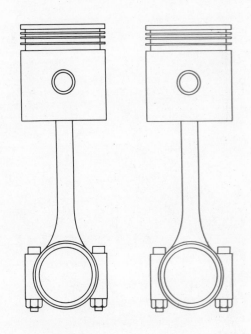

AUTOMOTIVE

McGRAW-HILL BOOK COMPANY, INC.

NEW YORK   CHICAGO   SAN FRANCISCO   DALLAS   TORONTO   LONDON

AUTOMOTIVE MECHANICS

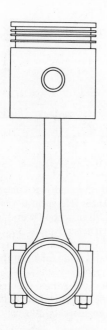
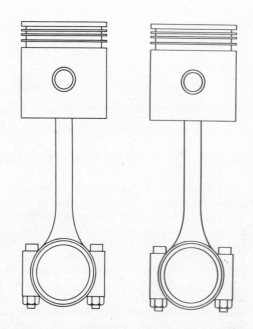

MECHANICS

FOURTH EDITION

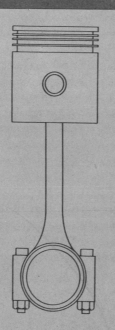

WILLIAM H. CROUSE

ABOUT THE AUTHOR

Behind William H. Crouse's clear technical writing is a background of sound mechanical engineering training as well as a variety of practical industrial experiences. He spent a year after finishing high school working in a tinplate mill, summers, while still in school, working in General Motors plants, and three years working in the Delco-Remy Division shops. Later he became Director of Field Education in the Delco-Remy Division of General Motors Corporation, which gave him an opportunity to develop and use his natural writing talent in the preparation of service bulletins and educational literature.

During the war years, he wrote a number of technical manuals for the Armed Forces. After the war, he became Editor of Technical Education Books for the McGraw-Hill Book Company. He has contributed numerous articles to automotive and engineering magazines and has written several outstanding books which are listed below.

William H. Crouse's outstanding work in the automotive field has earned for him membership in the Society of Automotive Engineers and in the American Society for Engineering Education.

BOOKS BY WILLIAM H. CROUSE

McGraw-Hill Automotive Mechanics Series

Automotive Chassis and Body
Automotive Electrical Equipment
Automotive Engines
Automotive Fuel, Lubricating, and Cooling Systems
Automotive Transmissions and Power Trains

Electrical Appliance Servicing
Everyday Automobile Repairs
Everyday Household Appliance Repairs
Understanding Science

AUTOMOTIVE MECHANICS

Library of Congress Catalog Card Number: 59-14444

Cover photograph courtesy of General Motors Corporation.

PREFACE

This is the fourth edition of *Automotive Mechanics*. When the author and publisher undertook to revise this book, they had two main purposes in mind: to include the most recent information about new models in the text and to improve its teachability. The author surveyed the most recent technical literature issued by the car manufacturers and has included the latest design, construction, and servicing information available. He has added a special chapter covering the features of the new compact cars. In preparing the third edition of *Automotive Mechanics,* the author rewrote the entire book with special attention to its readability level; he shortened sentences and paragraphs, defined terms when first used, and simplified the vocabulary. Again, with the preparation of this edition, he has reexamined the text and, where possible, made changes to clarify and simplify the text further. The publisher and author have added a second color throughout to emphasize important points, to clarify illustrations, to improve teachability, and to increase student interest in the text.

In the revision, the publisher and the author were guided by the comments and suggestions of classroom teachers who use the textbook. Their day-by-day experience in teaching from the book enabled them to contribute ideas for a revision. Thus, the improvements in the new edition can be traced directly to the cooperative interest of the teachers who took the time to offer their suggestions to the author and publisher. To these many friends the author wishes to express his deep appreciation.

Automotive Mechanics provides a complete introductory course on the subject. It covers the theory of operation and the construction, maintenance, repair, and adjustments of automotive components. With minor exceptions, it covers the full content of the automotive courses listed in the *Automotive Industry-Vocational Education Conference's Standards for Automotive Service Instructions in Schools*. The student who completes the *Automotive Mechanics* textbook, therefore, covers the full basic curriculum established by the top authorities in vocational education and in the automotive industry. No additional textbooks are required for the student to meet the standards set by the Automotive Industry and the American Vocational Association.

WILLIAM H. CROUSE

CONTENTS

vii

ACKNOWLEDGMENTS

Many individuals and organizations have contributed to the present and previous editions of *Automotive Mechanics*. The author gratefully acknowledges his indebtedness and tenders his sincere thanks to the many, many people in industry and in education who, by their advice and counsel, so ably assisted in the preparation of the present edition of the book. All cooperated with the aim of producing complete and accurate information that would be useful in the training of automotive mechanics. Special thanks are due to the following organizations for information and illustrations that they supplied: AC Spark Plug Division, Buick Motor Division, Cadillac Motor Car Division, Chevrolet Motor Division, Delco Products Division, Delco-Remy Division, Detroit Diesel Engine Division, Frigidaire Division, Oldsmobile Division, Pontiac Motor Division, Saginaw Steering Gear Division, and United Motors Service Division of General Motors Corporation; Allen Electric and Equipment Company; American Exporter's *Automotive World;* Akron Equipment Company; American Motors Corporation; Barrett Equipment Company; Bear Manufacturing Company; Bendix Products Division of Bendix Aviation Corporation; Black and Decker Manufacturing Company; Carter Carburetor Company; Chrysler Sales Division, De Soto Division, Dodge Division, and Plymouth Division of Chrysler Corporation; Clayton Manufacturing Company; Henry Disston and Sons, Inc.; Eaton Manufacturing Company; E. I. du Pont de Nemours & Company, Inc.; Electric Auto-Lite Company; Federal-Mogul Corporation; E. Edelmann and Company; Federal Motor Truck Company; Ford Motor Company; Gemmer Manufacturing Company; B. F. Goodrich Company; Greenfield Tap and Die Corporation; Hall Manufacturing Company; Jam Handy Organization, Inc.; Hercules Motors Corporation; Hobart Brothers; Hotpoint, Inc.; Houde Engineering Division of Houdaille-Hershey Corporation; International Harvester Company; Kaiser Motors Corporation; K-D Manufacturing Company; Kelsey-Hayes Wheel Company; Kent-Moore Organization, Inc.; Johnson Bronze Company; King-Seeley Corporation; Lincoln-Mercury Division of Ford Motor Company; Linde Air Products Company; Mack-International Motor Truck Corporation; Metalizing Company of America; Alexander Milburn Company; Monmouth Products Company; Monroe Auto Equipment Company; Muskegon Piston Ring Company; New Britain Machine Company; North American Electric Lamp Company; Perfect Circle Company; Ramsey Accessories Manufacturing Company; Rottler Boring Bar Company; A. Schrader's Son Division of Scovill Manufacturing Company, Inc.; Sealed Power Corporation; South Bend Lathe Works; Spicer Manufacturing Corporation; Standard Oil Company; Storm Manufacturing Company, Inc.; Studebaker-Packard Corporation; Sun Electric Corporation; Sunnen Products Company; Thompson Products Inc.; United Specialties Company; United States Rubber Company; Van Norman Company; Warner Electric Brake Manufacturing Company; Waukesha Motor Company; Weaver Manufacturing Company; Wilkening Manufacturing Company; and Zenith Carburetor Company.

Special thanks are also due to the hundreds of people in education who helped the publisher and the author plan the revision so that the new edition of *Automotive Mechanics* would be more useful to them than ever before. Hundreds of automotive-mechanics instructors offered advice, comments, and criticisms with the aim of making the new edition of the book a more useful and more perfect teaching tool. To all these people, and the organizations they represent, sincere thanks!

WILLIAM H. CROUSE

CHAPTER 1 | SHOP PRACTICE

THIS CHAPTER DESCRIBES THE various common hand tools used in automotive shopwork and explains how to use and take care of them. In addition, it discusses safety in the shop, that is, the safe way to work and to handle tools. It also discusses various fasteners. Here is what is meant by "fasteners"; the automobile (or any machine, for that matter) is put together by different types of screws, bolts, nuts, studs, washers, snap rings, and so on. These parts "fasten" the automobile parts together.

§ 1. Shopwork Work that is done in the automotive shop is quite varied. The automobile is made up of many different parts, and it may require many different service operations. You could fill a couple of pages just making a list of these operations. However, when you stop to think about it, all these jobs are made up of a few basically simple steps:

1. Measuring. You have to measure to find out what work the automobile requires. In some cases, you measure length or thickness or diameter. In other cases, you measure vacuum or power or voltage or speed or pressure. Taking some sort of measurement is often the first step in an automotive service job.

2. Disassembly. You may have to do a disassembly, or "teardown," job when the measurements show that something is wrong and repair work is needed.

3. Metalwork, or machining. Often, the repair job requires removal of metal from parts (as by filing, honing, drilling, and so on). When this is done by a machine (such as an electric drill or hone), the process is often called *machining.*

4. Installing new parts. Sometimes you find that old parts have worn out (such as piston rings, valves, bearings, and so on). So you must fit and install new parts. These actions usually require measuring and machining.

5. Reassembly. After necessary work is done on the different parts of the mechanism being repaired, the parts must be put back together. The mechanism must be reassembled and reinstalled on the car.

6. Adjustments. Some of the mechanisms on the automobile must be adjusted after a repair job. This compensates for wear, or restores the original specifications, and so on.

You will find how all these jobs are done on the engine and other automobile components as you study this book. Just remember this: Some of the service jobs may appear complicated. But every one of them can be broken down into the six steps listed above. And each step is basically simple.

Thus, not one of the automotive service jobs is really complicated. They are all made up of a series of simple steps. Keep this in mind as you move into the later chapters of the book that describe automotive service.

§ 2. **Specifications**   In the automotive shop, you often hear the word "specifications" or "specs." The specifications give you the correct measurements. The engineers who designed the car, the production men who built it, and the service engineers who figure out the proper ways to service it—all these men work out the proper measurements, or specifications, for the various parts and components of the car. They know, for example, that the generator should produce 40 amperes, that the exhaust valves should open 45 degrees before BDC (bottom dead center), that the piston-ring gap should be 0.002 inch, and so on. (We'll explain what all these things mean in due time.) All these measurements, or specifications, are listed in the automobile manufacturer's shop manual. Then, whenever the automotive mechanic is doing a service job, he goes to the shop manual to look up the specifications. In this way, he can compare the measurements he finds on the car with the measurements that the factory specifies. The amount that the measurements are off tells him what he must do. For example, suppose the engine cylinders, when new, measure 3 inches in diameter (this is the specification). But when the mechanic measures the cylinders on the car, he finds the cylinders have worn to a larger size. If they are only slightly oversize, he can take care of the wear by installing new piston rings. But if wear is considerable, then the cylinders must be machined (honed or bored).

The specifications tell you what the measurements should be. When things are not "up to specifications," then a repair or readjustment job may be required.

§ 3. **Fasteners**   Fasteners, to many people, mean pins or staples to fasten sheets of paper together. But, to the automotive engineer, fasteners are automotive parts that attach working components to each other or hold them in the proper relationship with each other. They include studs, bolts, screws, nuts, washers, lock washers, rivets, snap rings, keys, and cotter pins. Before we discuss these further, let us note the difference between bolts, screws, and studs. These are often confused.

1. Screws (Fig. 1–1). The term "machine screw" refers to the type of screw which is driven, or turned, into drilled and threaded holes in metal parts. The screw is turned down into the threaded hole to hold another part in place. There are many varieties and types of screw, as noted in a following section.

2. Bolts (Fig. 1–1). Bolts require nuts. The bolt is put through holes in parts to be attached to each other, and the nut is then turned onto the bolt.

3. Studs (Fig. 1–1). Studs, or stud bolts, as they are often called, are like bolts or screws except that they have no heads and are threaded at both ends. One end goes into a threaded

hole, and a nut is turned onto the other end.

§ **4. Threads** Screws, bolts, and studs have external threads. Nuts and threaded holes for screws, bolts, and studs have internal threads. Threads are made with taps and dies (see § 20). Threads (or *screw threads*, to use the full name) are designated in several ways. They are designated by size (by

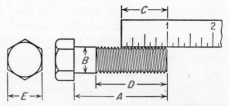

Fig. 1–2. A hex-head screw or bolt with parts named: **A**, length; **B**, diameter; **C**, pitch or threads per inch; **D**, length of thread; **E**, size of wrench required for head.

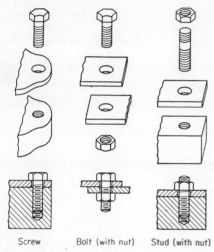

Screw   Bolt (with nut)   Stud (with nut)

Fig. 1–1. A screw, bolt, and stud. Top views show the attaching parts separated but aligned in readiness for assembly. Bottom views are sectional views. The diagonal lines are meant to show that the parts have been cut away (or sectioned). This permits the screw, bolt, or stud to show. Note that the screw, bolt, or stud does not show actual threads in the sectional views; the threads are indicated by the short and long horizontal lines. It is much easier to indicate threads in this way than actually to draw them in and it saves a great deal of the draftsman's time.

outside diameter or by a number), by the number of threads per inch (or *pitch*), by thread series (coarseness or fineness of thread), and by thread class (quality of finish and fit).

1. Size. Size means the diameter of the bolt or screw (Fig. 1–2); it is the outside diameter of the threads. Diameters above $\frac{1}{4}$ inch are classified by the actual measurement in fractions of an inch ($\frac{1}{4}$, $\frac{5}{16}$, $\frac{3}{8}$, and so on). Diameters below $\frac{1}{4}$ inch are classified by number (0, 1, 2, 3, and on up to 12). The table (Fig. 1–3) shows sizes of some of the smaller screws or bolts.

2. Pitch. Pitch is the number of threads per inch (Fig. 1–2). You can determine the pitch of the threads of any bolt or screw by counting the number of threads in an inch (see Fig. 1–2). Or you can use a regular thread-pitch gauge (Fig. 1–4). Notice that the gauge has a number of blades and that each blade has a different number of teeth per inch. Each blade is marked with the number of teeth it has per inch. To determine the number of teeth per inch, or pitch, of a bolt, you try different blades until you find the blade that fits the threads.

3. Thread series. Generally speak-

3

ing, the larger the diameter of a bolt, the coarser the thread. By "coarse" we mean largeness of the threads. A coarse thread is comparatively large, and there are relatively few threads per inch. The opposite of coarse is *fine*. A fine thread is comparatively small, and there are more per inch. There are six different series of threads as indicated in the table (Fig. 1–3). The coarse-thread series (designated as UNC, for Unified National Coarse,* or NC, for National Coarse) is for gray iron, soft metals, and plastics. A coarse thread

Size	Diameter (decimal)	Threads per inch					
		Coarse (UNC or NC)	Fine (UNF or NF)	Extra fine (UNEF or NEF)	8 thread series	12 thread series	16 thread series
0	0.0600	...	80				
1	0.0730	64	72				
2	0.0860	56	64				
3	0.0990	48	56				
4	0.1120	40	48				
5	0.1250	40	44				
6	0.1380	32	40				
8	0.1640	32	36				
10	0.1900	24	32				
12	0.2160	24	28	32			
$\frac{1}{4}$	0.2500	20	28	32			
$\frac{5}{16}$	0.3125	18	24	32			
$\frac{3}{8}$	0.3750	16	24	32			
$\frac{7}{16}$	0.4375	14	20	28			
$\frac{1}{2}$	0.5000	13	20	28		12	
$\frac{9}{16}$	0.5625	12	18	24		12	
$\frac{5}{8}$	0.6250	11	18	24		12	
$\frac{3}{4}$	0.7500	10	16	20	...	12	16
$\frac{7}{8}$	0.8750	9	14	20	...	12	16
1	1.0000	8	12	20	8	12	16
$1\frac{1}{8}$	1.1250	7	12	18	8	12	16
$1\frac{1}{4}$	1.2500	7	12	18	8	12	16
$1\frac{3}{8}$	1.3750	6	12	18	8	12	16
$1\frac{1}{2}$	1.5000	6	12	18	8	12	16

Fig. 1–3. Screw thread sizes and pitches.

shortens disassembly and reassembly time since a coarse-threaded bolt requires fewer turns to remove and install. The fine-thread series (designated UNF, for Unified National Fine,* or NF, for National Fine) is for applications where greater bolt strength and additional accuracy of assembly are required. The extra-fine-thread series (UNEF, for Unified National Extra Fine,* or NEF, for National Extra Fine) uses a thread that is still finer. There are also the 8 thread series, the 12 thread series, and the 16 thread series. These are for use in larger-size bolts. Each series has the same pitch regardless of bolt size. Thus, in the 16 thread series, there are 16 threads per inch on all size bolts (or ¾ inch up to 6 inches). Refer to the table (Fig. 1–3) for information on various thread series and sizes.

4. *Thread classes.* There are a number of different thread classes; the difference between classes is one of accuracy, or tolerance. That is, in one class of thread, the internal threads (or nut) fit the external threads (or bolt) rather tightly. Another class of thread has a looser fit. The intermediate fit is most widely used; the classes having a tight fit and a loose fit are confined to special applications. Actually, there are

* The term "Unified" refers to a thread form which is somewhat different from other thread forms. Before this thread form was designed, United States screw-thread standards did not conform with British and Canadian standards. Thus, British and Canadian screws did not always fit American machinery, and vice versa. However, in 1948, a standard for an interchangeable thread (Unified National Coarse and Unified National Fine) was adopted, and industry is changing over to it in the three countries.

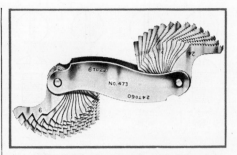

Fig. 1–4. A thread-pitch gauge.

two systems of classification, the new Unified thread-standard classification (see the footnote below for explanation of "Unified"), and a traditional American Standard. Ultimately, it is assumed that the American Standard will be dropped and the Unified classes used.

a. *Unified classes.* There are six Unified classes, 1A, 1B, 2A, 2B, 3A, and 3B. The letter A designates external threads (as on bolts, screws, and studs). The letter B designates internal threads (as in nuts). Classes 1A and 1B provide the loosest fits and permit easy and quick assembly even when threads are dirty or somewhat battered. Classes 2A and 2B provide fairly tight fits and are used for most commercial products. For close tolerances and exceptionally uniform fit, classes 3A and 3B are used.

b. *American Standard classes.* There are two of these standards, 2 and 3. These correspond to some extent to the Unified classes 2A and 2B, and 3A and 3B.

5. *Complete thread designation.* As we noted at the start of this section, screw threads are designated in four ways, size, pitch, series, and class. For example, consider a ¼-20 UNC-2A

5

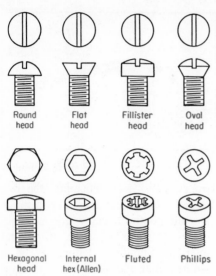

Fig. 1–5. Various types of screwheads.

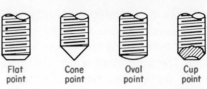

Fig. 1–6. Types of setscrew points.

thread. From this designation, we know the diameter is ¼ inch, that there are 20 threads to an inch, that the thread is a Unified National Coarse, and that it is an external class 2 thread.

§ **5. Screws and bolts** As already noted (§ 3), screws, or machine screws, enter threaded holes, while bolts are used with nuts. However, as far as appearance is concerned, they may be very similar. Actually, a great variety of screws and bolts are used on the automobile. Most bolts have hexagonal (six-sided) heads (Fig. 1–2). Screws may also have hexagonal (or "hex") heads, but they are also supplied with other provisions for driving (Fig. 1–5). Wrenches and screw drivers to drive the various types of bolts and screws are discussed on following pages.

The setscrew is a special type of screw (Fig. 1–6). Its purpose is to fasten a collar, gear, or similar part to a shaft. The setscrew is turned down in a threaded hole in the collar or gear until the inner end contacts the shaft. The inner end, or point, of the setscrew "bites" into the shaft and holds the collar or gear in the set position. Figure 1–6 shows various types of setscrew points.

One special type of screw cuts its own threads; this is a self-tapping screw (Fig. 1–7). The end of the screw is somewhat smaller and may have one or more slots cut in it. These slots form cutting edges on the threads so that, when the screw is turned into the hole, threads are cut in the hole.

§ **6. Nuts** Nuts are of various shapes (Fig. 1–8). The slotted and castle (or castellated) nut is used with a cotter pin (§ 7). Other nuts are used with lock washers (§ 8). Cotter pins and lock washers prevent the nuts from working loose and dropping off. Lock washers are also used under the heads of bolts or screws to keep them from loosening.

Another locking method uses two nuts. The second nut is turned down on and tightened against the first nut. The second nut locks the first nut in place and thereby keeps it from working loose.

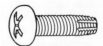

Fig. 1–7. Self-tapping screw.

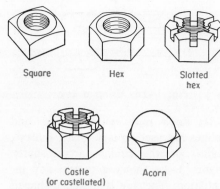

Square   Hex   Slotted hex

Castle (or castellated)   Acorn

Fig. 1—8. Several common nuts.

Fig. 1—10. Cotter pin before installation (*top*), and installation in hole in bolt and slots in nut.

Some nuts have a "built-in" locking feature (Fig. 1–9). The self-locking nut to the left in Fig. 1–9 has a slot cut in the side, and the upper threads are somewhat distorted. When the nut is turned down on a bolt, the separated sections of the nut are drawn slightly together. The spring effect produces friction on the threads that acts to prevent nut movement. The interference-type nut has a collar of fiber or soft metal. The bolt threads cut threads in the fiber or soft metal as the nut is turned on the bolt. The extra material jams in the bolt threads to keep the nut from loosening. The self-locking nut with the vertical slots is made with

the inner diameter of the upper section slightly smaller than the bolt diameter. Thus, the upper segments of the nut press against the bolt threads to hold the nut in position. The palnut is a single-thread lock nut.

§ 7. Cotter pins

Cotter pins (Fig. 1–10) are used with slotted or castle nuts. The bolt has a hole through which the cotter pin passes. To use the pin, the nut is tightened, and the nut slots are lined up with the hole in the bolt. Then the cotter pin is inserted and the two legs of the pin bent, as shown. They are shown only partly bent in the illustration. In practice, they would be bent back until they are snug around the nut.

§ 8. Lock washers

Lock washers (Fig. 1–11) are placed between the nut or screwhead and a flat washer (Fig. 1–12). The edges left by the split

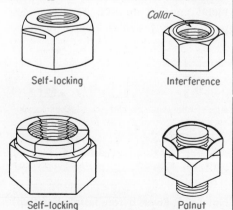

Collar

Self-locking   Interference

Self-locking   Palnut

Fig. 1—9. Self-locking nuts.

Plain   External   Internal   External-internal

Fig. 1—11. Lock washers.

7

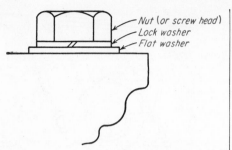

Fig. 1–12. Lock washer between flat washer and nut (or screwhead).

(in the plain lock washer) cut into the nut or screwhead and keep it from turning and loosening. The toothed lock washers provide many edges to improve the locking effect. In some assemblies, the flat washer is not used; the lock washer is placed between the nut or screwhead and the machine part.

§ 9. Snap rings External snap rings (Fig. 1–13) are used on shafts to prevent endwise movement of a gear or collar on the shaft. Internal snap rings are used in housings and similar machine parts to retain shafts or other components in position. The external snap ring must be expanded with special snap-ring pliers so that it slips over the shaft and into the undercut on the shaft. The internal snap ring must be contracted so that it can slip into the hole and into the undercut.

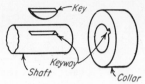

Fig. 1–14. Using a key.

§ 10. Keys and splines Keys and splines are used to lock gears, pulleys, collars, or other similar parts to shafts. Figure 1–14 shows a typical key installation. The key is a wedge-shaped piece of metal. It fits into slots (or keyways) cut into the shaft and collar (or pulley or gear) being installed on the shaft. The key thus locks the shaft and collar together.

Splines (Fig. 27–10) are internal and external teeth cut in both the shaft and the installed part. When the gear, pulley, or collar is installed, it is the same as having a great number of keys between it and the shaft. In many mechanisms, the splines fit loosely so that the gear or other part is free to move back and forth on the shaft. The splines, however, force both to rotate together.

§ 11. Rivets Rivets (Fig. 1–15) are metal pins that are used to more or less permanently fasten two parts together.

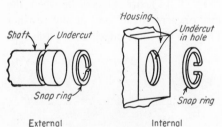

External   Internal
Fig. 1–13. Snap rings.

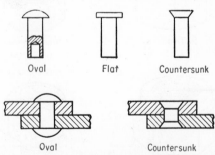

Fig. 1–15. Rivets before installation (top) and after installation (bottom).

In the automobile, the rivets are installed cold (in construction work, they may be heated). One end of the rivet has a head. After the rivet is in place, a driver, or a hammer and rivet set, is used to form a head on the other end of the rivet.

§ 12. **Screw drivers** The screw driver is used to drive, or turn, slotted screws. Do not use a screw driver as a pry bar or as a punch or chisel; you are likely to break it. Keep the tip properly ground (Fig. 1–16), with the sides practically parallel at the end. If the sides are tapered, the tip will tend to rise up out of the screw slot when it is turned. Always select the proper screw driver for the job; the tip should fit snugly in the screw slot. A screw driver that is too large or small is hard to use and may damage the screw or part being worked on.

The Phillips-head screw (Fig. 1–17) has two slots that cross at the center. It is widely used on automobile trim and molding; there is less chance that the screw driver will slip out of the slots and damage the finish. Three sizes of Phillips-head screw drivers, 4-, 6-, and 8-inch, handle most automotive work.

Offset screw drivers (Fig. 1–18) are handy for removing screws in places that are hard to get at. The two blades are at right angles; the ends can be reversed as a screw is tightened or loosened.

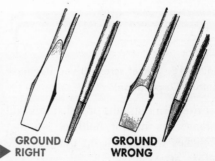

GROUND
▶ RIGHT

GROUND
WRONG

Fig. 1–16. Right and wrong ways to grind screw-driver tip. (*General Motors Corporation*)

§13. **Hammers** The ball-peen hammer (Fig. 1–19) is the one most commonly used by mechanics. It should be gripped on the end, and the face should strike the object squarely, as shown in Fig. 1–20. Hammers for striking on easily marred surfaces are shown in Fig. 1–21.

Check the hammer-head attachment to the handle occasionally. A wedge or screw is put into the head end of the handle (Fig. 1–22) to spread it and keep it from coming loose. Make sure the wedge or screw is tight each time you start to use the hammer. If the head should fly off, it might injure someone.

§ 14. **Pliers** A few of the many kinds of cutting and gripping pliers are shown in Fig. 1–23. Do not use pliers to grip hardened-steel surfaces; this will dull the teeth in the plier jaws. Do

Fig. 1–17. Phillips-head screw and screw driver. (*General Motors Corporation*)

Fig. 1–18. Offset screw driver. (*General Motors Corporation*)

not use pliers on nuts or bolts; this will damage the nut or bolthead so that wrenches will not fit on them.

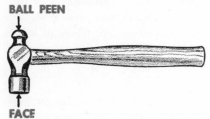

BALL PEEN

FACE

Fig. 1–19. Ball-peen hammer. (*General Motors Corporation*)

§ 15. Wrenches   Wrenches of many types are available, including open-end, box, combination open-end and box, adjustable, monkey, pipe, socket, setscrew, and spanner. Each has its special use.

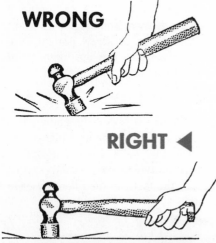

WRONG

RIGHT ◀

Fig. 1–20. Wrong and right ways to grip and use hammer. (*General Motors Corporation*)

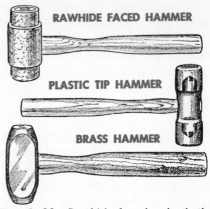

RAWHIDE FACED HAMMER

PLASTIC TIP HAMMER

BRASS HAMMER

Fig. 1–21. Rawhide-faced, plastic-tip, and brass hammers. (*General Motors Corporation*)

1. Open-end wrenches. Open-end wrenches are designed to tighten or loosen nuts or bolts (Fig. 1–24). The opening is usually at an angle to the body to permit turning a nut or bolt in a restricted space. After the nut or the bolt is turned as far as the restricted space will allow, the wrench can be turned over 180 degrees to permit further turning of the nut or bolt. By turning the wrench over after each swing, the nut or bolt can be loosened or tightened satisfactorily (Fig. 1–25). It is usually better to pull against the wrench rather than to push. If it is necessary to push, push with the palm

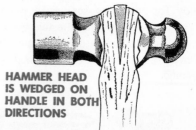

HAMMER HEAD IS WEDGED ON HANDLE IN BOTH DIRECTIONS

Fig. 1–22. Manner in which hammer head is wedged on handle. (*General Motors Corporation*)

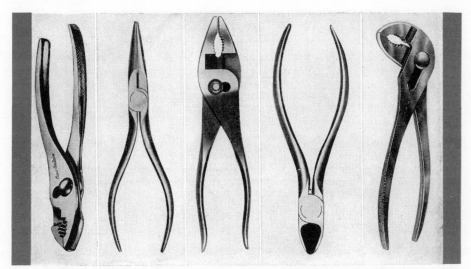

Fig. 1–23. Several types of pliers. (*New Britain Machine Company*)

of the hand and keep the fingers out of the way so that, if the nut or bolt suddenly gives, the knuckles will not be hurt. Make sure that the wrench fits the nut or bolthead snugly. If it fits loosely, excessive strain is thrown on the wrench and it may spring or break. The nut or bolthead may also be damaged. Do not use a pipe or another wrench on the end of the wrench to gain additional leverage. The wrench is designed to withstand the maximum leverage a man can apply by hand on its end; gaining added leverage with a pipe or another wrench may cause the wrench to break. Never use a hammer to strike on a wrench except where the wrench has been specially designed to be used in this manner.

2. Box wrenches. Box wrenches (Fig. 1–26) serve the same purpose as open-end wrenches. However, the opening into which the nut or bolthead fits completely surrounds, or boxes, the nut or bolthead. Box wrenches can be used in very restricted spaces because

of the thinness of the metal in the wrench head (Fig. 1–27). The wrench cannot slip off the nut. The 12-point box wrench, now almost universally used, has 12 notches in the head, so that a nut or bolt can be installed or removed even where there is a swing of only 15 degrees. Some box wrenches

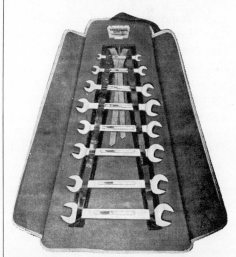

Fig. 1–24. A set of open-end wrenches. (*New Britain Machine Company*)

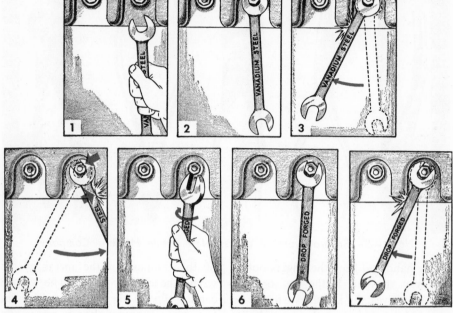

Fig. 1–25. Manner in which wrench may be turned over to turn nut in restricted space. (*General Motors Corporation*)

have the heads at an angle of 15 degrees to the handle to provide added clearance for the hand (Fig. 1–28).

3. Combination open-end and box wrenches. These have a box wrench on one end and an open-end wrench on the other. The box wrench is more convenient than an open-end wrench for final tightening or breaking loose of a nut or a bolt but is less convenient for otherwise turning the nut or the bolt. The box must be lifted completely off

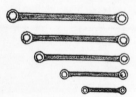

Fig. 1–26. Set of box wrenches. (*General Motors Corporation*)

the nut and then placed back on for each swing. On the other hand, the open-end wrench is less convenient for final tightening or breaking loose of a nut or a bolt, since it is more likely to

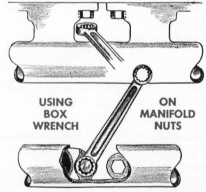

USING BOX WRENCH   ON MANIFOLD NUTS

Fig. 1–27. The box wrench can be used in a restricted space. (*General Motors Corporation*)

12

slip off, but it is more convenient for running a nut or a bolt off or on. Thus the combination open-end and box wrench enables the mechanic to use one type and then the other by merely reversing the ends.

4. *Socket wrenches*. These wrenches are somewhat similar to box wrenches, except that the sockets are detachable and are used with special handles. Figure 1–29 illustrates a set of socket wrenches with several types of handle. The sockets fit into the handles, the proper type of handle being selected for the job at hand. One type of handle has a sliding offset which permits application of added leverage by sliding the handle out. Another type has the handle attached through a hinge. The speed handle permits rapid running up or down of a bolt or nut. It works like a carpenter's brace, which is used with a bit to bore holes in wood. The ratchet handle has a ratchet that eliminates the necessity of lifting the socket off the nut or the bolt. The ratchet locks the socket as the handle is turned in one direction so that the socket turns with the handle. As the handle is moved back, the ratchet permits the handle to move without moving the socket. A universal joint is handy for working in restricted spaces where a straight wrench will not fit, since it allows the handle to be worked at an angle with the socket.

5. *Torque wrenches*. A torque wrench (Fig. 1–30) is necessary for working on the modern automotive vehicle, since many nuts and bolts must be tightened the correct amount—not too little or too much. Through long experience, it has been found that excessive tightening of nuts or bolts

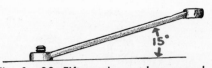

Fig. 1– 28. Fifteen-degree box wrench. *(General Motors Corporation)*

causes distortion of parts and danger of stripped threads or broken bolts, while insufficient tightening may permit the nut or the bolt to loosen. By using a torque wrench, the amount of torque being applied can be read on the dial, to permit tightening within the specified limits.

6. *Allen wrenches*. These are used on Allen screws (Fig. 1–31). This type of screw is not widely used on automobiles, although the caster and camber adjustments on the front wheels of many cars are made by turning an Allen screw type of pivot pin.

Figure 1–32 shows the wrong way and the right way to use an adjustable wrench. Be sure that the wrench jaws are tightened on the nut or bolt flats.

§ 16. **Chisels** Cold chisels are supplied in a number of different shapes (Fig. 1–33); all are for cutting metal by driving with a hammer. The chisel is normally held in the left hand. It should be held rather loosely so that, if the hammer does not strike square or misses, the hand will tend to give with the hammer blow and will be less subject to injury. For chipping with a chisel, goggles should be worn to prevent the possibility of chips flying into the eye. A chisel that has mushroomed on the end because of repeated hammer blows should not be used until the end has been dressed on a grinding wheel so that the turned-over metal is removed (Fig. 1–34).

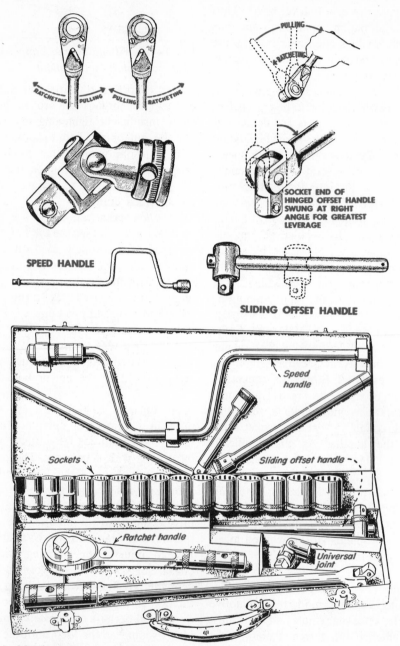

Fig. 1–29. Set of socket wrenches with handles. (*New Britain Machine Company and General Motors Corporation*)

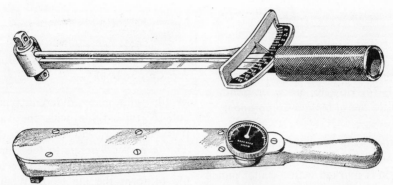

Fig. 1–30. Torque wrenches. (*General Motors Corporation*)

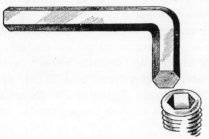

Fig. 1–31. Allen screw and wrench. (*General Motors Corporation*)

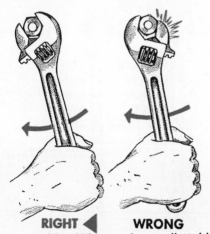

RIGHT ◄ WRONG

Fig. 1–32. When using adjustable wrench, pull on handle so that major load is carried by stationary jaw as shown at left. (*General Motors Corporation*)

§ **17. Punches** Punches are used to knock out rivets or pins, to align parts for assembly, and to mark locations of holes to be drilled. Punches for knocking out rivets or pins are of two kinds, the starting and the pin punch (Fig. 1–35). The starting punch is tapered and is used merely to break the rivet loose after the rivethead has been ground off or cut off with a chisel. The pin punch is then used to drive the rivet out.

The center punch (Fig. 1–36) is handy not only for marking hole locations for drilling but also for marking parts before they are disassembled, so

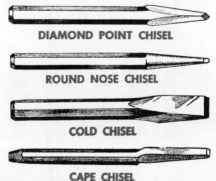

DIAMOND POINT CHISEL

ROUND NOSE CHISEL

COLD CHISEL

CAPE CHISEL

Fig. 1–33. Types of chisels. (*General Motors Corporation*)

15

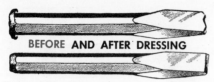

Fig. 1–34. How to dress, or grind, a chisel. (General Motors Corporation)

Fig. 1–36. Center punch. (General Motors Corporation)

that they can be reassembled in the same relative location. Unless the hole location is marked with a center punch before a hole is drilled, the drill may wander, or move around, on the surface of the piece through which the hole is to be drilled (Fig. 1–37). If the hole location is first center-punched, the drill will not do this.

§ 18. Files Files are cutting tools with a large number of cutting edges, or teeth. Files have many uses, and consequently there are hundreds of styles of file with many different types of cut. A typical file with the various parts named is shown in Fig. 1–38. The term "cut" refers to the cuts that have been made across the face of the file to form the file teeth. When the cuts are relatively far apart, the file is termed a "rough" or "coarse-cut" file. When they are close together, the file is termed a "smooth" or "dead-smooth" file. The terms indicating coarseness or fineness are, in order, rough, coarse, bastard, second-cut, smooth-cut, and dead-smooth. Figure 1–39 illustrates four of these. The coarser the file, the more metal it will remove with each file stroke.

When only one series of cuts has been taken across the face of the file,

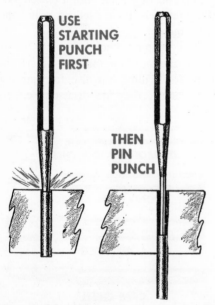

Fig. 1–35. Using starting and pin punches. (General Motors Corporation)

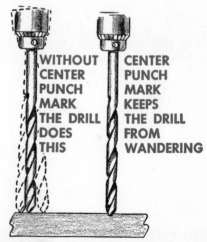

Fig. 1–37. Manner in which center-punching hole location will keep drill from wandering. (General Motors Corporation)

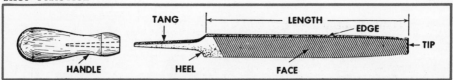

Fig. 1–38. A typical file with the parts named. (*General Motors Corporation*)

with all cuts parallel to each other, the file is known as a *single-cut file*, regardless of its coarseness. When the file has two series of cuts across its face in two different directions, it is known as a *double-cut* file (Fig. 1–40). Double cutting a file produces a large number of small teeth, each little tooth being much like the point of a chisel.

In addition to the above classification, files are classified according to their shape. Files may be flat, triangular, square, half-round, or round, either with or without taper from the heel to the top. Many special types of files are also available. Selection of the cut and shape of a file depends upon the work to be done. A few types of files are shown in Fig. 1–41.

A handle should be put on a file before it is used. Otherwise, you might accidentally drive the pointed tang into your hand. Handles are made in various sizes for various-sized files. To install the handle, place the file tang into the hole in the handle, and tap

the butt end of the handle on the bench (Fig. 1–42). Never hammer on the file to drive it into place. The file is brittle and may shatter.

Be sure that the part to be filed is held securely. Clamp it in a vise, if possible, and use the soft vise faces if necessary to protect the part from scarring. It is difficult to describe the exact procedure of using a file, since the procedure varies greatly with the type of job and the material. The forward, or cutting, stroke should be smooth and firm, with the proper amount of pressure. Insufficient pressure will allow the file teeth to slip over the work, so that the teeth are dulled. Excessive pressure tends to overload the file teeth, so that the cut is irregular. Use only enough pressure to keep the file cutting. On the back, or return, stroke, the file should be lifted clear of the work. Dragging the file back wears the cutting edge of the file teeth. However, if the file is used on soft metal, such as lead, the file should be dragged on the

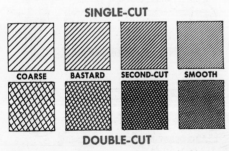

Fig. 1–39. File cuts. (*General Motors Corporation*)

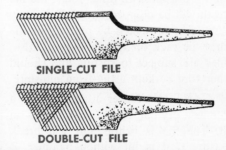

Fig. 1–40. Single-cut and double-cut files. (*General Motors Corporation*)

17

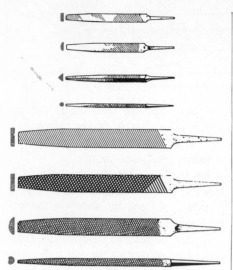

Fig. 1–41. Several types of files.

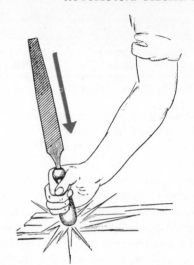

Fig. 1–42. Tapping butt end of file handle on bench to tighten file tang in handle. (*General Motors Corporation*)

return stroke, as this tends to clean the teeth. Also, in the process known as *drawfiling*, a finishing operation, the file is pushed along the work crosswise and may not be lifted for the return stroke.

If the file is not cutting, a file card should be used to clean the file teeth. The file card is a wire-bristled brush. Tapping the handle on the bench every few strokes during filing tends to keep the file clean, but the file card will also be required.

When a file is not in use, it should be carefully put away. If a file is thrown into a drawer with other tools, the file teeth will be chipped and dulled. They should be protected by putting the file in a file rack or by wrapping it. Also, files are subject to rusting and should therefore be kept away from moisture.

▶ *CAUTION:* Never attempt to use a file as a pry bar, and never hammer on it. The file is brittle and will break easily. If it is hit with a hammer, it is likely to shatter in a dangerous manner.

§ 19. Hack saws The hack saw is a special type of saw for sawing metal (Fig. 1–43). The blades are replaceable, and the frame is adjustable for various blade lengths. It is very important that the correct type of blade be selected for the work to be done. Blades are made with 14 to 32 teeth per inch. Using a blade with the wrong number of teeth will not only make the job more difficult but will also damage

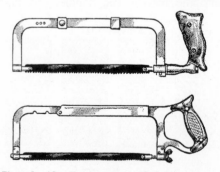

Fig. 1–43. Two types of hack saws. (*General Motors Corporation*)

18

or break the blade. Figure 1–47 illustrates correct and incorrect blades for various jobs.

After the correct blade for a job has been selected, it should be placed in the hack-saw frame and tightened to the proper tension (Fig. 1–44). Insufficient tension will cause the blade to bend and probably to break. The teeth should be pointed away from the handle so that they will cut when the hack saw is pushed (Fig. 1–45).

In using the hack saw, it should be held as shown in Fig. 1–46. On the forward, or cutting, stroke, move the hack saw evenly and with uniform pressure. Lift the blade slightly from the work on the return stroke to avoid wear on the back of the teeth, since this would soon dull them. Never twist or bend the blade when cutting, since such treatment may break it. In sawing

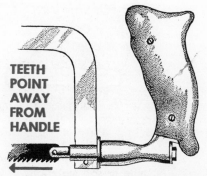

TEETH POINT AWAY FROM HANDLE

Fig. 1–45. Proper relationship of teeth with hack-saw handle. (*General Motors Corporation*)

sheet metal, it may be found that even with the 32-tooth blade only one tooth will be in contact with the metal. For such work, the sheet metal may be clamped in the vise between two blocks of wood and the cut taken through both the wood and the metal.

Take good care of the blades. Do not throw them into a toolbox with other tools and thus dull the teeth. Wipe the blades with an oily cloth occasionally to keep them from rusting.

§ 20. Taps and dies Taps and dies are devices used for cutting inside and outside threads. (See § 4 for information on threads.)

Taps are made in several styles (Fig. 1–48). The taper tap is used to thread a hole completely through a piece of metal, the plug tap to thread

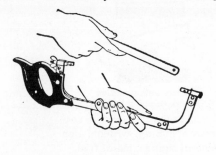

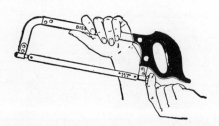

Fig. 1–44. Inserting and tightening blade in hack saw. (*Henry Disston and Sons, Inc.*)

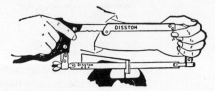

Fig. 1–46. Holding hack saw in sawing. (*Henry Disston and Sons, Inc.*)

CORRECT	INCORRECT
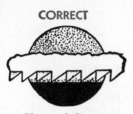	
Plenty of chip clearance	Fine teeth. No chip clearance. Teeth clogged

Use 14 teeth for cutting materials in thick sections made of mild or soft materials.

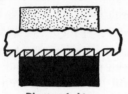	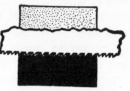
Plenty of chip clearance	Fine teeth. No chip clearance. Teeth clogged

Use 18 teeth for cutting materials thicker than $\frac{3}{64}$ inch in sections of annealed tool steel, high-speed steel, rail, bronze, aluminum, light structural shapes, copper.

Two teeth and more on section	Coarse teeth straddles work stripping teeth

Use 24 teeth for cutting material thicker than $\frac{1}{32}$ inch in sections of iron, steel, brass and copper tubing, wrought iron pipe, drill rod, conduit, light structural shapes, metal trim.

Two or more teeth on section	Coarse pitch straddles work

Use 32 teeth for cutting material similar to recommendations for 24 tooth blades but thinner than $\frac{1}{32}$ inch.

Fig. 1–47. Correct and incorrect number of teeth for various cutting jobs. The correct number is shown at left on each job. (*L. S. Starrett* Co.)

a hole only part way, and the bottoming tap to thread a hole to the bottom when the hole does not go all the way through the metal.

The tap is held in a tap wrench (Fig. 1–49). The wrench jaws are adjustable and can be tightened to hold the tap securely. The tap should be started square in the hole and the wrench turned smoothly and evenly, with both hands. A lubricant such as lard should be applied to the tap. Every time two complete turns of the tap have been made, the tap should be backed off about a quarter turn and lubricant applied.

Dies cut outside threads (Fig. 1–50). Dies are held in diestocks (Fig. 1–51) during the cutting operation. The procedure is similar to that required for tapping. The rod should be chamfered on the end, so that the die will start easily. Every two complete turns, the die should be backed off a quarter turn and lubricant such as lard applied.

§ 21. Measuring devices

The measuring of linear distances is one of the most important of all the jobs performed in an automotive service shop. In almost every step of automotive service, measurements are taken to determine size, fit, or clearance. And unless the measurements are properly taken, the service job will not be correct; improper operation or failure of the unit being serviced will result.

Almost everyone is familiar with the ruler, or scale, for measuring on flat surfaces. To measure the diameter of a shaft or the thickness of a part, an outside caliper or micrometer is used. To measure the diameter of a hole, an

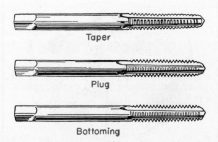

Fig. 1–48. Hand taps. (*Greenfield Tap and Die Corporation*)

inside caliper or micrometer is used. Special dial-indicator gauges are also available to take such measurements. Measurement of small clearances or gaps is required in brake work, setting valve tappets, fitting pistons, adjusting spark plugs, and so forth. For such work, feeler gauges are used. The procedures of using these measuring devices are detailed in the following paragraphs.

1. Feeler gauges. These gauges are essentially strips or blades of hardened and tempered steel or other metal, ground or rolled with extreme accuracy to the proper thickness. They are generally supplied in sets (Fig. 1–52), each blade marked with its thickness in thousandths of an inch. In Fig. 1–52, for example, the "3" means 0.003

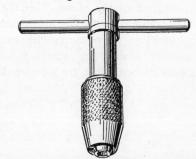

Fig. 1–49. Adjustable hand-tap wrench. (*Greenfield Tap and Die Corporation*)

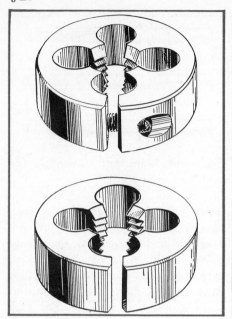

Fig. 1–50. Dies. (*Greenfield Tap and Die Corporation*)

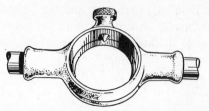

Fig. 1–51. Diestock. (*Greenfield Tap and Die Corporation*)

feelers are made of carefully calibrated steel wire of the proper diameter. They are useful in making spark-plug gap and similar checks.

Feeler gauges should never be forced into a space to be measured. They should not be allowed to become bent, torn, or battered. They should be wiped with a clean, oily cloth occasionally. With care, feeler gauges will last a long time without losing their accuracy.

inch, the "4" means 0.004 inch, and so on. Some feeler gauges have two steps, or thicknesses, and are called *stepped* feeler gauges (Fig. 1–53). The tip of the blade is somewhat thinner than the remainder of the blade. The blade marked "10–12" in Fig. 1–53, for example, is 0.010 inch thick at the tip and 0.012 inch thick on the thicker portion, which starts about ½ inch from the end of the blade. This type of feeler gauge is handy on certain jobs, such as valve-tappet-clearance adjustment where the specifications might call, for example, for a clearance of 0.006 to 0.008 inch. By making the adjustment so that the 0.006-inch gauge will fit and the 0.008-inch gauge will not fit, the specified clearance is obtained.

Wire feeler gauges are similar to the flat feeler gauges, except that the wire

2. *Calipers.* Calipers can be used to take a number of different measurements. Figure 1–54 illustrates the use of an outside caliper to measure the diameter of a shaft. The caliper should be adjusted to slip over the shaft easily of its own weight. It should not be forced, since this would spring the caliper and prevent accurate measurement. After the caliper has been adjusted, the caliper can be placed against a scale, as shown in Fig. 1–55, in order to determine the shaft diameter. One leg of the caliper should be held

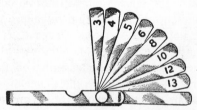

Fig. 1–52. Set of feeler gauges. (*General Motors Corporation*)

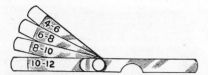

Fig. 1–53. Set of stepped feeler gauges. *(General Motors Corporation)*

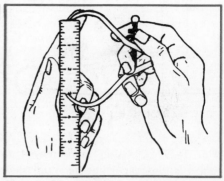

Fig. 1–55. Checking measurement to which outside caliper has been adjusted. *(South Bend Lathe Works)*

against the end of the scale and the reading on the scale at the other leg noted.

Inside calipers are used in a similar manner to measure the diameter of holes. Figure 1–56 illustrates an inside caliper in use. It should be entered in the hole at an angle, as shown by the dotted lines, and then slowly straightened. Adjust until it will slip in the hole with a slight drag. The caliper must be held square across the diameter of the hole. After the caliper is adjusted, the measurement can be read from the scale, as shown in Fig. 1–57.

The micrometer (Fig. 1–58), or "mike" as it is often called, is a special type of caliper designed to measure in thousandths of an inch. It is a precision instrument and must be carefully treated. When the thimble is turned clockwise, the spindle moves toward the anvil; when the thimble is turned

in the opposite direction, the spindle moves away from the anvil. The hub, or barrel, of the micrometer is marked off in uniform spacings, each of which is 0.025 inch. The thimble is spaced off into 25 graduations around its circumference, each graduation indicating 0.001 inch (Fig. 1–59). The internal threads of the thimble are such that every revolution of the thimble moves the thimble on the hub 0.025 inch. When the thimble has been turned to bring the spindle up against the anvil, the thimble will have been brought up to the "0" mark on the hub and the "0" mark on the thimble will have aligned with the lateral line on the hub.

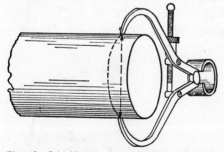

Fig. 1–54. Using an outside caliper to measure shaft diameter. *(South Bend Lathe Works)*

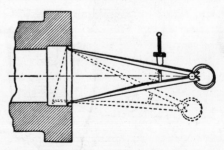

Fig. 1–56. Using an inside caliper to measure the diameter of a hole. *(South Bend Lathe Works)*

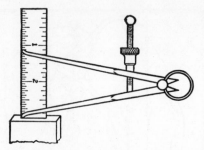

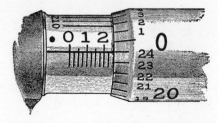

Fig. 1–59. Hub and thimble markings on micrometer. (*General Motors Corporation*)

Fig. 1–57. Checking measurement to which inside caliper has been adjusted. (*South Bend Lathe Works*)

If the thimble is backed off to give 0.010-inch clearance between the anvil and the spindle, the "10" marking on the thimble will align with the lateral line on the hub; this indicates 0.010 inch. If the thimble is backed off four revolutions exactly, the thimble will clear the "1" marking on the hub, which indicates 0.10 inch, or four times 0.025. If the thimble were then turned back part of a revolution, say to the "12" marking, then the total distance between the anvil and the spindle would be 0.10 inch plus 0.012

inch, or 0.112 inch. By thus adding the hub and thimble markings and remembering that each hub marking represents 0.025 inch and each spindle marking represents 0.001 inch, the measurement to which the micrometer has been adjusted can easily be read. Once the reading has been taken, it can be translated from decimals to fractions, if desired, by reference to the decimal-equivalent chart (Fig. 1–60).

Inside micrometers are also available for taking measurements of hole diameters (Fig. 1–61), as, for instance, the bore of an engine cylinder. Other

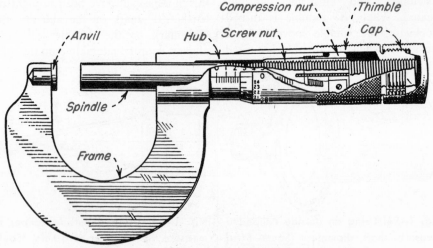

Fig. 1–58. A micrometer. (*General Motors Corporation*)

special micrometers find use in automotive shops. The special micrometer shown in Fig. 14–67 has long anvil and spindle jaws which permit easy measurement of the crankshaft-journal diameter. Much of the precision machinery used in the automotive shop has micrometer adjustments; cylinder honing or boring equipment, other hones, machine lathes, crankshaft lathes, precision grinders—all have such adjustments.

In the use of the micrometer, extreme care must be exercised to prevent damaging it. In particular, *it should never be clamped* on the piece to be measured. The micrometer should be tightened only enough to cause a slight drag as it is slid over the piece being measured. Clamping will distort the micrometer or ruin the screw threads.

3. *Dial indicators.* These are gauges that utilize a dial face and needle to register measurements. The needle is connected by gearing and linkage to a movable contact point. Movement of the contact point registers in thou-

$\frac{1}{64}$	.0156	$\frac{17}{64}$	.2656	$\frac{33}{64}$	.5156	$\frac{49}{64}$	.7656
$\frac{1}{32}$	.0312	$\frac{9}{32}$	.2812	$\frac{17}{32}$	.5312	$\frac{25}{32}$	.7812
$\frac{3}{64}$	.0468	$\frac{19}{64}$	.2969	$\frac{35}{64}$	.5469	$\frac{51}{64}$	.7969
$\frac{1}{16}$	.0625	$\frac{5}{16}$	.3125	$\frac{9}{16}$	.5625	$\frac{13}{16}$	.8125
$\frac{5}{64}$	.0781	$\frac{21}{64}$	.3281	$\frac{37}{64}$	.5781	$\frac{53}{64}$	.8281
$\frac{3}{32}$	.0937	$\frac{11}{32}$	.3437	$\frac{19}{32}$	.5937	$\frac{27}{32}$	.8437
$\frac{7}{64}$	.1094	$\frac{23}{64}$	.3594	$\frac{39}{64}$	.6094	$\frac{55}{64}$	.8594
$\frac{1}{8}$	.125	$\frac{3}{8}$	.375	$\frac{5}{8}$	.625	$\frac{7}{8}$	.875
$\frac{9}{64}$	.1406	$\frac{25}{64}$	.3906	$\frac{41}{64}$	.6406	$\frac{57}{64}$	.8906
$\frac{5}{32}$	.1562	$\frac{13}{32}$	.4062	$\frac{21}{32}$	.6562	$\frac{29}{32}$	.9062
$\frac{11}{64}$	.1719	$\frac{27}{64}$	.4219	$\frac{43}{64}$	.6719	$\frac{59}{64}$	.9219
$\frac{3}{16}$	.1875	$\frac{7}{16}$	.4375	$\frac{11}{16}$	.6875	$\frac{15}{16}$	.9375
$\frac{13}{64}$	.2031	$\frac{29}{64}$	.4531	$\frac{45}{64}$	.7031	$\frac{61}{64}$	.9531
$\frac{7}{32}$	.2187	$\frac{15}{32}$	.4687	$\frac{23}{32}$	.7187	$\frac{31}{32}$	.9687
$\frac{15}{64}$	.2344	$\frac{31}{64}$	.4844	$\frac{47}{64}$	.7344	$\frac{63}{64}$	.9843
$\frac{1}{4}$	.25	$\frac{1}{2}$	.5	$\frac{3}{4}$	.75	1	1.0

Fig. 1–60. Table of decimal equivalents.

sandths of an inch on the dial face. Figure 14–78 illustrates a dial indicator being used to check cylinder walls in an engine.

§ 22. **Drills** Drills are tools for making holes. The type of material into which a hole is to be made determines the type of drill bit that must be used. The drill bit, or twist drill, is a cylin-

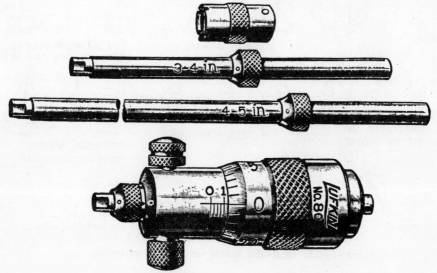

Fig. 1–61. Inside micrometer. (*General Motors Corporation*)

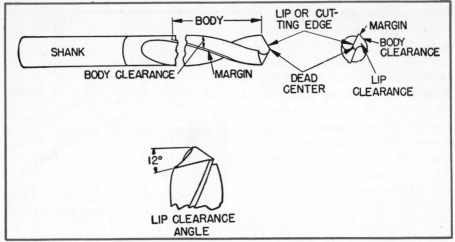

Fig. 1–62. The parts of a twist drill.

drical bar with helical grooves and a point (Fig. 1–62). The point is formed to provide cutting edges to cut into material. The helical grooves provide passages through which the chips that have been cut can pass away from the working surface. The shape of the point varies with the material (Fig. 1–63).

Grinding twist-drill points requires considerable skill. The two cutting edges must have the same angle with the center line of the drill, both edges must be of the same length, and the angle of clearance must be correct and the same for both cutting edges. Usually, when a considerable number of drills are used, a special grinding

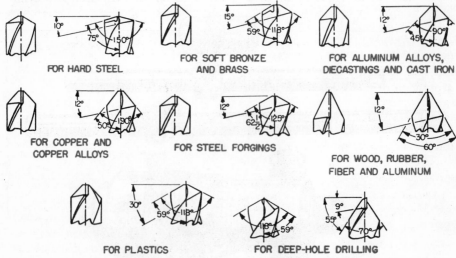

Fig. 1–63. Twist-drill points for various materials.

fixture is employed that assures the correctness of all angles (Fig. 1–64).

Twist drills have either a tapered or a straight shank, such as that shown in Fig. 1–62. The straight-shank drill is the more commonly used in ordinary shopwork.

For most shopwork, electrically operated drills are employed. These may be portable or permanently assembled into a floor- or bench-mounted press. The drill must have good care and must be correctly used. It must be kept clean and must be oiled periodically in line with the manufacturer's recommendations. Always turn off the drill before attempting to oil it. That is one of the fundamentals of safety practice in any shop. *Always turn off a machine before attempting to oil it.*

Never overload a drill so much that it stalls. This is very damaging. Do not click the switch off and on in an attempt to start a stalled drill. This is likely to burn out the switch or the motor. Relieve the feed pressure as the drill bit breaks through the finished work, to avoid stalling.

If a portable drill is used, do not drag it around by the cable, and do not leave it lying around on the floor so that the cable or the drill bit will be stepped on or run over and damaged.

§ 23. Removing broken studs

Occasionally studs or bolts will break off, and the removal of the broken part will be necessary. If the break is above the surface, it may be possible to file flats on two sides of the stud or the bolt, so that a wrench can be used to back it out. Also, a slot may be cut so that a screw driver can be used. If the break is below the surface, an extractor may

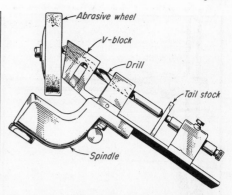

Fig. 1–64. Drill-grinding fixture for holding drill while it is being ground.

be required. The first step in the removal of a stud broken off below the surface is to center-punch the stud and drill a small hole down into it. Follow this with a larger drill that makes a hole in the stud nearly as large as the small diameter of the threads, leaving only a thin shell. Then the screw extractor is brought into use. One type, called the *Ezy-Out,* is tapered and has a coarse spiral thread with sharp edges. An extractor of the right size is se-

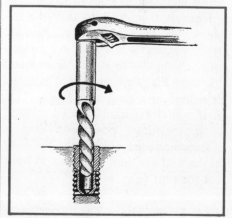

Fig. 1–65. Using stud extractor to remove broken stud. (*General Motors Corporation*)

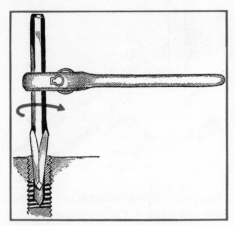

Fig. 1–66. Using a diamond-pointed chisel to remove a broken stud in an emergency. (*General Motors Corporation*)

the handle is turned, a screw in the base of the vise moves the movable jaw toward or away from the stationary jaw. To avoid marring or otherwise damaging finished surfaces of parts that are to be clamped in the vise, caps of copper or similar soft metal are placed over the steel jaws of the vise. These are usually referred to as "soft" jaws.

lected, inserted into the hole in the stud, and turned in a counterclockwise direction with a wrench (Fig. 1–65). The thread edges bite into the sides of the hole in the stud so that the stud is screwed out.

A second type of extractor is driven into the hole in the stud so that the edges bite into the sides of the hole. A wrench is then used to turn the extractor and back out the stud. Another type of extractor is similar in construction, except that it is not tapered and has three sharp splines instead of flutes. It is used in a similar manner.

If a stud extractor is not available, it is sometimes possible to tap a diamond-pointed chisel into the hole in the stud and turn the chisel to back out the stud (Fig. 1–66).

§ 24. Bench vise

The bench vise (Fig. 1–67) is used to hold a piece or part while it is being sawed, filed, chiseled, or otherwise worked on. When

§ 25. Arbor presses

Arbor presses have many uses in the automobile shop. The simplest (Fig. 1–68) has a handle that rotates a gear which is meshed with a rack. This causes the rack to move down or up as required. The lower end of the rack has a tool- or arbor-holding device. A considerable amount of pressure can be exerted on the arbor through the handle, and this makes it relatively easy to remove or install bearings and bushings, to burnish bushings, and to perform other similar jobs. The larger presses of this type may be operated hydraulically,

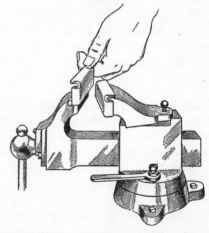

Fig. 1–67. Bench vise, showing soft jaws being put into place on vise jaws.

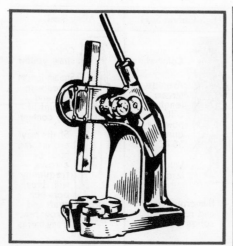

Fig. 1–68. Arbor press. (*Kent-Moore Organization, Inc.*)

that is, by liquid pressure acting in a cylinder.

§ 26. Oilstone

There are many types of oilstones, varying not only in shape and size but also in the fineness or coarseness of the abrasive dust that makes up the stone. Stones should always be moistened with oil when used, or they will become clogged or glazed and will no longer cut properly. If this should happen, the stone may be cleaned with solvent and then reoiled. Since stones are brittle, they should not be dropped or otherwise subjected to rough treatment.

§ 27. Grinding wheels

Grinding wheels can be broken by hard blows, by heavy pressure, or by excessive tightening of the spindle nut. Thus, reasonable caution should be exercised in the use of the grinding wheel. Goggles should always be worn, and the safety shield should be in place, when the wheel is used. Figure 1–69 shows the wheel being used to grind a screw

driver, while Fig. 1–64 shows the use of a special drill-grinding fixture. In general, the purpose of using the grinding wheel is to restore the working edges of the tool to their original shape and sharpness. Overheating of the tool should be avoided, since this would draw the temper of the steel. The tool should be repeatedly dipped in water during the grinding process, to prevent it from becoming too hot. The type of steel being ground can be determined by watching the sparks thrown off by the grinding operation (see Fig. 1–70).

§ 28. Taking care of yourself in the shop

Work quietly, and give your work your undivided attention. You should never indulge in horseplay or create an unnecessary disturbance. Such actions might distract someone and cause him to get hurt. Keep your tools and equipment under control. Don't scatter them about or lay them on operating machinery or equipment. Keep them out of aisles and working spaces where someone could trip over them. Use special care to keep jack handles and creepers out of the way; tripping over these is one of the most common causes of accidents in the automobile shop. Don't put sharp ob-

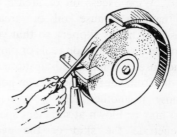

Fig. 1–69. Grinding wheel being used to grind screw driver.

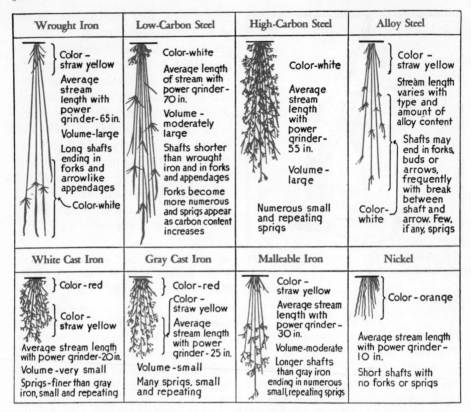

Wrought Iron	Low-Carbon Steel	High-Carbon Steel	Alloy Steel
Color – straw yellow. Average stream length with power grinder-65 in. Volume-large. Long shafts ending in forks and arrowlike appendages. Color-white	Color-white. Average length of stream with power grinder- 70 in. Volume - moderately large. Shafts shorter than wrought iron and in forks and appendages. Forks become more numerous and sprigs appear as carbon content increases	Color-white. Average stream length with power grinder- 55 in. Volume- large. Numerous small and repeating sprigs	Color – straw yellow. Stream length varies with type and amount of alloy content. Shafts may end in forks, buds or arrows, frequently with break between shaft and arrow. Few, if any, sprigs. Color-white
White Cast Iron	Gray Cast Iron	Malleable Iron	Nickel
Color-red. Color- straw yellow. Average stream length with power grinder-20 in. Volume -very small. Sprigs-finer than gray iron, small and repeating	Color-red. Color – straw yellow. Average stream length with power grinder-25 in. Volume -small. Many sprigs, small and repeating	Color – straw yellow. Average stream length with power grinder- 30 in. Volume-moderate. Longer shafts than gray iron ending in numerous small, repeating sprigs	Color - orange. Average stream length with power grinder- 10 in. Short shafts with no forks or sprigs

Fig. 1–70. Identification of different types of steel by spark test.

jects or tools into your pockets. You might cut your hand or get stabbed. Make sure that your clothing is suited to the job and that you do not have a dangling tie, loose sleeves, and so forth, that could get caught in moving machinery. Wipe excess oil or grease off your hands, because oil or grease makes your hands slippery so that you cannot get a good grip on tools or parts. Do not use a compressed-air hose to blow dirt from your clothes. Never point the hose at another person. Particles of dirt may be blown at sufficient speed to penetrate the skin or the eyes. Goggles should be worn when the air hose is used, as well as during chipping, grinding, or any other job where

there is danger to the eyes from flying particles. When using a car jack, make sure that it is centered, so that it will not slip and allow the car to drop. Never jack up a car when someone is working under it. Use car stands or supports, properly placed, before going under a car.

§ 29. Taking care of your tools Tools should be clean and in good condition, as noted in previous articles. Greasy or oily tools will be hard to hold and use; wipe them off before trying to use them. Always use the proper tool for the job; using the wrong tool may damage the tool or the part being worked on, or it might lead to personal injury.

Do not use a hardened hammer or punch on a hardened surface. Hardened steel is brittle—almost like glass —and may shatter from heavy blows. Slivers from the head of the hammer or from the punch might fly out and embed in the hand or, worse, in the eye. Use a soft hammer or punch on hardened parts.

§ 30. Using power-driven equipment

A great variety of power-driven equipment is used in the automobile shop. The instructions for using any equipment should be carefully studied before the equipment is operated. Hands and clothing should be kept away from moving machinery, such as the engine flywheel, fan, and so forth. Keep hands out of the way when using any cutting device, such as cylinder-boring equipment or a drum lathe. Do not attempt to feel the finish while the machine is in operation, since there may be slivers of metal that will cut your hands badly. When using any honing or grinding equipment, keep hands away from rotating parts and do not try to feel the finish with the machine in operation. When working on any device with compressed springs, such as clutches or valves, use great care to prevent the springs from slipping and jumping loose. If this should happen, the spring might take off at high speed and hurt someone.

Never attempt to adjust or oil moving machinery unless the instructions specifically state that this should be done.

§ 31. Fire prevention

The automobile requires gasoline to operate, and gasoline is a highly flammable substance. Therefore, you should be particularly careful around the shop to avoid spilling gasoline. If gasoline is spilled, it should be wiped up at once and the rags put outside or in a safe place to dry. Naturally, smokers should be very careful, since open flames in the presence of gasoline vapors will cause the vapors to explode. This is so great a danger that smoking is strictly prohibited in many automobile shops. Oily rags or waste are another potential source of fire, since they may ignite by spontaneous combustion, that is, by the oil on the rags (by chemical action) causing so much heat to develop that the rags catch fire. Oily rags or waste should be placed in covered metal containers provided for them.

An engine that has a gasoline leak in the fuel line, tank, pump, or carburetor is extremely dangerous, since the gasoline could catch fire very easily. Before such an engine is started, the leak should be repaired and all gasoline be wiped up. Care should be used to avoid shorts or grounds in the electric circuit which could cause sparks, especially around the carburetor or the fuel pump. In particular, the ground cable should be disconnected from the battery first when a battery is being removed from a car. This prevents the possibility of a ground when the cable clamp is being loosened from the insulated terminal. For the same reason, the grounded cable should be reconnected *last* on reinstallation of the battery.

REVIEW QUESTIONS

1. What are the six basic steps in automotive shopwork?
2. What are specifications, and how are they used in shopwork?

3. Name a few types of fastener.
4. Explain the difference between bolts, studs, and screws.
5. How are thread sizes designated?
6. What is meant by thread pitch? How is pitch measured?
7. What is meant by the term "thread series"?
8. What is meant by thread classes?
9. Name a few different kinds of nuts.
10. Explain the purpose of cotter pins.
11. Explain the purpose of lock washers.
12. Explain the purpose of snap rings.
13. What are some cautions to observe in using a screw driver?
14. What types of screw driver are there?
15. Describe the Phillips-type screw driver. Where are Phillips-head screws used?
16. What are offset screw drivers?
17. Describe the correct manner of using a hammer.
18. Name several types of wrench.
19. What is an open-end wrench?
20. What are box wrenches?
21. What are socket wrenches?
22. Name and describe the use of several types of socket-wrench handles.
23. What is a torque wrench, and why is it used?
24. Describe the proper method of using a chisel.
25. Name several uses of punches. What types of punch are there?
26. What is the purpose of a file?
27. What is a single-cut file? A double-cut file?
28. What terms designate the coarseness or fineness of a file?
29. Describe the procedure of using a file.
30. Describe the proper method of installing a blade in a hack-saw frame and the proper manner of using a hack saw.
31. What is a tap? A die? Describe how they are used.
32. Name three styles of tap.
33. Describe the procedure of measuring a shaft with an outside caliper.
34. Describe the procedure of measuring the diameter of a hole with an inside caliper.
35. Describe the procedure of taking a measurement with a micrometer.
36. What are feeler gauges? Stepped feeler gauges?
37. Name the important points to watch in practicing safety in the shop.
38. Name the important things to do in taking care of tools.
39. Name the important things to watch to prevent fires in the shop.

CHAPTER 2

FUNDAMENTALS OF THE AUTOMOBILE

THIS CHAPTER DISCUSSES BRIEFLY the various components of the automobile, describes their purpose, and explains how these different components operate together. The chapter will therefore serve as an introduction to automobile construction and operation.

§ 32. Components of the automobile

The average automobile driver views his car as a mechanism designed for his comfort and convenience that requires gasoline, oil, water, air, and occasional repairs. As long as he supplies these wants, he can sit in the driver's seat, manipulate a few controls, and be carried from one place to another.

The automobile engineer sees in the car a triumph of engineering and production skill. He sees the car as thousands of diverse parts that have been pressed, welded, riveted, stitched, bolted, hammered, screwed, buckled, and otherwise assembled into a smoothly functioning unit.

The automobile mechanic sees the car as a combination of thousands of parts that are under stress and are wearing in a thousand ways. He is familiar with these parts: he knows how they go together and the job each part does in the operation of the automobile. He knows how they wear and fail, what he must do to forestall failure, and what is required to restore the car to good running condition when failure occurs. When a car is difficult to start, does not develop rated power, steers hard, and so on, he knows how to adjust, repair, or replace the faulty parts causing the trouble.

To a person raising the hood of an automobile for the first time, the automobile may seem a very complex mechanism. Yet the functioning of the automobile is based on a few simple mechanical fundamentals that all of us use in our daily lives. Thus the study of the automobile is not so much the learning of new principles as it is applying things we already know to the mechanisms of the automobile.

Basically, the automobile consists of four components (Fig. 2–1 shows three of these). They are:

1. The engine, or source of power.
2. The framework, or support for the engine and wheels, which includes the steering and braking systems.
3. The power train, or mechanism that transmits the power from the engine to the wheels.
4. The body.

To these may be added a fifth component, the car-body accessories. These accessories include the heater, lights,

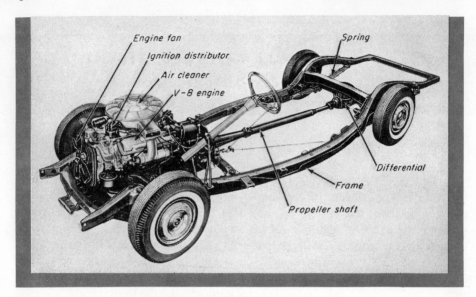

Fig. 2–1. Chassis of a passenger car. It contains the source of power, or engine; the frame which supports the engine, wheels, and body; the power train which carries the engine power to the rear wheels; the steering and breaking system. (*Mercury Division of Ford Motor Company*)

radio, and other devices that contribute to the convenience and comfort of the driver. Let us consider each of the five further.

§ 33. The engine
The engine (Fig. 2–2) is the source of power that makes the wheels go round and the car move. It is an *internal-combustion* engine because the fuel (gasoline) is burned *inside* it. (A steam engine is an *external-combustion* engine because the fuel is burned outside the engine.)

The burning of gasoline inside the engine produces high pressure in the engine combustion chambers. This high pressure forces *pistons* to move; the movement is carried by *connecting rods* to the engine crankshaft. The crankshaft is thus made to rotate; the rotary motion is carried through the power train to the car wheels so that they rotate and the car moves.

On a later page, we shall describe these parts and go into full detail on how the engine is constructed and how it operates. For the moment, we can remember that the engine requires a fuel system to supply it with a mixture of air and fuel. It also needs a cooling system; the combustion of the air-fuel mixture in the engine creates very high temperatures (as high as 4500°F). The cooling system removes part of this heat so that the engine does not become overheated and damaged. The engine also includes a lubricating system. The purpose of the lubricating system is to supply all moving parts inside the engine with lubricating oil; the oil keeps moving parts from wearing excessively. The engine requires a

Fig. 2–2. A typical six-cylinder engine, partly cut away so the internal construction can be seen. This engine is known as an "in-line six" because its six cylinders and pistons are one behind the other. Notice the cylindrical piston and its connecting rod shown in the cutaway view of the second cylinder. (*Ford Division of Ford Motor Company*)

fourth system, the ignition system. The ignition system provides high-voltage electric sparks that ignite, or set fire to, the charges of air-fuel mixture in the engine combustion chambers.

These four systems are discussed briefly in following sections. Then, in later chapters, we shall describe them in detail.

§ 34. Fuel system The fuel system (Fig. 2–3) consists of a tank in which

gasoline is stored, a pump which pumps gasoline from the tank, a carburetor which mixes the gasoline with air, and fuel lines (metal tubes) connecting the three.

1. Fuel pump. The fuel pump (Fig. 2–4) contains an airtight, flexible diaphragm attached by linkage to a rocker arm. This rocker arm moves back and forth when the engine is running (moved by an offset or eccentric section of the camshaft). This

35

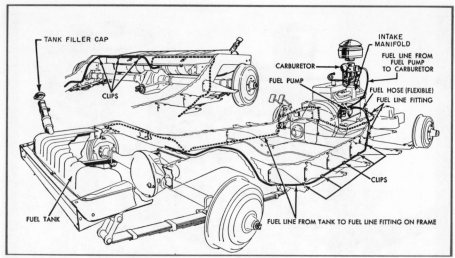

Fig. 2—3. Fuel system on an automotive chassis. Dotted line shows alternate fuel-line location.

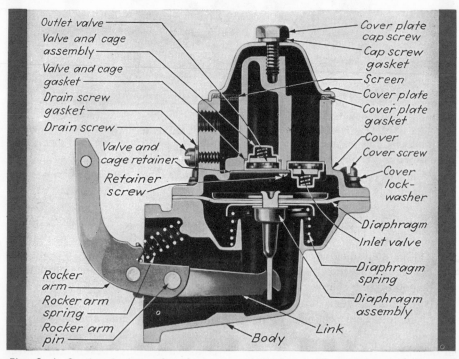

Fig. 2—4. Sectional view of a fuel pump. (AC *Spark Plug Division of General Motors Corporation*)

movement causes the diaphragm to move; gasoline is "drawn" from the gasoline tank and delivered to the carburetor. The fuel pump is discussed in detail in Chap. 8.

2. *Carburetor.* The carburetor (Fig. 2–5) is essentially a mixing device which mixes liquid gasoline with air. In this process, it throws a fine spray of gasoline into air passing through the carburetor (on its way to the engine). The gasoline evaporates and mixes with the air to form a highly combustible mixture. This mixture then enters the engine combustion chambers, where it is ignited. It burns to cause the engine to produce power. The carburetor is described in detail in Chap. 8.

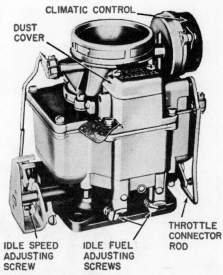

Fig. 2–5. A carburetor used on a six-cylinder engine.

§ 35. Ignition system

The ignition system is part of the electric system of the automobile. Its purpose is to produce high-voltage surges (of up to 20,-000 volts) and to deliver them to the combustion chambers in the engine. These high-voltage surges then cause electric sparks in the combustion chambers. The sparks ignite, or set fire to, the air-fuel mixture in the combustion chambers so that it burns and causes the engine to operate. Chapter 7 describes the ignition system in detail.

§ 36. Lubricating system

There are a great many moving metal parts in the engine. These parts must be protected by lubricating oil so that there will be no actual metal-to-metal contact. The moving parts, in effect, float on films of oil. You might compare this with a boat floating down a river. As long as the water is deep enough to float the boat, there will be no wear on either the bottom of the boat or the bed of the river. But suppose the water level should fall so that the boat makes contact with the river bed. If this should happen, then pushing the boat along on the river bed will wear both the bottom of the boat and the river bed. In a like manner, removing the oil film from between the moving metal parts in the engine would cause rapid wear and early failure of the engine.

The lubricating system is built into the engine. Figure 2–6 shows a lubricating system in an eight-cylinder engine. An oil pump takes oil from the oil pan and forces it through holes drilled in the engine block and crankshaft. This oil thereby reaches the various bearings that support rotating shafts and the different moving parts in the engine. It covers the surfaces of the moving parts to prevent metal-to-metal contact and undue wear of the parts.

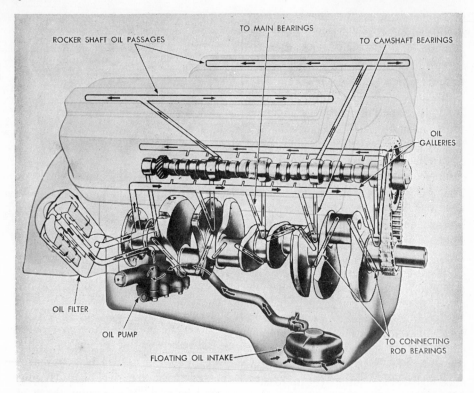

ROCKER SHAFT OIL PASSAGES

TO MAIN BEARINGS

TO CAMSHAFT BEARINGS

OIL GALLERIES

OIL FILTER

OIL PUMP

FLOATING OIL INTAKE

TO CONNECTING ROD BEARINGS

Fig. 2–6. Engine lubricating system in an eight-cylinder V-type engine. (*Chrysler Sales Division of Chrysler Corporation*)

§ **37. Cooling system** (Fig. 2–7) A great deal of heat is produced in the engine by the burning of the air-fuel mixture. Some of this heat escapes from the engine through the exhaust gases (the hot gases left after the gasoline burns). But enough remains in the engine to cause serious trouble unless removed by some other means. The cooling system takes care of this additional heat. The cooling system is built into the engine. There are hollow spaces around each engine cylinder and combustion chamber. These hollow spaces are called water jackets since they are filled with water when the engine is running. The water takes heat from the engine, becoming hot in the process. A water pump pumps the hot water from the engine water jackets into a radiator (see Fig. 2–7). The radiator has two sets of passages. One set carries water. The other set carries air (pulled through by car motion and the engine fan). As the hot water passes through, it gives up its heat to the air passing through. The cooled water then reenters the engine, where it can pick up more heat. In operation, water continuously circulates between the engine and radiator, carrying heat from the engine to the radiator. By this means, excessive engine temperatures are prevented.

TO RADIATOR
UPPER TANK

FROM RADIATOR
LOWER TANK

Fig. 2–7. Cooling system of a V-8 engine. Engine is partly cut away to show, by arrows, the circulation of water. The radiator is not shown, but see § 272 for a discussion of radiators. (*Mercury Division of Ford Motor Company*)

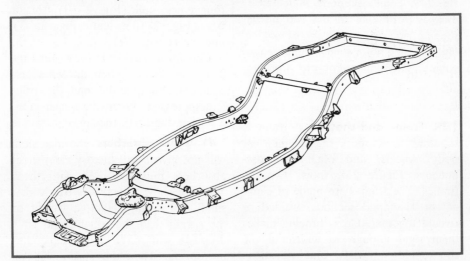

Fig. 2–8. Typical automobile frame. The frame curves upward at the rear (to right) to provide room for the rear springs. The frame narrows at the front to permit the front wheels to turn for steering. (*Ford Division of Ford Motor Company*)

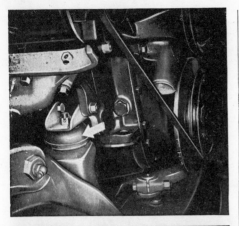

Fig. 2–9. Engine supports, indicated by arrows: (*Top*) One of the two biscuit-shaped mountings at front of engine. (*Bottom*) Long narrow mounting at rear of engine. (*Studebaker-Packard Corporation*)

§ 38. Frame and chassis

A frame is required to support the engine, car body, wheels, and other car components. Figure 2–8 shows two car frames. The frames are made of channel or U-shaped sections, welded or riveted together. Cross bracing makes them rigid enough to withstand the shock, blows, twists, and vibrations they meet in operation.

When the engine, wheels, power train, brakes, and steering system are installed on the frame, the assembly is called the chassis (Fig. 2–1).

§ 39. Engine support

The engine is usually supported by the frame at three or four places. The supporting arrangement includes rubber pads, or washers (Fig. 2–9), placed between the support lugs on the engine and the brackets on the frame. The rubber pads, or washers, prevent metal-to-metal contact. They thus absorb engine vibration and noise and prevent them from being carried directly to the frame and hence to the car body and passengers.

§ 40. Springs

The wheels are attached to the frame through springs (Fig. 2–10). The springs support the weight of the vehicle. They also allow the wheels to move up and down as the wheels meet holes or bumps in the road. Thus, little of this up-and-down movement is carried to the car frame, body, and passengers. Springs are of four types, coil (Fig. 2–10), torsion bar (Fig. 2–13), leaf (Fig. 29–3), and air (Chap. 29).

Coil-spring action is shown in Figs. 2–11 and 2–12. When the wheel encounters a bump in the road, the spring is compressed. When the wheel meets a hole in the road, the spring expands.

§ 41. Shock absorbers

Springs alone will not give a satisfactory ride; shock absorbers must be used with them. You can show why this is true with a small coil spring. Hang a weight on the spring. Lift the weight, and let it drop. It will move down, expanding the spring. Then the spring will rebound, pulling the weight up. The weight will move up and down (oscillate) for some time. On a car without

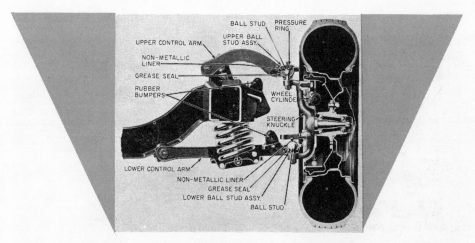

Fig. 2–10. Passenger-car front suspension using coil springs. Frame, wheel, and other parts partly cut away to show suspension parts. (*Pontiac Motor Division of General Motors Corporation*)

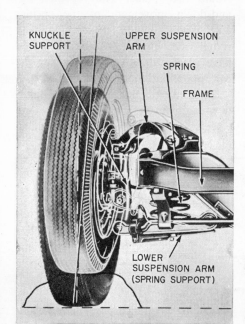

Fig. 2–11. Coil spring compresses as wheel encounters a bump in the road. Note how upward movement of wheel raises lower spring support to compress spring. (*Ford Motor Company*)

Fig. 2–12. Coil spring expands as wheel meets a hole in the road. Note how downward movement of wheel permits lower spring support to move down and expand spring. (*Ford Motor Company*)

41

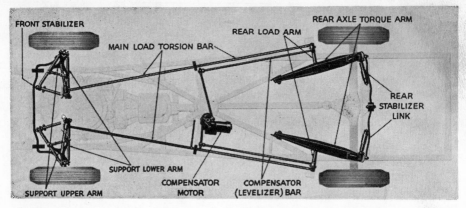

Fig. 2–13. Torsion-bar suspension system. (*Studebaker-Packard Corporation*)

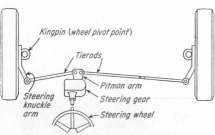

Fig. 2–14. Simplified drawing of a steering system.

shock absorbers, a similar action would take place. The repeated up-and-down movement of the springs and wheels would produce a very rough ride. Further, the driver would have great difficulty in controlling the car, particularly on curves.

To eliminate this excessive up-and-down movement of the springs and wheels, a shock absorber is placed at

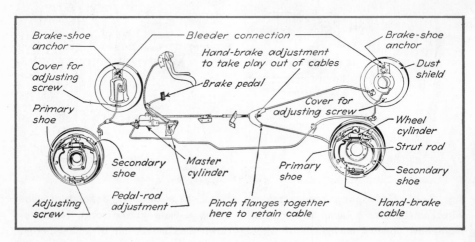

Fig. 2–15. Schematic view of a typical hydraulic-brake system. (*Cadillac Motor Car Division of General Motors Corporation*)

each wheel (**Fig. 2–10**). Shock absorbers are filled with fluid. In operation, wheel movement causes the shock absorber to force this fluid through small openings (orifices). Since fluid can pass through restricted openings rather slowly, this puts a restraint on wheel and spring movement. The restraint imposed prevents excessive wheel movement. It also damps out the spring oscillations quickly after the hole or bump is passed.

§ **42. Steering system** The steering system permits the front wheels to be pivoted on their supports to the right or left so that the car can be steered. Figure 2–14 is a simplified drawing of a steering system. The steering wheel is mounted on a steering shaft that ex-

tends into the steering gear. The bottom end of the shaft has a worm gear that rotates as the wheel is turned. A gear sector is meshed with the worm gear; rotation of the worm gear causes the gear sector to rotate. This movement causes the pitman arm, attached to the sector, to swing to the right or left. This action, in turn, pushes or pulls on the tie rods attached to the pitman arm. The steering-knuckle arms, attached to the front wheels, are therefore forced to swing the wheels to the right or left on their pivots.

§ **43. Brakes** Brakes are necessary to slow or stop the car. Practically all cars use hydraulic brakes (actuated by pressure on a fluid). A typical hydraulic-brake system is shown in Fig.

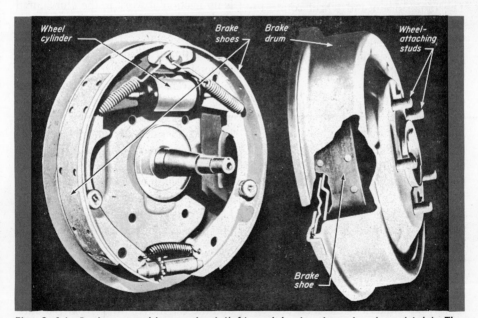

Fig. 2–16. Brake assembly at wheel (*left*) and brake drum in place (*right*). The drum is partly cut away so that one brake shoe can be seen. (*Oldsmobile Division of General Motors Corporation*)

2–15. When the brake pedal is pushed down, a piston, or plunger, is forced into the fluid-filled master cylinder. This forces brake fluid out of the master cylinder and through the brake lines, or tubes, into the brake wheel cylinders. There are wheel cylinders at each wheel (Fig. 2–16). Each wheel cylinder contains two pistons connected to the two brake shoes in the wheel brake assembly. As the brake fluid is forced into the wheel cylinder, it causes the two pistons to move outward. This, in turn, causes the brake shoes to move outward. The shoes are steel; the outer curved surface is covered with a tough asbestos material that can withstand wear and heat. As the shoes move outward, they are forced into contact with the curved inner surface of the rotating brake drum. The brake drum and wheel rotate together; when the brake shoes are forced tightly against the drum, they produce a frictional drag that slows or stops the wheel.

§ 44. **Tires**   The tires support the weight of the car. They absorb road shocks resulting from small bumps or holes. The older type of tire, used for many years, consists of an outer casing and an inner tube. In later tires, the two have, in effect, been combined; no inner tube is used. In the older type, air is retained in the inner tube. In the later type, the air is retained between the casing and the wheel rim. The car, in effect, rides on cushions of air which permit the tires to give slightly as road irregularities are encountered. This action provides a smoother ride. Tires also provide good frictional contact at the road surface.

§ 45. **Power train**   The power train (Fig. 2–17) contains several mechanisms which carry the engine power to the rear wheels. These are the clutch, transmission, propeller shaft, differential, and rear axles.

NOTE: Cars equipped with automatic transmissions normally do not have a clutch. On these, the transmission operates automatically so that the driver is not required to use a clutch and to shift gears.

The clutch is a friction-type uncoupling device. It is linked to a clutch pedal in the driver's compartment. When the driver pushes down on the clutch pedal, the linkage forces a flat disk, or plate, to move. This movement releases the pressure from a friction disk. With the pressure released, there is no friction at work in the clutch, and the power flow is therefore interrupted. That is, the engine runs without transmitting power to the power train. It is declutched from the transmission.

The transmission provides different *gear ratios* between the engine and wheels. This is necessary with the gasoline engine since the engine produces little power at low speed. Thus, for accelerating the car from a standing start, considerable power is required; the engine should be running at a fairly high speed. The driver therefore shifts the transmission gears into low; this gear position permits the engine to run at fairly high speed while turning the rear wheels at a fairly low speed. Thus, the engine develops high power, and the car moves away from the curb and accelerates quickly. Next, the driver shifts to second (momentarily declutching to permit movement of

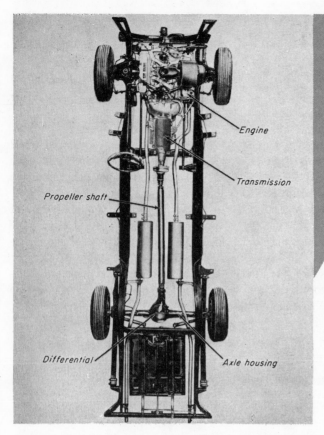

Fig. 2–17. View from top of a typical automotive chassis showing locations of engine, transmission, propeller shaft, differential, and rear axle housing. (*Dodge Division of Chrysler Corporation*)

the gears in the transmission). In second, the car accelerates to a higher speed. Finally, the driver shifts to high. In this gear position, there is a direct drive through the transmission; the propeller shaft turns at the same speed as the engine crankshaft. There is another gear position, reverse. In this position, the propeller shaft is made to rotate in a reverse direction so that the car is backed.

The propeller shaft is a drive shaft to carry the power from the transmission to the rear-wheel axles. It contains two devices, a universal joint (or joints) and a slip joint. These joints permit the shaft to lengthen and shorten and, in effect, to bend. This shaft flexibility is necessary because the rear wheels move up and down as a result of the spring actions at the rear of the car.

The differential contains gears that carry the driving power from the propeller shaft to the rear-wheel axles. A differential is necessary so that the two rear wheels can rotate different amounts when the car goes around a turn. As this happens, the outside wheel must turn more times than the inner wheel. The differential permits this action while still delivering power to both rear wheels.

All these power-train components,

as well as the other components of the automobile, are covered in detail in following chapters.

REVIEW QUESTIONS

1. What are the five basic components of the automobile?
2. Why is the automobile engine called an *internal-combustion* engine?
3. What are the four separate accessory systems required for operation of the engine?
4. What is the purpose of the fuel system?
5. What is the purpose of the fuel pump? The carburetor?
6. What is the purpose of the lubrication system?
7. What is the purpose of the cooling system?
8. What is the purpose of the car springs?
9. Why are shock absorbers used?
10. Describe briefly how the steering system operates.
11. How do brakes operate?
12. What is the purpose of the tires?
13. Of what mechanisms does the power train from the engine to the car wheels consist?
14. Describe briefly the operation of the clutch.
15. What is the purpose of the transmission?
16. Why are universal joints used?
17. What is the purpose of the slip joint?
18. Why is a differential required?

THE GOOD SHOPMAN

The good shopman works carefully and thoughtfully. He avoids doing things that will distract his fellow workers or cause them to get hurt. He is thinking about the job he is doing. He does his job in the most businesslike and efficient manner possible. He is not only a good worker, he is a safe worker.

This does not mean he is grim or glum. Quite the contrary. The good shopman is friendly and pleasant to others. He is capable of getting along with others, of working with them.

All this is important to the future of the good shopworker. People like the pleasant, hard-working fellow who minds his own business, who "knows his stuff" on the job he is doing. It is easy to have a good word for the fellow who is liked. It is easy for the foreman or manager to remember the fellow he likes when it comes time for that pay raise or better job.

THIS CHAPTER DISCUSSES THE fundamental principles that enter into the operation of automobile engines. It explains what takes place in the engine that causes the engine to produce power. In addition, the chapter describes the construction of a typical engine. Following chapters discuss various specific types of engine and explain in detail how they are constructed.

PHYSICAL PRINCIPLES

§ 46. Atoms You may think it somewhat strange for us to start this chapter with a description of atoms. However, if we have some understanding of these fundamental particles, we shall be able to understand engine operation more easily. In this modern world, almost everyone has heard of the atom bomb and of "splitting the atom" in the laboratory. There are more than ninety varieties of atoms. Each variety has a special structure and a special name, such as iron, copper, lead, hydrogen, oxygen, tin, and so on. A piece of iron, for example, is made up of a tremendous number of one particular variety of atom. A quantity of the gas oxygen is made up of a great number of another variety of atom. Any substance made up of one variety of atom is called an *element*. The atoms of the more than ninety

elements can be put together in thousands of different ways to form a great variety of compounds. This can be compared to the 26 letters of the alphabet, which can be combined in many ways to form the thousands of words of our language. Thus, salt, water, wood, glass, the very blood and bone of our bodies are made up of compounds produced by the combining of different atoms. Common table salt is made up of atoms of the elements sodium and chlorine. Water is made up of the elements hydrogen and oxygen.

§ 47. Size of atoms Atoms are far too small for us to see, even with the most powerful microscopes. There are billions of atoms in a single drop of water. To get an idea of how small they actually are, consider this: A cubic inch of hydrogen gas (at 32°F and atmospheric pressure) contains about 880,000,000,000,000,000,000 (880 billion billion) hydrogen atoms (Fig. 3–1). Suppose we were able to expand this cube until it was large enough to contain the earth. This means that each edge would measure 8,000 miles (instead of 1 inch). Now, if the atoms were expanded the same amount (or about 500,000,000 times), each atom would measure only about ten inches in diameter!

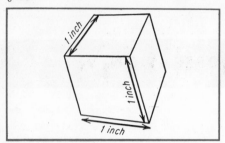

Fig. 3–1. A cubic inch of hydrogen gas at atmospheric pressure and at 32°F contains about 880 billion billion atoms.

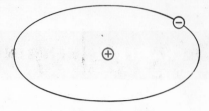

+ means plus or positive
− means minus or negative

Fig. 3–2. The hydrogen atom is made up of two particles, a proton with a positive electric charge and an electron with a negative electric charge.

NOTE: Since there are so many atoms, you might think they are packed closely together. But they are not. The distance between atoms is considerably greater than the diameter of the atoms.

§ **48. The hydrogen atom** The hydrogen atom is the simplest of all atoms. It is made up of two particles (Fig. 3–2). One of these, at the center, or *nucleus,* is a proton (it carries a positive electric charge). The other, whirling around the nucleus at tremendous speed, is an electron (it carries a negative electric charge).

NOTE: Positive charge is indicated by a plus (+) sign. Negative charge is indicated by a minus (−) sign.

The electron is kept in its path around the proton by two forces. One force is the attraction that two particles of opposing electric charges have for each other. Positive attracts negative, and negative attracts positive. This attraction tends to pull the electron in to the proton. But the attraction is balanced by the tendency the electron has to fly away in a straight line (instead of continuing to move in

a circle). This is somewhat similar to the balance of forces you have when you swing a ball on a rubber band around your hand (Fig. 3–3). The ball tries to fly away from your hand (and it would if the rubber band broke). But the rubber band (the attractive force) keeps the ball moving in its circular path around your hand.

§ **49. Helium** The next element above hydrogen, as we go from the simplest to the more complicated atoms, is helium, another gas. The helium atom has two protons (+ charges) in its nucleus and two electrons (− charges) circling the nucleus (Fig. 3–4). The nucleus of the helium atom also contains two other particles which are neutral electrically (and are thus

Fig. 3–3. The electron in a hydrogen atom circles the proton like a ball on a rubber band swung in a circle around the hand.

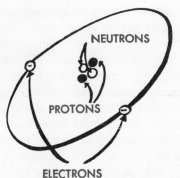

Fig. 3–4. A helium atom.

called *neutrons*). The neutrons seem to have the ability to hold the two protons (with their + charges) in the nucleus. Without the neutrons, the two protons would fly apart. For just as opposing electric charges (positive and negative) attract each other, so do like electric charges repel each other. Positive repels positive. Negative repels negative.

§ 50. More complex atoms The next element above helium in complexity is lithium, a very light metal. The lithium atom (Fig. 3–5) has 3 protons and 4 neutrons. Three electrons, one for each proton, circle the nucleus.

Next comes beryllium with 4 protons, 5 neutrons, and 4 electrons; boron with 5, 5, and 5; carbon with 6, 6, and 6; nitrogen with 7, 7, and 7; oxygen with 8, 8, and 8; and so on. Note that each atom normally contains the same number of electrons as it has protons. This makes the atom electrically neutral (since positive charges equal negative charges).

§ 51. Molecules We have already mentioned that the atoms of the various elements can combine in thousands

of ways to form a great variety of compounds. Whenever atoms combine, *molecules* are formed. A molecule of common table salt is made up of two atoms, one atom of sodium and one atom of chlorine. A molecule of water is made up of one atom of oxygen and two atoms of hydrogen. These are very simple molecules. Many molecules are very complicated and contain many atoms. The molecule of serum albumin (found in blood plasma) contains about ten thousand atoms.

The formation of molecules from atoms or from other molecules is called *chemical reaction*. During chemical reaction, electrons are interchanged, or shared, between the atoms involved. The nuclei of the atoms remain unchanged.

§ 52. Combustion Combustion, or fire, is a common chemical reaction in which the gas oxygen combines with other elements such as hydrogen or carbon. One type of combustion process occurs in the automobile engine; a mixture of air and gasoline vapor is compressed and then ignited, or set on fire. A following section describes engine processes in detail.

The air (our atmosphere) is about 20 percent oxygen. Gasoline is largely

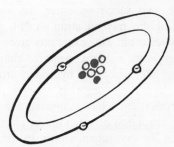

Fig. 3–5. A lithium atom.

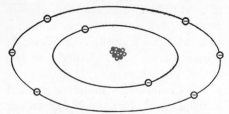

Fig. 3–6. An oxygen atom. The 8 electrons circle the nucleus in two paths, or orbits, 2 in an inner orbit and 6 in an outer orbit.

hydrogen and carbon (and is thus called a hydrocarbon). The chemical reaction during combustion is between these three elements (oxygen, hydrogen, and carbon).

The oxygen atom has 8 protons and 8 neutrons in its nucleus. Eight electrons circle the nucleus in two orbits (Fig. 3–6), 2 in an inner orbit and 6 in an outer orbit. The outer orbit is capable of carrying 8 electrons. It will, in fact, accept, or "grab," 2 additional electrons if any are nearby. The hydrogen atom has 1 electron, as already mentioned.

During the combustion process, the gasoline splits up into hydrogen and carbon. Then these two elements combine with oxygen. For instance, when the hydrogen and oxygen combine, two hydrogen atoms lose their electrons to one oxygen atom as shown in Fig. 3–7. These two electrons enter the outer orbit of the oxygen atom to "fill up" the outer orbit. However, this gives the oxygen atom a double negative charge. Meanwhile, since the hydrogen atoms have lost their negative charges (or electrons), each has a positive charge. Now, attraction between unlike charges causes the hydrogen atoms to attach themselves to the oxygen atom to form

a molecule. The molecule has the symbol H_2O and the name *water*.

Now, let us see what happens when carbon and oxygen unite. The carbon atom has 6 protons and 6 neutrons in its nucleus and 6 electrons circling its nucleus (Fig. 3–8). Two of the electrons are in the inner orbit, the other 4 in the outer orbit. During the combustion process, the 4 electrons in the outer orbit are "grabbed" by two oxygen atoms somewhat as shown in Fig. 3–9. This gives the oxygen atoms two negative charges each and the carbon atom four positive charges. The opposing electric charges therefore bring the three atoms together to form a molecule of the gas carbon dioxide, or CO_2.

Now see what we have. In the combustion process, oxygen in the air unites with hydrogen and carbon in the gasoline to form water and carbon dioxide. Since the combustion is accompanied with high temperatures (which may go above 4500°F), the water is in the form of vapor, or steam.

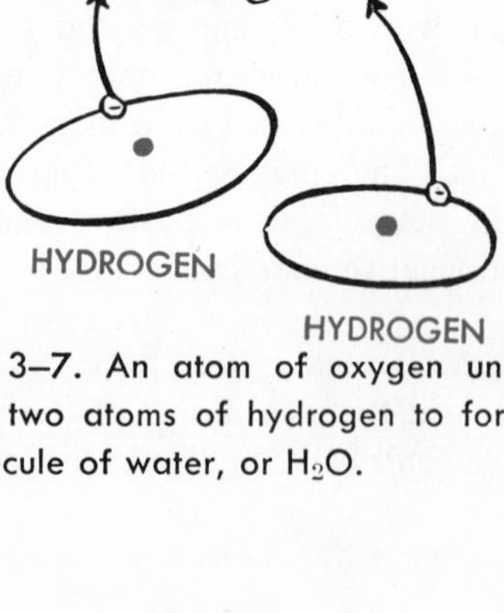

OXYGEN

HYDROGEN

HYDROGEN

Fig. 3–7. An atom of oxygen uniting with two atoms of hydrogen to form a molecule of water, or H_2O.

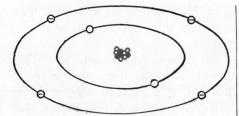

Fig. 3–8. An atom of carbon.

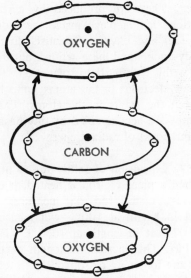

Fig. 3–9. Two atoms of oxygen uniting with one atom of carbon to form a molecule of carbon dioxide, or CO_2.

Both the water vapor and carbon dioxide are exhausted from the engine through the exhaust system.

§ 53. Heat We mentioned that combustion is accompanied with high temperatures. What is meant by the term "high temperature," or "heat"? From the scientific viewpoint, heat is simply *the rapid motion of the atoms or molecules of a substance.*

This may be a hard statement to understand. First, it is necessary to realize that the atoms and molecules

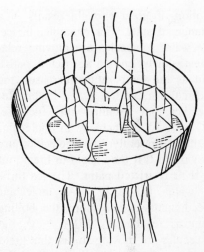

Fig. 3–10. When ice cubes are heated in a pan over a fire, they first melt, or turn to water. Then, the water boils, or turns to vapor.

of any substance are in rapid motion. Even though a piece of iron or the table top appears solid and motionless, the molecules and atoms composing them are in rapid motion. The atoms in a piece of hot iron are moving faster than the atoms in a piece of cold iron.

§ 54. Change of state You probably are still puzzled. But when we discuss change of state, the idea that heat is atomic (or molecular) motion will become clear.

If we put a pan of ice cubes over a fire, the ice cubes would soon melt, or turn to water. Then, the water would boil, or turn to vapor (Fig. 3–10). Most substances can exist in any of these three states, solid, liquid, gas (or vapor). When a substance changes from one state to another, it undergoes a *change of state.*

A change in the speed of molecular

51

motion, if great enough, results in a change of state. For example, in ice, the water molecules are moving relatively slowly and in restricted paths. But as the temperature increases, the molecules move faster and faster. Remember that a temperature increase, or *heat,* is an increase in molecular motion. Presently, the molecules are moving so fast they begin to break out of their restricted paths. The ice turns to water (at 32°F). As molecular speed increases still more, the boiling point is reached (212°F). Now, the molecules are moving so fast that great numbers of them fly clear out of the water. The water boils, or turns to vapor.

§ 55. Producing change of state

But what makes the water molecules move faster? Here is a somewhat simplified explanation: During combustion, as already noted, oxygen atoms unite with carbon or hydrogen atoms. The new molecules thus formed are set into extremely rapid motion. Rushing together of the atoms to satisfy the unbalance of electric charges can be said to produce this rapid motion. Now, the newly formed and rapidly moving molecules from the fire below the pan bombard the pan. This bombardment sets the molecules of metal in the pan into more rapid motion (the pan becomes hot). The metal molecules, in turn, bombard the ice molecules. The ice melts; the water turns to vapor.

§ 56. Light and heat radiations

This is only a partial description of what takes place in a fire. In addition to the swiftly moving molecules, the fire also produces *radiations*. We see these radiations as *light* and can feel them as *heat*. They are produced by certain actions taking place inside the atoms of fuel and oxygen. Scientists do not fully understand these actions, but they offer this as a partial explanation: The inner electrons in the atoms jump between the orbits in the atoms. These jumps are accompanied by tiny flashes (emissions) of radiant energy.

§ 57. Expansion of solids due to heat

When a piece of iron is heated, it expands. A steel rod that measures 10 feet in length at 100°F will measure 10.07 feet in length at 1000°F (Fig. 3–11). This increase in length occurs for the following reason:

As the rod is heated, the molecules in it move faster and faster. If the rod is heated enough, the steel will melt, or undergo a change of state. But even before this happens, the steel will expand a little. For as the molecules move faster and faster, they need more room. They "push" adjacent molecules away so that they all have, in effect, more room to move around in.

Fig. 3–11. A steel rod that measures 10 feet at 100°F will measure 10.07 feet at 1000°F.

§ 58. Expansion of liquids and gases

Not only solids, like iron, copper, or aluminum, but also liquids and gases expand when heated. A cubic foot of water at 39°F will become, when heated to 100°F, 1.01 cubic feet. A cubic foot of air at 32°F, heated to

100°F without a change in pressure, would become 1.14 cubic feet. These expansion effects result from more rapid molecular motion, which tends to push the atoms and molecules farther apart so that they "spread out" and take up more room.

§ 59. Increase of pressure

A different sort of effect results if the volume is held constant while the cubic foot of air is heated from 32 to 100°F. If we started with a pressure of 15 psi (pounds per square inch), we would find that the pressure would increase to about 17 psi at 100°F. This can be explained by the molecular theory of heat we have already discussed (§§52–58). But, first, let us look at the term "pressure" more closely.

Gas or air pressure in a container is due entirely to the unending bombardment of the gas molecules against the insides of the container (Fig. 13–12). As we have already said, gas or vapor molecules are moving about in all directions at high speed. They are continually bumping into each other and into any solid that is in their way. Thus, the walls of the container are bumped by these countless billions of molecules; these "bumps" add up to a definite combined "push," or pressure.

As temperature increases, the molecules of air move faster. They bump the walls of the container harder and more often to produce an increased pressure.

Now, let us look at what happens when air is compressed (as, for instance, in the engine cylinders). Compressing air pushes the molecules closer together. This means that the molecules will be bumping into each

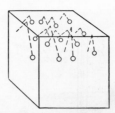

Fig. 3–12. Gas pressure in a container is the result of the ceaseless bombardment of the inner sides of the container by the fast-moving molecules of gas. This "bombardment" is shown on only one side of the container for simplicity. It actually takes place against all the inner sides. The molecules are shown tremendously enlarged. And, of course, there are billions of molecules entering into the action, and not a few as shown.

other, and into the walls of the container, more often. This more intense bombardment adds up to a greater pressure.

NOTE: Not only pressure, but temperature also increases when a gas is compressed. Moving the molecules closer together causes them to bump each other more often so that they are set into faster motion. Faster motion means a higher temperature. For example, in the diesel-engine cylinder, air is compressed to as little as a sixteenth of its original volume. During this action, the temperature of the compressed air goes up to as much as 1000°F. Of course, the heat produced by the action would soon escape from the compressed air and its container into the surrounding air. Any hot object tends to lose heat until its temperature falls to that of the surrounding medium.

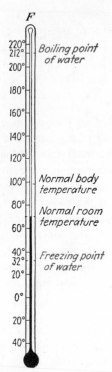

F

220°
212° — Boiling point
200° — of water

180° —

160° —

140° —

120° —

100° — Normal body
temperature

80° — Normal room
temperature
60° —

40°
32° — Freezing point
20° — of water

0° —

20° —

40° —

Fig. 3–13. A Fahrenheit thermometer.

§ 60. The thermometer

The ordinary glass-stemmed thermometer (Fig. 3–13) is a familiar application of the principle that liquids expand with increasing temperature. The liquid, usually mercury (a metal that is liquid at ordinary temperatures) or a special type of alcohol, is largely contained in the glass bulb at the lower end of the stem. As temperature increases, the liquid expands. Since it now needs more room, part of it is forced up into the hollow glass stem. The higher the temperature, the farther the liquid is forced up into the stem. The stem is marked off to indicate the temperature in degrees.

§ 61. The thermostat

Different metals expand different amounts with increasing temperature. For example, aluminum expands twice as fast as iron as their temperatures go up. This difference in expansion rates is used in thermostats. These devices are temperature-sensitive and can be made to do various jobs as temperature changes. For instance, the thermostat in your home heating system turns the furnace on when the temperature goes down and turns it off when the temperature comes up to the shutoff point. Various thermostats are used in the automobile to open and close electric circuits, to control the engine cooling system, and so on. One type of thermostat is shown in Fig. 3–14. It consists of a coil made of two strips of different metals, brass and steel, for example, welded together. When the coil is heated, one metal expands faster than the other. If the faster-expanding metal is on the inside of the strip, the coil will attempt to straighten out and will unwind. Various thermostats are described in the pages that follow.

Fig. 3–14. A coil-type thermostat. The coil winds up and unwinds as the temperature goes up and down. The resulting motion can be used to operate a control.

§ 62. Gravity

Gravity is the attractive force that exists between all objects. When we release a stone from our hand, it falls toward the earth. When a car is being driven up a hill, a considerable part of the engine power is being used in overcoming gravity (raising the car against gravitational attraction). Likewise, a car can coast down a hill with the engine turned off because of the gravitational attraction of the earth on the car.

Gravitational attraction is usually measured in terms of *weight*. We put an object on a scales and note that it "weighs" 10 pounds, for example. What we mean by this is that the object has sufficient mass for the earth to register that much pull on it. It is gravitational attraction, or the pull of the earth, that gives an object its weight.

§ 63. Atmospheric pressure

We do not usually think of the air as having any weight. But the air is an "object," and it has weight (is pulled toward the earth by gravitational attraction). At sea level and average temperature, a cubic foot of air weighs about eight-hundredths (0.08) of a pound, or about 1¼ ounces. This seems like very little. But we must consider that the blanket of air (our atmosphere) surrounding the earth is many miles thick. This means that there are, in effect, many thousands of cubic feet of air piled one on top of another, all adding their weight. Actually, we find that the total weight, or downward push, of this air amounts to about 15 psi at sea level. This means that the pressure of the air (atmospheric pressure) is about 2,160

pounds on every square foot. This is more than a ton per square foot (2,000 pounds = 1 ton). Since the human body has a surface area of several square feet, the body is sustaining a total atmospheric pressure of several tons!

When a person first realizes this, he is apt to wonder why all this tremendous pressure doesn't crush him. The reason is that the internal pressures in the body balance these outside pressures. Fish have been found thousands of feet down in the ocean, where pressures are more than 100,000 psi (which is about seven hundred tons per square foot). The fish can live because their internal pressures balance these enormous outside pressures.

§ 64. Vacuum

Vacuum is the absence of air or other matter. If we could journey far above the earth's surface, hundreds of miles, we should find practically no atmosphere at all. That is, there are only a few widely scattered atoms of air at this height. This is vacuum.

But we do not need to leave the earth to find a vacuum. We can produce a vacuum on earth with a long glass tube, closed at one end, plus a dish of mercury (a heavy metal that is liquid at normal temperatures). To produce the vacuum, we completely fill the tube with mercury and then close the end. Next, we turn the tube upside down and put the end in the dish of mercury. Finally, we open the end. Some of the mercury will run down out of the tube, leaving the upper end of the tube empty (Fig. 3–15). Since no air can enter the upper end of the

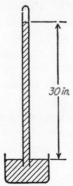

Fig. 3–15. A barometer. The mercury in the tube will stand at about 30 inches above the surface of the mercury in the dish at an atmospheric pressure of 15 psi.

tube, the upper part of the tube is a vacuum.

The device (Fig. 3–15) is called a *barometer* and is used to measure atmospheric pressure (Fig. 3–16). When atmospheric pressure increases, the increased push on the mercury forces the mercury higher in the tube. When atmospheric pressure goes down, there is a weaker push on the mercury and the mercury settles to a lower level in the tube.

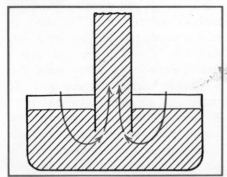

Fig. 3–16. The pressure of the air, acting on the surface of the mercury and through the mercury, holds the mercury up in the tube.

NOTE: The barometer is a useful device in forecasting weather changes. Before a storm, the atmospheric pressure usually drops. This is due to the heated, and lighter, air accompanying a storm. Thus, when the mercury "falls" in the barometer, it indicates a storm.

OPERATION OF ENGINE

§ 65. The engine cylinder Most automotive engines have six or eight cylinders. Since similar actions take place in all cylinders, let us concentrate on one cylinder to study engine operation. Figure 2–2 shows an engine in side view, partly cut away so that internal parts can be seen. Figure 3–17 shows an end view of an engine, cut away so that the cylinder, piston, valve, and other parts can be seen. Figure 3–18 shows this same cylinder at an angle; here, the cylinder is cut away, but the piston is not. Essentially, the cylinder is nothing more than a cylindrical air pocket, closed at one end. A movable metal plug—the piston—fits snugly into the open end of the cylinder. The piston is made of aluminum or other suitable metal. It is a snug fit, but it is still loose enough to slide easily up and down in the cylinder.

Figure 3–19 shows this action. In Fig. 3–19*a,* the piston is below the cylinder. The cylinder is drawn as though it were transparent so that the actions inside it can be seen. Figure 3–19*b* shows the piston pushed up into the cylinder. This upward movement of the piston traps air in the cylinder and compresses it (pushes it into a smaller space). If we could now put some gasoline vapor into the compressed air, and if we were able to

apply a lighted match or spark to the air-vapor mixture, it is obvious what would happen. The gasoline vapor would burn. High pressure would be created, and the piston would be blown out of the cylinder as shown in Fig. 3–19c. This is about what happens in the engine cylinder. A mixture of gasoline vapor and air enters the cylinder, the piston moves up to compress it, the compressed mixture is ignited, and the resulting combustion pushes the piston downward.

§ 66. **Piston rings** The piston must be a fairly loose fit in the cylinder. If it were a tight fit, then, as it became hot, it would expand and might stick in the cylinder. This, of course, could ruin the engine. On the other hand, if the piston fitted too loosely, excessive amounts of air-fuel mixture and combustion pressure would leak past. This loss would seriously reduce engine performance.

To provide a good sealing fit between the piston and cylinder, piston rings are used. The rings are split at one point and are fitted into grooves cut into the outside of the piston (Fig. 3–20). When the piston is installed in the cylinder, these rings are com-

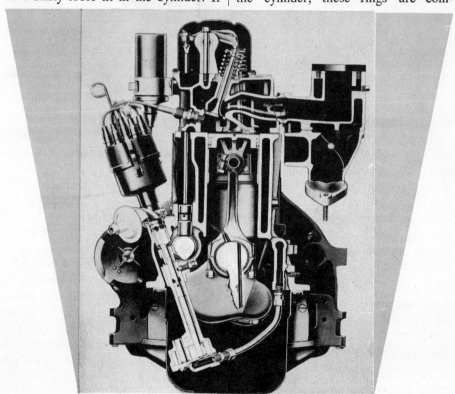

Fig. 3–17. Cross-sectional view of a six-cylinder engine. Piston is at top of stroke. Both piston and cylinder are shown cut in half. (*Chevrolet Motor Division of General Motors Corporation*)

57

Fig. 3–18. Cutaway view of an eight-cylinder, V-type engine. (*Mercury Division of Ford Motor Company*)

pressed into the grooves so that the split ends almost come together. The rings fit tightly against the cylinder wall and against the sides of the groove so that there is a good seal between the cylinder wall and piston. Little combustion pressure can escape past the rings. Even with the good seal the piston and rings can still slide freely up and down in the cylinder.

§ 67. Reciprocating to rotary motion

As we mentioned in § 65, the piston moves up and down in the cylinder. This up-and-down motion is called *reciprocating motion*. The piston moves in a straight line. This straight-line motion must be changed to rotary, or turning, motion in order for it to turn the car wheels. A crank and a connecting rod (Figs. 3–21 and 3–22) change reciprocating motion to rotary.

The crank is an offset section of the engine crankshaft. It swings around in a circle as the shaft rotates. The connecting rod connects the crankpin of the crank to the piston (Fig. 3–22). The crank end of the connecting rod is attached to the crankpin by the rod bearing cap. The cap is fastened to the connecting rod with the rod-cap bolts (Fig. 3–22). The cap and rod have bearings which permit the crankpin to rotate freely within the rod. The piston end of the rod is attached to the piston by the *piston pin,* or *wrist pin.* The piston pin is held in two bearings in the piston. A bearing in the piston-pin end of the connecting rod (or bearings in the piston) permits the rod to swing back and forth on the piston pin.

NOTE: Crank end of connecting rod is sometimes called rod "big end," while piston end is called rod "small end."

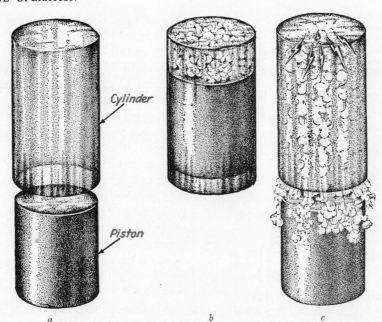

Fig. 3–19. Three views showing the actions in engine cylinder: (a) The piston is a metal plug that fits snugly up into the engine cylinder. (b) When the piston is pushed up into the cylinder, air is trapped and compressed. The cylinder is drawn as though it were transparent so that the piston can be seen. (c) The increase of pressure as the gasoline vapor and air mixture is ignited pushes the piston out of the cylinder.

Now, let us see what happens as the piston moves up and down in the cylinder (Fig. 3–23). As the piston starts down, the connecting rod tilts to one side so that the lower end can follow the circular path of the crankpin. If you follow the sequence of actions as shown in Fig. 3–23 (steps numbered 1 to 8), you will note that the connecting rod tilts or swings back and forth on the piston pin while the lower end moves in a circle along with the crankpin.

§ **68. The valves** There are two openings, or ports, in the enclosed end of the cylinder, one of which is shown in Fig. 3–18. One of the ports permits the

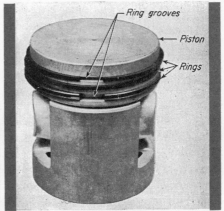

Fig. 3–20. A typical piston with piston rings in place. When the piston is installed in the cylinder, the rings are compressed into the grooves in the piston.

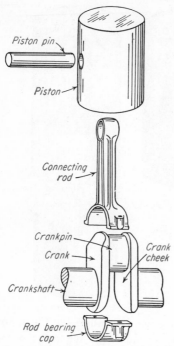

Fig. 3–21. A piston, connecting rod, piston pin, and crankpin on engine crankshaft in disassembled view. Piston rings are not shown.

mixture of air and gasoline vapor to enter the cylinder. The other port permits the burned gases, after combustion, to exhaust, or escape, from the cylinder.

The two ports have valves assembled into them. These valves close off one or the other port, or both ports, during the various stages of engine operation. The valves are nothing more than accurately machined metal plugs (on long stems) that close the openings when they are seated (have moved down into the openings). Figure 3–24 shows a valve and valve seat of the type generally used in automotive engines; the valve is shown raised up off the valve seat so that it is opened. This

type of valve is called a *poppet valve*.

When the valve closes, it moves down so that the outer edge rests on the seat. In this position, the valve port is closed so that air or gas cannot escape from the cylinder.

A spring on the valve stem (Fig. 3–25) tends to hold the valve on its seat (closed). The upper end of the spring rests against a flat section of the cylinder block. The lower end rests against a flat washer, or spring retainer, which is attached to the valve stem by a retainer lock (also called a keeper). The spring is under compression, which means it tries to expand and therefore spring-loads the valve in the closed position.

A valve-opening mechanism opens the valve, or lifts it off its seat, at certain times. This mechanism includes a

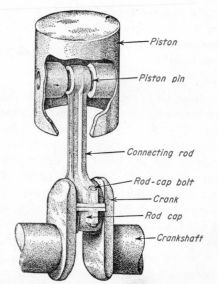

Fig. 3–22. Piston and connecting-rod assembly attached to crankpin on crankshaft. Piston rings not shown. Piston partly cut away to show how it is attached to connecting rod.

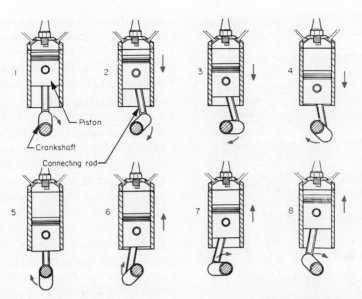

Fig. 3–23. Sequence of actions as crankshaft completes one revolution and piston moves from top to bottom to top again.

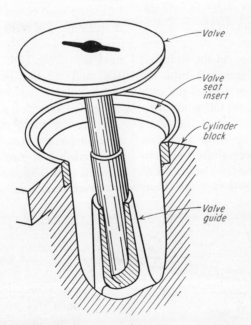

Fig. 3–24. A valve and valve seat in cylinder. The cylinder block, valve guide, and valve-seat insert have been partly cut away so that the valve stem can be seen.

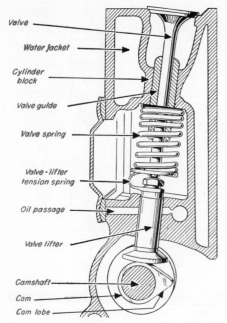

Fig. 3–25. Valve mechanism used in an L-head engine. Valve is raised off seat with every camshaft rotation. (*Studebaker-Packard Corporation*)

valve lifter and a cam on the camshaft (Fig. 3–25). As the camshaft turns, the "bump," or high spot (called the cam lobe), on the cam comes around under the valve lifter. This raises the lifter. As the lifter moves up, it pushes up on the valve stem, forcing the valve to move upward off its seat, or to open. After the cam lobe moves out from

under the valve lifter, the valve spring forces the valve down on its seat again.

Figure 3–26 shows a typical camshaft. It has a cam for each valve in the engine, or two cams per cylinder. The camshaft is driven by gears, or by a chain, from the crankshaft. It turns at one-half crankshaft speed. The cam lobes are so positioned on the camshaft as to cause the valves to open and close in the cylinders at the proper time with respect to the actions taking place in the cylinders.

§ 69. Action in a cylinder The actions taking place in the engine cylinder can be divided into four stages, or strokes. "Stroke" refers to piston movement; a stroke occurs when the piston moves from one limiting position to the other. The upper limit of piston movement (position 1 in Fig. 3–23) is called TDC (top dead center). The lower limit of piston movement is called BDC (bottom dead center). A stroke is piston movement from TDC to BDC or from BDC to TDC. In other words, the piston completes a stroke each time it changes its direction of motion.

Where the entire cycle of events in the cylinder requires four strokes (or two crankshaft revolutions), the engine is called a *four-stroke-cycle engine,* or a *four-cycle engine.* The term "Otto

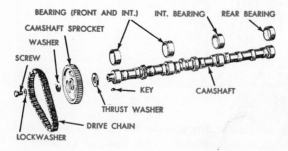

Fig. 3–26. Camshaft and related parts for six-cylinder engine. (*Ford Division of Ford Motor Company*)

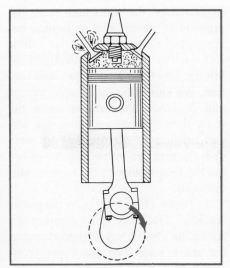

Fig. 3–27. Intake stroke. The intake valve (*left*) has opened, and the piston is moving downward, drawing air and gasoline vapor into the cylinder.

take stroke, the intake valve has opened. The piston is moving down, and a mixture of air and vaporized gasoline is being "drawn" into the cylinder through the valve port. The mixture of air and vaporized gasoline is delivered to the cylinder by the fuel system and carburetor (discussed in Chap. 8).

NOTE: Actually, the piston does not "draw" the air-fuel mixture into the cylinder. As the piston moves down, a partial vacuum is produced in the cylinder and atmospheric pressure (pressure of the air) outside the engine pushes air into the engine cylinder. This air passes through the carburetor, where it picks up a charge of gasoline vapor, and then through the intake manifold and intake-valve port (see Chap. 8).

cycle" is also applied to this type of engine (after Friedrich Otto, a German scientist of the nineteenth century). The four piston strokes are intake, compression, power, and exhaust. (Two-stroke-cycle engines are also in use; in these, the entire cycle of events is completed in two strokes, or one crankshaft revolution.)

NOTE: For the sake of simplicity in the following discussion, the valves are considered to open and close at TDC and BDC. Actually, they are not timed to open and close at these points, as is explained in a later chapter. Also, the illustrations showing the four strokes (Figs. 3–27 to 3–30) are much simplified. They show the intake and exhaust valves separated and placed on either side of the cylinder so that both can be seen.

1. Intake (Fig. 3–27). On the in-

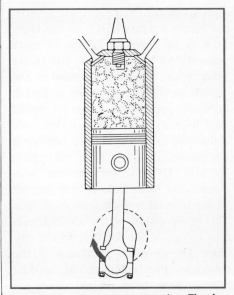

Fig. 3–28. Compression stroke. The intake valve has closed, and the piston is moving upward, compressing the mixture.

63

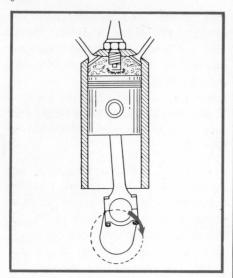

Fig. 3–29. Power stroke. The ignition system produces a spark that ignites the mixture. As it burns, high pressure is created which pushes the piston downward.

2. Compression (Fig. 3–28). After the piston reaches BDC, or the lower limit of its travel, it begins to move upward. As this happens, the intake valve closes. The exhaust valve is also closed, so that the cylinder is sealed. As the piston moves upward (pushed now by the revolving crankshaft and connecting rod), the air-fuel mixture is compressed. By the time the piston reaches TDC, the mixture has been compressed to as little as one-seventh of its original volume, or even less. This compression of the air-fuel mixture increases the pressure in the cylinder. Or, to say it another way, the molecules that compose the air-fuel mixture have been pushed closer together. They therefore bump into the cylinder walls and piston head more often. The increasing frequency of the bumps means that a stronger push is

registered on the walls and head; the pressure is higher. The molecules, being pushed closer together, also collide with each other more frequently. This, in turn, sets them into more rapid motion. We know that more rapid motion and increased temperature mean the same thing. Therefore, when the air-fuel mixture is compressed, not only does the pressure in the cylinder go up, but the temperature of the mixture also increases.

3. Power (Fig. 3–29). As the piston reaches TDC on the compression stroke, an electric spark is produced at the spark plug. The spark plug consists essentially of two wire electrodes, electrically insulated from each other. The ignition system (part of the electric system discussed in Chap. 7) delivers a high-voltage surge of electricity to the spark plug to produce the spark. The spark ignites, or sets fire to, the air-fuel mixture. It now begins to burn very rapidly, and the cylinder pressure increases to as much as 600 psi or even more. This means that the hot gases are pushing against every square inch of the combustion chamber and the piston head with a pressure of 600 pounds or more. For example, a piston 3 inches in diameter with a head area of about 7 square inches would have a pressure on it of over 2 tons. This terrific push against the piston forces it downward, and a power impulse is transmitted through the connecting rod to the crankpin on the crankshaft. The crankshaft is rotated as the piston is pushed down by the pressure above it.

Let us take a look at the activities we have just described from the molecular point of view. That is, let us see

how the increased pressure can be explained by considering the air-fuel mixture as a vast number of molecules. We have already noted, in the previous paragraph, that compressing the mixture increases both its temperature and its pressure. The molecules move faster (higher temperature) and bump the cylinder walls and pistonhead more often (higher pressure). Then, when combustion takes place, the hydrocarbon molecules of gasoline are violently split apart into hydrogen and carbon atoms. The hydrogen and carbon atoms then unite with oxygen atoms in the air (see § 52, Combustion). All this sets the molecules into extremely rapid motion (still higher temperature, which may momentarily reach 4500° F). The molecules begin to bombard the cylinder walls and piston head much harder and more often. In other words, the pressure goes up much higher.

It may be a little difficult, at first, to visualize a 2-ton push on the piston head as resulting from the bombardment of molecules far too small to be seen. But remember that there are billions upon billions of molecules in the combustion chamber, all moving at speeds of many miles a second. Their combined hammering on the piston head adds up to the high pressure that is registered.

4. Exhaust (Fig. 3–30). As the piston reaches BDC again, the exhaust valve opens. Now, as the piston moves up on the exhaust stroke, it forces the burned gases out of the cylinder through the exhaust-valve port. Then, when the piston reaches TDC, the exhaust valve closes and the intake valve opens. Now, a fresh charge of air-fuel

mixture will be drawn into the cylinder as the piston moves down again toward BDC. The above four strokes are continuously repeated during the operation of the engine.

§ 70. **Multiple-cylinder engines** A single-cylinder engine provides only one power impulse every two crankshaft revolutions and is delivering power only one-fourth of the time. To provide for a more continuous flow of power, modern engines use four, six, eight, or more cylinders. The power impulses are so arranged as to follow one another, or overlap (on six- and eight-cylinder engines). This gives a more nearly even flow of power from the engine.

§ 71. **Flywheel** The power impulses in a multicylinder engine follow each

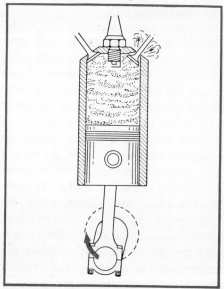

Fig. 3–30. Exhaust stroke. The exhaust valve (*right*) has opened, and the piston is moving upward, forcing the burned gases from the cylinder.

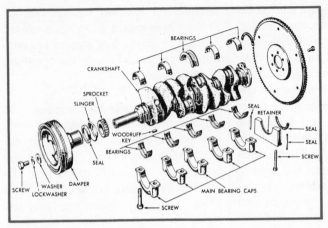

BEARINGS

CRANKSHAFT

SPROCKET
SLINGER

SEAL
RETAINER

WOODRUFF
KEY

BEARINGS

SEAL
SEAL

SCREW

SEAL

SCREW   WASHER   DAMPER
        LOCKWASHER

MAIN BEARING CAPS

SCREW

Fig. 3–31. Crankshaft
and related parts used
in an eight-cylinder, V-
type engine. (*Mercury
Division of Ford Motor
Company*)

other, or overlap, to provide a fairly even flow of power. However, additional leveling off of the power impulses is desirable. This would make the engine run still more smoothly. To achieve this, a flywheel is used (Fig. 3–31). The flywheel is a fairly heavy steel wheel, attached to the rear end of the crankshaft.

To get a better idea of how the flywheel does its job, let us look at a single-cylinder engine. This engine delivers power only one-fourth of the time—during the power stroke. During the other three strokes, it is absorbing power—to push out the exhaust gas, to "pull in" a fresh air-fuel charge, to compress the charge. Thus, during the power stroke, the engine tends to speed up. During the other strokes, it tends to slow down. Any rotating wheel, including the flywheel, resists any effort to change its speed of rotation (this is due to inertia; see § 76). When the engine tends to speed up, the flywheel resists it. When the engine tends to slow down, the flywheel resists it. Of course, in the single-cylinder engine, there would still be some speed-up and slowdown. But the flywheel minimizes

it. In effect, the flywheel absorbs power from the engine during the power stroke (or speed-up time) and then gives it back to the engine during the other three strokes (or slowdown time).

In the multicylinder engine, the flywheel acts in a similar manner to smooth out still more the peaks and valleys of power flow from the engine. In addition, the flywheel forms part of the clutch (§ 409). The flywheel also has teeth on its outer diameter that mesh with the electric cranking-motor drive pinion when the engine is being cranked to start it. This is explained in more detail in § 172.

REVIEW QUESTIONS

1. What two forces keep the electron circling the proton in the hydrogen atom?

2. What are molecules?

3. Define combustion. What element must be present before combustion can take place?

4. Describe the combustion of gasoline.

5. Define heat in terms of molecular activity.

6. What is a change of state?

7. Explain gas pressure in terms of molecular actions.
8. Why does the gas pressure in a container increase with increasing temperature?
9. Explain how a thermometer operates.
10. Explain how a thermostat operates.
11. Explain atmospheric pressure in terms of molecular activity.
12. What is vacuum?
13. Explain how a barometer operates.
14. What are the four stages, or strokes, of engine operation?
15. Describe the actions in the cylinder during each of the four strokes.
16. Explain how the reciprocating motion of the piston is changed to rotary motion.
17. Describe the construction and operation of the valves.
18. Explain why a flywheel is used.

STUDY QUESTIONS

1. Make a sketch of a cylinder with valve ports, spark plug, piston, piston rings, connecting rod, and crankshaft.
2. Make sketches showing the four strokes, or stages, of engine operation, and write a brief explanation of the actions taking place during each stroke.

KEEPING A NOTEBOOK

One of the secrets of success, say many successful students, is the keeping of a notebook. A notebook helps you in many ways. When you write down facts in your notebook, you must organize your thoughts. You must think about the facts. You cannot write down facts without thinking about them. And thinking about facts is the way to memorize them.

Take any sentence and write it down enough times and you will never forget it. Thus writing down facts helps you to remember them.

Furthermore, you are storing those facts in your notebook where you can look them up if they get hazy in your mind. The good student learns that his well-kept notebook is matched by the well-organized facts stored up in his mind.

A large, loose-leaf, ring-binder type of notebook is usually best. With a loose-leaf notebook, you can rearrange pages, replace old pages that have become dog-eared or dirty, and insert new pages. You can organize your notebook into sections (engines, steering, suspension, and so on) or keep separate notebooks on each topic.

MAKING NOTES

You should make notes of any important facts you run across as you study. It is just as necessary for you to write down the high spots of your day's activities in the shop. Making notes is explained in more detail on page 262.

CHAPTER 4

ENGINE MEASUREMENTS AND PERFORMANCE

THIS CHAPTER DESCRIBES VARIOUS ways in which engines and engine performance are measured. An engine may be measured in terms of cylinder diameter, piston stroke, and number of cylinders. It may be measured, performancewise, in terms of the torque and horsepower it develops, its efficiency, and the horsepower required to overcome internal friction (or friction horsepower). These various terms, their meanings, and their applications to engines are discussed below.

§ **72. Work**   The engineering definition of *work* is *changing of the position of an object against an opposing force.* The object must be moved by the application of a force (a push, a pull, a lift). For example, when a weight is lifted, work is done on the weight; it is moved against the force of gravity. In a similar way, when a coil spring is compressed, work is done on the spring (Fig. 4–1). A force, or push, is exerted through a distance.

Work is measured in terms of distance and force. If a 5-pound weight is lifted off the ground 1 foot, the work done on the weight is 5 foot-pounds (ft-lb) (or 1 times 5). If the 5-pound weight is lifted 2 feet, the work done is 10 foot-pounds.

Distance times force equals work.

§ **73. Energy**   Energy is the capacity, or ability, to do work. When work is done on a body, energy (ability to do work) is stored in that body. For example, when the spring is compressed (Fig. 4–1), work is done on the spring and energy is stored in it. The spring can do work (Fig. 4–2) if released.

§ **74. Power**   Work can be done

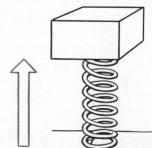

Fig. 4–2. When the spring is released, it can do work on another body, lifting a weight against the force of gravity, for example.

Fig. 4–1. When a spring is compressed, work is done on that spring and energy is stored in it.

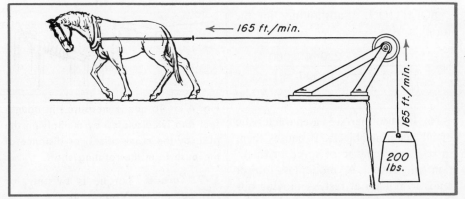

Fig. 4–3. One horse can do 33,000 foot-pounds of work a minute.

slowly, or it can be done rapidly. The rate at which work is done is measured in terms of power. A machine that does a great deal of work in a short time is called a *high-powered* machine. A machine that takes much longer to do a comparatively small amount of work is a *low-powered* machine.

Power is the rate, or speed, at which work is done.

§ 75. Horsepower A horsepower (hp) is the power of one horse, or a measure of the rate at which a horse can do work. Years ago, when engines were being developed, their ability to do work was compared with the work ability of horses. A 10-hp engine, for example, could do the work of 10 horses.

A horsepower is considered to be 33,000 foot-pounds per minute (Fig. 4–3). The horse walks 165 feet in 1 minute, lifting the 200-pound weight. The amount of work involved is 33,-000 foot-pounds, and the horse does this in a minute. If the 200-pound weight is lifted 165 feet in 2 minutes, then the horse is only "half" working; only ½ hp is required. The formula for horsepower is

$$hp = \frac{\text{ft-lb per min}}{33,000} = \frac{L \times W}{33,000 \times t}$$

where hp = horsepower
L = length, in feet, through which W is moved
W = force, in pounds, that is exerted through distance L
t = time, in minutes, required to move W through L

PROBLEM: You have a heavy box loaded with sand and want to drag it 500 feet across a level lot in 2 minutes. It requires a force of 2,000 pounds to pull the box. What is the horsepower required?

SOLUTION: Substituting in the formula,

$$hp = \frac{L \times W}{33,000 \times t} = \frac{500 \times 2,000}{33,000 \times 2} =$$
$$15.15 \text{ hp}$$

PROBLEM: You are asked to select a gasoline engine capable of raising a coal-mine elevator, which weighs 3,000 pounds, 220 feet in 1 minute. Ignoring friction and other power losses, what would be the minimum horsepower you could select?

69

SOLUTION: Substituting in the formula,

$$hp = \frac{L \times W}{33,000 \times t} = \frac{220 \times 3,000}{33,000 \times 1} = 20 \text{ hp}$$

§ 76. **Inertia** Inertia is a characteristic of all material objects. It causes them to resist any change of speed or direction of travel. A motionless object tends to remain at rest. A moving object tends to keep moving at the same speed and in the same direction.

Consider the automobile. When it is stationary, its inertia must be overcome by the application of power before it will move. To increase its speed, further power must be applied. To decrease its speed, the brakes must be applied. The brakes must overcome the inertia of the car to slow it down. In a similar manner, when the car goes around a curve, its inertia tends to keep it moving in a straight line. The tires on the road must overcome this tendency, or else the inertia of the car will send it into a skid.

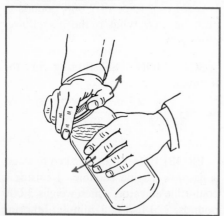

Fig. 4–4. Torque, or twisting effort, must be applied to loosen and remove the top from a screw-top jar.

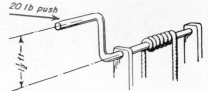

Fig. 4–5. Torque is measured in pound-feet and is calculated by multiplying the push by the crank offset, or distance of the push from the rotating shaft.

§ 77. **Torque** Torque is twisting, or turning, effort. You apply torque to the steering wheel to guide a car around a curve. You apply torque to the top of a screw-top jar when you loosen it (Fig. 4–4).

Do not confuse torque with work or with power. Torque is the twisting effort the engine applies, through the shafts and gears, to the car wheels. Power is something else—it is the rate at which the engine works. Work is the energy expended, or the product of force and distance. Both work and power indicate motion — something moves. Torque does not imply motion; it is merely a turning effort *which may or may not result in motion.*

Torque is measured in pound-feet (do not confuse this with foot-pounds of work). For instance, if you pushed on a windlass crank with a 20-pound push, and if the crank were 1½ feet long (from center to handle), you would be applying a torque of 30 pound-feet (lb-ft) to the crank (Fig. 4–5). You would be applying this torque, regardless of whether or not the crank were turning, so long as you applied a 20-pound push on the crank.

§ 78. **Friction** Friction is the resistance to motion between two objects in contact with each other. If you put this

book on a table top and then pushed the book across the table, you would find it took a certain amount of push. If you put a second book on top of the first book, you would find you had to push harder to push the two books together across the table top. Thus friction, or resistance to motion, increases with the load. The higher the load, the greater the resistance to motion (that is, the greater the friction). In the automobile engine, the bearings are heavily loaded. Some bearings sustain loads of well above 1,000 psi (pounds per square inch). With such heavy loads, the friction would be tremendous if it were not for the lubricating oil. However, the oil, in effect, floats the rotating journal so that actual metal-to-metal contact is avoided. The friction is then between moving layers of oil, rather than between solid objects. This friction is relatively low. Friction has been classified into three types, dry, greasy, and viscous.

1. Dry friction. This is the friction between two dry objects, a board being dragged across a floor, for instance. If the board and the floor are rough, the friction is relatively high. If the board and floor are smooth, the friction is lower. You can think of dry friction as an interference to motion between two objects caused by surface irregularities that tend to catch on each other. Even objects that have been machined to a very smooth finish still have very small irregularities; they offer resistance to relative motion.

2. Greasy friction. This is the friction between two objects thinly coated with oil or grease. It can be assumed that the thin film tends to fill in the low spots in the surfaces. This reduces the tendency for the surface irregularities to catch on each other. However, high spots will still catch and wear as the two surfaces move over each other. In an automobile engine, greasy friction may occur in an engine on first starting. Most of the lubricating oil may have drained away from the bearing surfaces and from the cylinder walls and piston rings. When the engine is started, only the small amount of oil remaining on these surfaces protects them from undue wear. Of course, the lubricating system quickly supplies additional oil, but before this happens, greasy friction exists on the moving surfaces. The lubrication between the surfaces where greasy friction exists is not sufficient to prevent wear. That is the reason why automotive engineers say that initial starting and warm-up of the engine is hardest on the engine and wears it the most.

3. Viscous friction. "Viscosity" is a term that refers to the tendency of liquids, such as oil, to resist flowing. A heavy oil is more viscous than a light oil and flows more slowly (has a higher viscosity, or higher resistance to flowing). Viscous friction is the friction, or resistance to relative motion, between adjacent layers of liquid. In an engine bearing supplied with sufficient oil, layers of oil adhere to the bearing and journal surfaces. In effect, these clinging layers of oil are carried around by the rotating journal and wedged under the journal (Fig. 4–6). The wedging action lifts the journal so that the oil itself supports the weight, or load. Now, since the journal is supported ("floats") on layers of oil, there is no metal-to-metal contact. However, the layers of oil must move over each

Fig. 4–6. Shaft rotation causes layers of clinging oil to be dragged around with it. The oil moves from the wide clearance A and is wedged into the narrow clearance B, thereby supporting the shaft weight W on an oil film.

other, and it does require some energy to make them so move. The resistance to motion between these oil layers is called *viscous friction.*

§ 79. **Bore and stroke**   The size of an engine cylinder is referred to in terms of the bore and stroke. The bore is the diameter of the cylinder. The stroke is the distance the piston travels from BDC (bottom dead center) to TDC (top dead center). (See Fig. 4–7.) The bore is always mentioned first. For example, in a $3\frac{1}{4}$- by $3\frac{1}{2}$-inch cylin-

der, the diameter, or bore, is $3\frac{1}{4}$ inches and the stroke is $3\frac{1}{2}$ inches. These measurements are used to figure the piston displacement.

§ 80. **Piston displacement**   Piston displacement is the volume that the piston displaces as it moves from BDC to TDC. Piston displacement of a $3\frac{1}{4}$- by $3\frac{1}{2}$-inch cylinder, for example, would be the volume of a cylinder $3\frac{1}{4}$ inches in diameter and $3\frac{1}{2}$ inches long or,

$$\frac{\pi \times D^2 \times L}{4} = \frac{3.1416 \times 3\frac{1}{4}^2 \times 3\frac{1}{2}}{4} =$$

$$\frac{3.1416 \times 10.5625 \times 3\frac{1}{2}}{4} = 29.036 \text{ cu in.}$$

If the engine has six cylinders, the total displacement would be 29.036 times 6, or 174.216 cubic inches.

§ 81. **Compression ratio**   The compression ratio of an engine is a measurement of how much the air-fuel charges are compressed in the engine cylinders. It is calculated by dividing the air volume in one cylinder with the

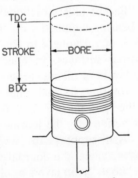

TDC

STROKE   BORE

BDC

Fig. 4–7. Bore and stroke of an engine cylinder.

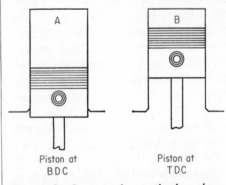

A

B

Piston at
BDC

Piston at
TDC

Fig. 4–8. Compression ratio is volume in cylinder with piston at BDC divided by volume with piston at TDC, or A divided by B.

piston at BDC by the air volume with the piston at TDC (Fig. 4–8).

NOTE: The air volume with the piston at TDC is called the *clearance volume* since it is the clearance that remains above the piston when it is at TDC.

For example, the engine of one popular car has a cylinder volume of 42.35 cubic inches at BDC (*A* in Fig. 4–8). It has a clearance volume of 6.05 cubic inches (*B* in Fig. 4–8). The compression ratio, therefore, is 42.35 divided by 6.05, or 7/1 (that is, 7:1). In other words, during the compression stroke, the air-fuel mixture is compressed from a volume of 42.35 cubic inches to 6.05 cubic inches, or to one-seventh of its original volume.

§ 82. Increasing compression ratio

In recent years, the compression ratios of automotive engines have been repeatedly increased. This increase offers several advantages. The power and economy of an engine increase as the compression ratio goes up (within limits) without a comparable increase of engine size or weight. In effect, an engine with a higher compression ratio "squeezes" the air-fuel mixture harder (compresses it more). This causes the air-fuel mixture to produce more power on the power stroke. Here is the reason: a higher compression ratio means a higher initial pressure at the end of the compression stroke. This means that, when the power stroke starts, higher combustion pressures will be attained; a harder push will be registered on the piston. The burning gases will also expand to a greater volume during the power stroke. It all adds up

to this: There is more push on the piston for a larger part of the power stroke. More power is obtained from each power stroke.

Increasing the compression ratio does, however, bring up special problems. For one thing, as the compression ratio goes up, the problem of detonation, or knocking, becomes more acute. There is a detailed discussion of knocking in Chap. 9. To summarize briefly, any particular fuel will stand a certain amount of squeezing without causing knocking. But if it is squeezed (compressed) further as a result of a higher compression ratio, it will then produce knocking. Thus, for the late higher-compression-ratio engines, the gasoline companies have brought out new types of fuel (which have a greater resistance to knocking).

NOTE: The antiknock value of gasolines is rated in terms of *octane*. A high-octane gasoline has a relatively high resistance against knocking (see Chap. 9).

§ 83. Delivery of air-fuel mixture

When the piston moves down on the intake stroke, a vacuum is produced in the cylinder. Atmospheric pressure then pushes air into the cylinder. The air must first pass through the carburetor (where it picks up a charge of fuel). Then the air (now charged with fuel) moves through the intake manifold and the intake-valve port to enter the cylinder. Note that the air must move through restricting passages and must change directions on its way to the cylinder. Under these conditions, it takes time for the air to get into the cylinder on the intake stroke. But even

during engine idle, there isn't much time available. For the intake stroke occurs in a few tenths of a second [at an idling speed of 350 rpm (revolutions per minute)]. At high speed, the time is reduced to as little as a hundredth of a second.

Thus, you can see that the vacuum in the cylinder is not going to be completely "satisfied." That is, the intake valve is going to close before the cylinder becomes completely filled with air. The higher the speed, the shorter the time available for air to flow into the cylinder and the smaller the amount of air that can enter.

§ **84. Volumetric efficiency** The amount of air-fuel mixture taken into the cylinder on the intake stroke is a measure of the engine's volumetric efficiency. If the mixture were drawn into the cylinder very slowly, a full measure could get in. But the mixture must pass very rapidly through a series of restricting openings and bends in the carburetor and intake manifold. In addition, the mixture is heated (from engine heat): it therefore expands. The two conditions, rapid movement and heating, reduce the amount of mixture that can get into the cylinder. A full charge of air-fuel mixture cannot enter because the time is too short and because the air becomes heated.

Volumetric efficiency is the ratio between the amount of air-fuel mixture that actually enters the cylinder and the amount that could enter under ideal conditions. For example, a certain cylinder has an air volume (*A* in Fig. 4–8) of 47 cubic inches. If the cylinder were allowed to completely "fill up," it would take in 0.034 ounce

of air (air at atmospheric pressure weighs about 1.25 ounces per cubic foot or about 0.00072 ounce per cubic inch). However, suppose that the engine were running at a fair speed so that only 0.027 ounce of air could enter during each intake stroke. This means that volumetric efficiency would be only about 80 percent (0.027 is 80 percent of 0.034). Actually, 80 percent is a good volumetric efficiency for an engine running at fairly high speed. Volumetric efficiency of many engines drops to as low as 50 percent at high speeds. This is another way of saying that the cylinders are only "half-filled" at high speeds.

This is one reason why engine speed and output cannot continue to increase indefinitely. At higher speed, the engine has a harder time "breathing," or drawing in air. It is "starved" for air and cannot produce any further increase in power output.

To improve volumetric efficiency, intake valves are made larger. Also, the intake-manifold passages are made larger and as straight and short as possible. Carburetors are often equipped with extra circuits, or air passages (additional barrels as noted in Chap. 8), which open at high speed to improve engine breathing. All these help the engine to produce more power at higher speeds.

§ **85. Engine power output** We have already noted that the output of engines is rated in terms of horsepower (§ 75). An engine that can deliver 33,000 foot-pounds of work in 1 minute is a 1-hp engine. An engine that can deliver 660,000 foot-pounds of work in 1 minute is a 20-hp engine

(660,000 divided by 33,000). The power that an engine actually delivers is called bhp (brake horsepower). Engines are usually rated in bhp although the letter "b" for "brake" is not always used. Thus, an engine rated at 160 bhp is often called a 160-hp engine.

§ 86. Brake horsepower The term "brake horsepower" came from the fact that a *prony brake* was once widely used to measure engine output. The prony brake (Fig. 4–9) contains a large drum, or wheel. A brake clamps around the outside of this drum. The brake can be tightened on the drum. A brake arm supports the brake and prevents it from turning. The end of the arm rests on a scale. The drum is driven by the engine. When the brake is tightened, friction on the drum imposes a load on the engine. At the same time, the friction tends to turn the brake and arm and the arm pushes down on the scale.

The prony-brake test is made by running the engine at a steady speed and gradually tightening the brake on the drum. This imposes an increasing load on the engine, and the throttle must be opened wider to maintain engine speed. At the same time, the load on the scale (*W* in Fig. 4–9) increases owing to the increased frictional drag of the brake on the drum. To find the maximum power that the engine can develop at the test speed, the load is increased gradually, the throttle being gradually opened at the same time in order to maintain speed. When the throttle is wide open, maximum power is being obtained. Any further loading would cause engine speed, and output, to drop off.

The following formula can then be used to determine horsepower:

$$\text{bhp} = \frac{2\pi RNW}{33,000} = \frac{RNW}{5,252}$$

where $R =$ length of arm (from center of drum)

$N =$ engine speed in rpm

$W =$ load, in pounds, on scale

For example, if the arm is 3 feet long, the load (*W*) is 100 pounds,

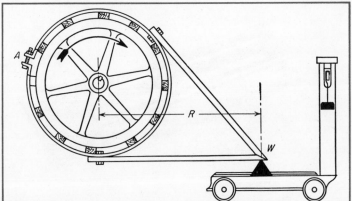

Fig. 4–9. Prony brake for determining power output of engine: A is adjustment for tightening brake on brake drum, R is length of arm (from center of shaft to end supported on scales), and W is weight, or force, exerted on scales.

75

Fig. 4–10. Dynamometer used for testing engines and measuring their power output. (*General Motors Corporation*)

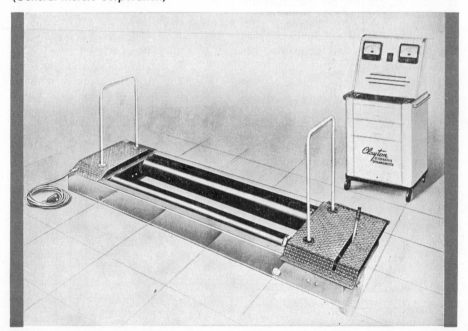

Fig. 4–11. Chassis dynamometer of the flush-floor type with the rollers set at floor level. The below-floor part is shown in phantom view. (*Clayton Manufacturing Company*)

Fig. 4–12. Automobile in place on chassis dynamometer. Rear wheels drive the dynamometer rollers, and instruments on test panel measure car speed, engine-power output, engine vacuum, fuel ratio, and so on. (*Clayton Manufacturing Company*)

and N is 1,000 rpm, then the bhp would be

$$\text{bhp} = \frac{3 \times 1,000 \times 100}{5,252} = 57.12 \text{ bhp}$$

§ **87. Rating engines with dynamometer** For testing engines today, a dynamometer is ordinarily used (Fig. 4–10). This device contains an electric dynamo, or generator, which is driven by the engine during the test. The amount of electric current produced is then a measure of the horsepower the engine is producing. A second type of dynamometer, or engine tester, uses a water brake. The water brake contains a rotating device with numerous blades. When water is put into the device, the rotating member has a restriction put upon it. The more water added, the greater the restriction. Thus, the water brake can apply varying loads on the engine.

Some dynamometers are used to test detached engines (Fig. 4–10). Others are so arranged as to permit testing of the engine while it is still in the car; these are called *chassis dynamometers* (Figs. 4–11 and 4–12). On these, the rear wheels of the car are placed on rollers. Then, the engine drives the wheels, and the wheels drive the rollers. The rollers can be loaded varying amounts so that engine output can be measured. The use of the chassis dynamometer is becoming more common in the automotive servicing field since it can give a very quick report on

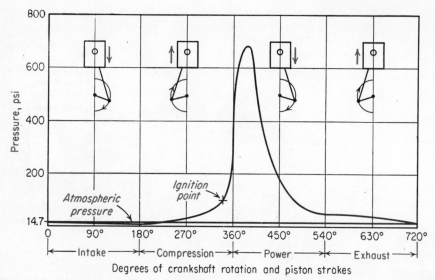

Fig. 4–13. Pressures in an engine cylinder during the four piston strokes. The four strokes require two crankshaft revolutions (360 degrees each), a total of 720 degrees of rotation. This curve is for a particular engine operating at one definite speed and throttle opening. Changing the speed and throttle opening would change the curve (particularly the power curve).

engine conditions (by measuring output at various speeds and loads). This type of dynamometer is also valuable in testing and adjusting automatic transmission since checks and adjustments can be made in the shop; no road testing is necessary.

§ 88. Indicated horsepower   The engine may also be evaluated in terms of ihp (indicated horsepower). Indicated horsepower is based on the power actually developed inside the engine cylinders by the combustion processes. A special indicating device (an oscilloscope) is required to determine ihp. This device measures the pressure continuously throughout the four piston strokes (intake, compression, power, exhaust). A graph of the cylinder pressures taken during a typical test of

engine ihp is shown in Fig. 4–13. The four small drawings show the crank rod, and piston positions as well as directions of motion, during the four strokes. Note that the pressure in the cylinder is about atmospheric at the beginning of the intake stroke. Then it falls a little below atmospheric as the delivery of air-fuel mixture to the cylinder lags behind piston movement (that is, volumetric efficiency is less than 100 percent). When the compression stroke begins, the pressure starts to increase as the piston moves upward in the cylinder. A little before the piston reaches TDC, ignition takes place. Now, the air-fuel mixture burns, and pressure goes up very rapidly. It reaches a peak of around 680 psi at about 25 degrees past TDC on the power stroke. Pressure then falls off

rapidly as the power stroke continues. But there is still a pressure of around 50 psi at the end of the power stroke. When the exhaust stroke begins, the pressure falls off and drops to about atmospheric at the end of the stroke.

A graph such as the one shown in Fig. 4–13 supplies the information needed to determine ihp. As a first step, the mep (mean effective pressure) is determined. The mep is the average pressure during the power stroke, minus the average pressures during the other three strokes. This is the pressure that, in effect, forces the piston down during the power stroke. The mep and other engine data being known, the following formula is used to determine ihp:

$$ihp = \frac{PLANK}{33,000}$$

where $P =$ mean effective pressure in psi

$L =$ length of stroke in feet

$A =$ area of cylinder section in square inches

$N =$ number of power strokes per minute (or rpm/2)

$K =$ number of cylinders

Some of the power developed in the engine cylinders (or ihp) is used in overcoming friction in the engine. Thus ihp is always greater than bhp (or power delivered by engine). Article 90 explains how bhp and ihp are related.

§ **89. Friction horsepower** Friction losses in an engine are sometimes referred to in terms of fhp (friction horsepower). This expression means the amount of horsepower used up in the engine to overcome friction. Friction horsepower is determined by driv-

ing the engine with an electric motor to measure the horsepower required to drive it. During this test, the engine is at operating temperature, but there is no fuel in the carburetor, and the throttle is held wide open. At low speed, friction is relatively low. But as engine speed increases, fhp goes up rapidly. The graph (Fig. 4–14) shows fhp in a typical engine at different speeds. At 1,000 rpm, the fhp is only about 4 hp. But, at 2,000 rpm, it is nearly 10 hp. At 3,000 rpm, it is up to 21 hp, and, at 4,000 rpm, it is about 40 hp.

One of the major causes of frictional loss (or fhp) in an engine is piston-ring friction. Under some conditions, the friction of the rings on the cylinder walls accounts for 75 percent of all friction losses in the engine. For example, Fig. 4–14 shows an fhp of 40 hp at 4,000 rpm. It could be that 75 percent, or 30 hp, is due to friction between the rings and cylinder walls Understanding this fact makes us more fully aware of the difficult job the rings have in the engine.

§ **90. Relating bhp, ihp, and fhp** Brake horsepower is the power delivered, ihp is the power developed in the engine, and fhp is the power lost owing

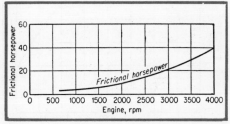

Fig. 4–14. Friction-horsepower curve, showing relationship of fhp to engine speed.

to friction. The relationship between the three is

$$bhp = ihp - fhp$$

That is, the horsepower delivered by the engine (bhp) is equal to the horsepower developed (ihp) minus the power lost owing to friction (fhp).

§ 91. **SAE horsepower** The SAE (Society of Automotive Engineers) horsepower rating of engines is used to compare engines on the basis of the number and diameter of the cylinders (usually for tax purposes), as follows:

$$SAE\ hp = \frac{D^2 \times N}{2.5}$$

where D = diameter of cylinder, or bore

N = number of cylinders

This formula does not take into consideration such factors as mep, length of stroke, rpm, and so forth.

§ 92. **Engine torque** As we have already noted (§ 77), torque is turning effort. When the piston is moving down on the power stroke, it is applying torque to the engine crankshaft (through the connecting rod). The harder the push on the piston, the greater the torque applied. Thus, the higher the combustion pressures, the greater the amount of torque.

Torque should not be confused with power. Torque is turning effort. Power is *rate of work.* (Reread § 77 if this is not clear.) The prony brake can be used to measure engine torque as well as power. To measure torque, we need to know only the load on the scale and the length of the brake arm. For instance, consider the example at the end of § 86. The brake arm is 3 feet long, and the load is 100 pounds. This means that the engine is developing a torque of 300 lb-ft.

§ 93. **Brake horsepower vs. torque** The torque that an engine can develop changes with engine speed (see Fig. 4–15). During intermediate speeds, volumetric efficiency is high (there is sufficient time for the cylinders to become fairly well "filled up"). This means that, with a fairly full charge of air-fuel mixture, higher combustion pressures will develop. With higher combustion pressures, the engine torque is higher.

But, at higher speed, volumetric efficiency drops off (there is not enough time for the cylinders to become filled

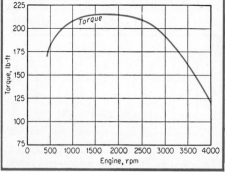

Fig. 4–15. Torque curve of an engine, showing relationship of torque to speed.

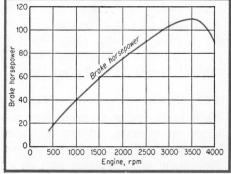

Fig. 4–16. Curve showing relationship of bhp to engine speed.

up with air-fuel mixture). Since there is less air-fuel mixture to burn, the combustion pressures will not go so high. There will be less push on the pistons, and thus engine torque will be lower. Note, in the graph (Fig. 4–15), how the torque drops off as engine speed increases.

The bhp curve of an engine is considerably different from the torque curve. Figure 4–16 is the bhp of the same engine for which the torque curve is shown in Fig. 4–15. It starts low at low speed and increases steadily with speed until a high engine speed is reached. Then, as still higher engine speeds are attained, bhp drops off. If you look at the formula for bhp (§ 86), you will see that engine speed is an important factor. But you will also note that torque ($W \times R$) is an important factor. Brake horsepower equals torque times rpm (divided by 5,252). Thus, as long as torque remains high and rpm continues to go up, bhp will also go up. But when torque drops off, then bhp stops increasing and also starts dropping off.

The drop-off of bhp is due not only to reduced torque at higher speed but also to increased fhp at the higher speed. Figure 4–17 compares the curves of these three factors, torque, bhp, and fhp, of an engine.

NOTE: The curves (Figs. 4–14 to 4–17) are for one particular engine only. Different engines have different torque, bhp, and fhp curves. Peaks may be at higher or lower speeds, and the relationships may not be as indicated in the curves shown.

§ 94. Engine efficiency   The term

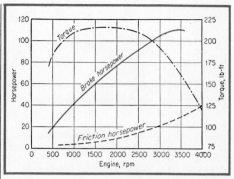

Fig. 4–17. Torque-bhp-fhp curves of an engine.

"efficiency" means the relationship between the effort exerted and the results obtained. As applied to engines, efficiency is the relationship between the power delivered and the power that could be obtained if the engine operated without any power loss. Engine efficiency can be computed in two ways, as *mechanical* efficiency and as *thermal* efficiency.

1. Mechanical efficiency. This is the relationship between bhp and ihp, or

$$\text{Mechanical efficiency} = \frac{\text{bhp}}{\text{ihp}}$$

EXAMPLE: At a certain speed, the bhp of an engine is 116, and its ihp is 135. Mechanical efficiency is thus bhp/iph = 116/135 = 0.86, or 86 percent. That is, 86 percent of the power developed in the cylinders is delivered by the engine. The remaining 14 percent, or 19 hp, is consumed as fhp.

2. Thermal efficiency. "Thermal" means of or pertaining to heat. Thermal efficiency of the engine is the relationship between the power output and the energy in the fuel burned to produce this output. We have already

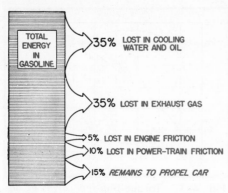

Fig. 4–18. Energy loss from cylinders to wheels.

noted that a considerable part of the heat produced by the combustion process is carried away by the cooling water (§ 37) and escapes in the exhaust gases. These are heat (thermal) losses that reduce the thermal efficiency of the engine. They do not add to the power output of the engine. The remainder of the heat, in causing the gases to expand and produce high pressure, forces the pistons down so that the engine develops power. Because there is a great deal of heat lost during engine operation, thermal efficiencies of the gasoline may be as low as 20 percent and are seldom higher than 25 percent. Practical limitations prevent higher thermal efficiencies.

§ 95. Over-all efficiency   The gasoline enters the engine with a certain energy content, a certain ability to do work. At every step in the process, from the burning of the gasoline in the cylinders to the rotation of the car wheels, energy is lost. Figure 4–18 illustrates these losses as determined for one engine and car during a test run. Note that as little as 15 percent

of the energy in the gasoline remains to actually propel the car. This energy is used to overcome rolling resistance and air resistance and to accelerate the car.

1. *Rolling resistance.* This results from irregularities in the road over which the wheels ride, as well as the flexing of the tires as the weight of the car is brought to bear on the various portions of the tire in turn.

2. *Air resistance.* Air resistance is the resistance the air offers to the passage of the car body through it. As car speed increases, so also does the air resistance. At 90 mph (miles per hour), tests show that as much as 75 percent of the power the engine is delivering is used up in overcoming air resistance. Streamlining the car body reduces this power loss from air resistance.

3. *Acceleration.* Power is required to increase car speed. In effect, the power applied to accelerate the car overcomes the inertia of the car. Energy in the form of car speed is built up, or stored, in the car.

REVIEW QUESTIONS

1. Define work. In what terms is it measured?
2. Define energy.
3. Define power.
4. Define a horsepower.
5. An engine raises 16,500 pounds 10 feet in 30 seconds. What horsepower is the engine delivering?
6. Define inertia.
7. Define torque. Explain the difference between torque and work.
8. Define friction. What are the three classes of friction?

9. What are the bore and stroke of an engine?

10. What is piston displacement? What is the piston displacement of an engine with a 3-inch bore and a 4-inch stroke?

11. Explain what the term "compression ratio" means.

12. The clearance volume in an engine is 6 inches, and the cylinder volume at BDC is 51 inches. What is the compression ratio of this engine?

13. What are some advantages of increasing compression ratio? What are some disadvantages?

14. Define volumetric efficiency.

15. Define brake horsepower. If the prony brake used to measure the horsepower of an engine has an arm 4 feet long and the load on the scales is 100 pounds at 2,500 rpm, what horsepower is the engine developing?

16. Define indicated horsepower.

17. Define friction horsepower.

18. What is the relationship between bhp, ihp, and fhp?

19. How can you use bhp and ihp to find the mechanical efficiency of an engine?

20. Define thermal efficiency.

STUDY QUESTIONS

1. Give the reasons in terms of inertia why quick stops and starts in driving a car waste gasoline.

2. If you were told to measure the piston displacement of an engine, how would you do it?

3. If you were told to measure the compression ratio of an engine, how would you do it?

4. As volumetric efficiency of an engine increases, does the engine tend to deliver more or less torque? Explain the reason for your answer.

5. If you can find the operating instructions for a chassis dynamometer, read them and then write a brief explanation of how to use a dynamometer.

6. Explain how to determine ihp.

7. Can you think of a way to measure the thermal efficiency of an engine?

THIS CHAPTER DISCUSSES VARIOUS ways in which engines are classified. All automotive engines are of the internal-combustion type. However, they are classified in different ways according to number of cylinders, arrangement of cylinders, valve arrangement, type of cooling, type of fuel burned, and so on.

§ **96. Cylinder arrangements** American passenger cars use four, six, or eight cylinders (some foreign cars use less than four).

1. Four-cylinder in-line engines. In the four-cylinder in-line engine, the cylinders are arranged in a single line with cylinders in a vertical position. All cylinders are cast together in the

Fig. 5–1. Six-cylinder engine with overhead valves, partly cut away to show internal construction. (*Ford Division of Ford Motor Company*)

Fig. 5–2. Eight-cylinder in-line passenger-car engine with overhead valves, partly cut away so that internal construction can be seen. (Buick Motor Division of General Motors Corporation)

cylinder block. The crankshaft is usually supported by three shaft bearings. Cylinders are numbered from front to back, and the firing order (order in which cylinders fire or produce power strokes) is either 1–3–4–2 or 1–2–4–3.

2. *Six-cylinder in-line engines.* The six-cylinder in-line engine is similar to the four, but it has two more cylinders (Figs. 2–2 and 5–1). The cylinders are arranged vertically and in line. The crankshaft is supported by three or four bearings, with the crankpins arranged in pairs 120 degrees apart. Cylinders are numbered from front to back, and the firing order is either 1–5–3–6–2–4 or 1–4–2–6–3–5.

NOTE: Considerable development work on V-6 engines has been done.

This type of engine has two banks of three cylinders each, placed at an angle to form a V as in the V-8 engine (see. below). However, a V-6 has not become available in American cars (except on an experimental basis) although at least one European manufacturer is supplying a V-6.

3. *Eight-cylinder in-line engines.* The eight-cylinder in-line engine has eight cylinders arranged vertically and in one line (Fig. 5–2). The crankshaft is usually supported on five bearings, although a greater number could be used. The crankpins are arranged in pairs and in planes that are perpendicular to each other. The firing order in practically universal use on eight-cylinder in-line passenger-car engines

Fig. 5–3. Front view of a V-8 engine. *(Buick Motor Division of General Motors Corporation)*

is 1–6–2–5–8–3–7–4, although 1–4–7–3–8–5–2–6 could also be used.

4. V-8 engines. In the V-8 engine (Figs. 5–3 to 5–6), the cylinders are arranged in two banks of four cylinders each, with the two banks set at a 90-degree angle (usually) to each other. This design permits a shorter and lighter but more rigid engine. The arrangement also permits the use of intake manifolding that assures relatively even distribution of the air-fuel mixture to all cylinders (since all cylinders are relatively close together). The crankshaft has only four crankpins; connecting rods from opposing cylinders in the two banks are attached to the same crankpin. Two rods are attached to each pin.

In recent years, there has been a great swing to V-8 engines. Such cars as Buick, Chevrolet, Chrysler, De Soto, Dodge, Oldsmobile, Packard, Plymouth, Pontiac, Studebaker, and others, have joined the ranks of those using V-8 engines. Cadillac, Ford, Lincoln, and Mercury have been using V-8 engines for a number of years. Engineers have mentioned several reasons for the swing to V-8 engines. One is that the shorter engine is more rigid; this permits higher running speeds and higher combustion pressures (higher power outputs) with less difficulty

from flexing, or bending, of the crank-shaft and cylinder block. Flexing, of course, throws the engine out of line, increases frictional losses and wear, and may set up internal vibrations. Also, the shorter engine makes possible more passenger space on the same wheel base, or a shorter-wheel-base car. Most of the V-8 engines, particularly the newer ones, use overhead valves (see § 97).

5. *Twelve- and sixteen-cylinder engines.* Twelve- and sixteen-cylinder engines have been used in passenger cars, buses, and trucks and in industrial installations. The cylinders are usually arranged in two banks (V type or pancake type), three banks (W type), or four banks (X type). The pancake engine is similar to a V engine except

that the two banks are arranged in a plane, but opposing; the cylinders work to the same crankshaft.

6. *Radial engine.* The radial engine, largely used in aircraft, has the cylinders radiating from a common center, like the spokes of a wheel. All connecting rods work to a common crankpin. The radial engine is air-cooled (§ 98).

§ **97. Valve arrangements** The intake and exhaust valves in the engine can be arranged in various positions in the cylinder head or block; these arrangements are termed "L," "T," "I," and "F" (Fig. 5–7). The L, I, and F arrangements are used in automotive engines.

1. *L-head.* In the L-head arrange-

Fig. 5–4. Sectional view, from end, of a V-8 engine with overhead valves. (De Soto Division of Chrysler Corporation)

87

(a)

(b)

Fig. 5–5. Sectional views from side (a), and from end (b), of a V-8 engine with overhead valves. (Chevrolet Motor Division of General Motors Corporation)

ment (Figs. 3–17 and 3–18), the combustion chamber and cylinder form an L. The intake and exhaust valves are located side by side, with all valves for the engine arranged in one line (except for . V-8 L-head engines, in which they would be in two lines as shown in Fig. 5–6). This arrangement permits the use of a single camshaft to operate all valves. Since the valve mechanisms are in the block, removal of the cylinder head for major overhaul of the engine is relatively easy. However, in the opinion of many automotive engineers, the L-head engine, while rugged and dependable, is not particularly adapted to higher-com-

pression engines. One reason is that the valves require a certain minimum space to move up into when they open. This space, plus the minimum clearance required above the top of the piston, determines the minimum possible clearance volume [volume with piston at TDC (top dead center)]. Since the clearance volume cannot be decreased below this minimum, there is a limit to how much the compression ratio of this engine can be increased. [Remember that compression ratio is the ratio between volume at BDC (bottom dead center) and clearance volume—or volume at TDC.] On the other hand, the overhead-valve

Fig. 5–6. Sectional view, from end, of a V-8 engine with L heads. (Ford Motor Company)

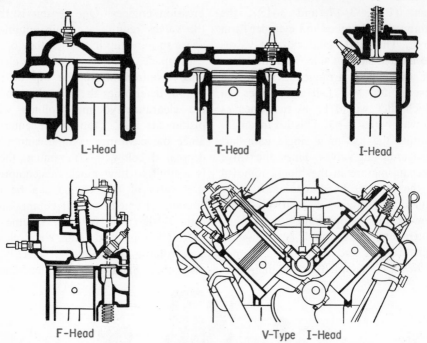

L-Head   T-Head   I-Head

F-Head   V-Type I-Head

Fig. 5–7. Valve arrangements. Compare these line drawings with the sectional views of various engines shown elsewhere in the book.

(I-head) engine is more adaptable to higher compression ratios, as explained in following paragraphs.

2. *I-head engine.* In the I-head, or overhead-valve, engine, the valves are carried in the cylinder head (Fig. 5–7). In in-line engines, the valves are in a single row as shown in Figs. 5–1 and 5–2. In V-8 engines, the valves may be arranged in a single row in each bank (Fig. 5–5), or they may be placed in a double row in each bank (Fig. 5–4). Regardless of arrangement, a single camshaft actuates all valves, with valve lifters, push rods, and rocker arms carrying the motion from the cams to the valves (Figs. 5–8*A* and 5–8*B*).

NOTE: Some overhead-valve engines—those used in racing cars, for example—have overhead camshafts. This arrangement eliminates the push rods and rocker arms. However, a chain and sprockets, or a gear train, is required to drive the camshaft.

The overhead-valve arrangement has come into more widespread use in recent years since it is more adaptable to the higher-compression-ratio engines. In an engine with overhead valves, it is practical to reduce the clearance volume a proportionally greater amount than in an L-head engine. If you will study the illustrations of the various L-head and I-head engines in the book, you will see that the method of grouping the valves directly above the piston permits a smaller clearance volume. In some I-head engines, there are pockets in the piston

90

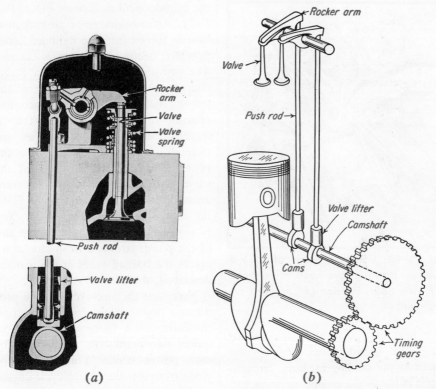

(a)   (b)

Fig. 5–8A. Valve-operating mechanism for I-head, or overhead-valve, engine. Sectional view of an actual engine is shown in *(a)*. In *(b)*, only the essential moving parts are shown, including the gears to drive the camshaft, the valve lifters, push rods, rocker arms, and valves for one cylinder. *(Buick Motor Division of General Motors Corporation)*

heads into which the valves can move when the valves are open with the piston at TDC. In some engines, the clearances between the piston and valves are only a few thousandths of an inch.

3. F-head engine. This engine is, in a sense, a combination L-head and I-head engine (Fig. 5–7). The intake valves are in the head, and the exhaust valves are in the block. Both sets are driven from the same camshaft.

4. V-8 arrangements. The V-8 engine may use L heads or I heads, as

has already been mentioned. Refer to the illustrations earlier in the chapter which show the two arrangements. The newer V-8 engines are all I-head.

§ 98. Classification by cooling Engines are classified as liquid-cooled or air-cooled. All present-day American automotive engines are liquid-cooled. Some earlier cars, however (such as the Franklin), were air-cooled. In the air-cooled engine, the cylinder barrels are separate and equipped with metal fins so that they can dispose of exces-

Fig. 5–8B. Cutaway view of a V-8 engine, showing overhead-valve train. (*Chrysler Sales Division of Chrysler Corporation*)

sive heat by radiation to the passing air. The liquid-cooled engine uses water as the cooling medium, circulating it between the engine water jackets and the cooling radiator (§ 37).

§ 99. Classification by cycles Engines can be classified as either two-stroke-cycle or four-stroke-cycle. In the four-stroke-cycle engine (usually called a four-cycle engine), already discussed (in § 69), the complete cycle of events requires four piston strokes (intake, compression, power, and exhaust). In the two-stroke-cycle, or two-cycle, engine, the intake and compression strokes, and the power and exhaust strokes, are in a sense combined. This permits the engine to produce a power stroke every two piston strokes, or every crankshaft rotation.

In the two-cycle engine, the piston acts as a valve, clearing valve ports in the cylinder wall as it nears BDC (Fig. 5–9). A fresh charge of air-fuel mixture is forced into the cylinder under pressure as the intake port is cleared. The pressure is produced by a supercharger, or blower. The shape of the piston head causes the incoming charge to be deflected upward; it thereby forces the burned gas out through the exhaust port. Then, as the piston starts upward, it shuts off the valve ports. The charge is then compressed, and as the piston nears TDC, the charge is ignited (Fig. 5–10). The power stroke then follows. At the end of the power stroke, a fresh charge replaces the burned gases in the manner described above.

Note that the two-cycle engine produces a power stroke every crankshaft revolution; the four-cycle engine requires two crankshaft revolutions for each power stroke. You might conclude from this that a two-cycle engine could produce twice as much horsepower as a four-cycle engine of the same size, running at the same speed. However, this is not true. In the first

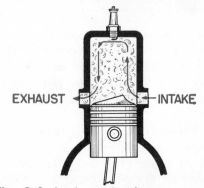

Fig. 5–9. Intake and exhaust on two-stroke-cycle engine. As piston moves downward, it clears the intake and exhaust ports.

place, some of the power is used to drive the blower that forces the air-fuel charge into the cylinder under pressure. Also, the burned gases are not completely cleared from the cylinder. There is also apt to be less charge entering than would be the case in the four-cycle engine. This is because the intake-valve port is open a much shorter period of time (as compared with the four-cycle engine). These factors reduce the amount of power that the engine can produce under given conditions.

A variation of the two-cycle engine uses an exhaust valve in the top of the cylinder (Fig. 5–11). As the piston nears BDC and clears the intake ports, the exhaust valve opens. The charging air is forced in under pressure, causing the burned gases to be forced up and out through the exhaust-valve port. Then, as the piston starts up on the compression stroke, the intake ports are sealed off and the exhaust valve closes. The engine shown in Fig. 5–11 is a two-cycle diesel engine.

§ **100. Classification by fuel** Internal-combustion engines can be classified according to the type of fuel they use. Automotive engines, in general, use gasoline. Some bus and truck engines use LPG (liquefied petroleum gas): these are essentially gasoline engines adapted for LPG. Diesel engines use diesel fuel oil. Chapter 9 describes these fuels in detail.

§ **101. Diesel engine** In the diesel engine, air alone enters the cylinder on the intake stroke, and air alone is compressed on the compression stroke. At the end of the compression stroke,

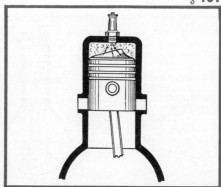

Fig. 5–10. As the piston moves upward on the compression stroke, it seals the valve ports and compresses the mixture.

the fuel is injected, or sprayed, into the combustion chamber. In diesel engines the compression ratios are as high as 15:1, and this produces pressures of about 500 psi (pounds per square inch) at the end of the compression stroke. When air is rapidly compressed to this pressure, it will be heated to a temperature of about 1000°F. This temperature is high enough to ignite fuel oil sprayed into the heated air. Thus, no separate ignition system is required; the oil is ignited by the heat resulting from the compression of the air.

The four-stroke-cycle diesel engine requires four piston strokes for the complete cycle of actions, just as in the gasoline engine. These are intake, compression, power, and exhaust. In the two-cycle diesel engine, a blower or rotary-type pump is used to produce the initial pressure on the ingoing air. The piston serves as a valve, or valves, clearing ports as it nears BDC. Fresh air enters the intake ports, and the burned gases exhaust through the exhaust ports. The type shown in Fig. 5–11 has an exhaust valve at the top

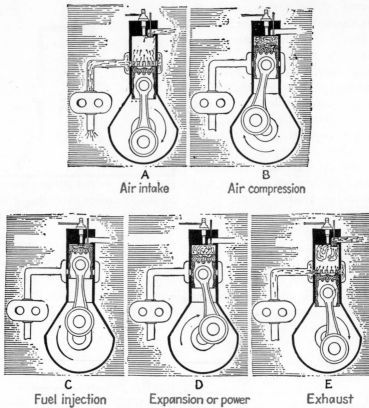

A   B
Air intake   Air compression

C   D   E
Fuel injection   Expansion or power   Exhaust

Fig. 5–11. Sequence of events in two-stroke-cycle diesel engine. (*Detroit Diesel Engine Division of General Motors Corporation*)

of the cylinder. The burned gases are forced through this exhaust-valve port as the valve opens and the piston moves down to clear the intake ports. Then, as the piston moves up, it closes off the intake ports. At the same time, the exhaust valve closes. Now, the air is trapped and compressed. The sequence of actions in a two-stroke-cycle engine is shown in Fig. 5–11.

§ 102. Gas turbine   The gas turbine, now making its appearance as an automotive power plant, consists, in es-

sence, of two sections, a gasifier section and a power section (Fig. 5–12). The compressor has a rotor with a series of blades around its outer edge. As it rotates, air between the blades is carried around and thrown out by centrifugal force. This action supplies the burner with air at relatively high pressure. Fuel is sprayed into the compressed air. The fuel used can be gasoline, kerosene, or oil. As the fuel burns, a further increase in pressure results. The high-pressure, high-temperature gas then passes through the

gasifier nozzle diaphragm. A series of stationary blades directs this high-pressure gas against a series of curved blades on the outer edge of the gasifier turbine rotor. The resulting high pressure against the curved blades causes the gasifier turbine rotor to spin at high speed. Since the gasifier turbine rotor and the compressor rotor are mounted on the same shaft, the compressor rotor is also spun at high speed. This action continues to supply the burner with an ample amount of compressed air. The action continues as long as fuel is supplied to the burner.

After the high-pressure, high-temperature gas leaves the gasifier section, it enters the power turbine. Here, it strikes another series of stationary curved blades which directs it against a series of curved blades on the outer edge of the power turbine rotor. The resulting high pressure against these rotor blades spins the rotor at high speed. In some models, the turbine may turn faster than 30,000 rpm. This high rpm is reduced by a series of transmission gears before the power is applied to the vehicle wheels.

§ 103. Free-piston engine Instead of a compressor-burner section, some engineers propose the use of a free-piston engine to supply high-pressure gas to drive a power turbine. The free-piston engine (Figs. 5–13 to 5–16) contains a pair of piston assemblies

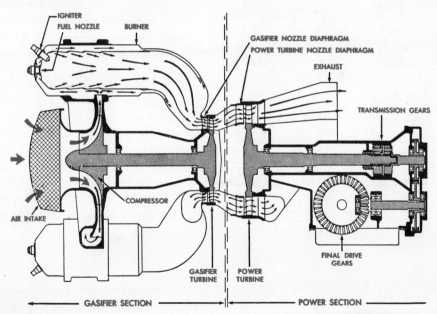

Fig. 5–12. Experimental gas turbine for automotive vehicles. The gasifier section burns fuel in a burner and delivers it to the power section, where it spins the power turbine. The power turbine then turns the vehicle wheels through a series of gears. (General Motors Corporation)

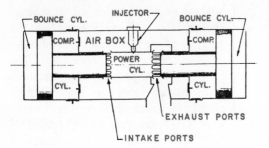

Fig. 5–13. Schematic drawing of a free-piston engine.

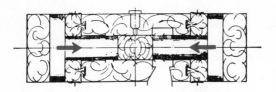

Fig. 5–14. Action as the compression cycle starts. The bounce pistons are moving inward, compressing air between the two power pistons.

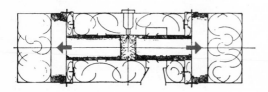

Fig. 5–15. Combustion starts when fuel is injected into the compressed and hot air between the power pistons.

Fig. 5–16. The combustion pressures drive the power pistons outward. As the right-hand piston clears the exhaust ports, the high-pressure gases escape from the power cylinder and drive the turbine. As the left-hand piston clears the intake ports, air from the air box enters the power cylinder and scavenges it.

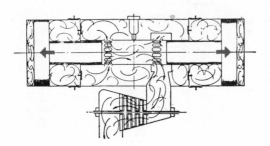

that oppose each other in a cylinder. Each piston assembly consists of a relatively small power piston attached to a relatively large bounce piston. The principle of operation is this: The piston assemblies are driven in (or bounced in) to compress air between the power pistons. As the pistons complete their inward travel, fuel is injected into the combustion space between the pistons. At this instant, the engine functions like a diesel engine

(see § 101). That is, the heat of compression ignites the fuel and combustion takes place. The resulting high pressure drives the pistons apart. They clear exhaust and intake ports, and fresh air enters the power cylinder. At the same time, the air back of the bounce pistons is compressed (in the bounce cylinders), and this pressure drives the piston assemblies toward each other again. The gas, as it exhausts from the power cylinder, still has sufficient pressure to drive a turbine (Fig. 5–16). This action continues as long as fuel is supplied to the engine.

The valves in the compression cylinders are spring-loaded to open against pressure. Thus, when the bounce pistons are moving inward, air is compressed ahead of them, and this forces the intake valves to open and admit this air to the air box. When the bounce pistons are moving outward, the pressure in the compression cylinders drops below atmospheric, and atmospheric pressure forces the intake valves open to admit air into the compression cylinders.

REVIEW QUESTIONS

1. What are five ways in which engines are classified?
2. What are four cylinder arrangements?
3. What are three valve arrangements?
4. Describe the actions in a two-cycle engine.
5. Explain the differences between gasoline and diesel engines.
6. Describe the action in a diesel engine.

STUDY QUESTIONS

1. What would be some of the advantages of a diesel engine in a passenger car? Some of the disadvantages?
2. Do you think diesel engines will ever come into widespread use in passenger cars? What are your reasons?
3. If you want further information on diesel engines, get a book on them from your library. Make a list of the different types and applications of diesel engines.

THIS CHAPTER DESCRIBES IN detail the construction of automotive engines and supplies you with the background information you need to move on into the engine troubleshooting and servicing sections of the book.

§ 104. The engine Thus far the engine has been considered from the viewpoint of its operation. We have seen how the mixture of air and fuel is delivered by the fuel system to the engine cylinder, where it is compressed, ignited, and burned. We have noted that this combustion produces a high pressure that pushes the piston down so that the crankshaft is rotated. Now, let us examine the various parts of the engine in detail.

§ 105. Engine cylinder block The cylinder block (Figs. 6–1 and 6–2) forms the basic framework of the engine. Other engine parts are attached to or assembled in it. The block is cast in one piece from gray iron or iron alloyed with other metals such as

Fig. 6–1. Cylinder block of six-cylinder L-head in-line engine, showing intake and exhaust valves of two cylinders removed. The screw driver is under a valve spring, prying it up and out. If a spring is removed in this manner, care must be used to keep it from flying and hurting someone. (Studebaker-Packard Corporation)

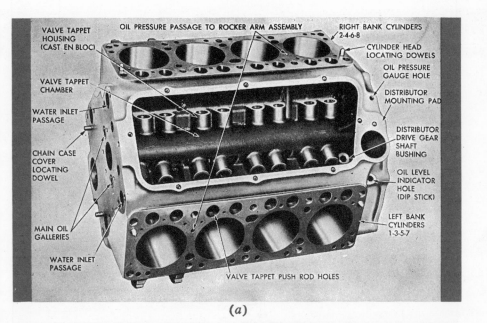

VALVE TAPPET HOUSING (CAST EN BLOC)

OIL PRESSURE PASSAGE TO ROCKER ARM ASSEMBLY

RIGHT BANK CYLINDERS 2-4-6-8

CYLINDER HEAD LOCATING DOWELS

OIL PRESSURE GAUGE HOLE

VALVE TAPPET CHAMBER

DISTRIBUTOR MOUNTING PAD

WATER INLET PASSAGE

DISTRIBUTOR DRIVE GEAR SHAFT BUSHING

CHAIN CASE COVER LOCATING DOWEL

OIL LEVEL INDICATOR HOLE (DIP STICK)

MAIN OIL GALLERIES

LEFT BANK CYLINDERS 1-3-5-7

WATER INLET PASSAGE

VALVE TAPPET PUSH ROD HOLES

(a)

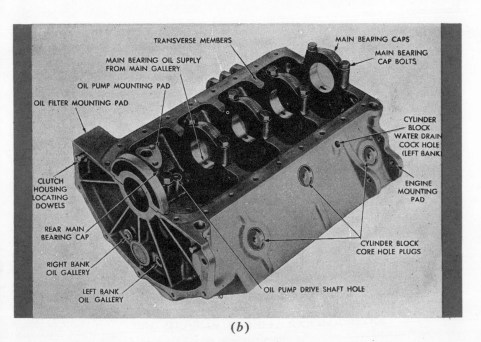

TRANSVERSE MEMBERS

MAIN BEARING CAPS

MAIN BEARING CAP BOLTS

MAIN BEARING OIL SUPPLY FROM MAIN GALLERY

OIL PUMP MOUNTING PAD

OIL FILTER MOUNTING PAD

CYLINDER BLOCK WATER DRAIN COCK HOLE (LEFT BANK)

CLUTCH HOUSING LOCATING DOWELS

ENGINE MOUNTING PAD

REAR MAIN BEARING CAP

RIGHT BANK OIL GALLERY

CYLINDER BLOCK CORE HOLE PLUGS

LEFT BANK OIL GALLERY

OIL PUMP DRIVE SHAFT HOLE

(b)

Fig. 6–2. (a) Top and (b) bottom views of a cylinder block from a V-8 overhead-valve engine. (De Soto Division of Chrysler Corporation)

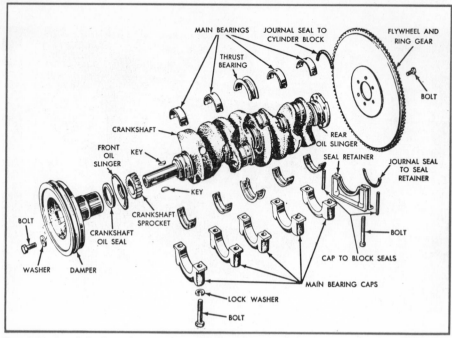

Fig. 6–3. Crankshaft and related parts for a V-8 engine. (*Ford Division of Ford Motor Company*)

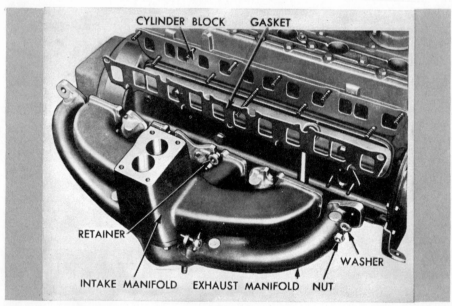

Fig. 6–4. Installation of intake and exhaust manifolds on the cylinder block of a typical L-head engine.

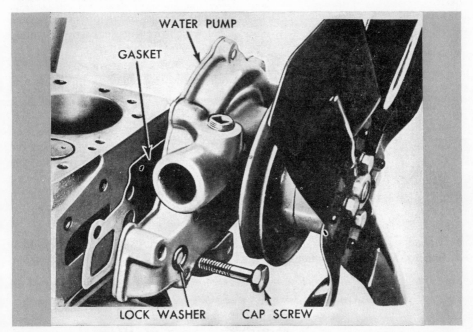

WATER PUMP

GASKET

LOCK WASHER   CAP SCREW

Fig. 6–5. Installation of the water pump on the cylinder block of a typical engine.

nickel or chromium. Some blocks are made from aluminum. The block contains not only the cylinders but also the water jackets that surround them. In aluminum blocks, cast-iron or steel cylinder sleeves are used. These metals have better wearing qualities than aluminum and can better withstand the wearing effect of the pistons and rings moving up and down in the cylinders. L-head engine blocks contain the passageways for the valves and valve ports. The lower part of the block supports the crankshaft (with main bearings and bearing caps) and also the oil pan. Figure 6–3 shows a crankshaft for a six-cylinder engine with bearing halves and caps.

The camshaft is supported in the cylinder block by bushings that fit into machined holes in the block (Fig. 3–26). On L-head in-line engines, the intake and exhaust manifolds are attached to the side of the cylinder block (Fig. 6–4). On L-head V-8 engines, the intake manifold is located between the two banks of cylinders. In this engine, there are two exhaust manifolds, one on the outside of each bank. On I-head engines, the manifolds are attached to the cylinder head.

Other parts attached to the block include the water pump (attached at the front as shown in Fig. 6–5), the timing gear or timing chain cover (at front), the flywheel and clutch housing (at rear), the ignition distributor, and the fuel pump. The cylinder head mounts on top of the block.

The various parts are attached to the cylinder block with sealing gaskets. The gaskets (§ 107) are placed between the part and the block. Then, tightening the attaching bolts or nuts

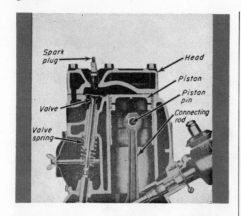

Fig. 6–6. Sectional view of the head from an L-head engine. (*Oldsmobile Division of General Motors Corporation*)

flattens the gasket to provide a good seal which prevents leakage (of water, oil, or gas).

Some parts are attached with bolts, others with nuts and studs. Studs are threaded at both ends; one end is tightened into a threaded hole in the block, the part to be attached is put into place, and a nut is tightened on the other end of the stud to hold the part in position. In some places, retaining or lock washers are put under the nuts or boltheads (see §§ 3–8).

§ 106. Cylinder head   The cylinder head is usually cast in one piece from

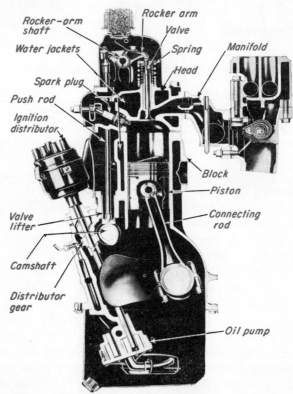

Fig. 6–7. Sectional view of I-head, or overhead-valve, type of engine. Note how the spark plugs, valves, valve mechanism, and manifolds are assembled to the head. (*Buick Motor Division of General Motors Coporation*)

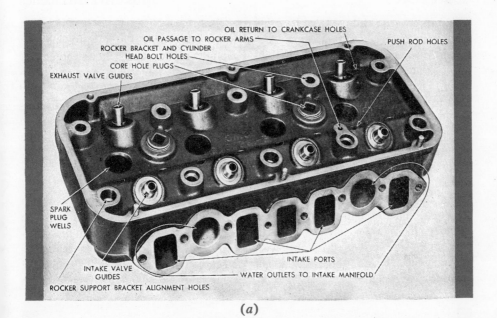

OIL RETURN TO CRANKCASE HOLES
OIL PASSAGE TO ROCKER ARMS
ROCKER BRACKET AND CYLINDER
HEAD BOLT HOLES
CORE HOLE PLUGS
EXHAUST VALVE GUIDES
PUSH ROD HOLES

SPARK
PLUG
WELLS

INTAKE VALVE
GUIDES
ROCKER SUPPORT BRACKET ALIGNMENT HOLES
INTAKE PORTS
WATER OUTLETS TO INTAKE MANIFOLD

(a)

HEMISPHERICAL COMBUSTION CHAMBERS
OIL PASSAGE TO ROCKER ARMS
PUSH ROD HOLES
INTAKE VALVE GUIDES
SPARK PLUG HOLES
WATER
PASSAGE
HOLES

EXHAUST
VALVE
SEAT
INSERT
EXHAUST MANIFOLD
MOUNTING STUDS
EXHAUST PORTS

(b)

Fig. 6–8. (a) Top and (b) bottom views of cylinder head from a V-8 overhead-valve engine. (De Soto Division of Chrysler Corporation)

103

iron, from iron alloyed with other metals, or from aluminum alloy. Aluminum has the advantage of combining lightness with high heat conductivity. That is, an aluminum head will tend to run cooler, other factors being equal. There are two types of head, L-head and I-head.

1. L head. This head is comparatively simple (Fig. 6–6). It contains water jackets for cooling; in the assembled engine, these water jackets are connected through openings to the cylinder-block water jackets. Sparkplug holes are provided, along with pockets into which the valves can move as they open.

2. I head. This head is somewhat more complex since it must include, along with the other items noted for the L head, the valves and valve-operating mechanisms (Figs. 6–7 and 6–8). Examine the various illustrations of I-head engines in the book to see how the valves are carried in the head. Later pages describe the valve-operating mechanisms.

§ 107. Gaskets The joint between the cylinder block and head must be tight and able to withstand the pressure and heat developed in the combustion chambers. The block and head cannot be machined flat and smooth

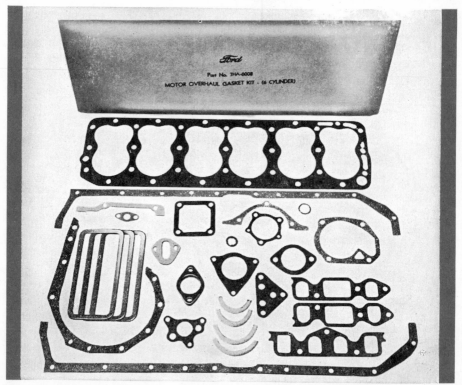

Fig. 6–9. Motor overhaul gasket kit for a six-cylinder engine, showing the various gaskets used in the engine. *(Ford Motor Company)*

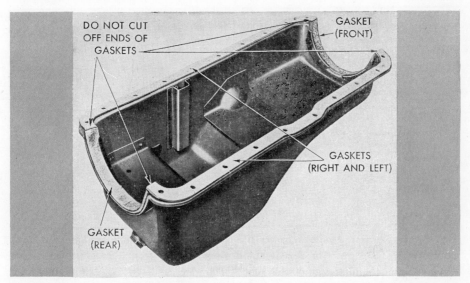

DO NOT CUT
OFF ENDS OF
GASKETS

GASKET
(FRONT)

GASKETS
(RIGHT AND LEFT)

GASKET
(REAR)

Fig. 6–10. Oil pan with gaskets in place, ready for pan replacement. *(Plymouth Division of Chrysler Corporation)*

enough to provide an adequate seal. Thus, gaskets are used (Fig. 6–9). Head gaskets are made of thin sheets of soft metal or asbestos and metal. All cylinder, water, valve, and head-bolt openings are cut out. When the gasket is placed on the block and the head installed, tightening of the head bolts (or nuts) squeezes the soft metal so that the joint is effectively sealed. Gaskets are also used to seal joints between other parts, such as between the oil pan, manifolds, or water pump, and the block.

§ 108. Oil pan   The oil pan is usually formed of pressed steel (Fig. 6–10). It holds 5 to 9 quarts of oil, depending on the engine design. The oil pan and the lower part of the cylinder block are called, together, the crankcase; they enclose, or incase, the crankshaft. The oil pump in the lubricating system draws oil from the oil pan and sends it to all working parts in the engine. The oil drains off and runs down into the pan. Thus, there is constant circulation of oil between the pan and working parts of the engine. (See Chap. 10 for details of engine lubricating systems.)

§ 109. Exhaust manifold   The exhaust manifold (Fig. 6–11) is essentially a tube for carrying the burned gases away from the engine cylinders. The exhaust manifold is attached to the side of the block on L-head engines and to the side of the cylinder head on I-head engines. On V-8 engines, there are two exhaust manifolds, one for each bank of cylinders. They are connected by a crossover pipe and exhaust through a common muffler and tail pipe.

§ 110. Exhaust system   The exhaust system includes the exhaust manifold,

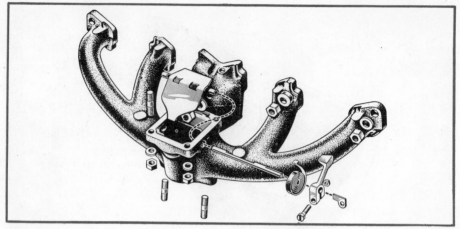

Fig. 6–11. Exhaust manifold for a six-cylinder L-head in-line engine with heat-control valve and parts in disassembled view.

exhaust pipe, muffler, and tail pipe (Fig. 6–12). Most V-8 engines use a crossover pipe to connect their two exhaust manifolds. However, at least one car uses two separate exhaust systems, one for each cylinder bank. This improves the "breathing" ability of the engine, allowing it to exhaust more freely and thus increases power output to some extent.

§ 111. **Muffler** The muffler (Fig. 6–13) contains a series of holes, passages, and resonance chambers to absorb and damp out the high-pressure surges introduced into the exhaust system as the exhaust valves open. This quiets the exhaust.

§ 112. **Intake manifold** The intake manifold (Fig. 6–14) is essentially a tube, or tubes, for carrying the air-fuel mixture from the carburetor to the engine intake-valve ports. The carburetor mounts on the intake manifold. The intake manifold is mounted on the side of the cylinder block in L-head engines and on the side of the

cylinder head in I-head engines. On V-8 engines, the intake manifold is situated between the two cylinder banks. The right-hand illustration in Fig. 6–14 shows the intake manifold for a V-8 engine. A two-barrel carburetor is used on this engine. The two-barrel carburetor is, in effect, two separate

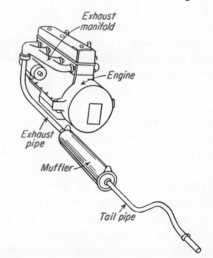

Fig. 6–12. Exhaust system. Exhaust gases from engine pass through the exhaust manifold, exhaust pipe, muffler, and tail pipe to the open air.

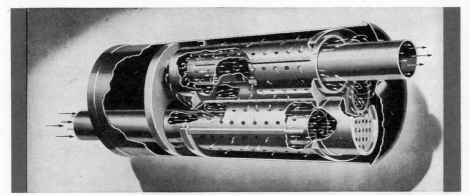

Fig. 6–13. Exhaust muffler in sectional view. The arrows show the path of exhaust-gas flow through the muffler. (*Chevrolet Motor Division of General Motors Corporation*)

carburetors assembled together. Each barrel feeds four cylinders, as shown by the white arrows. Chapter 8 discusses various carburetors in detail.

§ 113. Manifold heat control During initial warm-up of the engine, just after starting, evaporation of the gasoline in the air-fuel mixture entering the engine is relatively poor. Gasoline evaporates more slowly when it is cold (see § 240). In order to improve fuel evaporation and therefore cold-engine operation, a device is provided to heat the intake manifold when it is cold. This device, called the *manifold heat-control valve,* is built into the exhaust manifold. Two arrangements are used, one for in-line engines, another for V-8 engines.

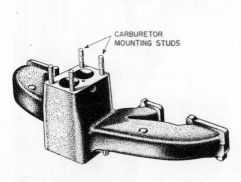

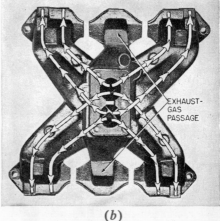

(*a*)   (*b*)

Fig. 6–14. Intake manifolds for (*a*) an L-head in-line six-cylinder engine and for (*b*) an I-head V-8 engine. The white arrows in (*b*) show the air-fuel-mixture flow from the two barrels of the carburetor to the eight cylinders in the engine. The central passage connects between the two exhaust manifolds; exhaust gas flows through this passage during engine warm-up.

107

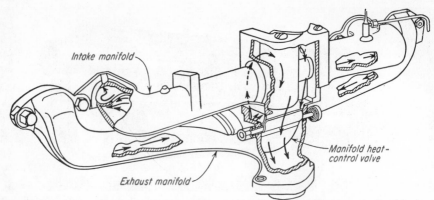

Fig. 6–15. Relationship between intake and exhaust manifolds, showing the thermostatically controlled manifold heat-control valve and directions of intake and exhaust gases with valve in cold-engine position.

1. In-line engines. In these engines, the exhaust manifold is located under the intake manifold. At a central point, there is an opening from the exhaust manifold into a chamber, or oven, surrounding the intake manifold (Figs. 6–15 and 6–16). A butterfly valve is situated in this opening (see Fig. 6–

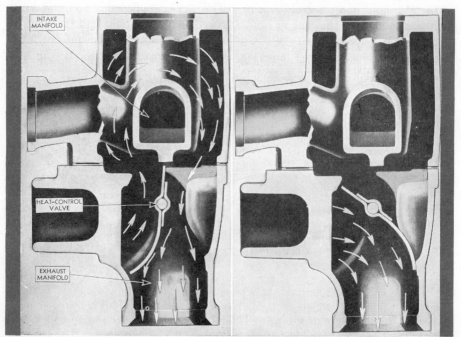

Fig. 6–16. The two extreme positions, in the exhaust manifold, of the manifold heat-control valve, which controls the flow of exhaust gases through the intake-manifold jacket. *(Chevrolet Motor Division of General Motors Corporation)*

11). When the valve is turned one way, the opening is closed off. The position of the valve is controlled by a thermostat (see § 61). When the engine is cold, the thermostat unwinds and moves the valve to the closed position (left in Fig. 6–16). Now, when the engine is started, the exhaust gases must pass through the opening and circulate through the oven around the intake manifold (Figs. 6–15 and 6–16). Heat from the exhaust gas quickly warms the intake manifold and helps the fuel to evaporate. Thus, cold-engine operation is improved. As the engine warms up, the thermostat winds up and moves the valve to the opened position (right in Fig. 6–16). Now, the exhaust gases pass directly into the exhaust pipe and no longer circulate in the oven around the intake manifold.

2. *V-8 engines.* In V-8 engines, the intake manifold between the two banks of cylinders has a special passage (indicated in the lower illustration shown in Fig. 6–14) through which exhaust gases can pass. One of the exhaust manifolds has a thermostatically controlled valve that closes when the engine is cold. This causes the exhaust gases to pass through the special passage in the intake manifold. Heat from

the exhaust gases then heats the air-fuel mixture in the intake manifold for improved cold-engine operation. As the engine warms up, the thermostatically controlled valve opens. Then, the exhaust gases from both exhaust manifolds pass directly into the exhaust pipes.

§ **114. Crankshaft** The crankshaft is a one-piece casting or forging of heat-treated alloy steel of considerable mechanical strength (Figs. 6–3 and 6–17). The crankshaft must be strong enough to take the downward thrusts of the pistons during the power strokes without excessive distortion. In addition, the crankshaft must be carefully balanced to eliminate undue vibration resulting from the weight of the offset cranks. To provide balance, crankshafts have counterweights opposite the cranks (see Fig. 6–3). Crankshafts have drilled oil passages (Fig. 6–17) through which oil can flow from the main to the connecting-rod bearings (see § 117, Bearing Lubrication).

The flow of power from the engine cylinders is not smooth. While the power impulses overlap (on six- and eight-cylinder engines), there are times when more power is being delivered than at other times (Fig. 6–18). This

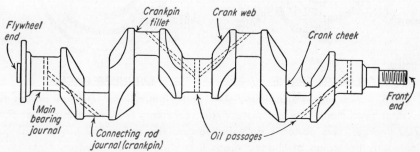

Fig. 6–17. Typical crankshaft with various parts named. (Johnson Bronze Company)

tends to make the crankshaft speed up and then slow down. However, the flywheel combats this tendency. The flywheel is a comparatively heavy wheel bolted to the rear end of the crankshaft (Fig. 3–31). The inertia of the flywheel tends to keep the flywheel turning at constant speed. Thus, the flywheel absorbs power as the crankshaft tries to speed up and gives back power as the crankshaft tries to slow down (see §§ 71 and 76).

In addition to this function, the flywheel also has gear teeth around its outer rim that mesh with the cranking-motor drive pinion for cranking the engine. The rear face of the flywheel also serves as the driving member of the clutch (on engines so equipped).

The front end of the crankshaft carries three devices, the gear or sprocket that drives the camshaft, the vibration damper (§ 115), and the fanbelt pulley. The pulley drives the engine fan, water pump, and generator by means of a V belt.

§ 115. Vibration damper The power impulses tend to set up torsional vibration in the crankshaft. When a piston

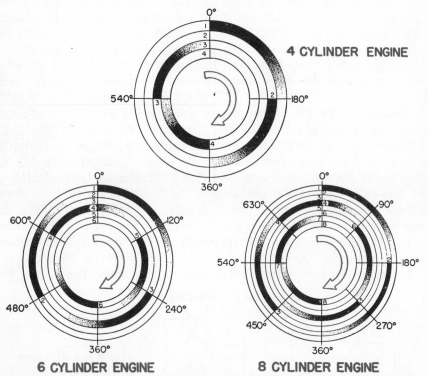

Fig. 6–18. Power impulse in four-, six-, and eight-cylinder engines during two crankshaft revolutions. The complete circle represents two crankshaft revolutions, or 720 degrees. Less power is delivered toward the end of the power stroke, as indicated by lightening of shaded areas that show power impulses. Note power overlap on six- and eight-cylinder engines.

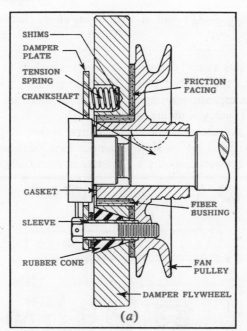

SHIMS
DAMPER PLATE
TENSION SPRING
CRANKSHAFT
FRICTION FACING
GASKET
FIBER BUSHING
SLEEVE
RUBBER CONE
FAN PULLEY
DAMPER FLYWHEEL

(a)

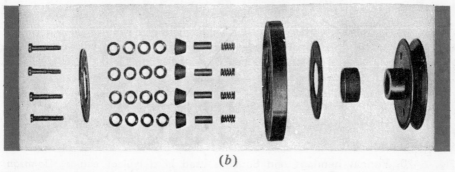

(b)

Fig. 6–19. (a) Sectional and (b) disassembled views of a typical vibration damper. (Studebaker-Packard Corporation)

moves down on its power stroke, it thrusts, through the connecting rod, against a crankpin with a force that may exceed 2 tons. This force tends to twist the crank ahead of the rest of the crankshaft. Then, a moment later, the force against the crank is relieved. The crank then tends to untwist, or move back into its original relationship with the rest of the crankshaft. This twist-untwist, repeated with every power im-pulse, tends to set up an oscillating motion in the crankshaft. This is tor-sional vibration; if it were not con-trolled, it would cause the oscillations to build up so much that the crank-shaft might actually break at certain speeds. To control torsional vibration, devices variously called *vibration damp-ers, torsional balancers,* or *crankshaft-torque-impulse neutralizers* are used. They are usually mounted to the front

111

of the crankshaft (Fig. 3–31) and include the fan-belt pulley.

Figure 6-19 shows one type of vibration damper. It contains a small damper flywheel mounted to the fan-belt pulley by rubber cones, springs, and screws. The fan-belt pulley is mounted on the crankshaft. As the crankshaft and pulley tend to speed up or slow down, the damper flywheel imposes a dragging effect (because of its inertia). This effect, which slightly compresses the rubber cones, tends to hold the pulley and crankshaft to a constant speed. This action tends to check the twist-untwist, or torsional vibration, of the crankshaft.

Several other types of vibration damper have been used. However, all operate in essentially the same manner.

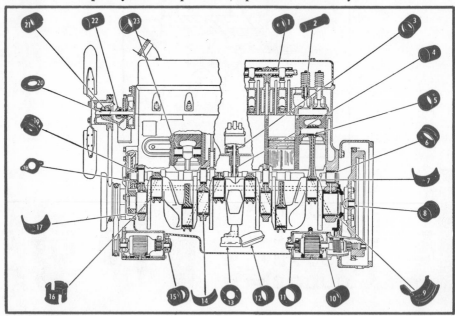

Fig. 6–20. Various bearings and bushings used in a typical engine. (*Johnson Bronze Company*)

1. Rocker-arm bushing
2. Valve-guide bushing
3. Distributor bushing, upper
4. Distributor bushing, lower
5. Piston-pin bushing
6. Camshaft bushing
7. Connecting-rod bearing
8. Clutch pilot bushing
9. End-thrust main bearing
10. Starter bushing, drive end
11. Starter bushing, commutator end
12. Oil-pump bushing
13. Distributor thrust plate
14. Intermediate main bearing
15. Generator bushing
16. Connecting-rod bearing
17. Front main bearing
18. Camshaft thrust plate
19. Camshaft bushing
20. Fan thrust plate
21. Water-pump bushing, front
22. Water-pump bushing, rear
23. Piston-pin bushing

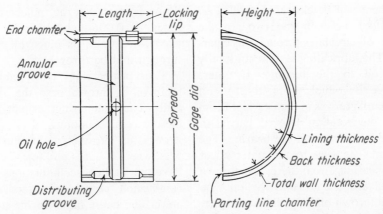

Fig. 6–21. Typical sleeve-type-bearing half with parts named. (Federal-Mogul Corporation)

§ 116. Engine bearings Bearings are installed in various places in the engine where there is relative motion between parts (Fig. 6–20). These bearings are called *sleeve bearings* because they are in the shape of a sleeve that fits around the rotating journal or shaft. Connecting-rod and crankshaft (or main) bearings are of the split, or half, type (Fig. 6–21). On main bearings, the upper half is installed in the counterbore in the cylinder block. The lower half is held in place by the bearing cap (Fig. 6–3). On connecting-rod big-end bearings, the upper half is installed in the rod, and the lower half is in the rod cap (Fig. 6–24). The small-end (or piston-pin) bearing in the connecting rod is of the full-round, or *bushing,* type (7 in Fig. 6–24).

The typical bearing half is made of a steel or bronze back to which a lining of bearing material is applied (Fig. 6–21). The bearing material is relatively soft. Thus, if wear takes place, it will be the bearing that wears rather than the more expensive engine part. Then, the bearing, rather than the

engine part, can be replaced when wear has progressed to the replacement point.

§ 117. Bearing lubrication As we have already noted, viscous friction causes the rotating journal to carry oil around the bearing; the journal load is supported by layers of oil (§ 78). The journal must be smaller in diameter than the bearing (Fig. 6–22) so

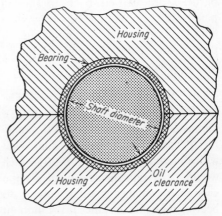

Fig. 6–22. Oil clearance between bearing and shaft journal. (Federal-Mogul Corporation)

that there will be clearance (called *oil clearance*) between the two. In the engine, oil circulates through this clearance. The lubricating system constantly feeds oil to the bearing. It enters through the oilhole (Fig. 6–21) and fills the oil grooves in the bearing. From there, the rotating journal carries it around to all parts of the bearing. The oil works its way to the outer edges of the bearing. From there, it is thrown off and drops back into the oil pan. The oil thrown off helps lubricate other engine parts such as the cylinder walls, pistons, and piston rings.

As the oil moves across the faces of the bearings, it not only lubricates them. It also helps to cool the bearings. The oil is relatively cool as it leaves the oil pan. It picks up heat in its passage through the bearing. This heat is then carried down to the oil pan and released to the air passing around the oil pan. The oil also flushes and cleans the bearings. It tends to flush out particles of grit and dirt that may have worked into the bearing. The particles are carried back to the oil pan by the circulating oil. They then tend to drop to the bottom of the oil pan or are removed from the oil by the oil screen or filter.

§ **118. Bearing oil clearances**   The greater the oil clearance (Fig. 6–22), the faster oil will flow through the bearing. Proper clearance varies somewhat with different engines, but 0.0015 inch would be a typical clearance. As the clearance becomes greater (owing to bearing wear, for instance), the amount of oil flowing through and being thrown off increases. With a 0.003-inch clearance (only twice 0.0015 inch), the oil

throwoff increases as much as five times. A 0.006-inch clearance allows twenty-five times as much oil to flow through and be thrown off.

Thus, as bearings wear, more and more oil is thrown onto the cylinder walls. The piston rings cannot handle these excessive amounts of oil; part of it works up into the combustion chambers, where it burns and forms carbon. Resulting carbon accumulations in the combustion chambers reduce engine power and cause other engine troubles (see Chap. 13). Excessive bearing oil clearances can also cause some bearings to fail from oil starvation. Here's the reason: The oil pump can deliver only so much oil. If the oil clearances are excessive, most of the oil will pass through the nearest bearings. There won't be enough for the more distant bearings; these bearings will probably fail from lack of oil. An engine with excessive bearing oil clearances usually has low oil pressure; the oil pump cannot build up normal pressure because of the excessive oil clearances in the bearings.

On the other hand, if oil clearances are not sufficiently great, there will be metal-to-metal contact between the bearing and shaft journal. Extremely rapid wear and quick failure will result. Also, there will not be enough oil throwoff for adequate lubrication of cylinder walls, pistons, and rings.

§ **119. Engine bearing types**   Early engines and some late-model heavy-duty engines use poured bearings. This bearing is prepared by fitting a journal-sized jig or mold into the counterbore and pouring molten bearing material into the opening. The resulting bearing

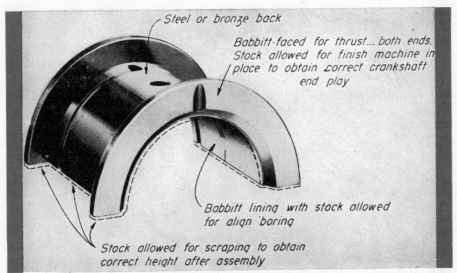

Fig. 6–23. Crankshaft thrust bearing of the semifitted type. (Federal-Mogul Corporation)

is then scraped and smoothed to provide the final fit and clearance.

In modern automotive engines, *precision-insert* (also called *precision-type*) bearings are used. These bearings are so precisely made that they can be installed without any machining or fitting. In many engines, it is possible to replace the main bearings without removing the crankshaft (see § 347)..

Some engines use semifitted bearings (Fig. 6–23). These have a few thousandths of an inch of extra bearing material that must be removed after the bearings are installed so as to establish the final fit. This procedure is described in § 349.

§ 120. Bearing requirements Bearings must be able to do other things besides carry the loads imposed on them, as noted below.

1. Load-carrying capacity. Modern engines are lighter and more powerful. They have higher compression ratios and thus impose greater bearing loads. Only a few years ago, bearing loads were around 1,600 to 1,800 psi (pounds per square inch). Today, connecting-rod bearing loads of 2,800 psi are not uncommon.

2. Fatigue resistance. When a piece of metal is repeatedly stressed so that it flexes or bends, it tends to harden and ultimately breaks. This is called fatigue failure. Repeatedly bending a piece of wire or sheet metal will demonstrate fatigue failure. Bearings are subjected to varying loads and are thus repeatedly stressed. The bearing material must be able to withstand these varying loads without failing from fatigue.

3. Embeddability. This term refers to the ability of a bearing to permit foreign particles to embed in it. Dirt and dust particles enter the engine

despite the air cleaner and oil filter. Some of them work onto the bearings and are not flushed away by the oil. A bearing protects itself by permitting such particles to sink into, or embed in, the bearing lining material. If the bearing were too hard to allow this, the particles would simply lie on the surface. They would scratch the shaft journal and probably gouge out the bearing. This, in turn, would cause overheating and rapid bearing failure. Thus, the bearing material must be soft enough for adequate embeddability.

4. *Conformability.* This is associated with embeddability. It refers to the ability of the bearing material to conform to variations in shaft alignment and journal shape. For example, suppose a shaft journal is slightly tapered. The bearing under the larger diameter will be more heavily loaded. If the bearing material has high conformability, it will "flow" slightly away from the heavily loaded areas to the lightly loaded areas. This redistributes the bearing material so that the bearing is more uniformly loaded. A similar action takes place when foreign par-

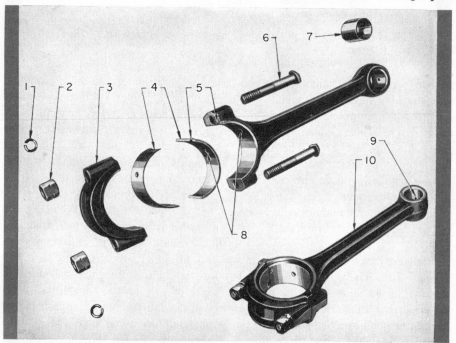

Fig. 6–24. Connecting rod with bearings and bearing cap in disassembled view (top) and assembled view (bottom). (Plymouth Division of Chrysler Corporation)

1. Cap-bolt-nut lock washer
2. Cap-bolt nut
3. Cap
4. Rod bearings
5. Tongue and groove
6. Cap bolt
7. Piston-pin bearing
8. Oilholes
9. Oilhole
10. Assembled rod

ticles embed in the bearing. As they embed, they displace bearing material, thus producing local high spots (Fig. 14–45). However, with high conformability, the material flows away from the high spots. This tends to prevent local heavy loading that could cause bearing failure.

5. *Corrosion resistance.* The bearing materials must be resistant to corrosion since some of the by-products of combustion may form corrosive substances.

6. *Wear rate.* The bearing material must be sufficiently hard and tough so that it will not wear too fast. At the same time, it must be soft enough to permit good embeddability and conformability.

§ **121. Bearing materials** The bearing back is usually of steel. The lining material is a combination of several metals, mixed, or alloyed, to provide the combination of desired characteristics. Such metals as copper, lead, tin, mercury, antimony, cadmium, and silver are used. Many combinations are possible. Each ingredient, or metal, supplies certain characteristics. The engine designer selects the combination of ingredients that will best suit his engine.

§ **122. Connecting rod** The connecting rod (Fig. 6–24) is attached at one end to a crankpin on the crankshaft and at the other end to a piston, through a piston pin or wrist pin. The connecting rod must be very strong and rigid and also as light as possible. The connecting rod carries the power thrusts from the piston to the crankpin. At the same time, the rod is in eccentric

motion (Fig. 3–23). To minimize vibration and excessive bearing loads, the rod must be light in weight.

The crankpin end of the rod is attached to the crankpin by the rod cap and bolts (Fig. 6–24). A split-style bearing is installed between the crankpin and the rod and rod cap.

The piston end of the rod is attached to the piston by means of a piston pin. The pin passes through bearings in both the piston and the connecting rod. There are three methods of attaching the rod and piston with the piston pin (Figs. 6–25 to 6–27). One type locks the pin to the piston with a lock bolt (Fig. 6–25); the connecting rod has a sleeve bearing that permits the rod to rock back and forth on the pin. A second design (Fig. 6–26) locks the pin to the con-

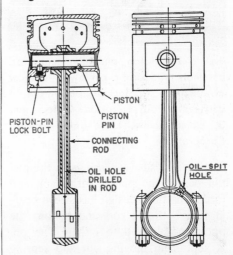

Fig. 6–25. Sectional view of a connecting rod and piston, showing oilhole to lubricate piston pin and oil-spit hole to lubricate cylinder wall. Note the lock bolt to lock the piston pin to the piston. *(Oldsmobile Division of General Motors Corporation)*

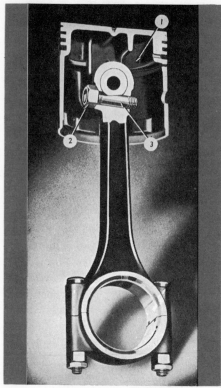

Fig. 6–26. Piston and connecting-rod assembly with piston cut away to show arrangement for locking piston pin to connecting rod: 1, piston; 2, lock nut; 3, clamp screw. (*Studebaker-Packard Corporation*)

ing. Oil reaches the piston-pin bearing by traveling the following path: from the oil pump to oil lines in the cylinder block; from these oil lines to the main bearings; from the main bearings through oil passages drilled in the crankshaft (Fig. 6–17); from the crankshaft oil passages to the connecting rod bearings; from the connecting-rod bearings through the rod oil passages to the piston-pin bearings.

To maintain good engine balance, connecting rods are carefully matched in sets for engines. All rods in an engine must have the same weight; if they do not, noticeable vibration may result.

§ **123. Pistons and piston rings**   As already noted (in § 65), the piston is essentially a cylindrical plug that moves up and down in the engine cylinder.

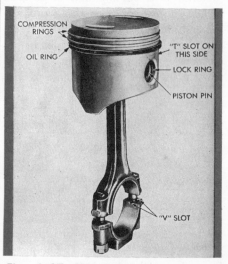

Fig. 6–27. Piston and connecting-rod assembly of type with lock rings to hold piston pin in position in piston and connecting rod. (*De Soto Division of Chrysler Corporation*)

necting rod; sleeve bearings in the piston permit the pin to turn back and forth. The third design has sleeve bearings in both the rod and piston; the pin is not locked to either. The pin is kept from moving out and scoring the cylinder wall by a pair of lock rings that fit into undercuts in the piston (Fig. 6–27).

To provide piston-pin lubrication, many connecting rods have an oil-passage hole drilled from the crankpin-journal bearing to the piston-pin bear-

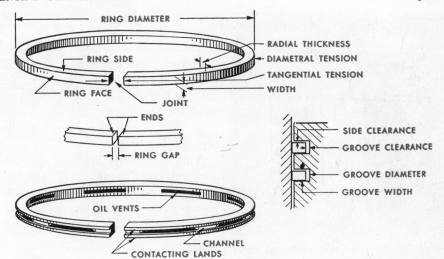

Fig. 6–28. A compression ring *(top)* and an oil-control ring *(bottom)* with various parts named. *(Sealed Power Corporation)*

It is equipped with piston rings to provide a good seal between the cylinder wall and piston. While the piston appears to be a simple part, it is actually quite complex from the design standpoint. But before we discuss pistons, let us examine piston rings.

§ 124. Piston rings A good seal must be maintained between the piston and cylinder wall to prevent blow-by. "Blow-by" is an expression used to describe the escape of burned gases from the combustion chamber, past the piston, and into the crankcase. In other words, these gases "blow by" the piston. It is not practical to fit the piston to the cylinder closely enough to prevent blow-by. Thus, piston rings must be used to provide the necessary seal.

The rings are installed in grooves in the piston as shown in Figs. 6–27, 6–29, and 6–36. Actually, there are two types of ring, compression rings

and oil-control rings. The compression rings seal in the air-fuel mixture as it is compressed and also seal in the combustion pressures as the mixture burns. The oil-control rings scrape off excessive amounts of oil from the cylinder wall and return it to the oil pan. Figure 6–28 shows typical compression and oil-control rings. Figure 6–29 shows a piston with two compression and two oil-control rings installed on it. The rings have joints (they are split) so that they can be expanded and slipped over the piston head and into the recessed grooves cut in the piston. The joint may be straight-edged (butt), angled, lapped, or of the sealed type (Fig. 6–30).

The rings are somewhat larger in diameter than they will be when in the cylinder. Then, when they are installed, they are compressed so that the joints are nearly closed. Compressing the rings gives them an initial tension; they press tightly against the cylinder wall.

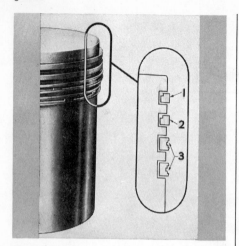

Fig. 6–29. External and sectional views of piston with four rings in place. The upper two (1 and 2) are top and second compression rings, while the lower two (3) are upper and lower oil-control rings. (*Plymouth Division of Chrysler Corporation*)

§ **125. Compression rings** Compression rings are made of cast iron. Typical compression rings are shown in Fig. 6–31. The counterbored (or grooved) and scraper types are used in many engines for top and second compression rings. Figure 6–32 shows the action of these rings during the intake stroke. Internal forces produced by cutting the grooves from the rings cause them to twist slightly, as shown. Thus, as they move down on the intake stroke, they produce a scraping action that scrapes off oil that might have been left on the cylinder wall by the oil-control rings. Then, on the exhaust and compression strokes, when the rings are moving upward, they tend to "skate" over the film of oil on the cylinder wall. This means they have less tendency to carry oil up into the com-

bustion chamber. At the same time, wear is minimized.

On the power stroke, combustion pressures press down on top of and back of the rings. This overcomes the internal tensions and causes them to untwist and thus present full-face contact with the cylinder walls for effective sealing (Fig. 6–33).

Various coatings are used on compression rings as an aid to effective wear-in and to prevent rapid wear. By "wear-in" we mean this: when new, the rings and cylinder wall have certain

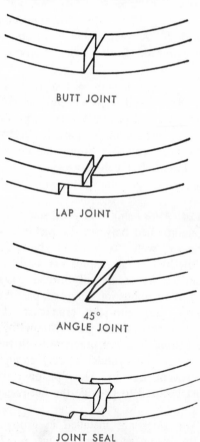

BUTT JOINT

LAP JOINT

45°
ANGLE JOINT

JOINT SEAL

Fig. 6–30. Various types of ring joints. (*Sealed Power Corporation*)

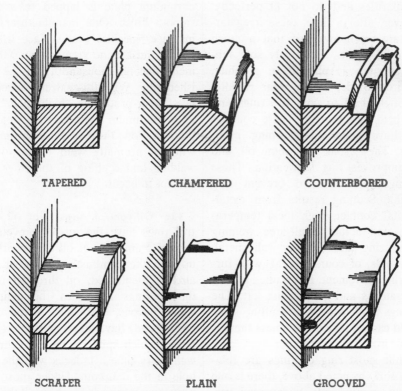

TAPERED	CHAMFERED	COUNTERBORED

SCRAPER	PLAIN	GROOVED

Fig. 6–31. Compression-ring shapes. *(Muskegon Piston Ring Company)*

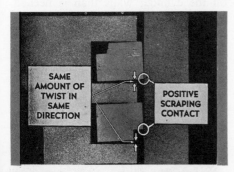

SAME AMOUNT OF TWIST IN SAME DIRECTION

POSITIVE SCRAPING CONTACT

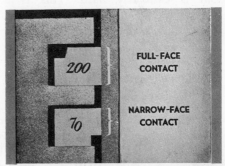

FULL-FACE CONTACT

200

NARROW-FACE CONTACT

70

Fig. 6–32. Action of counterbored compression rings during intake stroke. Internal forces of rings tend to twist them so that a positive scraping contact is established between rings and cylinder wall. This helps to remove any excessive oil that has worked past the oil-control rings. *(Perfect Circle Company)*

Fig. 6–33. Action of grooved compression rings during power stroke. The combustion pressure presses the rings against the cylinder wall with full-face contact, thus forming a good seal. *(Perfect Circle Company)*

irregularities and do not fit perfectly; however, after a time, these irregularities are worn away so that a much better fit results. Relatively soft substances such as phosphate, graphite, and iron oxide, which wear rapidly, are often used to coat the rings and thus help this wear-in. These coatings also have good oil-absorbing properties. They "soak up" some oil, and this improves ring lubrication. These coatings also tend to prevent ring scuffing. Scuffing results from metal-to-metal contact, high local temperatures, and actual small-area welding of the ring and cylinder-wall metal. The welds, of course, break with further ring movement. But scuffed places, or scratches and gouges, are left. The coatings tend to prevent scuffing since a weld cannot take place unless there is actual iron-to-iron contact.

While most ring coatings are relatively soft, as noted above, there is one coating, coming into widespread use, that is extremely hard. This is a chromium plate, or coating. You might think that a chromium-plated ring would cause rapid cylinder-wall wear. But actually, the use of such rings reduces cylinder-wall wear, according to many tests. The reason is this: the chromium plate is lapped to a very smooth finish. One manufacturer, for instance, specifies that surface irregularities must be no greater than 0.0001 inch (one ten-thousandth) in the finished ring. With this extreme smoothness, wear-producing "high spots" are at a minimum; cylinder-wall wear is therefore low. Further, since chromium will not normally weld to cast iron, welding and scuffing of the rings are not apt to occur.

§ **126. Oil-control rings** The oil-control rings have the job of preventing excessive amounts of oil from working up into the combustion chamber. As already mentioned, oil throwoff from the bearings lubricates the cylinder walls, pistons, and rings. Some connecting rods have an oil-spit hole (Fig. 6–25) which spits oil on the cylinder wall every time it indexes with the oil-hole in the crankpin. Under most circumstances, there is far more oil thrown on the cylinder walls than is needed. Most of it must be scraped off and returned to the oil pan. However, this scraped-off oil does several things. It carries away particles of carbon as well as dust and dirt particles. These particles are then removed by the oil

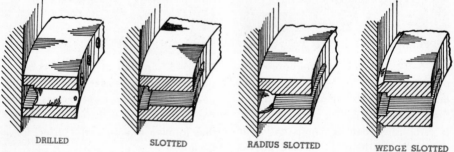

DRILLED   SLOTTED   RADIUS SLOTTED   WEDGE SLOTTED

Fig. 6–34. Types of integral, or one-piece, oil-control rings. (Muskegon Piston Ring Company)

screen or filter. The oil also provides some cooling effect. In addition, the oil on the rings helps to seal between the rings and the cylinder wall. Thus, the oil, as it circulates, lubricates and also cleans, cools, and seals.

Figure 6–34 shows various types of integral, or one-piece, oil-control rings. These rings have holes or slots between upper and lower bearings surfaces. These openings give the oil scraped from the cylinder walls someplace to go. The oil passes through the openings and through holes drilled in the back of the oil-ring grooves in the piston. From there, it returns to the oil pan.

Another type of oil-control ring is shown in Fig. 6–35 (bottom ring). This ring is made of flexible strip steel. The extremely open construction and great flexibility of the ring make it especially effective in handling large quantities of oil.

§ 127. Effect of speed on oil control

As engine speed increases, the oil-control rings have a harder time controlling the oil and preventing excessive amounts from passing them. There are several reasons for this. The engine and engine oil are hotter. Hot oil is thinner and can pass the rings more easily. More oil is pumped at high speed; more oil is thrown on the cylinder walls. This means the oil-control rings have a harder job to do. And they have less time to do it. Thus, at high speed, more oil gets past the rings and is burned in the combustion chamber. This increases oil consumption considerably. An engine may use two or three times as much oil at high speed as at low speed. Much, but not all, of

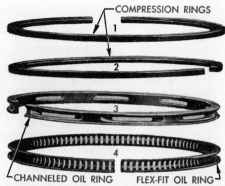

Fig. 6–35. Set of piston rings for one piston of an eight-cylinder engine. Note construction of the two oil rings (3 and 4). (*Buick Motor Division of General Motors Corporation*)

this is due to the reduced effectiveness of the rings at high speed in controlling the oil.

§ 128. Replacement rings

As mileage piles up, the rings and cylinders (among other parts) wear. Cylinders wear tapered and out of round (Fig 14–77). This means the rings become less and less effective in controlling oil and holding compression. There comes a time when the engine is losing so much power and is burning so much oil that repair is required. Then, when the engine is torn down, the first step is to decide whether the cylinder is so badly tapered that it must be honed or bored (§§ 352–358) or whether new replacement rings will make a satisfactory repair. If taper wear is not too great, satisfactory repair can often be made by installing a set of special rings. Figure 6–36 illustrates such a set of rings, installed on a piston.

The lower of the two compression rings (2 in Fig. 6–36) has a *ring expander* back of it. The ring expander is

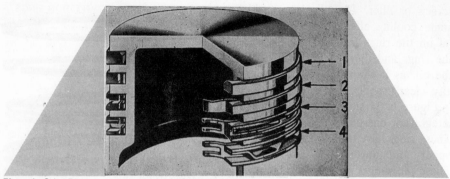

Fig. 6–36. Piston rings designed for installation in cylinder with tapered bore. Upper two rings are compression rings; lower two are oil-control rings. *(Plymouth Division of Chrysler Corporation)*

a steel spring in the shape of a wavy or humped ring (one is shown below the oil-control ring in Fig. 6–45). It adds tension, or cylinder-wall pressure, to the compression or oil-control ring. With the ring expander, the ring is made somewhat thinner (from back to front) so that it is more flexible. The ring expander then more than makes up for any loss of tension from the reduced thickness. Figure 6–37 shows a ring expander under a compression ring. The combination offers high flexibility with high tension. In a tapered or out-of-round bore, the ring must

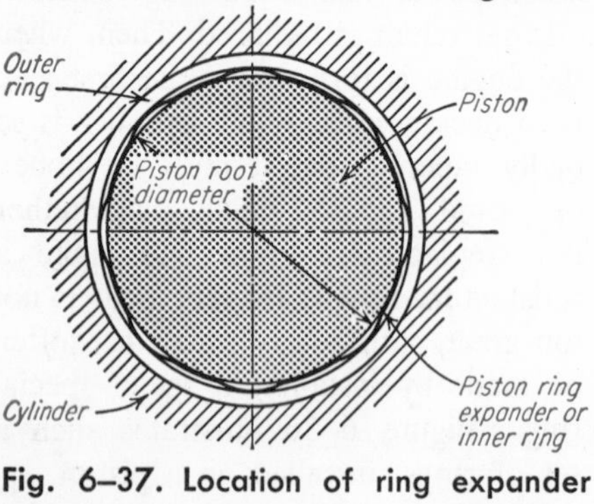

expand and contract—it must change shape—as it moves up and down. The combination (piston ring plus ring expander) gives the ring a better chance to conform to the changing shape of the bore as the ring moves up and down in the cylinder.

NOTE: Some late-model engines use expanders under the bottom (oil-control) rings. These engines use only one oil-control ring; this additional assistance (from the expander) is desirable since only one ring has the major oil-control job to do (see Figs. 6–40 and 6–45).

The oil-control rings in the replacement set shown in Fig. 6–36 are of two types. The upper one (3) is of the slotted, or channel, type. It uses a ring expander. The lower one (4) is made of three parts, upper and lower rails with an expanding spring between them.

Fig. 6–37. Location of ring expander under piston ring as seen in a top sectional view. *(Muskegon Piston Ring Company)*

§ **129. Pistons**   A typical piston with parts named is shown in Fig. 6–38. Pistons have been made of various metals, including cast iron, semisteel,

and aluminum. Aluminum is less than half as heavy as cast iron, and thus most automobile engines are equipped with aluminum-alloy pistons. Since aluminum expands more rapidly than cast iron as temperature increases, special provision must be made to maintain proper piston clearance at operating temperatures.

§ 130. **Piston clearance** Piston clearance is the distance between the piston and the cylinder wall. Proper clearance is in the neighborhood of 0.001 to 0.002 inch. If the clearance is excessive, piston slap will result. Piston slap is caused by the sudden tilting of the piston in the cylinder as the piston starts down on the power stroke. The piston shifts from one to the other side of the cylinder with sufficient force to produce a distinct noise. Usually, piston slap is a problem only in older engines with worn cylinder walls and worn or collapsed piston skirts, any of which produce excessive clearance. On the other hand, the clearance must be large enough. If it is too small, then the oil will not be able to get to the rings and upper part of the bore. Further, piston expansion, with increasing temperature, could cause the piston to

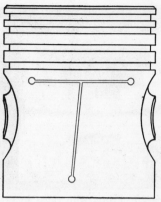

Fig. 6–39. Piston with horizontal and vertical slots cut in skirt. Horizontal slot reduces path for heat travel, and vertical slot allows for expansion without increase of piston diameter.

seize. In either event, engine failure would result.

There are several methods of keeping pistons from excessively changing dimensions with temperature. One method, used on aluminum pistons, is to cast into the piston special alloy-steel struts or rings. Since the alloy steel does not expand with temperature increase as much as aluminum, the struts or rings hold down piston expansion.

Another method is to keep heat away from the lower part of the piston as much as is possible. One way of doing this is to cut horizontal slots in the piston just below the lower oil-control ring (Fig. 6–39). These slots reduce the path for the heat traveling from the piston head to the piston skirt. Thus, the skirt does not become quite so hot and does not expand so much. On many pistons, vertical slots are cut in the skirt about halfway between the piston-pin holes (Fig. 6–39). These slots permit metal expansion without

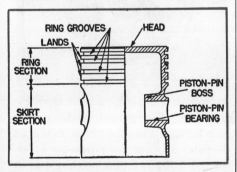

Fig. 6–38. A piston in partial sectional view with parts named.

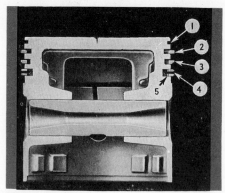

Fig. 6–40. Piston with rings in sectional view, showing heat dam and shapes of rings: 1, heat dam; 2, upper compression ring; 3, lower compression ring; 4, oil ring; 5, ring expander. *(Studebaker-Packard Corporation)*

appreciable increase of piston diameter. Another method of reducing heat travel to the piston skirt makes use of a heat dam (Figs. 6–40 and 6–44, left). The dam consists of a groove cut near the top of the piston. This reduces the size of the path the heat can travel from the piston head to the skirt. The skirt therefore runs cooler and does not expand so much.

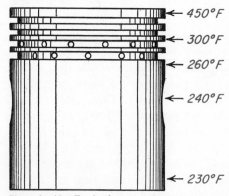

Fig. 6–41. Typical operating temperatures of various parts of a piston. *(Muskegon Piston Ring Company)*

126

Typical operating temperatures of a piston are shown in Fig. 6–41. Note, in the example shown, that there is a 220° difference between the top and the skirt of the piston. The piston rings help the heat accumulating in the piston head to escape; they transmit heat from the piston to the cylinder walls.

§ 131. **Cam-ground pistons** In many engines, pistons are slightly oval in shape when cold (Fig. 6–42). These pistons are *cam-ground* (so-called because they are ground on a machine that uses a cam to move the piston toward and away from the grinding wheel as the piston revolves). When cam-ground pistons warm up, they assume a round shape so that their area of contact with the cylinder wall increases (Fig. 6–43). "Contact" here must not be construed as meaning actual contact. There must be clear-

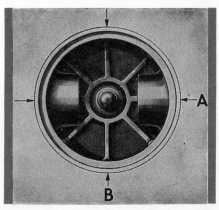

Fig. 6–42. Cam-ground piston viewed from bottom. When the piston is cold, its diameter at A, at the piston-pin holes, may be 0.002 to 0.003 inch less than at B. *(Plymouth Division of Chrysler Corporation)*

COLD   WARM   OPERATING TEMPERATURE

Fig. 6–43. As the cam-ground piston warms up, the expansion of the skirt distorts the piston from an elliptical to a round shape, so that the area of normal clearance between the piston and cylinder wall is increased.

ance between the piston and cylinder wall as noted in the previous section. What is meant is that, when cold, the oval shape of the piston permits normal clearance in only a small area (there being excessive clearance elsewhere). But as the piston warms up, this area of normal clearance increases.

§ **132. Piston shapes** Some pistons have a rather complex head formation (Fig. 6–44). The one to the left in the figure is designed to improve turbulence of the air-fuel mixture as it is compressed in the combustion cham-

ber. The one to the right has depressions on one side to provide sufficient clearance between the piston and the valves. By using a piston with depressions and a dome-shaped head, a smaller clearance volume, and thus a higher compression ratio, can be attained.

Some late-type engines are using a cutaway, or slipper, piston (Fig. 6–45). This permits a more compact engine. Cutting away the piston skirt permits the use of a shorter connecting rod without interference between the skirt and crankshaft counterweights.

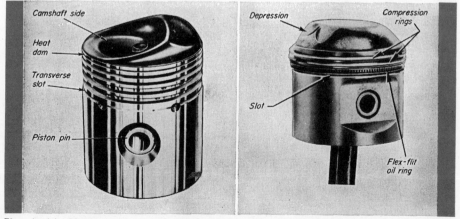

Fig. 6–44. Pistons with complex head formations. The one to the right is used in the Buick V-8 engine. (*Buick Motor Division of General Motors Corporation*)

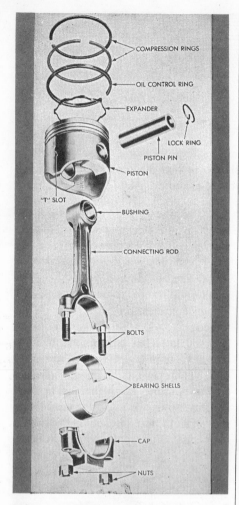

Fig. 6–45. Piston and connecting-rod assembly, disassembled so that the internal construction of the piston can be seen. Note that the piston skirt is short under the piston bosses. This allows clearance between the piston and crankshaft counterweights when the piston is at BDC. The arrangement permits a lower and more compact engine construction. (*De Soto Division of Chrysler Corporation*)

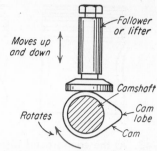

Fig. 6–46. A simple cam and follower (or lifter). As the cam revolves, the follower follows the cam surface by moving up and down.

Fig. 6–47. Crankshaft and camshaft sprockets with chain drive showing timing marks on sprockets: 1, camshaft-sprocket mark; 2, crankshaft-sprocket mark; 3, center line of shafts. Note that the larger of the two sprockets is on the camshaft so that it turns at one-half crankshaft speed. (*Plymouth Division of Chrysler Corporation*)

128

On some engines (Buick V-8, for instance), the crankshaft counterweights are contoured, instead of the piston skirt being cut away, to avoid interference between the two.

§ 133. **Cams and camshaft** A cam is a device that can change rotary motion into linear, or straight-line, motion. The cam has a high spot, or lobe; a follower riding on the cam will move away from or toward the camshaft as the cam rotates (Fig. 6–46).

In the engine, cams on the camshaft cause the intake and exhaust valves to open. Figures 3–25 and 5–8 show the valve mechanisms (or *valve trains*) on L-head and I-head engines. There is a cam on the camshaft for each valve, or two cams per cylinder. In addition, the camshaft has an eccentric to operate the fuel pump and a gear to drive the ignition distributor and oil pump. The camshaft is driven from the crankshaft by sprockets and chain (Figs. 6–47 and 6–57) or by two gears (Fig. 6–48). The camshaft sprocket or gear has twice as many teeth as the sprocket or gear on the crankshaft. This gives a 1:2 gear ratio; the camshaft turns at half the speed of the crankshaft. Thus, every two revolutions of the crankshaft produce one revolution of the camshaft and one opening and closing of each valve (in the four-cycle engine).

The camshaft is mounted in bearings in the lower part of the cylinder block in in-line engines. It is located between the two banks of cylinders in V-8 engines (Figs. 5–4 to 5–6).

§ 134. **Valves** As already noted, each cylinder has two valves, an intake valve and an exhaust valve. The cam lobes on the camshaft are so related to the crankshaft crankpins (through the gears or sprockets and chain) as to cause the valves to open and close with the correct relationship with the piston strokes (see § 146, Valve Timing).

Various types of valves have been used in the past, among them sliding-sleeve and rotary. But the valve in general use today is the mushroom, or poppet, valve (Fig. 6–49). The valve is normally held closed and firmly seated by one or more heavy springs and by pressures in the combustion chamber. The manner in which springs are attached to the valves is described in § 138.

§ 135. **Valve cooling** The intake valve runs relatively cool since it passes only air-fuel mixture. But the exhaust valve must pass the very hot burned gases. The exhaust valve may actually become red-hot in operation. Figure 6–50 shows a typical temperature pattern of an exhaust valve. Note that

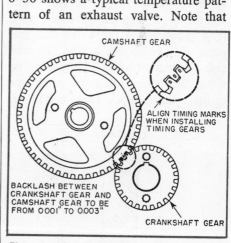

Fig. 6–48. Camshaft and crankshaft gears to drive camshaft. Note timing marks on gears. *(Studebaker-Packard Corporation)*

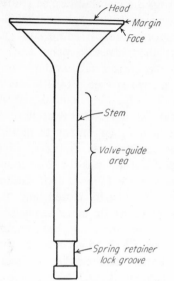

Fig. 6–49. Valve with parts named.

L-head engines. Water nozzles are used in cylinder heads of I-head engines. These devices provide for additional water circulation in and cooling of the critical areas.

Figure 6–50 also emphasizes the importance of proper valve seating. If the valve face and valve seat do not mate properly or are rough or worn, then full-face contact will not take place. This means that there is a smaller area of contact through which heat transfer (and valve-face cooling) can take place. At the same time, uneven contact may mean that hot exhaust gases will leak between the valve face and seat in some spots. These spots will naturally run hotter. Actually, a poor seat may cause a valve to run several hundred degrees hotter than normal; there might be local hot

the valve stem is coolest, the part near the valve face being next coolest. This is because the valve stem passes heat to the valve guide and this helps keep the valve stem cool. Likewise, the valve face passes heat to the valve seat, and this helps keep the valve face cool. It is obvious that the valve seat and guide must be cooled, in turn. To provide adequate cooling of these parts, water-distributing tubes are often put in the cylinder block (Fig. 6–51) on

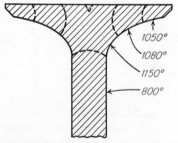

Fig. 6–50. Temperatures in an exhaust valve. Valve is shown in sectional view. (Eaton Manufacturing Company)

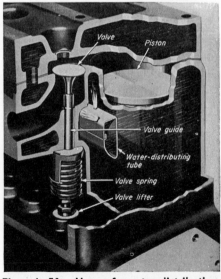

Fig. 6–51. Use of water-distributing tube to cool valve. This picture also gives a good view of the valve location in an L-head engine. (Pontiac Motor Division of General Motors Corporation)

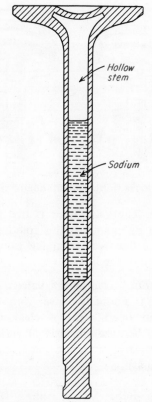

Fig. 6–52. Sectional view of a sodium-cooled valve. *(Eaton Manufacturing Company)*

spots at even higher temperatures. Naturally, these higher temperatures greatly shorten valve life: the hot spots wear or burn away more rapidly.

§ 136. **Sodium-cooled valve** To aid valve cooling and thus increase valve life, many heavy-duty engines use sodium-cooled valves. This valve has a hollow stem partly filled with metallic sodium (Fig. 6–52). Sodium melts at 208°F. Thus, at operating temperatures, the sodium is liquid. As the valve moves up and down, the sodium is thrown upward into the hotter part

of the valve. It absorbs heat, which it then gives up to the cooler stem as it falls down into the stem again. This circulation cools the valve head. The valve therefore runs cooler. A sodium-cooled valve will run as much as 200°F cooler than a solid-stem valve of similar design. This means, other factors being equal, longer valve life.

§ 137. **Valve seat** The exhaust-valve seat is also subjected to the extremely high temperatures of the burned gases. For this reason, the exhaust-valve seat in many engines is made of a special, heat-resistant steel-alloy insert ring (Fig. 6–53). This ring holds up better than the block or head materials. Also, when it does become worn so much that it cannot be refinished with a valve-seat grinder, it can be replaced.

§ 138. **L-head valve train** The L-head-engine valve train (Fig. 3–25) consists of the camshaft, valve lifter, valve spring, and valve. The valve spring is compressed between the cylin-

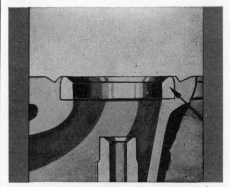

Fig. 6–53. Cutaway view ot a valve-seat insert. The insert is indicated by the arrow. *(Plymouth Division of Chrysler Corporation)*

131

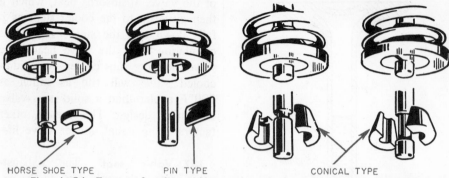

HORSE SHOE TYPE   PIN TYPE   CONICAL TYPE
Fig. 6–54. Types of valve-spring-retainer locks (also called keepers).

der block and a spring retainer. The spring retainer is attached to the end of the valve stem with a retainer lock (Fig. 6–54). The retainer holds the lock in place in the undercut or slot in the valve stem. The valve rides in the valve guide; this is essentially nothing more than a hollow steel tube, carefully dimensioned to be a tight fit in the block and have a close clearance fit with the valve stem.

The valve lifter includes an adjusting screw that can be turned in or out to attain the correct clearance between the screwhead and valve stem. This clearance, called *tappet clearance* or *valve lash,* is included to assure valve seating. If there were no clearance, then dimension changes due to temperature changes might so lengthen the valve stem as to keep it from closing. This could lead to quick valve

Fig. 6–55. Rocker arm used in overhead-valve engine. (Chevrolet Motor Division of General Motors Corporation)

failure. The valve lifter is free to rotate in its mounting; this rotation distributes the wear from the cam over the face of the lifter.

NOTE: Hydraulic valve lifters (§ 145) normally have zero valve lash in operation. No clearance is needed because dimensional variations in the valve train are taken care of hydraulically.

§ 139. I-head valve train   In the I-head or overhead-valve engine, a push rod and rocker arm are required in addition to the parts used in the valve train of the L-head engine (see Fig. 5–8). There are two general designs of rocker arm. In one type, the rocker arm has an adjusting screw (Fig. 6–55). The lower end of the adjusting screw is ball-shaped and rests in a socket in the upper end of the push rod. This type of arm is mounted on a rocker-arm shaft as shown in Figs. 6–56 and 6–57. Note that the rocker arms are lined up on the shaft with their adjusting-screw ends resting on the push rods. The push rods extend through openings in the cylinder head and block to the valve lifters above the cams.

Fig. 6–56. Rocker-arm assembly for six-cylinder overhead-valve engine. (*Chevrolet Motor Division of General Motors Corporation*)

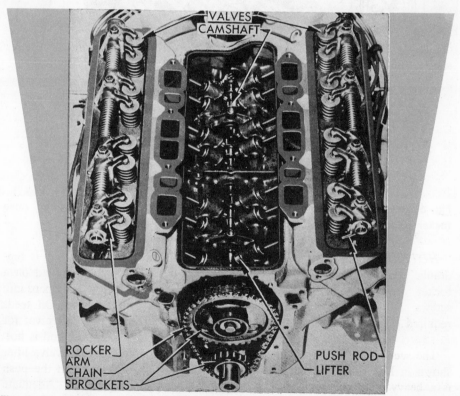

Fig. 6–57. Valve mechanism of a V-8 overhead-valve engine. (*Buick Motor Division of General Motors Corporation*)

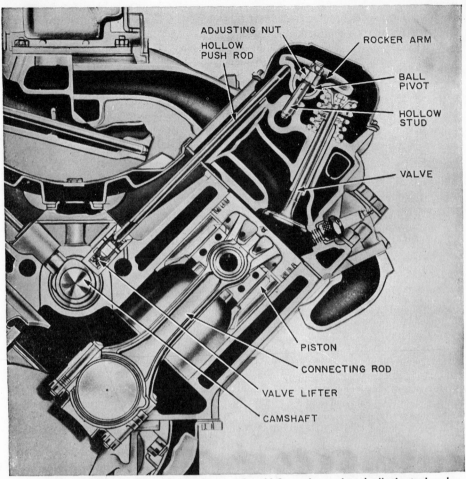

Fig. 6–58. Sectional view of one bank of a V-8 engine using ball-pivoted valve rocker arms. *(Pontiac Motor Division of General Motors Corporation)*

NOTE: On many engines using hydraulic valve lifters (§ 145), the rocker arms do not have adjusting screws. No valve-lash adjustment is required on these engines.

The second design of rocker arm is shown in Fig. 6–58. This rocker arm is a heavy steel stamping, shaped as shown. The push-rod end is formed into a socket in which the end of the push rod rides. The rocker arm is supported by a ball pivot mounted on a stud. The stud is hollow and opens into an oil gallery in the head. Oil feeds through the stud to the ball pivot for lubrication. Also, the push rod is hollow and feeds oil from the valve lifter to the contact area between the push rod and the rocker arm. Adequate lubrication of the moving parts of the valve train is thus assured. The valve

clearance on this design is measured between the rocker arm and valve stem, as with the other design. However, on this design, adjustment is made by turning the adjusting nut above the ball pivot up or down on the mounting stud. This raises or lowers the rocker arm to increase or decrease valve clearance.

In many I heads, the valves are carried in replaceable valve guides. In other I heads (for example in late Ford and Chevrolet V-8 engines), the guides are part of the head. That is, they are holes bored in the head and are not separate parts. On these, if the guides become worn, they can be reamed to a larger size and valves with oversize stems installed.

§ 140. F-head valve trains   In the F-head engine, one valve is in the head and the other valve is in the block. Usually, the exhaust valve is located in the block (see Fig. 5–7). Thus, this engine is a combination L-head and I-head engine and has valve trains as described in the previous two sections.

§ 141. Valve rotation   If the exhaust valve were to rotate a little each time it opened, many valve troubles would be minimized. For example, one common cause of valve burning is deposits on the valve face. These deposits, which are products of combustion, tend to prevent normal valve seating so that the valve overheats and burns. Another valve trouble is sticking. This condition usually results from accumulations of carbon (from burned oil) on the valve stem. These deposits work

into the clearance between the valve stem and valve guide; the valve sticks. or "hangs up," in the guide and does not close. Then, the valve overheats and burns.

If the valve rotates as it opens and closes, there will be less chance of valve-stem accumulations causing the valve to stick. Further, there will be a wiping action between the valve face and seat; this tends to prevent any build-up of face deposits. In addition, valve rotation results in more uniform valve-head temperatures, for this reason: some parts of the valve seat may be hotter than others; actual hot spots may develop. If the same part of the valve face continued to seat on the hot spot, a corresponding hot spot would develop on the valve face. That hot spot on the valve face would wear, or burn away, faster. But if the valve rotates, no one part of the face will be continuously subjected to the higher temperature. Thus, longer valve life will result.

§ 142. Valve rotators   There are several types of valve rotators. In one type, the valve is relieved of all spring pressure so that it is free to rotate. Engine vibration then causes it to rotate. This is the "free type" of valve rotator. Another type assures positive rotation of the valve by imposing a rotating force on the valve stem each time the valve opens.

§ 143. Free-type valve rotator   Figure 6–59 shows the details of a free-type valve rotator. Instead of the usual spring-retainer lock, this design uses a split washer lock and a tip cup. As the valve lifter moves up, the adjust-

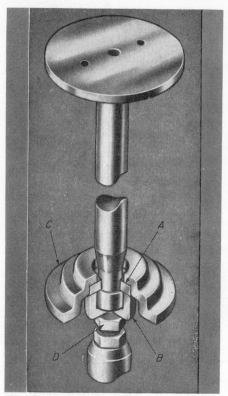

Fig. 6–59. Construction of "free-type" valve rotator: A, spring-retainer lock; B, tip cup; C, spring retainer; D, lifter adjusting screw. (Thompson Products, Inc.)

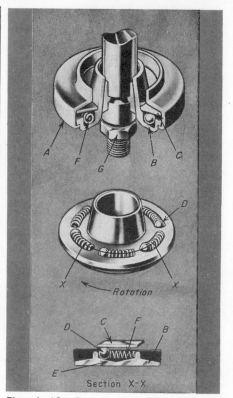

Fig. 6–60. Construction of positive-rotation type of valve rotator: A, seating collar; B, spring retainer; C, flexible washer; D, balls; E, inclined race; F, ball-return springs; G, lifter adjusting screw. (Thompson Products, Inc.)

ing screw pushes up on the tip cup. The tip cup then carries the motion to the lock and valve retainer. The retainer is lifted, thereby taking up the valve-spring pressure. Note that the spring pressure is taken off the valve stem; the valve is free. Since it is free, it can rotate when it is open.

§ 144. Positive-type valve rotator Figure 6–60 shows the details of one positive-type valve rotator. This design applies a rotating force on the valve stem each time it opens, thus assuring positive rotation of the valve. A seat-

ing collar (A) is spun over the outer lip of the spring retainer (B). The valve spring rests on the seating collar. The collar encloses a flexible washer (C) placed above a series of spring-loaded balls (D). The middle view shows how the balls and springs are positioned in grooves in the spring retainer. The bottoms of the grooves (races) are inclined as shown in the bottom view (E), which is a section (X–X) cut from the middle view. When the lifter is raised, the adjusting

screw (G) lifts the valve and applies an increasing pressure on the seating collar. This flattens the flexible washer (C) so that the washer applies the spring load on the balls (D). As the balls receive this load, they roll down the inclined races. This causes the retainer to turn a few degrees and thus turn the valve a few degrees. When the valve closes, the spring pressure is reduced so that the balls return to their original positions, ready for the next valve motion.

§ 145. Hydraulic valve lifter   This type of lifter, now used in many engines, is very quiet in operation because it assures zero tappet clearance (or valve lash). Also, as a rule, this lifter requires no adjustment; variations due to temperature changes or to wear are taken care of hydraulically.

Figure 6–61 shows the details of a hydraulic valve lifter as used in a V-8 I-head engine. Figure 6–62 shows the operation of this valve lifter. Oil is fed into the valve lifter from the oil pump and through an oil gallery that runs the length of the engine. When the valve is closed, oil from the pump is forced

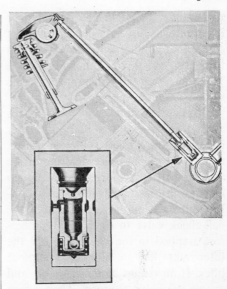

Fig. 6–61. Sectional view of a V-8 I-head engine, showing location of hydraulic valve lifter in valve train. The insert shows the construction of the lifter. (*Cadillac Motor Car Division of General Motors Corporation*)

into the valve lifter through the oil-holes in the lifter body and plunger. The oil forces the ball-check valve in the plunger to open. Oil then passes the ball-check valve and enters the

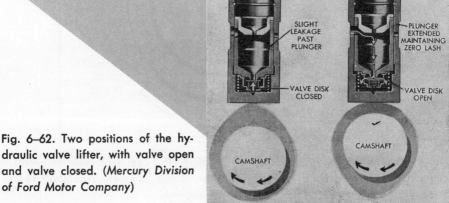

Fig. 6–62. Two positions of the hydraulic valve lifter, with valve open and valve closed. (*Mercury Division of Ford Motor Company*)

space under the plunger. The plunger is therefore forced upward until it comes into contact with the valve push rod (or valve stem in L-head·engines). This takes up any clearance in the system.

Now, when the cam lobe moves around under the lifter body, the lifter is raised. Since there is no clearance, there is no tappet noise. Raising of the lifter and the valve produces a sudden increase in pressure in the body chamber under the plunger. This causes the ball-check valve to close. Oil is therefore trapped in the chamber, and the lifter acts like a simple, one-piece lifter. It moves up as an assembly and causes the valve to open. Then, when the valve closes, the lifter moves down and the pressure on the plunger is relieved. If any oil has been lost from the chamber under the plunger, oil from

the engine oil pump can cause the ball-check valve to open so that engine oil can refill the chamber, as noted above.

§ 146. **Valve timing** In previous discussions of valve action, it was assumed that the intake and exhaust valves were opening and closing at TDC and BDC. Actually, as can be seen from Fig. 6–63, the valves are not timed in this manner. In the valve-timing diagram shown, the exhaust valve starts to open at 45 degrees before BDC on the power stroke and stays open until 5 degrees after TDC on the intake stroke. This additional time that the exhaust valve is opened gives more time for the exhaust gases to leave the cylinder. By the time the piston reaches 45 degrees before BDC on the power stroke, the combustion pressures have dropped considerably

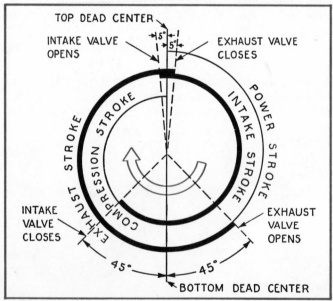

Fig. 6–63. The intake- and exhaust-valve timing. The complete cycle of events is shown as a 720-degree spiral, which represents two complete crankshaft revolutions. Timing of valves differs for different engines.

(see Fig. 4–13). Little power is lost by giving the exhaust gases this extra time to exhaust from the cylinder.

In a similar manner, leaving the intake valve open for 45 degrees past BDC after the intake stroke gives additional time for air-fuel mixture to flow into the cylinder. As you will recall from our discussions of volumetric efficiency (§ 84), delivery of adequate amounts of air-fuel mixture to the engine cylinders is a critical item in engine operation. Actually, the cylinders are never quite "filled up" when the intake valve closes (volumetric efficiency is well below 100 percent). Leaving the intake valve open for a number of degrees past BDC after the intake stroke does increase volumetric efficiency.

Timing of the valves is due to the shape of the lobe on the cam and the relationship between the gears or sprockets and chain on the camshaft and crankshaft. Changing the relationship between the driving and driven gears or sprockets changes the timing at which the valves open and close. For example, if the camshaft gear were de-meshed and moved ahead one tooth and then re-meshed, the valves would open and close earlier. Suppose this moved the valve action ahead 15 degrees. Then the exhaust valve would open at 60 degrees before BDC on the power stroke and close at 10 degrees before TDC on the exhaust stroke (in the example shown in Fig. 6–63). The intake-valve actions would likewise be moved ahead. These valve-action advances would seriously reduce engine performance. Also, in the newer engines where there are very small clearances between the valves and piston

heads, there would be danger of the pistons striking the valve heads. This, of course, could severely damage the engine. To prevent such troubles, the gears or sprockets are marked so that they can be properly aligned (See Figs. 6–47 and 6–48).

REVIEW QUESTIONS

1. What part forms the basic framework of the engine?
2. Describe briefly how the cylinder block is made.
3. Name six items that are attached to the cylinder block.
4. What is the purpose of a gasket? Name several places where gaskets are used in the engine.
5. What is the purpose of the oil pan?
6. Why is the muffler used?
7. What function does the intake manifold perform? The exhaust manifold?
8. What is the purpose of the manifold heat control? How does it work?
9. What is the purpose of the crankshaft vibration damper?
10. What is the main purpose of the flywheel? What are the two other duties the flywheel often has?
11. What are some of the characteristics of a good bearing?
12. What is the common name of the bearings that support the crankshaft? Describe the manner in which they support the crankshaft.
13. Describe the operation of preparing and installing a poured bearing.
14. What are semifitted bearings? Precision-insert bearings?
15. What are exhaust-valve-seat inserts, and why are they used?

16. What is the purpose of the connecting rod?
17. What three methods of attaching the piston and connecting rod with the piston pin are in common use?
18. In what way is the piston pin often lubricated?
19. What two functions must piston rings perform?
20. What is the purpose of the coatings on piston rings?
21. What is the effect of engine speed on oil control?
22. Describe a ring expander, and explain its purpose.
23. What is piston slap?
24. What is blow-by?
25. Why are slots sometimes cut in the piston skirt?
26. Describe the action of cam-ground pistons as they warm up in operation.
27. Does the camshaft turn at the same, at one-half, or at twice crankshaft speed?
28. Describe the action of an intake valve; an exhaust valve.
29. Describe the action of a sodium-cooled valve when it is in operation.
30. What are the advantages of valve rotation? Describe two types of valve rotators.
31. Describe the operation of a hydraulic valve lifter.
32. What does the term "valve timing" mean?
33. In Fig. 6–63, how many degrees of crankshaft rotation does the exhaust valve stay open? How many degrees of crankshaft rotation does the intake valve stay open?

STUDY QUESTIONS

1. What advantage might there be in making an engine with separate cylinders, instead of making the cylinder block in one casting? What disadvantages?
2. Which is more important to the operation of the engine, the intake manifold or the exhaust manifold? Why?
3. Make a sketch of the valve-operating mechanism for an L-head engine, starting with the camshaft and ending with the valve seat.
4. Make a sketch of the valve-operating mechanism for an I-head engine, starting with the camshaft and ending with the valve seat.
5. Is the following statement true? "The more cylinders an engine has, the larger the flywheel must be." Give the reason for your answer.
6. Define torsional vibration.
7. How does the vibration damper on the crankshaft operate?
8. Can you think of any advantages the precision-insert bearing might have over other types of bearings? Disadvantages?
9. Make a sketch of a piston, and name essential parts.
10. If an engine is operating at 2,150 rpm, how many times would the exhaust valve in cylinder 1 open in 1 minute?
11. Draw a valve-timing chart in which the intake valve opens at TDC and closes at 30 degrees after BDC and the exhaust valve opens at 30 degrees before BDC and closes at 5 degrees after TDC.

THIS CHAPTER DISCUSSES electric systems used in automobiles. The electric system does several jobs. It cranks the engine for starting. It supplies the high-voltage surges that ignite the compressed air-fuel mixture in the combustion chambers. It includes the battery, cranking motor, generator, regulator, ignition system, radio, lights, heater motor, indicating gauges, and so on. All these are discussed in the pages that follow.

§ 147. Function of electric system
The operation of the engine lubrication system depends upon a flow of oil through channels and lines. The fuel system carries gasoline through lines and air through tubes and manifold. The cooling system operates by means of a flow of water through jackets, tubes, and the radiator. Note that in all these the operation of the system depends upon the flow of a substance. The electric system also depends upon the flow of a substance. However, since this substance cannot normally be seen, weighed, or otherwise examined, it seems very mysterious. There is no reason for this, however. The substance that flows in the electric system (called *electric current*) is no more mysterious than the substances that flow in the lubrication, fuel, or oiling system. Understanding the action of electric current is as easy as under-

standing the action of these other systems in the vehicle.

The electric current, as it moves through various wires, conductors, and electrically operated devices, performs several jobs on the car (Fig. 7–1). It cranks the engine, furnishes electric sparks at the spark plugs that ignite the compressed mixture in the cylinders, operates the radio and heater motor, supplies lights for night driving, and operates gauges on the dash of the car that indicate charging rate in amperes, oil pressure, engine temperature, and the amount of fuel in the tank.

§ 148. Components of electric system
The electric system (Fig. 7–1) consists of the storage battery, cranking motor, generator, regulator, ignition distributor, coil, and spark plugs, as well as the wires and switches that connect these various units. Lights, radio, heater, indicating gauges, and other electrically operated devices, while a part of the electric system, are usually considered as accessory devices, since they are not absolutely necessary to the operation of the car.

1. *Storage battery*. The storage battery (Fig 7–16) is an *electrochemical* device. This means that its operation depends on both chemical and electrical actions. The battery supplies electric current when the engine is being

141

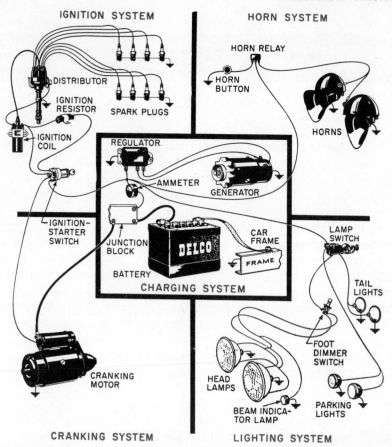

IGNITION SYSTEM

HORN SYSTEM

HORN RELAY

HORN BUTTON

DISTRIBUTOR

IGNITION RESISTOR   SPARK PLUGS

HORNS

IGNITION COIL

REGULATOR

AMMETER

GENERATOR

IGNITION-STARTER SWITCH

JUNCTION BLOCK

CAR FRAME

LAMP SWITCH

DELCO

FRAME

BATTERY

CHARGING SYSTEM

TAIL LIGHTS

CRANKING MOTOR

HEAD LAMPS

FOOT DIMMER SWITCH

PARKING LIGHTS

BEAM INDICA-TOR LAMP

CRANKING SYSTEM

LIGHTING SYSTEM

Fig. 7–1. A typical car electric system, illustrating the electric units and the connections between them. The symbol ⏚ means ground, or the car frame. By using the car frame as the return circuit, only half as much wiring is required. (*Delco-Remy Division of General Motors Corporation*)

cranked with the electric cranking motor and also during the times when the generator is not supplying enough current for connected electric units. When current is withdrawn from the battery, chemical actions take place that produce the flow of current. The chemicals in the battery are, in a sense, used up by this chemical action. Thus, after a certain amount of current has been withdrawn, the battery becomes

"discharged." To "recharge" the battery, current from some external source, such as a generator, must be forced through it in the opposite direction.

2. Cranking motor. The cranking motor (Fig. 7–32) is a special direct-current electric motor that starts the engine by rotating the crankshaft when the cranking-motor switch is closed. Closing the switch connects the motor

to the battery. There is a special gearing arrangement between the cranking-motor drive pinion and the engine flywheel that will be discussed below.

3. Generator. The generator (Fig. 7–41) is a device that converts mechanical energy (from the automobile engine) into a flow of electric current. This current restores the battery to a charged condition when it has become discharged. It also operates electrical devices, such as the ignition system, lights, radio, etc. The generator is usually mounted to the side of the engine block and is driven by the engine fan belt.

4. Regulator. Under some conditions, the generator could produce too much current, and this would damage the various electrical devices turned on. To prevent such damage, a generator-output regulator (Fig. 7–51) is used. The regulator controls the amount of current the generator produces. It allows the generator to produce a high current when the battery is in a discharged condition and electric units are turned on. When the battery becomes charged and electric units are turned off, the regulator cuts down the current produced to the amount needed to meet the operating requirement of the system.

5. Ignition system. The ignition system (Fig. 7–53) provides the electric sparks that ignite, or set fire to, the compressed air-fuel mixture in the engine cylinders. Each spark is timed by the ignition system to appear at the correct instant with respect to the piston as it approaches the end of the compression stroke.

6. Lights, heater, radio, indicating devices. The lights, radio, and heater add to the flexibility, comfort, and convenience of the car, while indicating devices keep the driver informed as to engine temperature, oil pressure, amount of fuel, and battery charging rate.

7. Wiring and switches. The wiring (Fig. 7–1) that connects the various electric units serves as paths, or circuits, through which the current can flow from one to another unit. Switches placed in these circuits are forms of valves that can close or open the circuits to permit or prevent the flow of current. The wires are made up of *conducting* materials, such as copper, that freely conduct the current between the electric units. Some materials, such as rubber or glass, are *nonconductors,* or insulators, that will not allow current to flow through them. Such substances are used to cover and insulate the wires so that the current will be kept within the proper circuits, or paths.

§ 149. **Characteristics of electricity**
The study of electricity properly starts with a study of atoms. We have already discussed atoms (§§ 46–50) and learned that the electrons circling the atomic nuclei have negative electric charges. These negatively charged electrons are held in their circular paths by the positive charges of the protons in the atomic nucleus.

However, despite the attraction between the electron and proton, electrons do break free from the atoms. When these electrons mass in one place, they are called a *charge of electricity.* When the electrons move from

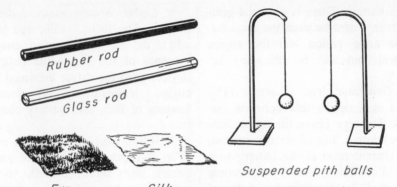

Fig. 7–2. Experiments with static electricity can be made with a rubber rod, a glass or lucite rod, a piece of fur, a piece of silk, and two suspended pith balls.

one place to another, they are called a *current of electricity*.

§ 150. Static electricity "Static" means at rest. Static electricity is produced by a massing of electrons in one place. With the equipment shown in Fig. 7–2, several static-electricity experiments can be performed. For example, rubbing the rubber rod with fur and then touching the rod to a suspended pith ball "charges" the ball with electrons. The electrons transfer from the fur to the rod and then to the ball. If the glass rod is rubbed with silk and the glass rod is touched to the second pith ball, free electrons will be removed from the ball. The pith ball thus develops an electron shortage and becomes positive in charge. During this second action, the silk attracts electrons from the glass rod; so it becomes positive in charge. Then, when the glass rod is touched to the pith ball, it attracts some electrons from the pith ball, leaving the pith ball positively charged.

If the negatively charged and the positively charged pith balls are brought near each other (Fig. 7–3), it will be found that they attract each

other. This shows that opposite electric charges attract.

Just as opposite electric charges attract, so do like electric charges repel. This can be proved by charging both pith balls positively and bringing them together (Fig. 7–4). Also, they may be charged negatively and brought together. In either case, the balls repel each other.

NOTE: The attractive and repulsive forces are tremendously large. For example, if two 1-ounce iron weights were placed 100 yards apart, and if it were possible for all electrons in one weight suddenly to apply their combined repulsive force against all the electrons in the second weight, the re-

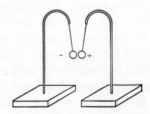

Fig. 7–3. When the pith balls are given opposite electric charges, they attract each other.

pulsive force, pushing the two weights apart, would be something like 760 million tons! The attractive force between unlike electric charges is similarly great.

§ 151. **Electric current** The repulsive force between electrons causes electrons to attempt to move away from each other. If there is a path along which the electrons can easily move, they will always move away from areas where there are many electrons to areas where there are few electrons. This movement of electrons is called an *electric current*.

A generator or a battery may be considered a device for concentrating electrons at one place, or *terminal*, and removing electrons from another place, or *terminal*. When these two terminals are connected by an electron path (or electric circuit), the electrons move through the circuit from one terminal to the other. That is, electric current flows between the terminals.

The terminal with large numbers of electrons is called the *negative*, or *minus*, terminal (indicated by —). The terminal with an electron shortage is called the *positive*, or *plus*, terminal (indicated by +).

§ 152. **Conductors and insulators** A typical electron path, or electric circuit, is a copper wire. A typical insulator is rubber. The copper wire forms a good electric circuit because it is a good conductor of electricity. A copper wire is made up of tremendous numbers of copper atoms. Each copper atom has 29 electrons circling the nucleus (and 29 protons in the nucleus). The outer electron is so loosely tied to the nu-

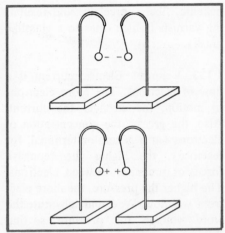

Fig. 7–4. When the pith balls are given like electric charges, they repel each other.

cleus by the attractive force (between negative and positive) that it can easily escape from the atom. Thus, in a copper wire, there are great numbers of free electrons. These free electrons move about in all directions. However, if the copper wire were attached between the terminals of an operating generator, then the electrons would all tend to move in the same general direction. In other words, the free electrons form an electric current.

Insulators, or nonconductors, are made up of atoms which do not easily lose electrons. Since the atoms hold on to their electrons, there are few free electrons in an insulator. As a result, electric current, or electrons, cannot easily move through the insulator. Wires and other current- (or electron-) carrying parts of electric circuits and machinery are usually covered with insulation. This prevents electrons from flowing away from the circuit so that electrical loss would occur. Such insulation consists of mica, rubber,

145

bakelite, fiber, porcelain, and insulating varnish (which dries to a glasslike finish).

§ **153. Voltage**   Electric current is a flow of electrons. The more electrons in motion, the stronger the current. Also, the greater the concentration of electrons (at a generator terminal, for instance), the higher the repulsive force, or pressure, between electrons. The higher the pressure, the more electrons will flow. We could substitute the word "voltage" for "pressure" so that the statement would read "The higher the voltage, the more electrons (or current) will flow." For voltage is simply the term used to indicate electrical pressure. A high voltage means a high electrical pressure, or a massing of many electrons. Voltage is measured in *volts*.

§ **154. Amperage**   Electric current, or electron flow, is measured in amperes of electric current, or, simply, *amperes*. When few electrons flow, the amperage is low. When many electrons flow, the amperage is high. The actual number is enormous. For instance, a 1-ampere generator (capable of lighting a single small light bulb) will supply about 6 billion billion electrons a second.

§ **155. Resistance**   Even the best of conductors offers some resistance to the movement of electrons through it. This is because the electrons could be said to "prefer" to move about in all directions in the conductor; they "resist" the electrical pressure, or force, that makes them all move in the same direction. A heavy wire has a lower resistance than a fine wire, because it offers a bigger electron path. On the other hand, a long wire has a greater resistance than a short wire of the same size, because the electrons have a longer path to travel. Resistance is measured in ohms, just as current is measured in amperes or voltage in volts.

§ **156. Ohm's law**   The relationship between resistance, amperage, and voltage can be summed up in a statement known as Ohm's law: *Voltage is equal to amperage times ohms.* This law can also be stated as a mathematical formula:

$$E = I \times R$$

In this formula, E is voltage in volts, I is current in amperes, and R is resistance in ohms.

It can be seen that, as resistanc increases (voltage remaining unchanged), the current will decrease. For example, if the cranking-motor circuit in an automobile has a low resistance, enough current can flow for normal cranking. If, on the other hand, the resistance is excessive, then not enough current can get through for normal cranking to take place. Likewise, if the headlight circuit has excessive resistance, insufficient current can get through and the lights will be dim. Thus, it can be seen that Ohm's law illustrates the importance of preventing excessive resistance in automotive electric circuits. Since bad connections or defective leads are the usual causes of excessive resistance, these are the things to look for when excessive resistance is found.

146

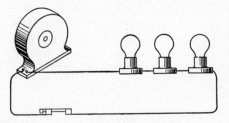

Fig. 7–5. Light bulbs connected in series. Same current flows through all.

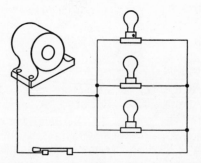

Fig. 7–6. Light bulbs connected in parallel to current source. Current divides, part flowing through each light bulb.

§ 157. Series and parallel circuits In a series circuit, each electrical device is connected to other electrical devices so that the same current flows in all (Fig. 7–5). If any device is turned off, then the circuit is opened and no current flows to any device.

In a parallel circuit (Fig. 7–6), the various devices are connected by parallel wires. The current divides, part of it flowing into one device, part into another. Practically the same voltage is applied to each device, and each can be turned on or off independently of the others. Most automotive circuits are parallel circuits, or, more accurately, series-parallel circuits. For instance, even though the headlights are connected to the battery in parallel, they are connected to the battery in series with a lighting switch.

§ 158. Voltage drop in circuits The electrical pressure, or voltage, expends itself from one to the other end of an electric circuit. For example, if the voltages across the resistors in the circuit shown in Fig. 7–7 were checked with a voltmeter, they would be found to add up to 6 volts. The voltage across the 4-ohm resistor would be found to be 2 volts. This could also be calculated if the amperage were known by using Ohm's law ($E = I \times R$, or $E = 0.5 \times 4 = 2$ volts). Measuring or calculating the voltages across the other resistors would give 1.0, 2.5, and 0.5 volts for a total, for all resistors, of 6 volts.

Thus, in any circuit, the voltage becomes "used up" from one to the other

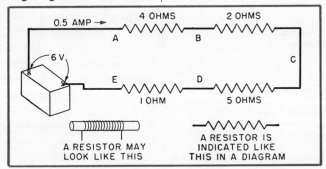

Fig. 7–7. A series circuit made of four resistors of varying resistances.

147

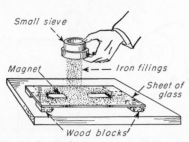 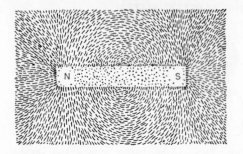

Fig. 7–8. (Left) Demonstrating magnetic lines of force. (Right) Magnetic lines of force of a bar magnet as shown by iron filings.

end of the circuit. In other words, the voltage drops, or there is a voltage drop, between different parts of an electric circuit.

§ 159. **Magnetism** Magnetism is a connecting link between mechanical energy and electricity. By means of magnetism in the car generator, some of the power produced by the engine is transformed into a flow of electrons that lights the headlights, charges the battery, operates the ignition. Likewise, a flow of electrons from the battery is transformed by magnetism into mechanical power in the cranking motor, so that the engine is cranked.

1. Magnets. A few simple experiments with magnets will demonstrate some of the principles of magnetism. If a bar or a horseshoe magnet is laid

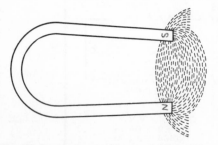

Fig. 7–9. Magnetic lines of force of a horseshoe magnet.

in iron filings, the ends (poles) of the magnet will be heavily covered with the filings. The iron filings are magnetically attracted to the magnetic poles. If a bar magnet is laid on a table with a sheet of glass on top of it and iron filings are sprinkled on the glass, the filings will fall into the lines shown in Fig. 7–8 when the glass is tapped. With a horseshoe magnet, the pattern will be as shown in Fig. 7–9.

2. Lines of force. These patterns illustrate what are termed "magnetic lines of force." Lines of force are used to explain many of the principles of magnetism. They are assumed to be extremely fine, threadlike lines stretching between magnetic poles. They tend to parallel each other and do not cross, but push adjacent lines of force away. This "push-apart" characteristic opposes the "rubber-band" characteristic, which attempts to pull the lines of force to minimum length.

These two characteristics of lines of force explain two actions of magnets. When unlike magnetic poles of two magnets are brought near each other, they will be strongly attracted (Fig. 7–10). On the other hand, like poles repel. With unlike poles, the lines of force stretch between the poles and, with the rubber-band characteristic,

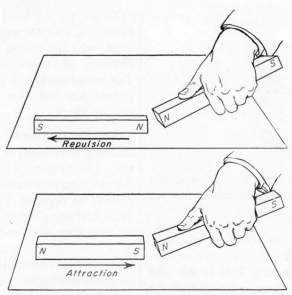

Fig. 7–10. Showing repulsion between like magnetic poles and attraction between unlike magnetic poles.

try to shorten and thus pull the poles together. However, when like poles are brought together, many lines of force are brought into parallel. The repulsions between the parallel lines of force tend to push the poles apart. The attractions and repulsions between like and unlike magnetic poles are used in electric motors to make the armature spin.

NOTE: It should be remembered that the so-called "lines of force" are merely a convention adopted to make it easier to understand the characteristics of magnetism. Strictly speaking, there is no such thing as a magnetic line of force.

§ 160. **Electromagnetism** A current of electricity (flow of electrons) always produces magnetic lines of force. This can be demonstrated by putting a wire through a piece of cardboard, sprinkling iron filings on the cardboard,

and then passing current through the wire (Fig. 7–11). The lines of force circle the wire in one direction or the other, depending on the direction of current flow through the wire.

1. Left-hand rule. By use of the left-hand rule, the direction that the lines of force circle the conductor can be determined. For example, when a wire has electricity flowing in it as shown in Fig. 7–12, the lines of force circle

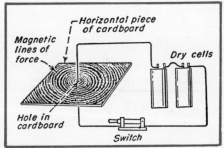

Fig. 7–11. Iron filings on the cardboard demonstrate magnetic lines of force around a conductor carrying an electric current.

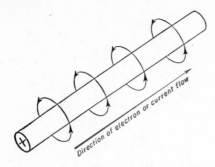

Fig. 7–12. Direction in which magnetic lines of force circle a current-carrying conductor.

the wire in the direction indicated. Note that the current is shown as flowing away from you. This is indicated by the small cross in the end of the conductor. If the current were flowing toward you, this would be indicated by a dot. Remember this by thinking of an arrow. If the arrow were coming toward you, you would see the point as a dot. If it were moving away, you would see the tail feathers as a cross. Note (Fig. 7–12) that the lines of force are shown as circling the conductor in a *counterclockwise* direction, or in the direction opposite to, or counter to, the direction in which the hands of a clock move.

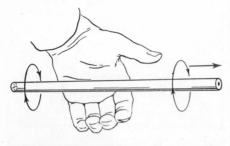

Fig. 7–13. The left-hand rule to determine direction in which lines of force circle a current-carrying conductor.

To use the left-hand rule, circle the conductor with the fingers of the left hand, with the thumb pointing in the direction of current (electron) flow. The curled-up fingers point in the direction that the lines of force circle the conductor (Fig. 7–13).

NOTE: The reader should not be confused if he hears of a "right-hand" rule. The right-hand rule is based on the old concept of current flowing from positive to negative. This old concept came into being before the true nature of electricity was understood. However, now that it is generally accepted that electric current is a current of electrons flowing from negative to positive, the left-hand rule has come into widespread use.

2. Electromagnets. When many turns of wire are wrapped into a coil and current is passed through the coil, the lines of force around the turns add so that a combined magnetic field is produced. You can demonstrate this by placing a sheet of glass over such a coil, sprinkling iron filings on the glass, and connecting the coil to a battery. When the glass is tapped, the iron filings will fall into a pattern much like that for the bar magnet (Fig. 7–8). The coil is known as an *electromagnet,* because it produces magnetism by electric means.

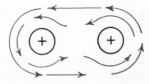

Fig. 7–14. Magnetic field around two current-carrying conductors seen in end view.

The reason the lines of force around the coil turns combine can be explained by reference to Fig. 7–14, which shows two adjacent coil turns in end view. Current flows through both in the same direction, and thus lines of force circle both in the same direction. Any lines of force between the two, being in opposite directions, cancel out, so that a combined magnetic field circles both, as shown. In the same manner, a combined magnetic field is produced around many parallel current-carrying conductors, or coil turns.

The north pole of the electromagnet can be found by use of the left-hand rule (Fig. 7–15). This is done by placing the left hand around the coil with the fingers pointing in the direction of current flow (assuming it flows from negative to positive). The thumb will point toward the north pole of the electromagnet.

3. Permeability. If strips of iron were inserted in the coil, its magnetic field would become much stronger. This is because the iron offers an easier path for the magnetism than does air. That is, the iron is more *permeable* to

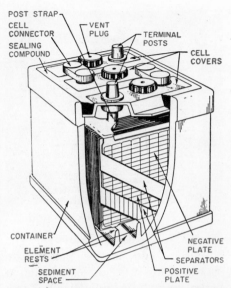

Fig. 7–16. Cutaway of a 6-volt storage battery. The case has been cut away to show the construction of one of the three cells.

magnetic lines of force. Iron in one form or another is used in motors, generators, ignition coils, and other electrical machinery so as to conduct the magnetism to the proper areas in the device.

STORAGE BATTERY

§ **161. Purpose of battery** The battery (Fig. 7–16) supplies current for operation of the cranking motor and the ignition system when the engine is being cranked for starting. It also supplies current for lights, radio, and other electrical accessories at times when the generator is not operating fast enough to handle the electrical load. The amount of current the battery can supply is strictly limited by the "capacity" of the battery, which in turn depends upon the amount of chemicals it contains.

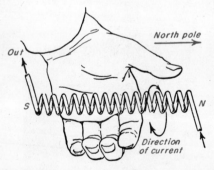

Fig. 7–15. Using the left-hand rule to determine the north pole of an electromagnet.

151

Fig. 7–17. A battery plate grid.

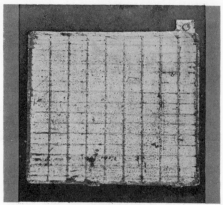

Fig. 7–18. A battery plate. Lead-oxide paste has been applied to the plate grid, and the plate is ready to be attached to the plate strap. The plate is attached, by lead burning the lug (*to upper right*), to the plate strap.

§ 162. Chemicals in battery The chemicals used in the battery are sponge lead, a solid; lead oxide, a paste; and sulfuric acid, a liquid. These three substances are brought together in such a way that they can react chemically to produce a flow of current. The lead oxide and sponge lead are held in plate grids to form positive and negative plates.

The plate grid (Fig. 7–17) consists of a framework of antimony-lead alloy with interlocking horizontal and vertical bars. The plate grids are made into plates (Fig. 7–18) by the application of lead oxide pastes; the horizontal and vertical bars serve to hold the pastes in the plate.

After the plates are assembled into the battery, the battery is given an initial "forming" charge; this changes the lead oxide paste in the negative, or minus, plate to sponge lead and changes the lead oxide paste in the positive, or plus, plate to lead peroxide.

§ 163. Battery construction In making the battery, several similar plates are properly spaced and welded or

lead-burned to a strap to form a plate group (Fig. 7–19). Plates of two types are used, one for the positive plate group, the other for the negative plate group. A positive plate group is nested with a negative plate group, with separators placed between the plates to form an element (Fig. 7–20). Separators (Fig. 7–21) are designed to hold

Fig. 7–19. A battery plate group.

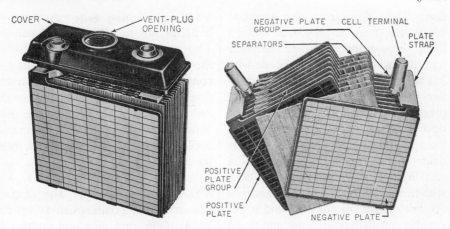

Fig. 7–20. A battery element, assembled and partly assembled.

the plates apart so that they do not touch, and at the same time they must be porous enough to permit liquid to circulate between the plates. Wooden sheets, spun glass matted into sheets, and porous sponge-rubber sheets are used as separator material.

The elements are placed in cells in the battery case. Covers are then put on and sealed around the edges with sealing compound. Then, terminals are built up through the covers from the positive- and negative-group plate straps (Fig. 7–16). Adjacent negative and positive terminals are connected by connector straps. Each cover has an opening through which liquid can be added when the filler cap or vent plug is unscrewed. After the liquid has been added and the battery given an initial charge, it is ready for operation.

§ **164. Chemical activities in battery**
The liquid, called the *electrolyte,* is made up of about 40 percent sulfuric acid and about 60 percent water. When sulfuric acid is placed between the

plates, chemical actions take place that remove electrons from one group of plates and mass them at the other. This transfer of electrons is carried on by chemical activity until there is sufficient unbalance of electrons to create a 2-volt pressure between the two groups of plates. This results in a pressure of 2 volts between the two terminals of the battery cell. If the two terminals are not connected by any circuit, no further appreciable chemical activity takes place. However, when the two terminals do become connected by an electric circuit, electrons (current) will

Fig. 7–21. Battery separator.

flow. They flow from the terminal where chemical activity has massed them, through the circuit, to the other terminal where the chemical activity has taken them away. Chemical activities now begin again; so the 2-volt pressure is maintained, and the current flow continues. The chemical actions "use up" the sponge lead, lead peroxide, and sulfuric acid. Thus, after a certain amount of current has been withdrawn, the battery is *discharged* (or "run down" or "dead") and is not capable of delivering any additional current. When the battery has reached this state, it may be *recharged*. This is done by supplying it with a flow of current from some external source, such as a generator, which forces current through the battery in a reverse direction. This reverses the chemical activities in the battery. Thus, the chemicals are restored to their original form, and the battery becomes recharged. It is then ready to deliver additional current.

The chemical actions that take place are rather complicated and are not fully understood. The sponge lead (negative plate) and lead peroxide (positive plate) change to lead *sulfate* during the discharge process. The sulfate comes from the sulfuric acid; the electrolyte loses acid and gains water as the sulfate goes into the plates. Thus, discharging the battery changes the two different chemicals in the battery plates to a third chemical, lead sulfate. Recharging the battery causes the lead sulfate to change back to sponge lead in the negative plates and lead peroxide in the positive plates. Meantime, the sulfuric acid reappears in the electrolyte.

§ **165. Connecting cells** Automotive batteries are usually either 6-volt or 12-volt units. There are three cells in the 6-volt battery; the three cells are connected in series. In series connections, the voltages add. There are six cells in the 12-volt battery, the cells being connected in series. Some special applications use 24-volt batteries; these have 12 cells.

§ **166. Battery ratings** The amount of current that a battery can deliver depends upon total area and volume of active plate material and the amount and strength of electrolyte. Batteries are rated in several ways, the most important of which are listed below.

1. Twenty-hour rate. The 20-hour rate represents the amount of current a battery can deliver for 20 hours without cell voltage dropping below 1.75 volts, starting with a temperature of 80°F. A battery delivering 5 amperes for 20 hours would be rated as a 100-ampere-hour battery (5 × 20).

2. Twenty-five-ampere rate. The 25-ampere rate measures battery performance at a moderate constant-current output at 80°F to a final limiting voltage of 1.75 volts per cell. This figure indicates the ability of the battery to carry the electrical operating load (lights, ignition, etc.) when the generator is not operating.

3. Cold rate. This rating indicates the number of minutes a battery can deliver 300 amperes at 0°F before the cell voltage drops below 1.0 volt. It gives an indication of the cold-weather starting ability of the battery. A typical rating applying to a particular 100-ampere-hour battery is that the battery will supply 300 amperes for about 3.6

minutes at 0°F before cell voltages drop to 1.0 volt.

§ **167. Battery efficiency** The ability of the battery to deliver current varies within wide limits, depending upon temperature and rate of discharge. At low temperature, chemical activities are greatly reduced; the sulfuric acid cannot work so actively on the plates, and thus the battery is less efficient and cannot supply as much current for as long a time. High rates of discharge will not produce as many ampere-hours as low rates of discharge because the chemical activities take place only on the surfaces of the plates; the chemical activities do not have time to penetrate the plates and utilize the materials below the plate surfaces.

§ **168. Variations in terminal voltage** Because the battery produces voltage by chemical means, the voltage varies according to a number of conditions. These conditions and their effect on battery voltage may be summed up as follows:

1. Terminal voltage, battery being *charged,* increases with:
   a. Increasing charging rate. To increase charging rate (amperes input), the terminal voltage must go up.
   b. Increasing state of charge. As state of charge goes up, voltage must go up to maintain charging rate.
   c. Decreasing temperature. Lower battery temperatures require a higher voltage to maintain charging rate.
2. Terminal voltage, battery being discharged, decreases with:

a. Increasing discharge rate. As the rate of discharge goes up, chemical activities increase and cannot penetrate plates so effectively; therefore, voltage is reduced.
b. Decreasing state of charge. With less active materials and sulfuric acid available, less chemical activity takes place, and voltage drops.
c. Decreasing temperature. With lower temperature, the chemical activities cannot go on so effectively, and the voltage drops.

CRANKING MOTOR

§ **169. Function of cranking motor** The cranking, or starting, motor (Fig. 7–22) electrically cranks the engine for starting. It is a special direct-current motor operating on battery voltage and is mounted on the engine flywheel housing as shown in Fig. 7–22. To understand how the cranking motor operates, let us consider the basic principles of motors.

§ **170. Basic motor principles** We have already seen that, when current moves through a conductor, a magnetic field builds up around that conductor (§ 160). If the conductor is held in a magnetic field, as from a horseshoe magnet, force will be exerted on the conductor. Figure 7–23 illustrates the conductor held in a magnetic field. Figure 7–24 shows the conductor in end view with the resulting magnetic field indicated. The cross in the center of the conductor indicates that the current is flowing away from the reader. This causes the magnetic field from this current flow to circle the

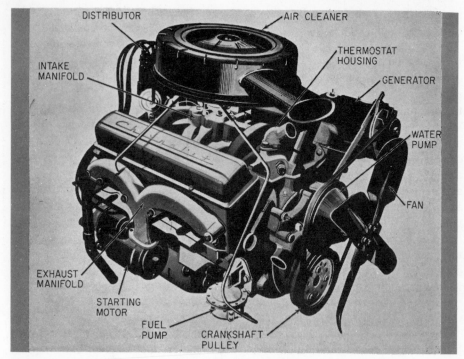

Fig. 7–22. Manner in which starting motor is mounted on engine. Distributor, fuel pump, and other accessories are mounted on the block. (*Chevrolet Motor Division of General Motors Corporation*)

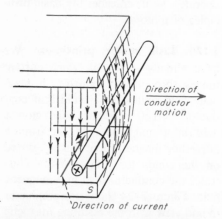

Fig. 7–23. Conductor held in magnetic field from magnet. Direction of current flow and encircling magnetic field around the conductor are shown by arrows.

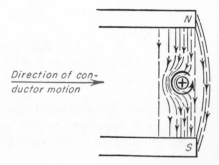

Fig. 7–24. End view of conductor shown in Fig. 7–23.

156

conductor in a counterclockwise direction. The circular magnetic field to the left of the conductor is in the same direction as the straight-line magnetic field from the magnet. To the right of the conductor, it is in the opposite direction. This weakens the magnetic field to the right of, and strengthens the magnetic field to the left of, the conductor, causing the resulting magnetic field to distort around the conductor as shown in Fig. 7–24.

Magnetic lines of force have a rubber-band characteristic of trying to shorten up to a minimum length. Thus the magnetic-field pattern shown in Fig. 7–24 will cause a push toward the right to be exerted on the conductor as the bent lines of force try to straighten out. The more current flowing, the more the lines of force will be distorted around the conductor, and the stronger will be the push. Increasing the straight-line magnetic field will have a similar result.

§ 171. **Motor construction** If we should bend the conductor into a U and connect the two ends to the two halves of a split copper ring, we should have the elements of an electric motor (Fig. 7–25). Stationary brushes, connected to a battery and resting on the split ring, and two poles of a magnet complete the elementary motor. The U-shaped conductor loop and the split ring (which is called the *commutator*) are so designed as to be able to rotate together. Current flows from the battery, through the right-hand brush and segment of the commutator, through the conductor and left-hand segment and brush, back to the battery as shown. This causes the left-hand part

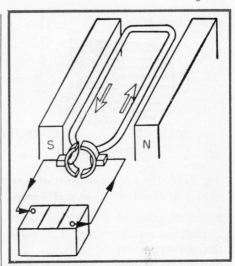

Fig. 7–25. Simple electric motor with a two-segment commutator.

of the conductor to be pushed upward and the right-hand part to be pushed downward (see Fig. 7–24). Thus the loop rotates in a clockwise direction. As the two sides of the loop reverse positions, the direction of the current flow through the two sides reverses. The force thus continues to rotate the loop clockwise.

The cranking motor must use more than one loop to develop any appreciable power. Actually, many loops or conductors are used, as shown in Fig. 7–26, which illustrates a cranking-motor armature. The ends of the conductors are connected to the commutator segments.

To obtain sufficient magnetic-field strength for powerful cranking-motor action, the natural magnetic strength of the magnetic poles is aided by field windings. Current flows through the field windings in such a direction as to aid the magnetic field between the two poles. Figure 7–27 illustrates a simple

157

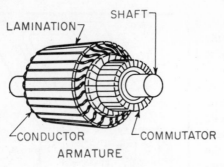

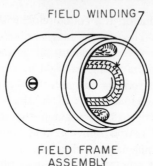

FIELD FRAME
ASSEMBLY

Fig. 7–26. The two major parts of a cranking motor: the armature and the field assembly. (*Delco-Remy Division of General Motors Corporation*)

wiring diagram of a cranking motor. Current enters the motor and passes through the two field windings, then through the armature, and back to the battery. If the battery connections were reversed, the current would flow through the armature first, as shown in Fig. 7–28, which illustrates schematically a simple motor. This type of motor is called a *series-wound,* or *series,* motor, since the armature and field windings are connected in series.

The wiring diagram illustrated in Fig. 7–27 is of a two-pole two-brush cranking motor. Many cranking motors have four brushes and four poles. Some also have one or two shunt windings (and are called *series-shunt,* or *compound,* units). The shunt windings prevent overspeeding (see Fig. 7–29).

A typical cranking motor with the main parts disassembled is shown in Fig. 7–30. The cranking motor consists of the commutator end head, holding the brushes, the field frame, into which the field windings are assembled around pole shoes, the drive housing, which houses the drive assembly and supports the motor on the engine flywheel housing, the armature, and the drive assembly. Some cranking motors also have a solenoid that operates the shift lever (§ 175).

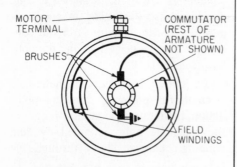

Fig. 7–27. Wiring circuit of cranking motor.

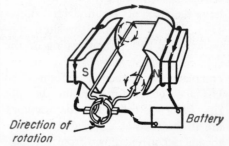

Direction of rotation

Fig. 7–28. Schematic drawing of a cranking motor. Heavy arrows show direction of current flow, and light circular arrows indicate direction of magnetic field. Compare this with Fig. 7–25.

§ 172. **Drive arrangement** The drive assembly contains a small pinion that, in operation, meshes with teeth cut in the flywheel (Fig. 3–31). This provides considerable gear reduction, so that the armature must rotate about fifteen times to cause the flywheel to rotate once. The cranking motor thus requires only about one-fifteenth as much power as would an electric motor directly coupled to the crankshaft, since the armature turns fifteen times for each flywheel revolution. The armature may revolve about 2,000 to 3,000 rpm (revolutions per minute) when the cranking motor is operated, thus causing the flywheel to spin at speeds as high as 200 rpm. This is ample for starting the engine.

After the engine starts, it may in-

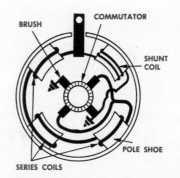

Fig. 7–29. Wiring circuit of four-pole series-shunt, or compound, cranking motor. (*Delco-Remy Division of General Motors Corporation*)

crease in speed to 3,000 rpm or more. If the cranking-motor drive pinion remained in mesh with the flywheel, it would be spun at 45,000 rpm because of the 15:1 gear ratio. This means the

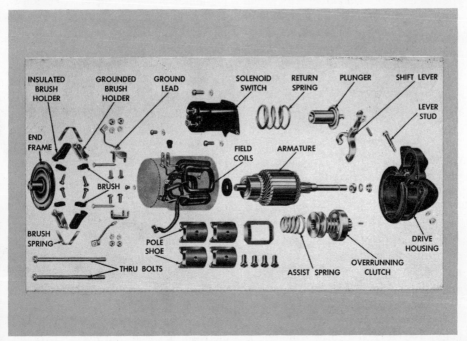

Fig. 7–30. Disassembled view of a cranking motor. (*Delco-Remy Division of General Motors Corporation*)

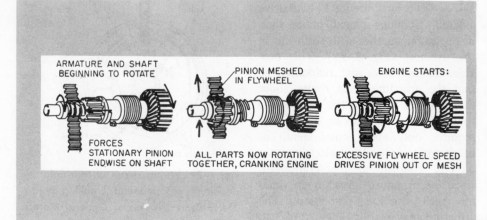

ARMATURE AND SHAFT
BEGINNING TO ROTATE

PINION MESHED
IN FLYWHEEL

ENGINE STARTS:

FORCES
STATIONARY PINION
ENDWISE ON SHAFT

ALL PARTS NOW ROTATING
TOGETHER, CRANKING ENGINE

EXCESSIVE FLYWHEEL SPEED
DRIVES PINION OUT OF MESH

Fig. 7–31A. Operation of Bendix drive. (*Delco-Remy Division of General Motors Corporation*)

armature would be spun at this terrific speed, and centrifugal force would cause the conductors and commutator segments to be thrown out of the armature, ruining it. To prevent such damage, automatic meshing and de-meshing devices are used. For passenger cars they are of two general types, inertia and overrunning clutch.

§ **173. Inertia drive** The inertia drive depends upon the inertia of the drive pinion to produce meshing. As has already been mentioned (§ 76), inertia is the property that all things have that resists any change in motion. When the drive pinion is not rotating, it resists any force that attempts to set it into motion. Two types of inertia drive are discussed below, the Bendix and the Folo-Thru.

1. Bendix drive. In the Bendix drive (Fig. 7–31*A*), the drive pinion is mounted loosely on a sleeve that has screw threads matching internal threads in the pinion. When the cranking motor is at rest, the drive pinion is not meshed with the flywheel teeth. As the cranking-motor switch is closed, the armature begins to rotate. This causes the sleeve to rotate also, since the sleeve is fastened to the armature shaft through the heavy spiral Bendix spring. Inertia prevents the pinion from instantly picking up speed with the sleeve. The sleeve thus turns within the pinion, just as a screw would turn in a nut held stationary. This forces the pinion endwise along the sleeve so that it goes into mesh with the flywheel teeth. As the pinion reaches the pinion stop, the endwise movement stops. The pinion must now turn with the armature, causing the engine to be cranked. The spiral spring takes up the shock of meshing.

After the engine begins to run and increase in speed, the flywheel rotates the drive pinion faster than the armature is turning. This causes the pinion

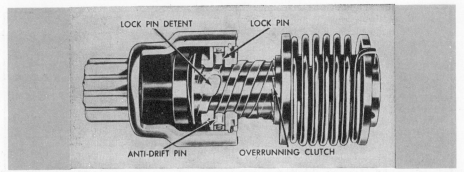

Fig. 7-31B. The Folo-Thru cranking-motor drive. Skirt of pinion has been cut away so that lock and antidrift pins can be seen. (Ford Motor Company)

to be spun back out of mesh from the flywheel. That is, the pinion turns on the sleeve, and the screw threads on the pinion and sleeve cause the pinion to be backed out of mesh from the flywheel.

2. Folo-Thru drive. This drive (Fig. 7-31B) is very similar in many respects to the Bendix drive. It has a sleeve attached through a spiral spring to the armature shaft. The sleeve has threads which match internal threads in the pinion base. Also included in the pinion base are two small spring-loaded pins. One is an antidrift pin that prevents the pinion from drifting into mesh with the flywheel when the engine is running. It imposes a frictional drag that holds the pinion in the de-meshed position. The other pin is a lock pin that drops into a detent in the sleeve thread as the pinion moves out to the cranking position. This holds the pinion in mesh with the engine flywheel during cranking. It prevents the pinion from being kicked out of mesh by a false start (during which the engine might fire a few times and then die). The pinion is thus held in mesh and cranking continues until the engine really gets started. Then, as the engine

speed increases to around 400 rpm, centrifugal force on the lock pin moves it out of the detent and the pinion de-meshes from the flywheel in the same manner as in the Bendix drive.

§ 174. Overrunning clutch The overrunning clutch (Fig. 7-32) is operated by a shift lever that causes the drive pinion to be moved along the armature shaft and into mesh with the flywheel

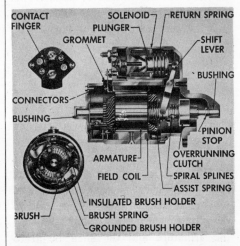

Fig. 7-32. Sectional view of enclosed shift-lever cranking motor. (*Delco-Remy Division of General Motors Corporation*)

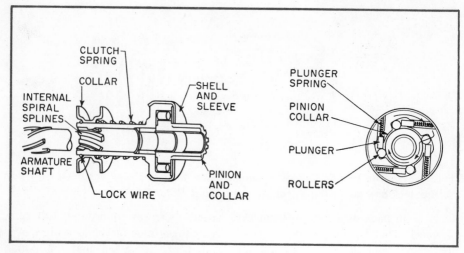

Fig. 7–33. Cutaway and end sectional views of overrunning clutch. (*Delco-Remy Division of General Motors Corporation*)

teeth. As the shift lever completes its travel, it closes the cranking-motor switch so that cranking takes place. Straight or spiral splines cut in the armature shaft and the clutch sleeve cause both to rotate together. A spiral spring is placed between the clutch housing and the shift-lever collar. This spring compresses if the pinion and the flywheel teeth should happen to butt instead of mesh. Then, after the cranking-motor switch is closed and the armature starts to rotate, meshing is completed by the spring pressure, so that cranking can take place.

The clutch (Fig. 7–33) consists of the outer shell, which has four hardened steel rollers, fitted into four notches, and the pinion and collar assembly. The notches are not concentric but are smaller in the end opposite to the plunger springs (Fig. 7–33). When the armature and the shell begin to rotate, the pinion is momentarily stationary. This causes the rollers to rotate into the smaller sections of the notches, where they jam tight. The pinion must now rotate with the armature, cranking the engine. After the engine starts, it spins the pinion faster than the armature is turning, so that the rollers are rotated into the larger sections of the notches, where they are free. This allows the pinion to spin independently of, or *overrun*, the remainder of the clutch. A spring on the shift lever pulls the pinion back out of mesh when the shift lever is released.

§ **175. Cranking-motor   controls**
Cranking-motor controls may vary from a simple foot-operated pedal to automatic devices that cause the cranking motor to operate when the ignition key is turned and the accelerator pedal is depressed. On the foot-operated type, linkages from a foot pedal operate a lever that closes the cranking-motor switch and, on the overrunning-clutch-drive motor, also meshes the drive pinion. The lever may be linked to the carburetor throttle valve so that

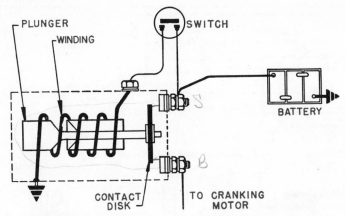

Fig. 7–34. Magnetic-switch schematic wiring circuit.

the throttle is opened a few degrees during starting. This allows ample air and fuel to be delivered to the intake manifold for good starting (§ 230).

Magnetic switches are used with some Bendix-drive cranking motors to close the motor switch (Fig. 7–34). The operating switch is usually of the push-button type placed on the dash. Closing this switch allows current to flow through the magnetic-switch winding. This creates a strong magnetic field that pulls in the magnetic-switch steel plunger. The plunger movement forces a contact disk across two terminals, completing the circuit between the battery and the motor.

On some overrunning-clutch motors, a magnetic switch may be used not only to close the cranking-motor circuit but also to shift magnetically the drive pinion into mesh. This type of magnetic switch is usually referred to as a *solenoid* (Fig. 7–35). Its operation is similar to the magnetic switch, except that it usually has a second winding and a solenoid control relay. The two windings in the solenoid consist of a pull-in winding and a hold-in

winding. They work together to pull the core in, meshing the pinion and closing the cranking-motor circuit. As the switch contacts close, the pull-in winding is shorted out, since it is connected between the two solenoid terminals. By this combination of windings, the magnetic strength is considerably increased. This provides sufficient pulling power to accomplish the twofold job of meshing the pinion and closing the switch. After the pinion is meshed and the switch is closed, less magnetism is required to hold the core in. Consequently, the pull-in winding becomes shorted out to reduce the drain on the battery during the cranking operation.

The relay is included to provide more positive control of the solenoid. The relay circuit is closed either by a push-button switch or by automatic controls, as shown in Fig 7–35, and this energizes the relay winding. The current flowing through the relay winding creates a magnetic field that pulls down the flat steel armature held above the winding by a spring. The relay contacts close, connecting the solenoid

163

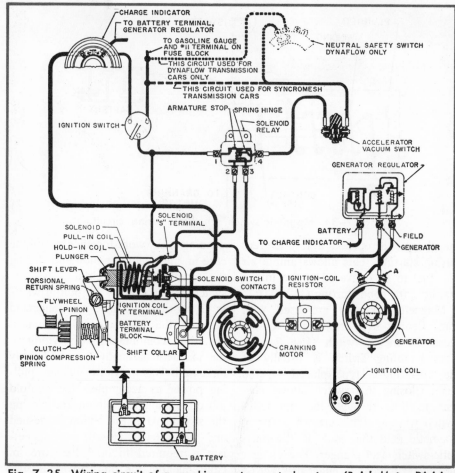

Fig. 7–35. Wiring circuit of a cranking-motor control system. *(Buick Motor Division of General Motors Corporation)*

windings to the battery so that the solenoid operates as described above.

In the circuit shown in Fig. 7–35, note that there is an ignition-coil resistor. Note also that it is a 12-volt system. During normal running, the resistor is in series with the ignition coil. It protects the coil, and distributor contact points, from excessive voltage. But when the cranking-motor solenoid operates, it shorts out the resistor and connects the coil directly to the battery. This imposes full battery voltage on the coil and improves ignition performance during cranking.

Vacuum switches are used on some applications to provide more automatic control of the cranking motor (Figs. 7–36 and 7–37). Two general types of switch have been used, the diaphragm type and the ball type. The diaphragm type (Fig. 7–36) has a spring-loaded, airtight, flexible diaphragm, one side of which is open to the intake manifold. The other side of the diaphragm is connected by mechan-

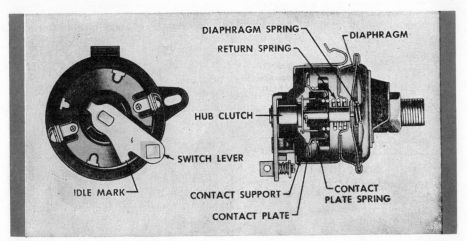

Fig. 7–36. End and sectional views of a manifold-mounted vacuum switch. *(Delco-Remy Division of General Motors Corporation)*

ical linkage to switch contacts. A linkage is provided to the accelerator pedal, so that when the ignition switch is turned on and the accelerator pedal is depressed, the vacuum-switch contacts close, completing the circuit to the solenoid relay. The relay, solenoid, and cranking motor all operate. As soon as the engine starts and vacuum develops in the intake manifold, the vacuum moves the diaphragm. This action moves the switch contacts and locks them open. This brings the cranking motor to a stop and prevents further action until such time as the engine is stopped, intake-manifold vacuum is lost, and the accelerator pedal is released.

The ball-type vacuum switch is built into the carburetor and uses a steel ball to control the closing and opening of the solenoid relay circuit (Fig. 7–37). When the engine is stopped, the steel ball drops down into an opening left by

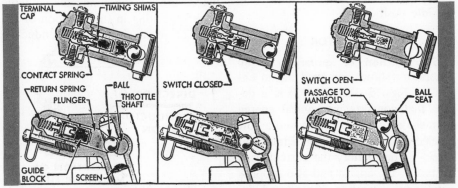

Fig. 7–37. Ball-type vacuum-controlled switch showing three positions: with engine stopped, engine being started, and engine running. *(Buick Motor Division of General Motors Corporation)*

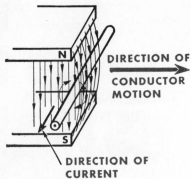

Fig. 7–38. Conductor moving through a magnetic field as shown will have a flow of current induced in it as indicated.

a flat spot on the throttle shaft. When the throttle is depressed for starting, the steel ball is forced up against a plunger and this movement pushes a W-shaped contact spring between the two switch terminals, so that the circuit is completed through the switch. When the engine starts, the manifold vacuum lifts the steel ball up into the ball seat, so that the plunger is pushed down by a coil spring. This plunger movement opens the circuit in the switch. The ball cannot return to its original position until the engine is stopped and the throttle returns to the idle position.

GENERATOR

§ 176. Function of generator   The generator (shown mounted on an engine in Figs. 5–3 and 7–22) is a device that converts mechanical energy from the automobile engine into a flow of electric current. The generator replaces in the battery the current used in starting the engine and also supplies current for operation of electrical devices, such as the ignition system, lights, radio, etc. The generator usually

is mounted on the side of the engine block (Fig. 7–22) or, on some V-type engines, between the two banks of cylinders. It is driven by the engine fan belt.

§ 177. Basic generator principles   We learned (§ 170) that, when a current-carrying conductor is held in a magnetic field, the conductor will be moved. It is also true that, when a conductor is moved through a magnetic field, current will be induced to move or flow through the conductor. If a conductor is held in a magnetic field and moved as shown in Fig. 7–38, a flow of current will be induced in the conductor in the direction shown, that is, toward the reader. This is indicated by the dot in the end of the conductor. Figure 7–39 illustrates the distortion of the magnetic field produced as the conductor moves through it. The magnetic lines of force tend to pile up ahead of the conductor and wrap around it, circling the conductor in a clockwise direction. Use of the left-hand rule indicates the direction of the current flow. If the left hand is placed around the conductor with the fingers pointing in the direction of the lines of force circling the conductor,

DISTORTION OF
MAGNETIC FIELD
Fig. 7–39. Distortion of magnetic field as conductor is moved through it and current flows in conductor.

the thumb will point in the direction of the current flow. The conductor must move across the magnetic field so that it cuts through lines of force. If the conductor moved parallel to the lines of force (for instance, from the top to the bottom of Fig. 7–39), no lines of force would be cut and no current would be induced in the conductor. The rate at which lines of force are cut determines the amount of current (or number of electrons) that will flow in the conductor. Thus, if the conductor is moved more rapidly through the magnetic field, more lines of force per second will be cut and more current will flow through the conductor. Likewise, if the magnetic field is strengthened (number of lines of force increased), the current flow will be increased as the conductor moves through the magnetic field.

§ 178. **Generator construction** If the conductor is bent into the shape of a U and the two ends connected to the two halves of a split copper ring, we have the elements of a generator (Fig. 7–40). Stationary brushes, connected to the "load" (an electric light or other current-consuming device) and resting on the split ring, and two poles of a magnet with windings around them complete the elementary generator. The U-shaped conductor and the split ring (called the *commutator*) are designed to rotate together. When they rotate in a clockwise direction as shown, current is induced in them as indicated by the arrows. The current flows toward the reader in the left-hand half of the loop and away from the reader in the right-hand half. The current flows out through the left-hand brush, most of it

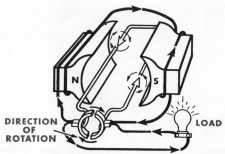

Fig. 7–40. Simplified schematic diagram of generator. Heavy arrows show direction of current flow, and light circular arrows show direction of magnetic fields around the conductors.

flowing to the load, to the right-hand brush, and back into the loop. Part of the current induced in the conductor flows through the two field windings assembled around the two magnetic poles. This current flow strengthens the magnetic field between the poles, thus increasing the amount of current induced in the conductor as it moves through the magnetic field. The left-hand rule can be used to check the direction of the magnetic field produced by the two field windings. Place the left hand around the winding with the fingers pointing in the direction in which the current flows. The thumb will point in the direction of the magnetic lines of force. In the generator assembly (Fig. 7–41), the magnetic poles (called *pole shoes*) are placed on the opposite sides of an iron field frame. The field frame forms the return magnetic circuit for the lines of force from the south to the north pole.

The commutator is designed to allow the generator to produce a flow of direct current, that is, the current continues to flow in the same direction. As

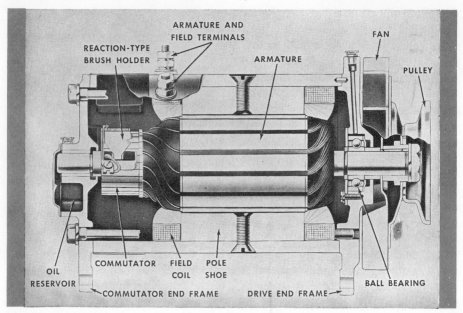

Fig. 7–41. Sectional views of a passenger-car generator. (Delco-Remy Division of General Motors Corporation)

the two sides of the loop (Fig. 7–40) rotate and change positions with respect to each other, the two segments of the commutator also change positions so that the current continues to be fed to the left-hand brush in the same direction.

The generator must use many rotating loops in order to produce an appreciable amount of current. These loops, or conductors, are assembled into the armature (Fig. 7–42) and are connected to the segments of the commutator. To obtain a strong magnetic field, the field windings are made of many turns of wire. The field windings are connected in series as shown in Fig. 7–40 and shunted across the two main brushes. In some earlier generators, one end of the field circuit was connected to a *third* brush. This provided some control of the generator

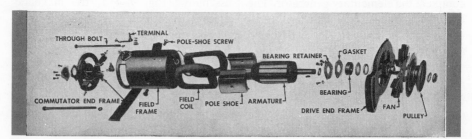

Fig. 7–42. Disassembled view of a passenger-car generator. (Delco-Remy Division of General Motors Corporation)

output, preventing it from increasing to excessive values (§ 180).

Figure 7–41 illustrates a sectional view of a typical generator, while Fig. 7–42 shows an exploded view of a similar unit. The generator consists of a field frame, into which the field windings are assembled; the armature, which contains the moving conductors; brushes, which rest on the armature commutator; the two end heads, which support the armature in bearings; and the drive pulley, assembled to the armature shaft for driving the generator.

§ **179. Generator-output control** Generators produce a flow of current as a result of the electric pressure, or voltage, that is induced in the generator. If the generator had no controlling device, increasing speed could cause the generator to build up an excessively high voltage. This would cause it to produce an excessively high current output. Thus, at high speeds, the electric units would be subjected to damaging high voltage, and the battery would be excessively overcharged. To prevent these conditions, various generator-control devices have been used. For full control, a voltage-regulating device plus a current-regulating device must be used.

§ **180. Third-brush generator** The *third-brush* generator was commonly used some years ago because it is partially self-regulating. The third-brush effect prevents the generator from producing an excessive amount of current. This effect results from the distortion and shifting of the magnetic field because of the current flow in the armature conductors. As has already been shown (Fig. 7–39), movement of a conductor through a magnetic field causes distortion of the magnetic field. This distortion increases with the amount of current flowing in the conductor, which in turn is dependent on the speed with which the conductor moves through the magnetic field. Thus, if a number of conductors are rotated in the magnetic field as shown in Fig. 7–43, the field will shift, or distort, as indicated, concentrating at the trailing edges of the poles. The trailing edges are the edges that the conductors pass last in revolving. The faster the conductors move, the greater the shift will be. In the simple shunt generator shown in Fig. 7–40, this shifting would have little effect, since the field windings are shunted across the armature and the brushes are placed to pick up the maximum voltage.

However, in third-brush generators, the third brush (*B* in Fig. 7–44), to which one end of the field circuit is connected, is not placed on the commutator where maximum voltage is available but some distance back of this point. Full voltage is not, therefore, available to the field windings. The voltage is sufficient to provide an adequately strong magnetic field for normal generator operation. Generator output increases with speed until some

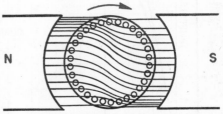

Fig. 7–43. Distortion of magnetic field produced by rotation of current-carrying conductors in magnetic field.

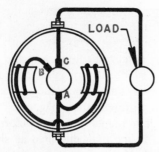

Fig. 7–44. Wiring circuit of third-brush generator. A and C are main brushes, and B is the third brush.

intermediate speed is reached. At higher speeds, the field distortion becomes more pronounced (Fig. 7–43), so that more of the magnetic field shifts *past* the third brush. Or, more accurately, the magnetic field shifts past the conductors connected to the third brush through the commutator bars. This means that a smaller amount of magnetic field is left to be cut by the conductors feeding the field windings. The voltage on the field windings drops, less current is pushed through the windings, and the magnetic strength is lowered. This tends to decrease the generator output. Still higher generator armature speed causes additional field distortion and a further drop of generator output. The amount of output obtained at various speeds thus approximately follows the lower curve shown in Fig. 7–45. At higher speeds, the generator output drops off to lower values. The third-brush effect is a current-limiting device, preventing an excessive amount of generator output. The maximum amount of current that can be obtained may be changed by shifting the third brush. Thus, when the third brush is moved toward the main brush (Fig. 7–44), it picks up a greater part of the total voltage available and consequently supplies the field windings with a stronger magnetic field. The magnetic field must undergo a greater amount of distortion before enough of the field has shifted past the third brush to cause a reduction of output. Therefore, a higher output can be obtained. Moving the third

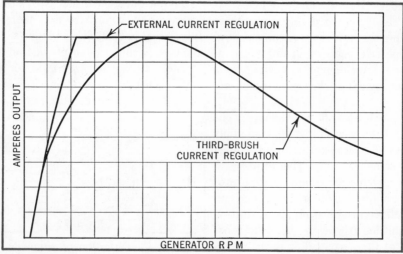

Fig. 7–45. Output curves of third-brush generator and generator employing an external form of current regulation.

brush away from the main brush reduces the generator output.

The third brush has been largely replaced on modern motor vehicles by a shunt generator using some form of external regulation. The reason for this is that the third-brush generator is not flexible enough for today's varied operations. It cannot supply enough output in the low- and high-speed ranges because of the third-brush effect, which causes a slow build-up of output and a tapering off of output at high speed.

§ 181. **External regulation** When a shunt generator is used, some device is required that will provide control of the output. Without control, shunt-generator output will continue to increase with speed until the generator becomes so overloaded that it overheats and burns up. The faster the conductors move through the magnetic field, the greater will be the voltage induced. Since this voltage is impressed on the field windings, the magnetic field will strengthen, causing a further increase of generator voltage. This process will continue, causing the generator output to increase further until it destroys itself. External regulation is designed to prevent this excessive voltage and output rise. It prevents this by inserting resistance into the generator field circuit when the voltage or current output approaches a predetermined maximum value. Figure 7–46 illustrates one system of connecting this resistance. The regulator switch, a pair of points, remains closed so long as voltage or output is not excessive. This directly connects the external end of the field circuit to the grounded brush. When voltage, or output, increases to maximum values, the regulator switch is caused to open in a manner to be explained below (§§ 183–187). This inserts resistance into the field circuit. The resistance reduces the amount of current flowing in the field windings, which in turn weakens the magnetic field. Thus, the generator output, or voltage, is reduced or kept from increasing beyond safe values. The manner of connecting the resistance shown in Fig. 7–46 is used in some systems. Other systems use the connections shown in Fig. 7–47. In the first system, the resistance is inserted between the field windings and ground, and the field circuit is connected to the insulated brush inside the generator. The

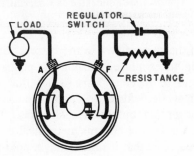

Fig. 7–46. Generator with externally grounded field circuit. (Auto-Lite and Delco-Remy standard-duty units)

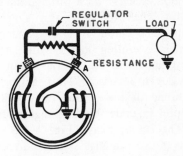

Fig. 7–47. Generator with internally grounded field circuit. (Heavy-duty Auto-Lite and Delco-Remy and Ford units)

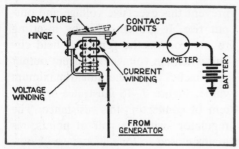

Fig. 7–48. Schematic wiring circuit of cutout relay.

second system (Fig. 7–47) grounds the field circuit to the grounded brush inside the generator, and the resistance is connected into the field circuit between the insulated brush and the field windings. It is necessary to bear in mind these two systems of connecting the field circuit in any analysis of generators: testing procedures are different for the two systems. This will be referred to again in § 370, which covers testing of generators.

CUTOUT RELAY

§ 182. Cutout relay, or circuit breaker
The cutout relay, or circuit breaker, is designed to close the circuit between the generator and the battery when the generator is producing current. Also, it opens this circuit so that the battery cannot discharge back through the generator when the generator slows or stops. The cutout relay is a magnetic switch, operating on the same principles that cause the various regulating devices to operate. Thus an understanding of the cutout relay will be helpful in understanding regulators.

The cutout relay (Fig. 7–48) consists of two windings assembled around a core, and a flat steel armature mounted on a hinge above the core. A contact point on the armature is placed just above a stationary point that is connected to the battery. When the generator is not operating, a spring on the armature holds the two points apart. This keeps the circuit between the generator and the battery open. The two windings consist of a current, or series, winding of a few turns of heavy wire and a voltage, or shunt, winding of many turns of fine wire. When the generator begins to operate, its voltage builds up, imposing voltage on the two windings. This creates a magnetic field that attracts the flat steel armature. Increasing generator voltage increases the magnetic attraction until operating voltage is reached. At this point, the attraction is strong enough to overcome the armature spring tension and pull the armature toward the winding core. This causes the two contact points to come together so that the generator is connected to the battery. Current flows from the generator to the battery. As it does this, it passes through the current, or series, winding in the right direction to add to the magnetic pull holding the points closed. Note the application of the left-hand rule to the two windings in the illustration.

When the generator stops, current begins to flow from the battery to the generator. A reversal in the direction of the current flow in the current winding takes place, causing its magnetic field to reverse. This means that the magnetic fields of the two windings no longer aid but buck each other. The result is that the magnetic field is so weakened that it can no longer hold the armature down. The armature spring tension pulls the armature up, separating the contact points. This opens the

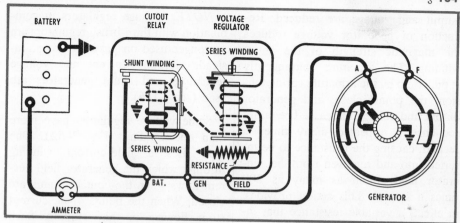

Fig. 7–49. Wiring circuit of vibrating voltage regulator and cutout relay.

circuit between the battery and the generator.

REGULATORS

§ 183. **Function of regulators** Regulators, as already mentioned, control the generator output so that damaging high-voltage and high-current output is prevented. High voltage in the electric system would soon damage the electrical devices, since excessive current would be forced through them by the high voltage. The battery would be seriously damaged by overcharging as a result of the high current flowing through it. In addition, excessive current flow through the generator windings would overheat and ruin the generator. Various types of regulating devices have been used to prevent these conditions. The type now used on automobiles, the vibrating voltage regulator, is described in the following article.

§ 184. **Vibrating voltage regulator**
The vibrating voltage regulator (Fig. 7–49) prevents the circuit voltage from exceeding a predetermined safe maximum. A practically constant voltage

is maintained in the system. This causes the generator to provide a charging rate in reverse ratio to the state of charge of the battery. That is, when the battery is low, it is supplied current at a high charging rate, and when it is charged, the charging rate tapers off to a few amperes.

The voltage regulator, normally mounted on the same base as the cutout relay, consists of a shunt winding and a flat steel armature mounted on a hinge above the winding core. When the battery is in a low state of charge, the regulator does not operate. Thus generator output increases to a value determined by speed and third-brush position. As the battery approaches a charged condition, its voltage increases. There is then an increasing magnetic pull from the shunt winding on the armature. When the regulating voltage is reached, the magnetic pull is sufficient to overcome the spring tension holding the armature away from the winding core. The armature is pulled down, causing the points to separate. This inserts resistance into the generator field circuit so that the generator

173

output and voltage are reduced. Reduction of generator voltage reduces the magnetic strength of the shunt winding. The armature consequently is pulled up by the armature spring tension, the points close, and generator output and voltage increase. The entire sequence is repeated many times a second, causing the resistance to be inserted into and removed from the generator field circuit as many as 200 times a second. This action provides, in effect, a variable resistance that increases or decreases the effective resistance in the generator field circuit, according to the state of charge of the battery and the connected electrical load. When the battery is fully charged and there are no electrical devices connected to the generator, the points vibrate in such a way that the resistance remains in the generator field circuit most of the time. It is as if a high resistance were inserted into the generator field circuit. The generator output consequently drops to a low value. When the battery becomes partly discharged or electrical devices are turned on, the points vibrate in such a way as to keep the resistance in the field only a small part of the time. This allows a higher generator output. Thus the generator output varies between wide limits. The action of the voltage regulator allows the generator to produce the correct amount of current for every condition of operation up to the limits imposed by generator speed and third-brush position. When full generator output is required, the voltage regulator does not operate and output is controlled by the third-brush setting through the full-speed range.

NOTE: Voltage regulators in combination with third-brush regulators are no longer used on passenger cars. Instead, vibrating current and voltage regulators and shunt generators are used (see § 186).

Some voltage regulators have more than one winding (Fig. 7–52). One type uses a field-current winding through which the generator field current flows when the contact points are closed. When the points open, current stops flowing in this winding. Such action speeds up the operation of the regulator armature, causing the regulator to provide a more even voltage with less fluctuation.

§ 185. Vibrating current regulator

The third-brush generator-output curve (Fig. 7–45) discloses that the generator output is low at low and high speed. To obtain sufficient output at these speeds, a shunt generator is used. The shunt generator requires some form of external current regulation to prevent the generator from producing too much output. Figure 7–50 illustrates a current regulator and generator. This system, as portrayed, is not used; the illustration is merely for the purpose of explanation.

The current regulator is constructed in a manner similar to the voltage regulator, except that the winding consists of a few turns of heavy wire through which full generator output passes. When the generator output reaches rated maximum, the current passing through the regulator winding is sufficient to overcome the armature spring tension and separate the regulator points. This inserts the resistance

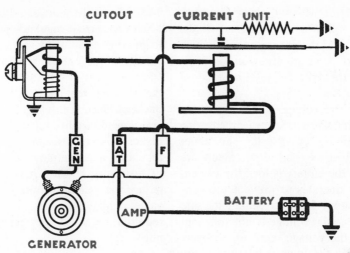

Fig. 7–50. Wiring circuit of current regulator and cutout relay. Current-regulator points are shown open.

into the generator field circuit, causing the generator output to drop off. As soon as the generator output is reduced, the magnetic pull of the regulator winding is reduced also, so that it can no longer hold the points open. They close, the generator field circuit is directly grounded, and the output increases. This cycle is repeated very rapidly, causing the current regulator to limit the current output of the generator to the value for which the generator is rated.

Some designs of current regulators use more than one winding. As with the voltage regulator, the added windings cause the points to vibrate more rapidly, producing a more even current output.

§ 186. Current and voltage regulator As was mentioned above, the current regulator is not used alone with a shunt generator. A voltage regulator is also included in the regulating device, so

that it is known as a current and voltage regulator. This combination unit also includes the cutout relay. Figure 7–51 shows a typical current and volt-

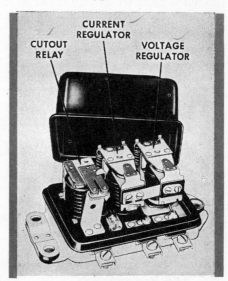

Fig. 7–51. Current and voltage regulator with cover removed. (Delco-Remy Division of General Motors Corporation)

age regulator with the cover removed. Figure 7–52 is a wiring circuit of the regulator and the generator with which it is used. Current and voltage regulators of this type are used on modern passenger cars.

Either the voltage regulator or the current regulator operates at any one time; they never operate simultaneously. When the load requirements are high and the battery is low, the current regulator operates to prevent the generator output from exceeding its safe maximum. The voltage is not sufficient to cause the voltage regulator to operate. But if the load requirements are reduced, or if the battery begins to come up to charge, the line voltage will increase to a value sufficient to cause the voltage regulator to operate. When this happens, the generator output is reduced; it falls below the value required to cause the current regulator to operate. All regulation is then dependent on the voltage regulator.

Many current and voltage regulators use two resistances, as shown in Fig. 7–52. They are connected in parallel when the current-regulator points open to provide a low value of resistance— enough to prevent the generator output from exceeding a safe maximum. When the voltage regulator operates, only one resistance is inserted into the generator field circuit and this provides a higher value of resistance. The voltage regulator must employ a higher value of resistance because it is required to *reduce* the generator output to a lower value, while the current regulator is required merely to *limit* generator output.

§ 187. Temperature compensation
Most voltage regulators and some current regulators are temperature-compensated. This means that they will have higher settings when cold than when hot. As previously explained (§ 168), low battery temperatures make it necessary to apply higher voltages to obtain current input to the battery. Temperature compensation of the voltage regulator allows this increase of

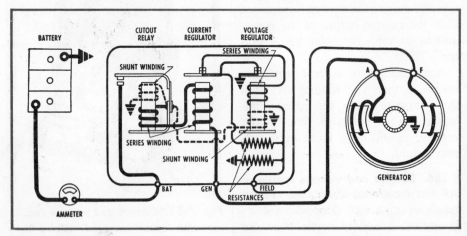

Fig. 7–52. Wiring circuit of the regulator shown in Fig. 7–51. (Delco-Remy Division of General Motors Corporation)

voltage with low temperature. Some current regulators are temperature-compensated to permit a higher generator output when cold than when hot, the generator output reducing as their temperature increases. This safely allows generator output to remain high, if required, until it reaches operating temperature. Then, the output is reduced to a value in line with the safe hot-generator output.

Temperature compensation can be achieved in either of two ways. One design makes use of a bimetal thermostatic hinge on the regulator armature. The hinge adds tension at low temperatures, so that a higher voltage (current on current regulators) is required to open the regulator points. As temperature increases, the hinge loses tension, so that less voltage (current) is required.

The second design makes use of a magnetic bypass. This passes more magnetism at low temperatures; thus less magnetism is left over to attract the regulator armature. The voltage (current) must go higher to cause regulator operation. As temperature increases, less magnetism is bypassed and the regulator setting is, in effect, reduced.

IGNITION SYSTEM

§ 188. Function of ignition system
The ignition system supplies high-volt-

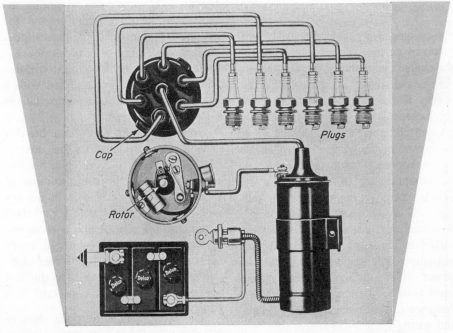

Fig. 7–53. Typical ignition system. It consists of the battery (source of power) ignition switch, ignition coil, distributor (shown in top view with cap removed and placed above it) spark plugs, and wiring. Units are not in proportion. (*Delco-Remy Division of General Motors Corporation*)

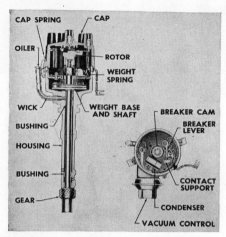

Fig. 7–54. Sectional and top views of an ignition distributor. In the top view, the cap and rotor have been removed so that the breaker plate may be seen. (Delco-Remy Division of General Motors Corporation)

age surges (of as much as 20,000 volts) of current to the spark plugs in the engine cylinders. These surges produce at the spark-plug gaps the electric sparks that ignite, or set fire to, the compressed air-fuel mixture in the combustion chamber. Each spark is timed to appear at the plug gap just as the piston approaches top dead center on the compression stroke when the engine is idling. At higher speed or during part-throttle operation, the spark is advanced so that it occurs somewhat earlier in the cycle; the mixture thus has ample time to burn and deliver its power (§ 192). The ignition system consists of the battery, switch, ignition distributor, ignition coil, spark plugs, and wiring (Fig. 7–53).

§ 189. Ignition distributor The ignition distributor (Figs. 7–54 and 7–55) has two jobs. First, it closes and

opens the circuit between the battery and the ignition coil. When the circuit closes, current flows in the ignition coil and builds up a magnetic field. When the circuit opens, the magnetic field in the coil collapses and a high-voltage surge of current is produced by the coil. The distributor's second job is to distribute each high-voltage surge to the correct spark plug at the correct instant by means of the distributor rotor and cap.

The distributor consists of a housing, drive shaft with breaker cam and advance mechanism, a breaker plate with contact points, a rotor, and a cap. The shaft is usually driven by the engine camshaft through spiral gears, and it rotates at one-half crankshaft speed. Figure 7–22 shows the mounting arrangement of a distributor on the cylinder block of an eight-cylinder engine, and Fig. 6–7 illustrates the drive arrangement. Note that the distributor drive shaft is coupled with a shaft that drives the oil pump. This is a common arrangement.

Rotation of the shaft and breaker cam causes the distributor contact points to open and close. The breaker cam usually has the same number of lobes as there are cylinders in the engine.* It rotates at half crankshaft speed, and the contact points close and open once for each cylinder with every breaker-cam rotation. Thus one high-voltage surge is produced by the coil for each cylinder every two crankshaft

* On some applications, the breaker cam has only one-half as many lobes as engine cylinders, but there are two sets of contact points that are arranged to close and open alternately. This produces the same effect as the breaker-cam and contact-point arrangement discussed above.

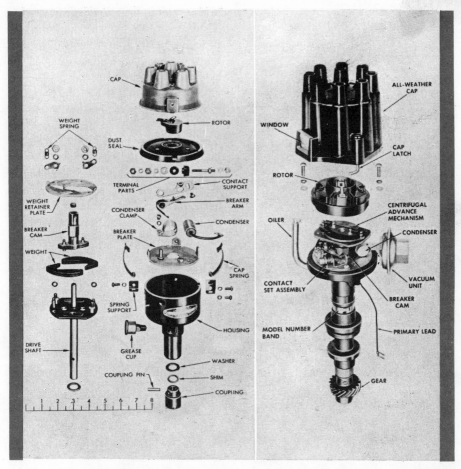

Fig. 7–55. Disassembled and partly disassembled views of distributors. (*Delco-Remy Division of General Motors Corporation*)

revolutions. This ignites the air-fuel mixture compressed in each cylinder every other crankshaft revolution.

The rotor rotates with the breaker cam, on which it is mounted. As it does so, a metal spring and segment on the rotor connect the center terminal of the cap with each outside terminal in turn, so that the high-voltage surges from the coil are directed first to one spark plug and then to another, and so on, according to the firing order.

§ 190. Spark plugs   The spark plug (Fig. 7–56) consists of a metal shell, to which is fastened a porcelain insulator, and an electrode extending through the center of the insulator. The metal shell has a short electrode attached to one side and bent in toward the center electrode. There are threads

179

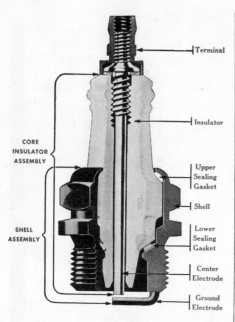

CORE
INSULATOR
ASSEMBLY

SHELL
ASSEMBLY

Terminal

Insulator

Upper
Sealing
Gasket

Shell

Lower
Sealing
Gasket

Center
Electrode

Ground
Electrode

Fig. 7–56. Sectional view of a spark plug. (AC Spark Plug Division of General Motors Corporation)

on the metal shell that allow it to be screwed into a tapped hole in the cylinder head. Figure 6–7 illustrates the location of the spark plug in the cylinder head of an overhead-valve engine, while Fig. 3–17 illustrates its location in an L-head engine. The two electrodes are of heavy wire, and there is a gap up to 0.040 inch between them. The electric spark jumps this gap to ignite the air-fuel mixture in the combustion chamber, passing from the center, or insulated, electrode to the grounded, or outer, electrode. The seals between the metal base, porcelain, and center electrode, as well as the porcelain itself, must be able to withstand the high pressure and temperature created in the combustion chamber during the power stroke.

§ 191. Ignition coil   The ignition coil transforms, or steps up, the 6 or 12

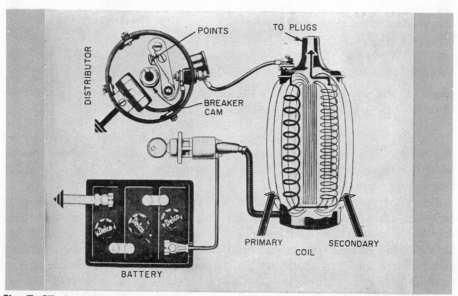

Fig. 7–57. Ignition primary circuit with coil primary and secondary windings shown schematically. The secondary is connected to the plugs through the distributor cap and rotor. (Delco-Remy Division of General Motors Corporation)

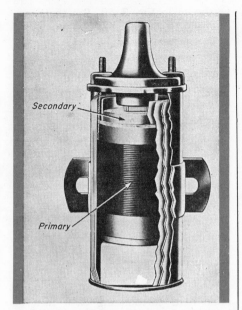

Fig. 7–58. Ignition coil with case cut away to show how primary winding is wound around outside of secondary winding. (Delco-Remy Division of General Motors Corporation)

volts of the battery to the high voltage required to make the current jump the spark-plug gap. A high voltage is required because the air-fuel mixture between the two electrodes presents a high resistance to the passage of current. The voltage (pressure) must go very high in order to push current (electrons) from the center to the outside electrode. Let us consider in detail the actions in the ignition coil that enable it to produce high-voltage surges.

The ignition coil has two circuits through it, a primary circuit and a secondary circuit (Fig. 7–57). The secondary circuit is made up of a winding of many thousands of turns of a fine wire. The primary circuit is made up of a winding of a few hundred turns

of relatively heavy wire, wrapped or wound around the outside of the secondary winding as shown in Fig. 7–58. When the distributor contact points close and current flows in the primary circuit, a magnetic field builds up. When the distributor contact points open and current stops flowing, the magnetic field collapses. The collapsing magnetic field induces high voltage in the secondary winding. This creates the high-voltage surge that is conducted through the distributor rotor and cap to a spark plug.

1. *Creating the magnetic field.* We have already seen that current flowing through a winding causes a magnetic field (§ 160). The magnetic field does not, however, spring up instantly when the circuit is closed to the battery. It takes a small fraction of a second (called the *build-up time*) for this to occur. The reason for this lies in the fact that the winding has self-induction. This term expresses the action that each turn of wire in the winding has on adjacent turns. Figure 7–59 illustrates the magnetic fields surrounding two adjacent turns of wire in the winding, seen in end view, as current flows in them. The current is flowing away from the reader as indicated by the crosses. When the current first starts to flow, the encircling magnetic fields begin to move outward from the wires in a manner somewhat like the ripples on a pool of water moving out from where a stone has been dropped. Fig-

Fig. 7–59. Magnetic fields surrounding two adjacent turns of wire in a winding through which current is passing.

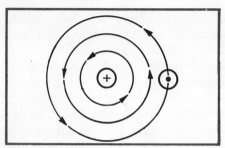

Fig. 7–60. Effect on an adjacent wire of an increasing magnetic field from one wire.

ure 7–60 illustrates the effect of this action on the right-hand wire. The increasing magnetic field cuts across the right-hand wire. It thus attempts to induce in that wire a flow of current in the opposite direction. This is indicated by the dot, which means the current is flowing toward the reader. To understand how current can be induced in the wire, consider the generator.

The generator causes a flow of current by moving conductors through a stationary magnetic field. However, if the conductors are held stationary and the magnetic field is moved, a flow of current also will be induced. This is the effect illustrated in Fig. 7–60. The turns of wire are stationary, but the expanding magnetic field from the left-hand wire moves across the right-hand wire. And since the magnetic field distorts around the right-hand wire in a clockwise direction, a flow of current is induced in a direction toward the reader. The left-hand rule will confirm this.

Actually, the current could not flow in this direction in the right-hand wire, because the battery is already forcing current through the winding and every turn of wire in the opposite direction,

as shown in Fig. 7–59. But there is a tendency for a flow of current to be induced in the reverse direction in every turn of wire. The tendency is brought about by the expanding magnetic fields from adjacent turns of wire. The result is that this tendency combats any increase in current flow through the winding. It takes a fraction of a second for the battery voltage to overcome this tendency and build up the magnetic field in the winding.

2. Effect on primary winding of collapsing the magnetic field. When the distributor contact points open, the current stops flowing and the magnetic field from the primary winding begins to collapse. This means that the magnetic field surrounding each turn of wire begins to collapse back toward the wire. Thus, instead of the field's moving to the right as shown in Fig. 7–60, the field moves to the left. This attempts to induce a flow of current in the right-hand wire in a direction opposite to that shown, or in the direction in which it flowed when the winding was connected to the battery. Such action, again, is self-induction.

3. Condenser effect. As the contact points separate in the distributor, the flow of current from the battery through the primary winding of the coil is interrupted. Instantly, the magnetic field begins to collapse, and this collapse attempts to reestablish the flow of current. If it were not for the condenser (also called a *capacitor*), the flow of current would be reestablished. This means a heavy electric arc would take place across the separating contact points. The points would burn, and the energy stored in the ignition coil as magnetism would be consumed by

the arc. The condenser prevents this, however, because it momentarily provides a place for the current to flow as the points begin to move apart.

The condenser is made up of two thin metallic plates separated by an insulator. The plates are two long, narrow strips of lead or aluminum foil, insulated from each other by special condenser paper and wrapped on an arbor to form a winding. The winding is then installed in a container. A condenser is shown in Fig. 7–61. The two plates provide a large surface area onto which the electrons (flow of current) can move during the first instant that the contact points separate. As will be remembered, it is the massing of electrons in one place in a circuit that causes them to move and produce what we know as a flow of current. Since the condenser provides a large surface area, many electrons can flow onto this large surface area without producing an excessive massing of electrons in one spot.

The number of electrons the condenser can accept is, however, limited, and it quickly becomes charged. But, by this time, the contact points are sufficiently far apart to prevent an arc from forming between them. In effect, the condenser acts as a reservoir into which electrons can flow during the first instant that the points begin to separate. By the time the reservoir is filled, the points are too far apart for the electrons to jump across them. The electrons, or current, consequently must stop flowing in the primary circuit. Since it is a current flow that sustains the magnetic field, the quick stoppage of the current causes the magnetic field to collapse rapidly. It is this rapid col-

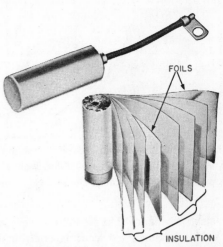

Fig. 7–61. A condenser assembled and with the winding partly unwound.

lapse that induces the high voltage in the secondary winding of the ignition coil.

4. Effect on secondary winding of magnetic-field collapse. The rapid collapse of the magnetic field causes the magnetic lines of force to move rapidly across the thousands of turns of wire in the secondary winding. This means that each turn will have voltage induced in it. Since all turns are connected in series so that the total voltage induced is the sum of the voltage of each turn, the winding will supply a high voltage during the magnetic-field collapse. One end of the secondary winding is connected through ground to the side electrode in the spark plug. The other end of the secondary winding is connected through the cap and the rotor of the distributor and through the wiring to the center electrode in the spark plug. This high voltage, suddenly imposed on the spark plug, causes electrons (current) to jump across the gap, producing an

183

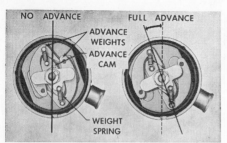

Fig. 7–62. Centrifugal-advance mechanism showing "no-" and "full-advance" positions. (Delco-Remy Division of General Motors Corporation)

electric spark. The instant that the spark is timed to occur is controlled by the spark-advance mechanisms in the distributor (§ 192).

5. *Summary.* Let us review briefly the action taking place in the ignition system. As the piston in one of the engine cylinders starts up on the compression stroke, one of the distributor breaker-cam lobes moves away from the contact-point breaker arm. The contact points close, current flows through the primary winding of the ignition coil, and a magnetic field builds up. At the instant that the piston reaches the position in the cylinder at which ignition of the compressed air-fuel mixture should take place, the next cam lobe has moved around to where it strikes against the contact-point breaker arm so that the contact points separate. The current stops flowing in the primary circuit; the magnetic field collapses. This induces high voltage in the secondary winding. The rotor on top of the breaker cam, in the meantime, has moved into position opposite the outside distributor cap terminal connected to the cylinder spark plug. The spark plug is thus connected to the secondary winding of the igni-

tion coil through the cap and rotor at the instant that the high voltage is induced, and a spark therefore occurs at the spark-plug gap.

6. *Ignition-coil resistor.* In many passenger-car 12-volt systems, there is an ignition-coil resistor connected in series with the coil when the engine is operating. The resistor reduces the voltage imposed on the coil and distributor contact points, thus protecting them from excessive current. However, during cranking, the cranking-motor solenoid shorts out the resistor (see Fig. 7–35). Full battery voltage is thus imposed on the coil, and ignition performance during cranking is therefore improved. This tends to eliminate the adverse effect of the reduced battery voltage brought about by the cranking-motor operation.

§ **192. Spark-advance   mechanisms** There are two general types of spark-advance mechanisms, centrifugal and vacuum. These mechanisms vary the spark timing for different engine-operating conditions as explained in the following paragraphs.

1. *Centrifugal.* When the engine is idling, the spark is timed to occur just before the piston reaches top dead center on the compression stroke. At higher speeds, it is necessary to deliver the spark to the combustion chamber somewhat earlier. This will give the mixture ample time to burn and deliver its power to the piston. To provide this advance, a centrifugal-advance mechanism is used (Fig. 7–62). It consists of two weights that throw out against spring tension as engine speed increases. This movement is transmitted through a toggle arrangement to

the breaker cam, causing it to advance or move ahead with respect to the distributor drive shaft. This, in turn, causes the cam to open and close the contact points earlier in the compression stroke at high speeds. Since the rotor, too, is advanced, it comes into position earlier in the cycle, also. The timing of the spark to the cylinder consequently varies from no advance at low speed to full advance at high speed when the weights have reached the outer limits of their travel. Maximum advance may be as much as 45 degrees of crankshaft rotation before the piston reaches top dead center; it varies considerably with different makes of engines. The toggle arrangement and springs are designed to give the correct advance for maximum engine performance.

2. Vacuum. Under part throttle, a partial vacuum develops in the intake manifold. This means that less air and fuel will be admitted to the cylinder (volumetric efficiency is lowered). Thus, the mixture will be less highly compressed. The mixture will burn more slowly when ignited, and, in order to realize full power from it, the spark should be somewhat advanced. To secure this advance of the spark, a vacuum-advance mechanism is used.

Figure 7–63 illustrates one type of vacuum-advance mechanism. It contains a spring-loaded and airtight diaphragm connected by a linkage, or

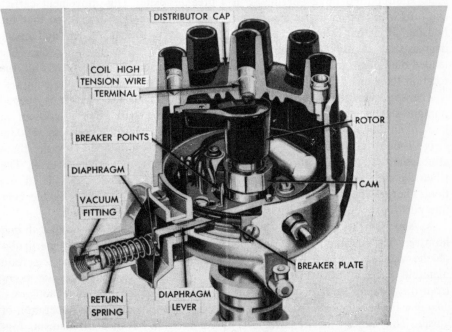

Fig. 7–63. Cutaway view of distributor showing construction of vacuum-advance mechanism. (*Ford Division of Ford Motor Company*)

185

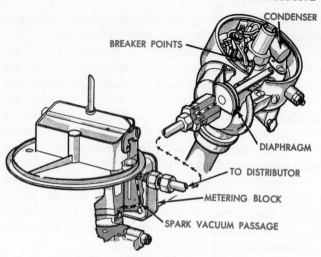

Fig. 7–64. Connection of vacuum line between carburetor and vacuum-advance mechanism on distributor. (*Ford Division of Ford Motor Company*)

lever, to the breaker plate. The breaker plate is supported on a bearing so it can turn with respect to the distributor housing. It actually turns only a few degrees since the linkage to the spring-loaded diaphragm prevents any greater rotation than this.

The spring-loaded side of the diaphragm is connected through a vacuum line to an opening in the carburetor (Fig. 7–64). This opening is on the atmospheric side of the throttle valve when the throttle is in the idling position. There is no vacuum advance in this position.

As soon as the throttle is opened, however, it swings past the opening of the vacuum passage. The intake-manifold vacuum can then draw air from the vacuum line and the airtight chamber in the vacuum-advance mechanism. This causes the diaphragm to move against the spring. The linkage

to the breaker plate then rotates the breaker plate. This movement carries the contact points around so that the cam, as it rotates, closes and opens the points earlier in the cycle. The spark consequently appears at the spark-plug gap earlier in the compression stroke. As the throttle is opened wider, there will be less vacuum in the intake manifold and less vacuum advance. At wide-open throttle, there will be no vacuum advance at all. The spark advance under this condition will be provided entirely by the centrifugal-advance mechanism.

3. Combination of centrifugal and vacuum advances. At any particular engine speed, there will be a certain definite centrifugal advance due to engine speed plus a possible additional spark advance due to the operation of the vacuum-advance mechanism. Figure 7–65 illustrates this. At 40 mph

(miles per hour), the centrifugal-advance mechanism provides 15 degrees spark advance on this particular application. The vacuum mechanism will supply up to 15 degrees additional advance under part-throttle conditions. However, if the engine is operated at wide-open throttle, this added vacuum advance will not be obtained. The advance in the usual application will vary somewhat between the straight line (centrifugal advance) and the curved line (centrifugal advance plus total possible vacuum advance) as the throttle is closed and opened.

4. *Full vacuum control.* The distributor illustrated in Fig. 7–66 does not

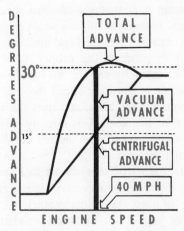

Fig. 7–65. Centrifugal- and vacuum-advance curves for one particular application.

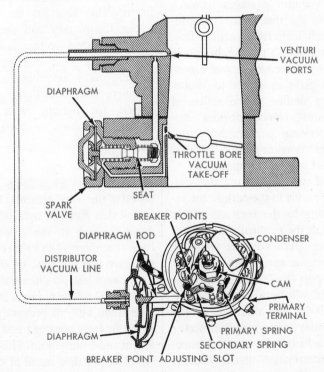

Fig. 7–66. Vacuum-line connections between carburetor and distributor having full vacuum control. (*Ford Division of Ford Motor Company*)

contain a centrifugal-advance mechanism. Instead, it utilizes vacuum from the carburetor venturi and intake manifold to produce the proper advance. Full control by vacuum means alone is possible because air speed through the carburetor air horn, and thus the vacuum in the venturi, is directly related to engine speed. Let us see how the system functions.

In the carburetor shown in Fig. 7–66, there are two vacuum openings in the air horn, one at the venturi and the other just above the throttle when it is closed. The lower, or throttle, vacuum take-off opening may have two ports on some models as shown in Fig. 7–66. These openings are connected by vacuum passages to each other and to the distributor vacuum-advance mechanism by a vacuum line. Vacuum imposed on the diaphragm in the vacuum-advance mechanism causes the breaker-plate assembly to rotate. This is very similar to the action of other vacuum-advance devices discussed in previous paragraphs. Rotation of the breaker-plate assembly causes an advance of the spark.

As engine speed increases, the vacuum at the venturi in the carburetor increases, owing to the increase of air speed through the venturi. This causes an increasing spark advance which is related to engine speed. At the same time, under part-throttle operating conditions, there will be a vacuum in the intake manifold; and this acts at the throttle vacuum ports in the carburetor to produce a further vacuum advance. Thus, the interrelation of the vacuum conditions at the two points in the carburetor produces, in effect, a combined

speed advance (as with a centrifugal device) and vacuum advance.

§ 193. Relays The various relays in the automobile are all switches that are magnetically operated. We have already discussed the cutout relay that is connected in the circuit between the battery and generator and the cranking-motor solenoid switch relay that energizes the solenoid when it closes. In addition, horn and lighting relays are used on some cars. The horn relay is a single-winding relay. When the horn-button switch is closed, the winding is energized, causing the relay contact points to close. Current flows from the battery through the points to the horns. This shortens the circuit between the battery and the horns, so that full battery voltage is available at the horns for good horn operation. The lighting relay operates in a similar manner; when the lighting switch is closed, the lighting relay closes its points to connect the battery and the lights.

§ 194. Lights Headlights are composed of three components: the light filament that gives off light when current flows through it, the reflector at the back that directs the light forward, and the lens that refracts, or distorts, the light beam into an illuminating pattern (Fig. 7–67). The filament is incased in an airtight bulb to prevent the oxygen in the air from causing the white-hot filament to be burned up. The reflector is either of polished metal or of mirrored glass, and it serves to throw all light rays into a cylindrical beam. The lens

is made up of a series of glass prisms molded together. The prisms bend the beam of light into an oval pattern that is aimed forward and somewhat downward. Part of the light is spread out in front of the car to provide local illumination; the remainder is focused into a hot spot that provides distant illumination. The patterns from the two headlights furnish satisfactory illumination for night driving.

There are two filaments in each headlight, one for normal country driving and the other for city or passing driving. The latter is somewhat displaced so that, when lit, it throws the beam of light downward. This illuminates the road but prevents the driver of an oncoming car from being blinded. A foot selector switch enables the driver to select either the driving or passing beam.

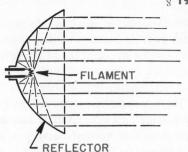

Fig. 7–67. Filament and reflector of headlight.

Cars today use sealed-beam headlights. This type of light has the filament, reflector, and lens assembled into one unit (Fig. 7–68). No focusing is necessary, and the reflector or lens cannot become dirty or corroded so that lighting efficiency is impaired. The only service required on this type of headlight is the aiming of the headlights.

Fig. 7–68. Sealed-beam headlight together with parts to hold it in place in fender: A, sealed-beam unit; B, subbody; C, retainer ring; D, lamp housing; E, coil springs; F, vertical-adjustment screw; G, horizontal-adjustment screw; H, lug; I, rim. (*Buick Motor Division of General Motors Corporation*)

189

§ 195 Indicating devices Most cars have four indicating devices on the dash for the convenience of the driver. These are ammeter, fuel level, oil pressure, and engine temperature.

The ammeter is connected between the battery and generator. It indicates the amount of current being put into or withdrawn from the battery. The typical ammeter consists of a pivoted vane to which a needle is attached, a permanent magnet, and a heavy conductor (Fig. 7–69). When no current flows to or from the battery, the pivoted vane is held between the two poles of the permanent magnet as shown. In this position, the needle indicates zero. When current does flow, it passes through the conductor. This current produces a magnetic field around the conductor; this magnetic field forces the vane to move. The stronger the current, the farther the vane moves. The needle, therefore, swings around to register the amount of current flowing through. If current is flowing to the battery, the needle swings to the "charge" side. If current is flowing from the battery, the needle swings to the "discharge" side.

The other indicating devices (fuel, oil, temperature) are of two types, magnetic and thermostatic. In the thermostatic type, there is a thermostat in the pickup unit and a thermostat in the dash unit. The pickup unit, in the fuel gauge, is located in the fuel tank. It is in the oil line from the oil pump in the oil-pressure indicator. And, in the engine temperature indicator, the pickup unit is in an engine water jacket, immersed in the cooling water. The pickup unit passes varying amounts of current to the dash unit (in accordance with changing fuel level, oil pressure, or temperature). This current heats the dash-unit thermostat, causing it to bend. If the current is relatively high, the thermostat will bend considerably. If low, it will bend only slightly. An indicating needle linked to the thermostat moves to indicate the fuel level, oil pressure, or temperature.

The magnetic type of indicating device also uses a pickup unit that passes varying amounts of current. In the dash unit, there are two coils with a magnetic vane between them. There is a needle mounted on the vane. The coils are so connected that the varying amounts of current passed by the pickup unit change the magnetic pattern between the coils. This causes the vane to swing around, carrying the needle with it to produce the correct indication (of fuel level, oil pressure, or temperature).

These indicating devices are described in detail in the chapters that

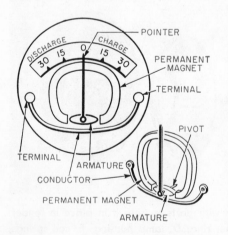

Fig. 7–69. Car ammeter, or charge indicator.

follow, dealing with fuel systems, cooling systems, and lubricating systems.

REVIEW QUESTIONS

1. Name several jobs that the electric current performs on the automobile.
2. Name the main components of the electric system.
3. What is the purpose of the storage battery?
4. What is the purpose of the cranking motor? Where is it mounted on the engine?
5. What is the purpose of the generator? Where is it mounted on the engine, and how is it driven?
6. What is the purpose of the generator regulator?
7. What is the purpose of the ignition system?
8. Give a brief explanation of electric current.
9. Give a brief explanation of voltage.
10. What is resistance in an electric circuit?
11. Does a storage battery actually store electricity?
12. When a battery is being discharged, does the sulfuric acid in the electrolyte increase or decrease?
13. What are three common methods of rating batteries? Which rating is most commonly used in referring to battery capacity?
14. When a battery is being charged, does increasing battery temperature require a higher or a lower charging voltage to maintain the same charging rate?
15. Why must the cranking-motor drive pinion be de-meshed from the engine flywheel after the engine starts?
16. Describe briefly the operation of the Bendix drive. Of the Folo-Thru drive.
17. Describe briefly the operation of the overrunning clutch drive.
18. Describe briefly the operation of the solenoid relay and solenoid in the cranking-motor control circuit.
19. What is the purpose of the vacuum switch in some cranking-motor control circuits?
20. Why is a generator output control required?
21. In an adjustable third-brush generator, in which direction is the third brush moved to increase generator output?
22. What would happen to a shunt generator if it were not controlled as it increased in speed?
23. What are the two systems of connecting the generator field circuit when an external regulating device is used?
24. What is the purpose of the cutout relay? What other name does this device have?
25. What is the essential difference between the voltage regulator and the current regulator in so far as the physical construction is concerned? In so far as the operation is concerned?
26. What is temperature compensation in the regulator? In what two general ways is temperature compensation obtained?
27. What two jobs does the ignition distributor have?

28. What is the purpose of the spark plugs?
29. What is the purpose of the ignition coil?
30. What two types of spark advance are incorporated in many ignition distributors?
31. Name several indicating devices that can be read from the driver's compartment and explain their purpose.

STUDY QUESTIONS

1. What is meant by a "one-wire" system?
2. Draw the symbol for ground, and explain what this term means.
3. Find out the locations of the battery on various automobiles.
4. Where is the regulator usually mounted on the automobile?
5. Ohm's law is $E = I \times R$. From this formula, figure out how much voltage would be required to force 3 amperes through 2 ohms of resistance. How much current would flow through a 4-ohm resistance if 6 volts were applied? If you had a 6-volt battery and wanted to have 15 amperes flowing in a circuit, what resistance would the circuit require?
6. Lay a flat piece of cardboard on top of a bar or horseshoe magnet, and sprinkle some iron filings on the cardboard just over the magnet. Tap the cardboard lightly, and the iron filings will form in lines that will indicate the magnetic lines of force. Make a sketch of these lines of force.

7. Do magnetic lines of force actually exist?
8. Make a sketch similar to Fig. 7–12, showing a magnetic field surrounding a conductor that is carrying current, but in your sketch make the flow of current in a direction opposite to that in Fig. 7–12.
9. Describe briefly the construction of a battery.
10. Make a sketch of a schematic cranking motor such as is shown in Fig. 7–28, but reverse the direction of current and indicate the direction of rotation.
11. Make a wiring diagram of a cranking motor with solenoid and solenoid relay, and write a sequence story of their operation starting with "1. The relay winding becomes magnetically energized as it is connected to the battery."
12. Name the main parts of a cranking motor.
13. Referring to Fig. 7–37, write a sequence story of the operation of the ball-type vacuum switch.
14. Make a sketch of a schematic generator, such as is shown in Fig. 7–40, but reverse the north and south poles. Indicate the direction of the current flow with the rotation as shown in Fig. 7–40.
15. Name main parts of a generator.
16. Make a wiring diagram of a cutout relay, and name the windings.
17. Make a wiring diagram of a current and voltage regulator, and name the windings.
18. Make a wiring diagram of an ignition system, naming all parts.

192

SERVICE TOOLS

A great variety of tools are available to help the serviceman test, adjust, and repair automotive components. They include special meters, gauges, punches, hammers, wrenches, lathes, vises, grinders, and so on; each tool has its special purpose and is designed to do a particular job well. This book describes many of these tools and explains how to use them.

In the early days of the automotive service business, there were few special tools. The automotive mechanic had to use standard mechanics tools or invent his own for special jobs. Gradually, as the automobile became more complex and such new devices as automatic transmissions and power steering were introduced, increased attention was focused on the designing of special tools to simplify servicing operations. Automotive engineers became increasingly aware that the reputation of their products depended on the continued good performance of their products and that this depended, in turn, on the quality of service their products received. Good service requires well-trained servicemen using proper service tools to make the correct adjustments and repairs.

Thus the designing of service tools became part of the automotive designer's job. Whatever the component, however it fit into the automobile, the job that it did, it had to be serviced and serviced with relative ease. Often this meant redesigning the component several times until it not only performed as it should, but also lent itself to ready servicing. Sometimes, an early component design would require numerous special tools for proper servicing. Engineers would then alter the design to reduce the number of special service tools required. Work on design ordinarily does not stop until all requirements are met: proper performance, simplest possible design, maximum simplicity of manufacture, ease of servicing.

Today specialty tool manufacturers work with automotive manufacturers devising a complete line of servicing tools for each new car model. Handmade models of new tools are often tried out in the laboratory before they are released for production. Great effort goes into producing the exact tool that is going to work most efficiently and easily for the serviceman in the shop.

A good automotive mechanic can get along with a minimum number of tools. But some of the new tools coming out of the laboratories of the automotive and tool manufacturers will enable him to do a better job, faster and more efficiently. Further, if he attempts to service some of the new components such as automatic transmissions, it becomes an absolute must for him to have the special tools designed specifically to do the servicing job.

Over a period of time, a good automotive mechanic acquires a comprehensive arsenal of servicing tools. With care, good tools will last many years. The good automotive mechanic knows that the proper tools make the job go faster, better; quality tools are a good investment and will last years if not a lifetime.

THIS CHAPTER DESCRIBES THE operation of automotive-engine fuel systems and discusses various types of fuel pumps, carburetors, and other components used in fuel systems. The major part of the chapter is concerned with gasoline-fuel systems using carburetors since this type of system is, by far, the most commonly used automotive-engine fuel system.

§ 196. **Purpose of fuel system** The fuel system has the job of supplying a combustible mixture of air and fuel to the engine. The fuel system must vary the proportions of air and fuel to suit the requirements of the engine under different operating conditions. For example, when the engine is being cranked for starting and the engine is

cold, the mixture must be comparatively rich (that is, it must have a comparatively high proportion of fuel). Under such conditions, the fuel system would supply a mixture of about 9 pounds of air to 1 pound of gasoline. After the engine has warmed up, it will operate satisfactorily on a leaner mixture of about 15 pounds of air to 1 pound of gasoline. But for acceleration and high-speed or full-load operation, the mixture must again be enriched.

§ 197. **Fuel-system components** The fuel system consists of the fuel tank, fuel pump, carburetor, intake manifold, and fuel lines, or tubes, connecting the tank, pump, and carburetor (Fig. 8–1). Some gasoline engines use a fuel-injection system; in this system, a fuel-

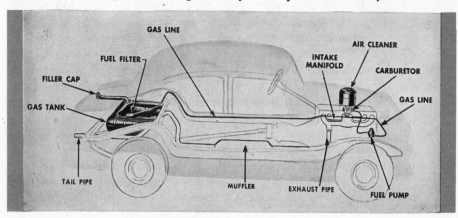

Fig. 8–1. Fuel system in phantom view.

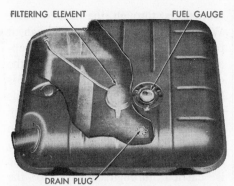

FILTERING ELEMENT   FUEL GAUGE

DRAIN PLUG

Fig. 8–2. Fuel tank, partly cut away to show filtering element and drain plug. (Plymouth Division of Chrysler Corporation)

injection pump replaces the carburetor. Details of these components are discussed in following sections.

§ 198. Fuel tank   The fuel tank (Fig. 8–2) is normally located at the rear of the vehicle. It is made of sheet metal and is attached to the frame. The filler opening of the tank is closed by a cap. The tank end of the fuel line is attached at or near the bottom of the tank. In some tanks, there is a filtering element at the fuel-line connection. The tank also contains the sending unit of the fuel gauge.

§ 199. Fuel filters and screens   Fuel systems have filters and screens to prevent dirt in the fuel from entering the fuel pump or carburetor. Dirt could, of course, prevent normal operation of these units and cause poor engine performance. The filter is often incorporated in the fuel pump. It may also be a separate unit connected into the fuel line between the tank and pump. In addition, carburetors often contain filter screens.

§ 200. Fuel gauges   The hydrostatic fuel gauge, commonly used years ago, is rarely seen today. It included an indicating tube on the dash, partly filled with colored liquid. This tube was connected to a vertical tube in the fuel tank. Variations in fuel level produced variations in the level of the liquid in the indicating tube.

The electric-type fuel gauge is generally used today. There are two types, *balancing coil* and *thermostatic*. Each type has a tank unit and a dash unit.

1. Balancing coil (Fig. 8–3). The tank unit in this fuel gauge contains a sliding contact that slides back and forth on a resistance as the float moves up and down in the fuel tank. This changes the amount of electrical resistance the tank unit offers. Thus, as the tank empties, the float drops and the sliding contact moves to reduce the resistance. The dash unit contains two coils, as shown in Fig. 8–3. When the ignition switch is turned on, current from the battery flows through the two coils. This produces a magnetic pattern that acts on the armature to which the pointer is attached. When the re-

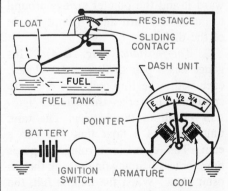

Fig. 8–3. Schematic wiring circuit of balancing-coil fuel-gauge indicating system.

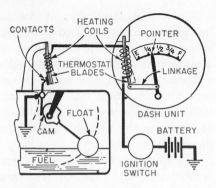

Fig. 8–4. Schematic wiring circuit of thermostatic fuel-gauge indicating system.

sistance of the tank unit is high (tank filled and float up), then the current flowing through the E (empty) coil also flows through the F (full) coil. Thus the armature is pulled to the right so that the pointer indicates on the F, or "full", side of the dial. But when the tank begins to empty, the resistance of the tank unit drops. Thus, more of the current flowing through the empty coil passes through the tank unit. Since less thus flows through the full coil, its magnetic field is weaker. As a result, the empty coil pulls the armature toward it and the pointer swings around to indicate toward the E (empty) side of the dial.

2. *Thermostatic (Fig. 8–4).* This gauge has a pair of thermostat blades, each with a heating coil. The coils are connected in series through the ignition switch to the battery. The tank unit also has a float that actuates a cam. The cam, in turning, imposes more or less bending on the tank thermostat blade. When the tank is full, the float is up and the cam puts a considerable bend in the blade. Then, when the ignition switch is turned on, cur-

rent flows through the heater coils. When the tank blade is hot enough, it bends farther so that the contacts separate. Then, the blade cools, and the contacts close. Again the blade is heated, and the points reopen. This action continues as long as the ignition switch is on. Meantime, the blade in the dash unit is heated and bends a like amount. Movement of this blade is carried through linkage to the pointer, which then moves to indicate on the "full" side of the dial. However, if the tank is nearly empty, then the float is down and the cam bends the tank thermostat blade only a little. As a result, only a small amount of heating is enough to bend the blade farther and open the contacts. Thus, the dash-unit blade bends only a little, and the pointer indicates toward the "empty" side.

§ 201. **Fuel pumps** Earlier fuel systems depended on gravity or on air pressure to cause gasoline to flow to the carburetor. Today, fuel systems use a fuel pump to deliver fuel from the tank to the carburetor. The pump is mounted on the side of the cylinder block on in-line engines (Fig. 7–22) and is mounted between the two cylinder banks in many V-8 engines. A rocker arm on the pump extends through an opening provided for it in the cylinder block. The rocker arm rests on an eccentric on the camshaft. On V-8 engines which have the fuel pump mounted in the V, the rocker arm rests on a push rod; the lower end of the push rod rides on the camshaft eccentric.

As the camshaft rotates, the eccentric causes the rocker arm to rock back

and forth. The inner end of the rocker arm is linked to a flexible diaphragm which is clamped between the upper and lower pump housings (Fig. 8–5). There is a spring under the diaphragm that maintains tension on the diaphragm. As the rocker arm rocks, it pulls the diaphragm down and then releases it. The spring then forces the diaphragm up. Thus, the diaphragm moves up and down as the rocker arm rocks.

This diaphragm movement alternately produces vacuum and pressure in the space above the diaphragm. When the diaphragm moves down, a partial vacuum is produced. Then, atmospheric pressure, acting on the fuel in the tank, forces fuel through the fuel line and into the pump. The inlet valve in the pump opens to admit fuel as shown by the arrows in Fig. 8–5. Note that the fuel first passes through a filter bowl and screen.

When the diaphragm is released by the return movement of the rocker arm, the spring forces the diaphragm upward, producing pressure in the space above the diaphragm. This pressure closes the inlet valve and opens the outlet valve. Now, fuel is forced from the fuel pump through the fuel line to the carburetor.

The fuel enters the carburetor past a needle valve in the float bowl (these are discussed in a following article). If the float bowl is filled, the needle valve closes so that no fuel can enter. When this happens, the fuel pump cannot deliver fuel to the carburetor. In this case, the rocker arm continues to rock. However, the diaphragm remains at or near its lower limit of travel; its spring cannot force the diaphragm upward so long as the carburetor float bowl will not accept further fuel. However, as the carburetor uses up fuel, the needle valve opens to admit fuel

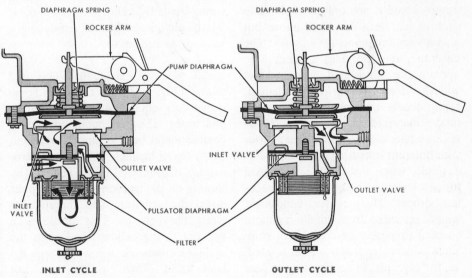

Fig. 8–5. Sectional views of a fuel pump showing the inlet and outlet cycles. (*Mercury Division of Ford Motor Company*)

197

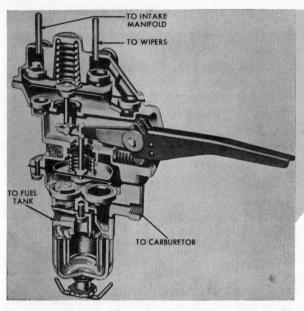

TO INTAKE MANIFOLD

TO WIPERS

TO FUEL TANK

TO CARBURETOR

Fig. 8–6. Cutaway view of fuel and vacuum pump. The vacuum unit is at the top, the fuel pump at the bottom. (Mercury Division of Ford Motor Company)

to the float bowl. Now the diaphragm can move up (on the rocker-arm return stroke) to force fuel into the carburetor float bowl.

§ 202. **Combination pumps** These pumps contain not only a fuel pump such as has been described above but also a vacuum pump (Fig. 8–6). The vacuum pump provides a vacuum to operate the windshield wipers. Most windshield wipers operate on vacuum; some obtain their vacuum from the intake manifold of the engine. However, intake-manifold vacuum varies with different operating conditions. For example, when the throttle is opened for acceleration, intake-manifold vacuum drops. This causes windshield wipers operated from intake-manifold vacuum to nearly or completely stop. Thus, when clear vision is most needed, as, for example, in accelerating to pass another car, the windshield wipers are likely to be operating poorly. To pro-

vide a steadier vacuum, a vacuum pump is incorporated with the fuel pump. Both operate from the same rocker arm. The vacuum pump is similar in construction and action to the fuel pump. It has a pair of valves and a spring-loaded diaphragm. However, it pumps air instead of fuel, producing a vacuum as it does so.

§ 203. **Electric fuel pump** This fuel pump (Fig. 8–7) is used on some heavy-duty equipment such as trucks and buses. The fuel pump contains a flexible metal bellows that is operated by an electromagnet. When the electromagnet is connected to the battery (by turning on the ignition switch), it pulls down the armature and thereby extends the bellows. This produces a vacuum in the bellows; fuel from the fuel tank enters the bellows through the inlet valve. Then, as the armature reaches its lower limit of travel, it opens a set of contact points. This discon-

nects the electromagnet from the battery. The return spring therefore pushes the armature up and collapses the bellows. This forces fuel from the bellows through the outlet valve and to the carburetor. As the armature reaches the upper limit of its travel, it closes the contacts so that the electromagnet is again energized and pulls the armature down once more. This series of actions is repeated so long as the ignition switch is turned on.

§ 204. **Air cleaners** As already noted, the fuel system mixes air and fuel to produce a combustible mixture. A great deal of air passes through the carburetor and engine—as much as 100,000 cubic feet of air every 1,000 car-miles. This is a great volume of air, and it is likely to contain a great amount of floating dust and grit. The

grit and dust could, if it entered the engine, cause serious engine damage. Thus, an air cleaner is mounted on the air horn, or air entrance, of the carburetor to keep out the dirt (Fig. 8–8). All air entering the engine through the carburetor must first pass through the air cleaner. The upper part of the air cleaner contains a ring of filter material (fine-mesh metal threads or ribbons) through which the air must pass. This material provides a fine maze that traps most of the dust particles. Most air cleaners have an oil bath. This is a reservoir of oil past which the incoming air must flow. The moving air picks up particles of oil and carries them up into the filter. There the oil washes accumulated dust back down into the oil reservoir. The oiliness of the filter material also improves the filtering action.

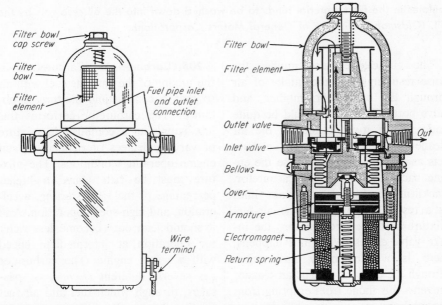

Fig. 8–7. (a) External and (b) sectional views of electric fuel pump. The bellows and electromagnet are in the lower part of the pump.

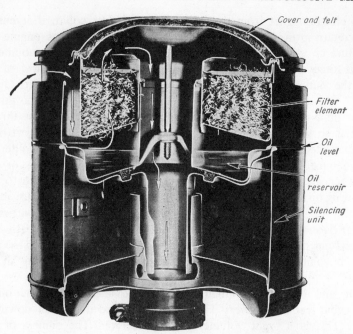

Cover and felt

Filter element

Oil level

Oil reservoir

Silencing unit

Fig. 8–8. Carburetor air cleaner and intake silencer of the oil-bath type. It incorporates an oil reservoir past which the air must flow. The sharp turn that the air must take throws particles of oil from the oil bath up into the filter. Dust that accumulates in the filter material tends to be washed down into the oil reservoir by the oil. *(Oldsmobile Division of General Motors Corporation)*

The air cleaner also muffles the noise resulting from the intake of air through the carburetor, muffler, and valve ports. This noise would be quite noticeable if it were not for the air cleaner. In addition, the air cleaner acts as a flame arrester in case the engine backfires through the carburetor. Backfiring may occur at certain times as a result of ignition of the air-fuel mixture in the cylinder before the intake valve closes. When this happens, there is a momentary flash back through the carburetor. The air cleaner prevents this flame from erupting from the carburetor and possibly igniting gasoline fumes outside the engine.

§ 205. Carburetion Carburetion is the mixing of the gasoline fuel with air so that a combustible mixture is obtained. The carburetor performs this job, supplying a combustible mixture of varying degrees of richness to suit engine operating conditions. The mixture must be rich (have a higher percentage of fuel) for starting, acceleration, and high-speed operation. And it should lean out (become less rich) for operation at intermediate speed with a warm engine. The carburetor has several different *circuits,* or passages, through which fuel and air-fuel mixture flows under different operating conditions to produce the varying rich-

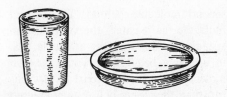

Fig. 8–9. Water will evaporate from the shallow pan faster than from the glass: the greater the area exposed to air, the faster the evaporation.

ness of the air-fuel mixture. All this is explained in following articles.

§ 206. Evaporation   When a liquid changes to a vapor (undergoes a *change of state*), it is said to evaporate. Water placed in an open pan will evaporate: it changes from a liquid to a vapor. Clothes hung on a line will dry: the water in the clothes turns to vapor. When the clothes are well spread out, they will dry more rapidly than when they are bunched together. This illustrates an important fact about evaporation. The greater the surface exposed, the more rapidly evaporation takes place. A pint of water in a tall glass will take quite a while to evaporate. But a pint of water in a shallow pan will evaporate much more quickly (Fig. 8–9).

§ 207. Atomization   In order to produce very quick evaporation of the liquid gasoline, it is sprayed into the air passing through the carburetor. Spraying the liquid turns it into many fine droplets. This effect is called *atomization* because the liquid is broken up into small droplets (but not actually broken up into atoms, as the name implies). Each droplet is exposed to air on all sides so that it evaporates very

quickly. Thus, during normal running of the engine, the gasoline sprayed into the air passing through the carburetor turns to vapor, or evaporates, almost instantly.

§ 208. Carburetor fundamentals   A simple carburetor could be made from a round cylinder with a constricted section, a fuel nozzle, or tube, and a round disk, or valve (Fig. 8–10). The round cylinder is called the *air horn,* the constricted section the *venturi,* and the valve the *throttle valve.* The throttle valve can be tilted more or less to open or close the air horn (Fig. 8–11). When the throttle is turned to the horizontal position, it shuts off, or *throttles,* the air flow through the air horn. When the throttle is turned away from this position, air can flow through the air horn.

§ 209. Venturi effect   As air flows through the constriction, or venturi, a partial vacuum is produced at the venturi. This vacuum then causes the fuel nozzle to deliver a spray of gasoline into the passing air stream. The venturi effect (of producing a vacuum) can be illustrated with the setup shown

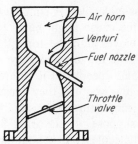

Fig. 8–10. Simple carburetor consisting of air horn, fuel nozzle, and throttle valve.

Fig. 8–11. Throttle valve in air horn of carburetor. When throttle is closed, as shown, little air can pass through. But when throttle is opened, as shown dotted, there is little throttling effect.

in Fig. 8–12. Here, three dishes of mercury (a very heavy metallic liquid) are connected by tubes to an air horn with a venturi. The greater the vacuum, the higher the mercury is pushed up in the tube by atmospheric pressure. Note that the greatest vacuum is right at the venturi. Also, it should be remembered that, the faster the air flows through, the greater the vacuum.

You can visualize the reason for the vacuum in the venturi if you will remember that the air is made up of countless molecules. A simple explanation of the cause might be as follows: As air moves into the top of the air horn, all the air molecules are moving at the same speed. But if all are to get through the venturi, they must speed up and move through faster. For instance, suppose we see what happens to two molecules, one behind the other. As the first molecule enters the venturi, it speeds up, tending to leave the

second molecule behind. The second molecule, as it enters the venturi, also speeds up. But the first molecule has, in effect, a head start. Thus, the two molecules are farther apart in the venturi than they were before they entered it. Now visualize a great number of particles going through the same action. Note that, as they pass through the venturi, they are farther apart than before they entered. This is just another way of saying that a partial vacuum exists in the venturi. For as already noted (§ 64), a partial vacuum is a thinning out of the air, a more than normal distance between air molecules.

§ 210. Fuel-nozzle action The partial vacuum occurs in the venturi, just where the end of the fuel nozzle is located. The other end of the fuel nozzle is in a fuel reservoir (the float bowl) as shown in Fig. 8–13. With the vacuum at the upper end of the nozzle, atmospheric pressure (working through

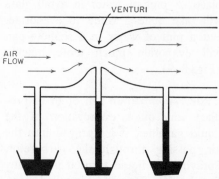

Fig. 8–12. Three dishes of mercury and tubes connected to air horn show differences in vacuum by the distance mercury rises in tubes. Venturi has highest vacuum.

a vent in the float-bowl cover) pushes fuel up through the nozzle and out into the passing air stream. The fuel enters the air stream as a fine spray which quickly turns into vapor as the droplets of fuel evaporate. The more air that flows through the air horn, the greater the vacuum in the venturi and the more fuel delivered.

§ 211. Throttle-valve action As already mentioned, the throttle valve can be tilted in the air horn to allow more or less air to flow through (Fig. 8–11). When it is tilted to allow more air to flow through, then larger amounts of air-fuel mixture are delivered to the engine. The engine develops more power and tends to run faster. But if the throttle valve is tilted so as to throttle off most of the air, then only small amounts of air-fuel mixture are de-

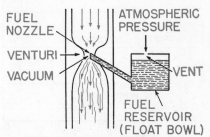

Fig. 8–13. The venturi, or constriction, causes a vacuum to develop in the air stream just below the constriction. Then atmospheric pressure pushes fuel up and out the fuel nozzle.

livered and the engine produces less power and tends to slow down. Linkage between the throttle valve and an accelerator pedal in the driver's compartment permits the driver to position the throttle valve to suit operating requirements (Fig. 8–14).

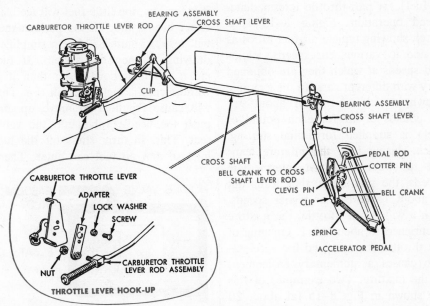

Fig. 8–14. Linkage between accelerator pedal and carburetor throttle valve.

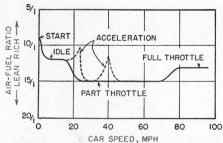

Fig. 8–15. Graph of air-fuel ratios for different car speeds. The graph is typical only; car speeds at which the various ratios are obtained may vary with different cars. Also, there may be some variation in the ratios.

§ 212. Air-fuel ratio requirements As already noted, the fuel system must vary the air-fuel ratio to suit different operating requirements. The mixture must be rich (have a high proportion of fuel) for starting but must be relatively lean (have a lower proportion of fuel) for part-throttle intermediate-speed operation. Figure 8–15 is a graph showing typical air-fuel ratios as related to various car speeds. Ratios and speeds at which they are obtained vary with different cars. In the example shown, a rich mixture of about 9:1 (9 pounds of air for each pound of fuel) is supplied for initial starting. Then, during idle, the mixture leans out to about 12:1. At intermediate speeds, the mixture further leans out to about 15:1. But at higher speeds, with a wide-open throttle, the mixture is enriched to about 13:1. Opening of the throttle at any speed for acceleration causes a momentary enrichment of the mixture. Two examples of this are shown in Fig. 8–15 [at about 20 mph (miles per hour) and at about 30 mph]. Following articles describe

the various circuits, or passages, in the carburetor that function to produce these variations in air-fuel ratio.

§ 213. Carburetor circuits The various circuits in the carburetor are:
1. Float circuit
2. Idling- and low-speed circuit
3. High-speed part-load circuit
4. High-speed full-power circuit
5. Accelerator-pump circuit
6. Choke

Following articles discuss each of these in detail.

§ 214. Float circuit The float circuit includes the float bowl and a float and needle-valve arrangement. The float and needle valve operate to maintain a constant level of fuel in the float bowl. If the level is too high, then too much fuel will feed from the fuel nozzle. If it is too low, too little fuel will feed. In either event, poor engine performance will result. Figure 8–16 is a simplified drawing of the float system. If fuel enters the float bowl faster than it is withdrawn, the fuel level will rise. This will cause the float to move up and push the needle valve into the valve seat. This, in turn, shuts off the fuel inlet so that no fuel can enter. Then,

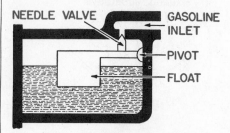

Fig. 8–16. Simplified drawing of a carburetor float system.

if the fuel level drops, the float moves down and releases the needle so that the fuel inlet is opened. Now, fuel can enter. In actual operation, the fuel is maintained at a practically constant level. The float tends to hold the needle valve partly closed so that the incoming fuel just balances the fuel being withdrawn.

Figure 8–17 shows a float circuit for a carburetor. Figure 8–18 shows an actual carburetor partly disassembled so that the floats can be seen. This is a dual carburetor; it has two barrels. It is used on an eight-cylinder engine, and each barrel supplies four cylinders (see § 235). The carburetor has a float bowl that surrounds the two barrels. The two floats are attached by a U-shaped lever and operate a single needle valve. Figure 8–19 shows the

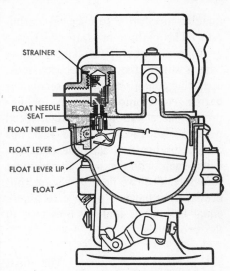

Fig. 8–17. Sectional view of a carburetor, showing float system. Fuel enters as shown by curved arrow. (Studebaker-Packard Corporation)

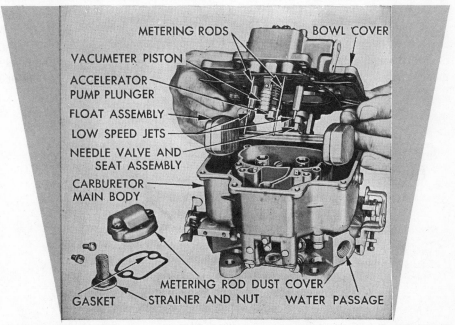

Fig. 8–18. Dual carburetor (two-barrel) partly disassembled so that the dual-float assembly can be seen. (Chrysler Sales Division of Chrysler Corporation)

float circuit for a four-barrel carbu-retor. This carburetor is, in effect, two two-barrel carburetors. The primary barrels supply the engine during most operating conditions, but the secondary barrels come into operation for im-proved acceleration and high-speed performance (§ 236). Note that this carburetor has two separate float cir-cuits, each with its own double-float assembly. The two float bowls are con-nected by a balance passage to assure equal fuel levels and air pressures in the two bowls.

§ 215. **Float-bowl vents**   The float bowls of many carburetors are vented into the carburetor air horn at a point above the choke valve. The carburetor shown in Fig. 8–19 is vented in this manner. The purpose of this arrange-ment is to equalize the effect of a clogged air cleaner. For example, sup-pose the air cleaner has become clogged with dirt so that the passage of air through it is restricted. This means that a partial vacuum will de-velop in the carburetor air horn. As a result, a somewhat greater vacuum is applied to the fuel nozzle (since this vacuum is added to the venturi vac-uum). If the float-bowl vent opens to the atmosphere (as shown in Fig. 8–13), the atmospheric pressure will then cause greater amounts of fuel to be delivered. The mixture will be too rich.

However, if the float bowl is vented into the carburetor air horn, then there will be a balance between the float bowl and air horn; air pressure will be the same in both. The effect of a clogged air cleaner is eliminated. Car-buretors vented in this manner are called *balanced* carburetors. Carbure-tors with float bowls vented to the at-mosphere are *unbalanced* carburetors.

§ 216. **Idle- and low-speed circuits**   When the throttle is closed or only slightly opened, only a small amount of air can pass through the air horn. The air speed is low, and practically no vacuum develops in the venturi.

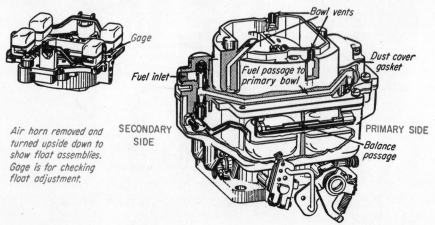

Fig. 8–19. Float system of four-barrel carburetor. (Oldsmobile Division of General Motors Corporation)

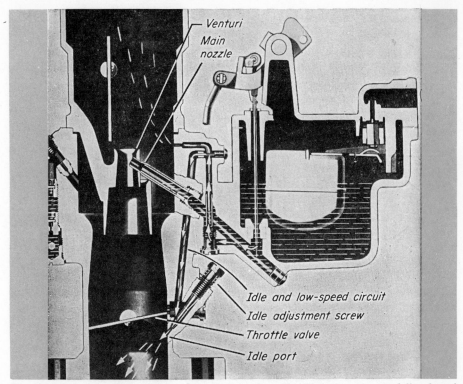

Fig. 8–20. Idle- and low-speed circuit in carburetor. Throttle valve is fully closed, and all gasoline is being fed past the idle adjustment screw. Lines indicate air; arrows indicate gasoline. (*Chevrolet Motor Division of General Motors Corporation*)

This means that the fuel nozzle will not feed fuel. Thus, the carburetor must have another circuit to supply fuel during operation with a closed or slightly opened throttle.

This circuit, called the idle- and low-speed circuit, is shown in operation in a typical carburetor in Fig. 8–20. It consists of passages through which air and fuel can flow. With the throttle closed as shown, there is a high vacuum below the throttle from the intake manifold. Atmospheric pressure pushes air and fuel through the passages as shown. They mix and flow past the tapered point of the idle adjustment screw. The mixture has a high propor-

tion of fuel (is very rich). It leans out somewhat as it mixes with the small amount of air that gets past the closed throttle valve. But the final mixture is still satisfactorily rich (see Fig. 8–15) for good idling. The mixture richness can be adjusted by turning the idle adjustment screw in or out to permit less or more air-fuel mixture to flow past the screw.

§ 217. Low-speed operation When the throttle is opened slightly as shown in Fig. 8–21, the edge of the throttle valve moves past the low-speed port in the side of the air horn. This port is a vertical slot or a series of small

207

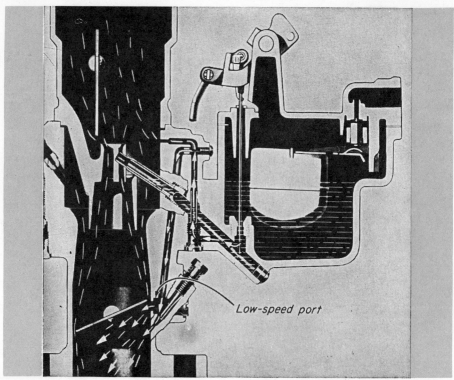

Fig. 8–21. Idle- and low-speed circuit in carburetor. Throttle valve is slightly opened, and gasoline is being fed through low-speed port. Lines indicate air; arrows indicate gasoline. *(Chevrolet Motor Division of General Motors Corporation)*

holes one above the other. Additional fuel is thus fed into the intake manifold through the low-speed port. This fuel mixes with the additional air moving past the slightly opened throttle valve to provide sufficient mixture richness for part-throttle low-speed operation.

§ 218. **Other idle- and low-speed circuits** There are many varieties of idle- and low-speed circuits in addition to the one shown in Figs. 8–20 and 8–21. In two-barrel carburetors, each barrel has its own idle- and low-speed circuit. In many four-barrel carburetors, only the primary barrels have idle- and low-speed circuits (§ 236). A

somewhat different type of idle circuit is shown in Fig. 8–22. This is an *updraft* carburetor; it is mounted below the intake manifold, and air flows *upward* through the carburetor to the intake manifold. (Other carburetors previously discussed are *downdraft* units; air flow is *downward* to the intake manifold.) On this unit, the idle adjustment screw serves a somewhat different purpose from the idle adjustment screws on carburetors previously discussed. On this unit, the idle adjustment screw admits air into the fuel flowing through the idle circuit. The more air that is admitted, the less fuel will flow. The fuel flows upward

through the idle jet and calibration (or restricting orifice), past the idle adjustment screw (or needle) and idle-port plug. Turning the idle adjustment screw out to admit more air results in a leaner mixture. Turning it in enriches the mixture. This arrangement is used in both updraft and downdraft carburetors.

§ 219. High-speed part-load circuit
When the throttle valve is opened sufficiently so that its edge moves well past the low-speed port, there is little difference in vacuum between the upper and lower part of the air horn. Thus, little air-fuel mixture will discharge from the low-speed port. How-

ever, under this condition, enough air is moving through the air horn to produce an appreciable vacuum in the venturi. As a result, the fuel nozzle centered in the venturi (called the *main nozzle* or the *high-speed nozzle*) begins to discharge fuel (as explained in § 210). The main nozzle supplies the fuel during operation with the throttle partly to fully opened. Figure 8–23 shows this action. The circuit from the float bowl to the main nozzle is called the *high-speed circuit*.

The wider the throttle is opened and the faster that air flows through the air horn, the greater the vacuum in the venturi. This means that additional fuel will be discharged from the main nozzle

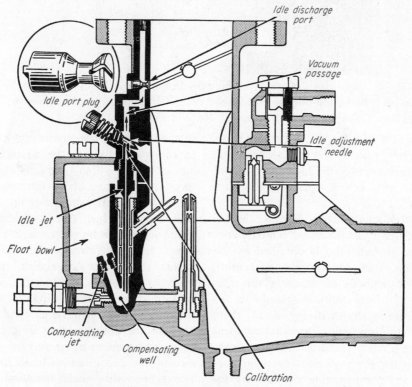

Fig. 8–22. Idle circuit in updraft carburetor. (Zenith)

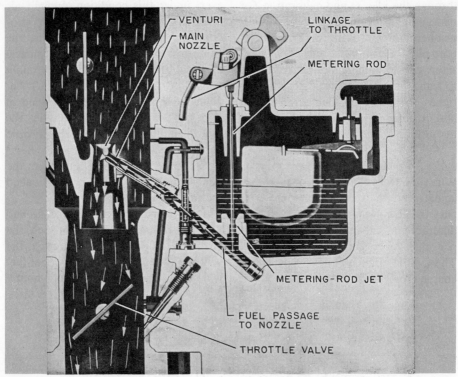

Fig. 8–23. High-speed circuit in carburetor. Throttle valve is fairly well open, and gasoline is being fed through high-speed nozzle. Lines indicate air; arrows indicate gasoline. *(Chevrolet Motor Division of General Motors Corporation)*

(because of the greater vacuum). As a result, a nearly constant air-fuel ratio is maintained by the high-speed circuit from part- to wide-open throttle.

§220. Compensating system In the carburetor just discussed, a nearly constant air-fuel ratio is obtained by the design of the main nozzle and venturi. Other methods of attaining this uniform air-fuel ratio are used. In the carburetor shown in Fig. 8–24, there is a compensating system that compensates for any variation in fuel delivery from the main nozzle. The main nozzle and compensating nozzle work together to deliver fuel. Fuel for the

compensating nozzle enters the compensating well through the compensating jet (Fig. 8–24). At low engine speed (and low air speed through the air horn), the main nozzle is not discharging much fuel. But the compensating nozzle discharges enough additional fuel to provide the correct air-fuel ratio. But as engine speed increases, fuel flows through the compensating nozzle faster than it can enter the well through the jet. The fuel level in the compensating well falls. Now, air begins to bleed into the well through the uncovered air-bleed holes. The compensating nozzle therefore discharges a leaned-out mixture. Mean-

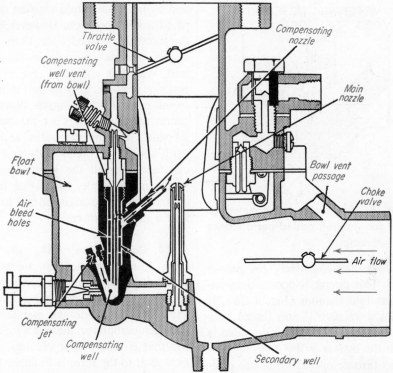

Fig. 8–24. Compensating system in an updraft carburetor. (Zenith)

time, however, the main nozzle is discharging more fuel. The combination provides the properly proportioned mixture for the operating condition.

§ 221. Full-power circuit For high-speed full-power wide-open-throttle operation, the air-fuel mixture must be enriched (see Fig. 8–15). Additional devices are incorporated in the carburetor to provide this enriched mixture during high-speed full-power operation. They are operated mechanically or by intake-manifold vacuum.

§ 222. Mechanically operated full-power circuit This circuit includes a metering-rod jet and metering rod with

two or more steps of different diameters (Fig. 8–25). The metering rod is attached to the throttle linkage (Fig. 8–23). When the throttle is opened, the metering rod is lifted. But when the throttle is partly closed, then the larger diameter of the metering rod is in the metering-rod jet. This somewhat restricts fuel flow to the main nozzle. However, adequate amounts of fuel do flow for normal part-throttle operation. When the throttle is opened wide, the rod is lifted enough to cause the smaller diameter, or step, to move up into the metering-rod jet. Now, the jet is less restricted, and more fuel can flow. The main nozzle is therefore supplied with more fuel, and the resulting air-fuel mixture is richer.

211

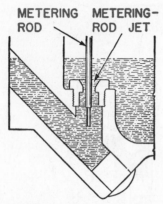

METERING   METERING-
ROD   ROD JET

Fig. 8–25. Metering rod and metering-rod jet for securing added performance at full throttle.

§ 223. Vacuum-operated full-power circuit This circuit is operated by intake-manifold vacuum (Fig. 8–26). It includes a vacuum piston linked to a valve in a bypass circuit. The valve is held in the bypass jet by a spring during part-throttle operation; in this position, all fuel to the main nozzle flows through the main metering jet. The vacuum piston is held in its upper posi-

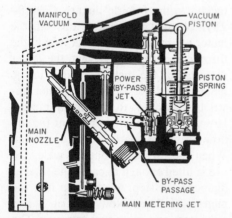

MANIFOLD
VACUUM   VACUUM
                                          PISTON

POWER   PISTON
(BY-PASS)   SPRING
JET

MAIN
NOZZLE

                         BY-PASS
                         PASSAGE
                MAIN METERING JET

Fig. 8–26. Vacuum-operated full-power circuit in carburetor. *(Studebaker-Packard Corporation)*

tion by intake-manifold vacuum during part-throttle operation. However, when the throttle is opened wide, there is no appreciable vacuum in the intake manifold. With this condition, the vacuum piston is released. It is pushed down by spring pressure. As it moves down, the piston rod pushes against the bypass-jet valve, causing the valve to open. With this valve open, additional fuel can feed through the bypass passage to the main nozzle. More fuel is discharged from the main nozzle to provide a richer mixture.

§ 224. Combination full-power circuits In some carburetors, a combination full-power circuit is used that is operated both mechanically and by vacuum from the intake manifold. In one such carburetor, there is a metering rod that is linked to a vacuum piston as well as to the throttle linkage. Thus, mechanical movement of the throttle to "full open" lifts the metering rod to enrich the mixture. Or loss of intake-manifold vacuum (as during a hard pull up a hill or during acceleration) will cause the vacuum-piston spring to raise the metering rod for an enriched mixture.

§ 225. Accelerator-pump circuit For acceleration, the engine requires a relatively rich mixture (Fig. 8–15). An accelerator-pump circuit temporarily enriches the mixture for acceleration by supplying additional fuel when the throttle is moved to the "open" position. Figure 8–27 shows one type of accelerator-pump circuit. The pump piston is connected to the throttle through linkage. When the throttle is

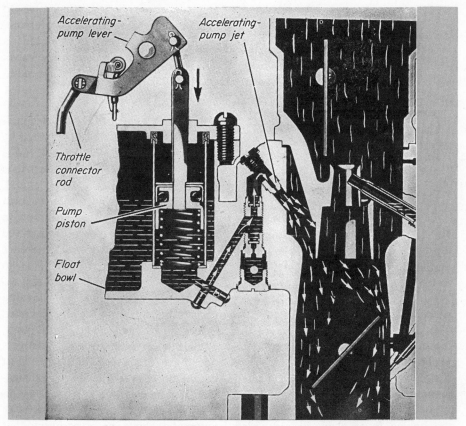

Fig. 8–27. Accelerator-pump system in carburetor. When the piston moves down, fuel is sprayed from the pump jet as shown by the arrows. (*Chevrolet Motor Division of General Motors Corporation*)

opened, the piston is forced down; this movement forces fuel through the accelerating-pump jet as shown (Fig. 8–27). A small check valve in the accelerator-pump circuit prevents the circuit from discharging fuel at other times. The circuit discharges fuel only when the pump piston is moved down as the throttle is opened.

An accelerator-pump circuit for a dual carburetor is shown in Fig. 8–28. This carburetor has two barrels; there is a discharge nozzle for each. The fuel flow from the accelerator pump is split between the two barrels.

§ 226. Choke When the engine is being cranked for starting, a very rich mixture must be delivered to the cylinders. But during this time air speed through the carburetor air horn is very low. Vacuum from the venturi action and vacuum below the throttle would be insufficient to produce adequate fuel flow for starting. Thus, to produce sufficient fuel flow during cranking, the

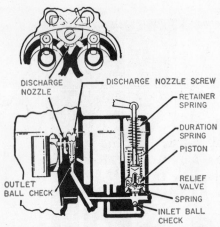

Fig. 8–28. Accelerator-pump system and location of discharge nozzles in a dual carburetor. *(Studebaker-Packard Corporation)*

carburetor has a choke (Fig. 8–29). The choke consists of a valve in the top of the air horn controlled mechanically, or by an automatic device. When the choke valve is closed, only a small amount of air can get past it (the valve "chokes off" the air flow). Then, when the engine is cranked, a fairly high vacuum develops in the air horn. This vacuum causes the main nozzle to discharge a heavy stream of fuel. The quantity delivered is sufficient to produce the rich air-fuel mixture needed for starting the engine.

As soon as the engine starts, its speed increases from cranking speed [of around 100 rpm (revolutions per minute)] to over 400 rpm. Now, more air and a somewhat leaner mixture are required. One method of satisfying this requirement is to mount the choke valve off center and to have a spring arrangement in the choke linkage. With this arrangement, the additional air the engine requires causes the valve to partly open against the spring pressure. Another arrangement is to include a small spring-loaded section in the valve; this section opens to admit the additional air.

§ 227. **Automatic chokes** Mechanically controlled chokes are operated by a pull rod on the dash. The pull rod is linked to the choke valve; when it is pulled out, the choke valve is closed. With this arrangement, the driver must remember to push the control rod in to the dechoked position as soon as the engine begins to warm up. If he does not, the carburetor will continue to supply a very rich mixture to the engine. This excessive richness will cause poor engine performance and carboned valves, piston rings, and spark plugs.

To prevent such troubles, most cars now have an automatic choke. Most automatic chokes operate on exhaust-manifold temperature and intake-manifold vacuum. Figure 8–30 shows an automatic choke on a carburetor. It includes a thermostatic spring and a vacuum piston, both linked to the choke valve. The thermostatic spring is made up of two different metal strips welded together and formed into a spiral. Owing to differences in expansion rates of the two metals, the thermostatic spring tends to wind up or unwind with changing temperature (§ 61). When the engine is cold, the spring has wound up enough to close the choke valve and spring-load it in the closed position. Now, when the engine is cranked, a rich mixture is delivered to the engine. As the engine starts, air movement through the air horn causes the

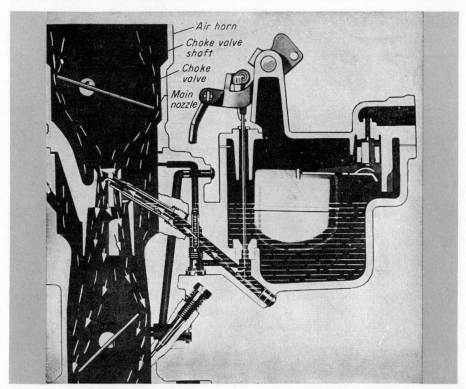

Fig. 8–29. Operation of choke in starting engine. *(Chevrolet Motor Division of General Motors Corporation)*

choke valve to open slightly (working against the thermostatic-spring pressure). In addition, the vacuum piston is pulled outward by intake-manifold vacuum to produce some further opening of the choke valve.

The choke valve is thus positioned properly to permit the carburetor to supply the rather rich mixture the engine requires for cold-engine idling operation. When the throttle is opened, the mixture must be enriched. The accelerator pump provides some additional fuel, but still more fuel is required when the engine is cold. This additional fuel is secured by the action of the vacuum piston. When the throttle is opened, intake-manifold vacuum is lost. The vacuum piston releases and is pulled inward by the thermostatic-spring tension. The choke valve therefore moves toward the "closed" position and causes the mixture to be enriched. During the first few moments of operation, the choke valve is controlled by the vacuum piston.

However, the thermostatic spring begins to take over as the engine warms up. The thermostatic spring is in a housing that is connected to the exhaust manifold through a small tube. Heat passes through this tube and enters

215

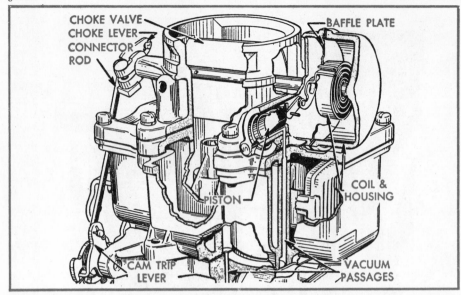

Fig. 8–30. Carburetor cut away so that the automatic-choke construction can be seen. *(Buick Motor Division of General Motors Corporation)*

the thermostatic-spring housing. Soon, the thermostat begins to warm up. As it warms up, it unwinds. This causes the choke valve to move toward the "opened" position. When operating temperature is reached, the thermostat has unwound enough to fully open the choke valve. No further choking takes place.

When the engine is stopped and cools, the thermostatic spring again winds up as noted above to close the choke valve and spring-load it in the "closed" position.

Figure 8–30 shows a carburetor partly cut away so that the construction of the automatic choke can be seen. The vacuum passage to the vacuum piston is shown, but the heat tube to the exhaust manifold is not. The heat tube introduces heat from the exhaust manifold into the thermostatic-spring housing.

The choke shown in Fig. 8–31 is operated electrically. It has an electromagnet that is energized when the engine is cranked. This causes the armature to be pulled upward. Linkage between the armature and choke then causes the choke valve to close. After the engine starts and the cranking motor is stopped, the electromagnet

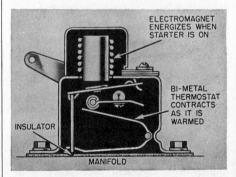

Fig. 8–31. Construction of electric choke. *(Plymouth Division of Chrysler Corporation)*

216

is deenergized and it releases the armature. The position that the choke valve then takes is determined by the thermostat. If the engine is cold, the thermostat keeps the choke nearly closed. But as the engine warms up, the thermostat warps to cause the choke valve to move toward the opened position.

NOTE: See § 113, which discusses the part that the manifold heat control plays in carburetor operation during engine warm-up.

§ 228. Other carburetor features
The different circuits discussed in the past several pages are basic for most carburetors. While the circuits may vary to some extent from one carburetor to another, they operate in a very similar manner. Various other features may be found on different carburetors as noted in the following articles.

§ 229. Anti-icing   When fuel is sprayed into the air passing through the air horn, it evaporates, or turns to vapor. This is a change of state (§ 54). During evaporation, the fuel takes on heat. That is, it takes heat from the surrounding air and metal parts. This is the same effect you get when you pour alcohol on your hand. Your hand feels cold. If you blow on your hand, thus causing the alcohol to evaporate faster, your hand will feel still colder. The faster that evaporation takes heat away from your hand, the cooler your hand will feel.

Now, let us see how this affects the carburetor. Spraying and evaporation of the fuel "rob" the surrounding air and carburetor of heat. Under certain

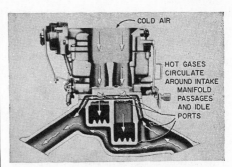

Fig. 8–32. Intake manifold and carburetor idle ports heating passages. Hot exhaust gases heat these areas as soon as the engine starts. *(Cadillac Motor Car Division of General Motors Corporation)*

conditions, the surrounding metal parts are so cooled that any moisture in the air will condense and actually freeze on the metal parts. The ice can build up sufficiently, if conditions are right, to cause the engine to stall. Conditions that would lead to this include high humidity (air very damp) and near-freezing temperature.

To prevent such icing, many carburetors have special anti-icing circuits. One arrangement for a V-8 engine is shown in Fig. 8–32. During the warm-up period, the manifold-heat-control valve shunts hot exhaust gases from one exhaust manifold to the other (see § 113). Part of this hot exhaust gas circulates around the carburetor idle ports and near the throttle-valve shaft. This adds enough heat to guard against ice formation. Another carburetor has water passages in the carburetor. You can see one of the water passages into the throttle body of the carburetor shown in Fig. 8–18 (lower right). The water comes from the engine cooling system; a small amount of the cooling

217

water bypasses through a special water manifold in the carburetor throttle body. This adds enough heat to the carburetor to prevent icing.

§ **230. Throttle cracker** When the engine is cranked, the throttle must be opened slightly, or *cracked,* so that enough air can get past it for starting. This action is accomplished by special linkage between the cranking-motor and the throttle linkage. Operating the cranking motor causes the throttle to be opened slightly.

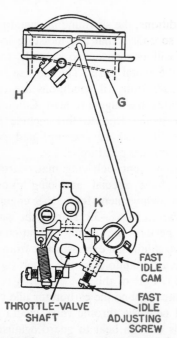

Fig. 8–33. Linkage between choke valve G, fast-idle cam, and throttle. When the fast-idle cam is in position shown, fast-idle adjusting screw does not allow throttle to close completely. *H,* adjusting screw; *K,* cam tang. *(Buick Motor Division of General Motors Corporation)*

§ **231. Fast idle** When the engine is cold, some throttle opening must be maintained so that the engine will idle faster than it would when warm. Otherwise, the slow idle with the engine cold might cause the engine to stall. With fast idle, enough air-fuel mixture gets through, and air speeds are great enough, to produce adequate vaporization and a sufficiently rich mixture. Fast idle is obtained by a fast-idle cam which is linked to the choke valve (Fig. 8–33). When the engine is cold, the automatic choke holds the choke valve closed. In this position, the linkage has revolved the fast-idle cam so that the adjusting screw rests on the high point of the cam. The adjusting screw therefore prevents the throttle valve from moving to the "fully closed" position. The throttle valve is held partly open for fast idle. As the engine warms up, the choke valve opens. This rotates the fast-idle cam so that the high point moves from under the adjusting screw. The throttle valve closes for normal hot-engine slow idle.

§ **232. Air bleed** In the high-speed circuits of various carburetors, small openings are incorporated to permit air to enter, or *bleed* into, the circuit. This action produces some premixing of the air and fuel so that better atomization and vaporization are attained. The action also helps to maintain a more uniform air-fuel ratio. At higher speeds, a proportionately larger amount of fuel tends to discharge from the main nozzle. But at the same time the faster fuel movement through the high-speed circuit causes more air to bleed into the circuit. Thus, the air-bleed

holes tend to equalize the ratio for different operating conditions.

§ 233. Antipercolator Under certain conditions, heat build-up in the engine will tend to cause the fuel in the carburetor to boil. One such condition that might cause this is idling after a hard run. If the fuel boils, the vapor pressure in the float bowl might cause fuel to be forced out of the main nozzle (somewhat in the manner that a coffee percolator works). To prevent this, carburetors include an antipercolating device. One type has a small valve that is so hinged as to be opened when the throttle is closed. Opening the valve releases any vapor pressure that might build up in the main circuit. Another type uses a tube connected from the high-speed circuit to the upper part of the air horn. This tube releases vapor pressure into the air horn to prevent percolation of the fuel.

§ 234. Special carburetor devices Other special devices in carburetors include:

1. Vacuum circuits to control the ignition-distributor spark advance (see § 192).
2. Electric switches to operate starting-motor controls (§ 175).
3. Throttle-return checks and magnetically controlled dashpots to retard throttle closing (on cars with automatic transmissions).
4. Electric kick-down switches (on some cars equipped with automatic transmissions).
5. Governors to control or limit top engine speed.

Figure 8–34 shows a throttle-return check on a carburetor. The throt-

tle-return check contains a spring-loaded diaphragm which traps air behind it when the throttle is opened. Then, when the throttle is released, the return check slows the throttle movement so that it closes slowly. This guards against sudden throttle closing that might cause the engine to stall. The electric kick-down switch, used on some cars with automatic transmissions, provides an electrical means of downshifting the transmission into a lower gear when the throttle is opened wide (under certain conditions). Use of governors is largely confined to heavy-duty vehicles; they prevent overspeeding and rapid wear of the engine. In one type, control is directly on the throttle valve; it tends to close the valve as rated speed is reached. Another type interposes a throttle plate between the carburetor throttle valve

Fig 8–34. Throttle-return check on carburetor. (Chevrolet Motor Division of General Motors Corporation)

and the intake manifold. The throttle plate moves toward the "closed" position as rated speed is reached to prevent delivery of additional amounts of air-fuel mixture and any further increase in engine speed.

§ 235. Dual carburetors As already noted, the dual carburetor is essentially two single-barrel carburetors in a single assembly (Fig. 8–18). Each barrel handles air-fuel requirements of half the engine cylinders. For example, the lower part of Fig. 6–14 shows the air-fuel delivery pattern in a V-8 engine. One carburetor barrel supplies cylinders 3, 4, 5, and 6. The other barrel supplies cylinders 1, 2, 7, and 8. The arrows indicate the pattern in Fig. 6–14. Each barrel has a complete set of circuits; the throttle valves are fastened to a single throttle shaft, and so both open and close together.

§ 236. Four-barrel carburetor The four-barrel carburetor (Figs. 8–19 and 8–35) consists essentially of two dual carburetors combined into a single assembly. The carburetor has four barrels and four main nozzles and thus is sometimes called a *quadrijet carburetor*. One pair of barrels makes up the primary side, the other pair the secondary side (Fig. 8–35). Under most operating conditions, the primary side alone takes care of engine requirements. However, when the throttle is moved toward the "wide-open" position for acceleration or full-power operation, the secondary side comes into operation. It supplies additional amounts of air-fuel mixture. Thus, the

engine receives more air-fuel mixture, volumetric efficiency (§ 84) is higher, and the engine produces greater horsepower.

§ 237. Diesel-engine and LPG fuel systems These are two special fuel systems designed to handle the special types of fuel the engines require.

1. Diesel-engine fuel system. In the diesel engine, air alone is compressed. Then, at the end of the compression stroke, the fuel system injects fuel oil (§ 101). A typical diesel-engine fuel system is shown in Fig. 8–36. The fuel pump delivers fuel oil at a comparatively low pressure to the injector (there is an injector in each cylinder). The injector (Fig. 8–37) contains a plunger that is operated and forced downward by a rocker arm. The rocker arm is actuated by a push rod and cam on the camshaft (the arrangement is much like the overhead-valve train). When the plunger is forced down, oil is forced from the spray tip at high pressure; it sprays into the compressed air in the cylinder and ignites from the heat of compression (§ 101). Power output from the engine is changed by altering the effective length of the plunger stroke. If the effective length is short, then only a small amount of fuel will be sprayed into the cylinder and the engine will produce relatively little power and run slowly. But as the effective length of the plunger stroke is increased, more oil is injected and power output also increases.

2. LPG fuel system. Liquefield petroleum gas (LPG) is a fuel that is liquid only under pressure (see Chap.

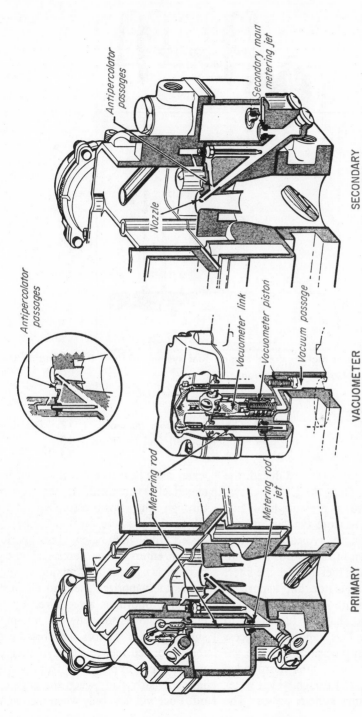

Antipercolator passages

Secondary main metering jet

Nozzle

SECONDARY

Antipercolator passages

Vacuometer link

Vacuometer piston

Vacuum passage

Metering rod

Metering rod jet

PRIMARY   VACUOMETER

Fig. 8–35. High-speed circuit of four-barrel carburetor. The primary and secondary sides of the carburetor are shown separated although they are actually assembled side by side. The view in the center shows in detail the construction of the vacuometer full-power circuit. (Oldsmobile Division of General Motors Corporation)

221

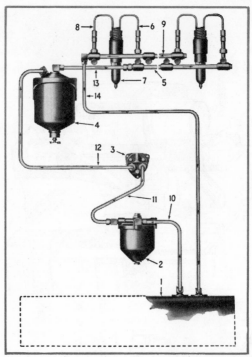

Fig. 8–36. General Motors diesel-engine fuel system. *(Detroit Diesel Engine Division of General Motors Corporation)*

1. Fuel tank	6. Inlet tube to injector	10. ⎫
2. Primary filter	7. Injector	11. ⎪
3. Fuel pump	8. Outlet tube from injector	12. ⎬ Fuel lines
4. Secondary filter	9. Upper (outlet) fuel manifold	13. ⎪
5. Lower (inlet) fuel manifold		14. ⎭

9). When the pressure is reduced, the fuel vaporizes. Thus, the LPG fuel system must have a pressure-tight fuel tank in which to store the fuel at adequate pressures. A typical LPG fuel system is shown in Fig. 8–38. Pressure in the tank forces fuel through the filter, high-pressure regulator, and vaporizer. The high-pressure regulator reduces the pressure so that the fuel starts to turn to vapor. This vaporizing process is completed in the vaporizer. The vaporizer has an inner tank surrounded by a water jacket through which water from the cooling system passes. The water adds heat to the fuel so that it is effectively vaporized. It then passes through the low-pressure regulator, where the pressure on it is further reduced (to slightly below atmospheric). It then enters the carburetor. The carburetor is essentially a mixing valve; it mixes the vaporized fuel and air in the proper proportions as required by the engine. The reason why the low-pressure regulator reduces the pressure on the vaporized fuel to slightly *below* atmospheric is to prevent it from flowing into the carburetor when the engine is off. Fuel will flow only when the engine

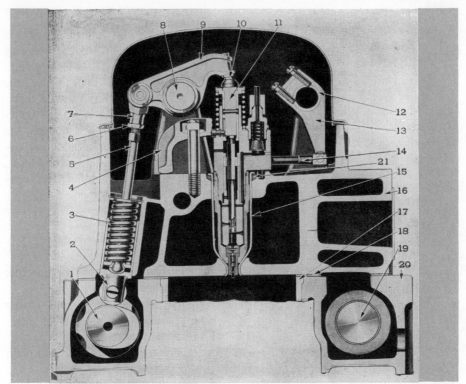

Fig. 8–37. Mounting of fuel injector above the engine cylinder. (Detroit Diesel
Engine Division of General Motors Corporation)

1. Camshaft
2. Cam follower
3. Following spring
4. Injector clamp
5. Push rod
6. Lock nut
7. Clevis

8. Rocker-arm shaft
9. Injector rocker arm
10. Ball stud and seat
11. Injector assembly
12. Control tube
13. Rack-control lever
14. Injector control rack

15. Copper tube
16. Cylinder head
17. Cylinder liner
18. Cylinder-head gasket
19. Balancer shaft
20. Cylinder block
21. Copper-tube sealing ring

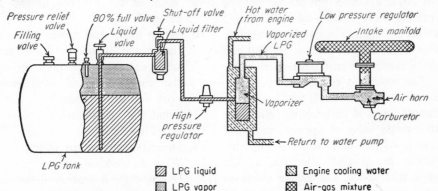

Fig. 8–38. Fuel system for LPG fuel system shown schematically.

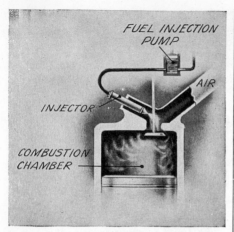

Fig. 8–39. Simplified schematic drawing of a gasoline fuel-injection system.

is running and there is a vacuum in the carburetor venturi (or air horn).

§ 238. Gasoline fuel-injection systems
The gasoline fuel-injection system, used on a number of engines, eliminates the carburetor. In place of the carburetor, a fuel-injection pump and an injector are used (Fig. 8–39). This system works much like the diesel-engine fuel system (Figs. 8–36 and 8–37); that is, there is a fuel-injection pump that delivers liquid gasoline to the injectors. The injectors then spray the liquid gasoline into the air streams entering the cylinders when the intake valves are open. The gasoline is rapidly vaporized in this process so that the air-fuel mixture can burn efficiently.

The system is controlled by an air-throttle valve which is similar to the throttle valve in carburetors. When the air-throttle valve is opened, more air enters. At the same time, the fuel-injection pump and injectors provide more fuel. Thus, the engine develops more power and increases in speed. In

some systems, the air-throttle valve is linked mechanically to a metering valve in the fuel-injection system. This mechanical linkage then varies the amount of fuel delivered as the throttle position and amount of air delivered are varied. In other systems, the variation of the amount of fuel delivered is determined on a speed basis, through mechanical or electric controls.

REVIEW QUESTIONS

1. What is the purpose of the fuel system?
2. What are the components of the fuel system?
3. Describe a fuel tank.
4. Is the fuel tank airtight? Explain the reason for your answer.
5. How does the balancing-coil type of fuel gauge work?
6. How does the the bimetal-thermostat type of fuel gauge work?
7. What is the purpose of the fuel pump? Describe briefly how the fuel pump operates.
8. What is a combination fuel pump? Why is this type of pump used?
9. What is the purpose of the air cleaner?
10. When the piston moves down on the intake stroke in the engine, what causes air to pass through the carburetor and intake-valve port into the cylinder?
11. What is evaporation?
12. What is volatility?
13. Describe the venturi effect.
14. What is atomization?
15. Describe the operation of the carburetor float system.

16. Describe the operation of the carburetor idling- and low-speed circuits.

17. Describe the operation of the carburetor high-speed part-load circuit.

18. Describe the operation of the carburetor high-speed full-power circuit that is mechanically operated. Vacuum-operated. Operated by combined vacuum and mechanical action.

19. What is the difference between an updraft and a downdraft carburetor?

20. Why is an accelerator-pump system required in a carburetor?

21. How does the accelerator-pump system operate?

22. What is the purpose of the choke?

23. Explain why an antipercolator device is desirable, and describe how such a device operates.

24. What is the purpose of the air bleed in carburetors?

25. Which fuel system is the more complicated, the one used on a gasoline engine or the one used on a diesel engine?

26. What three jobs must the diesel-engine fuel system perform in delivering the fuel oil to the engine cylinder?

27. Describe the construction and operation of an LPG fuel system.

STUDY QUESTIONS

1. Make a sketch of a gasoline-engine fuel system, naming the units, and write a brief essay describing how the system operates.

2. Make a sketch of the electric circuit of the balancing-coil type of fuel-gauge system.

3. Make a sketch of the electric circuit of the bimetal-thermostat type of fuel-gauge system.

4. One gallon equals 0.134 cubic foot. If a cubic foot of air weighs 0.08 pound and a gallon of gasoline weighs 6.4 pounds, how many gallons of air would be used with 1 gallon of gasoline with a mixture ratio of 15:1 (15 pounds of air for 1 pound of fuel)?

5. Make a sketch of a simple carburetor, showing the float system and the idling circuit.

6. Make a sketch of a simple carburetor, showing the same parts as in the previous question, plus the venturi and high-speed circuit.

7. Write a sequence story describing the action of the automatic choke, starting with "1. Engine is cold; thermostatic spring has wound up and closed the choke valve."

8. Describe what takes place when a liquid is "atomized," and explain why this action helps to evaporate the liquid.

9. Thousands of miles out in space from the earth's surface, there is no atmosphere. Explain why a gasoline engine would not operate at such a distance from the earth without special apparatus. What special apparatus would be required to make it operate?

THIS CHAPTER DISCUSSES THE origin and characteristics of various fuels used in automotive-type engines, including gasoline, LPG (liquefied petroleum gas). and diesel-engine fuel oil.

§ 239. Gasoline Gasoline is a hydrocarbon (made up of hydrogen and carbon compounds). These compounds split into hydrogen and carbon atoms when gasoline burns; these atoms then unite with oxygen atoms (see (§ 52). Gasoline is produced by a complex refining process from crude oil, or petroleum. No one knows exactly how petroleum originated. It is found in "pools," or reservoirs, underground. When a well is drilled down to a reservoir, the underground pressure forces the petroleum up and out of the well. The petroleum must then be put through an intricate process; the resulting products include gasoline, many grades and kinds of lubricating oil and fuel oil. and many other products.

§ 240. Volatility of gasoline Actually, gasoline is not a simple substance. It is a mixture of a number of different hydrocarbons; each has its own characteristics. Aside from its combustibility, one of the important characteristics of gasoline is volatility.

Volatility refers to the ease with which a liquid vaporizes. The volatil-

ity of a simple compound like water or alcohol is determined by increasing its temperature until it boils, or vaporizes. A liquid that vaporizes at a relatively low temperature has a high volatility; it is highly volatile. If its boiling point is high, its volatility is low. A certain heavy oil, with a boiling point of 600°F, has a very low volatility. Water has a relatively high volatility (boils at 212°F at atmospheric pressure).

Gasoline is blended from different hydrocarbon compounds, each having a different volatility or boiling point. The proportions of high-volatility and low-volatility hydrocarbons must be correct for the operating conditions, as noted below.

1. Easy starting. For easy starting with a cold engine, gasoline must be highly volatile so that it will vaporize readily at low temperature. Thus, a percentage of the gasoline must be highly volatile. For the colder Northern states, the percentage must be higher than for the South.

2. Freedom from vapor lock. If the gasoline is too volatile, engine heat will cause it to vaporize in the fuel line and fuel pump. This would prevent normal fuel delivery to the carburetor and would probably produce stalling of the engine. Thus, the percentage of highly volatile gasoline must be kept low to prevent vapor lock.

3. Quick warm-up. The speed with

which the engine warms up depends in part on the percentage of gasoline that will vaporize immediately after the engine starts and thus contribute to engine operation. Volatility for this purpose does not have to be quite so high as for easy starting. But it must be fairly high.

4. Smooth acceleration. When the throttle is opened for acceleration, there is a sudden increase in the amount of air passing through. At the same time, the accelerator pump delivers an extra amount of gasoline. If this gasoline does not vaporize quickly, there will be a momentary interval during which the air-fuel mixture will be too lean. This will cause the engine to hesitate, or stutter. Immediately after, as the gasoline begins to evaporate, the mixture will become temporarily too rich. Here again there will be poor combustion and a tendency for the engine to hesitate. A sufficient proportion of the gasoline must be sufficiently volatile to assure adequate vaporization for smooth acceleration.

5. Good economy. For good economy, or maximum miles per gallon, the fuel must have a high heat content, or energy, and low volatility. High overall volatility tends to reduce economy since it may produce an overrich mixture under many operating conditions. On the other hand, the lower-volatility fuels tend to burn more efficiently (and have a higher heat content). However, the lower-volatility fuels increase starting difficulty, reduce speed of warm-up, and do not give quite as good acceleration. Thus, only a limited percentage of the gasoline can be of low volatility.

6. Freedom from crankcase dilution.

Crankcase dilution results when part of the gasoline enters the engine cylinders in an unvaporized condition. It does not burn but runs down the cylinder walls and enters the oil pan, where it dilutes the oil. This process washes lubricating oil from the cylinder walls (thus increasing wear of walls, rings, and pistons). Also, the diluted oil is less able to provide lubrication for other engine parts such as the bearings. To avoid damage from crankcase dilution, the gasoline must be sufficiently volatile so that little, if any, enters the cylinders in liquid form.

7. The volatility blend. As can be seen from the discussion above, no one volatility would satisfy all engine operating requirements. On the one hand, the fuel must be of high volatility for easy starting and good acceleration. But it must also be of low volatility to give good fuel economy and combat vapor lock. Thus, gasoline must be blended from various amounts of different hydrocarbons having different volatilities. The blend then satisfied the various operating requirements.

§ 241. Antiknock value During normal combustion in the engine cylinder, an even increase of pressure occurs. But if the fuel burns too rapidly, there is a sudden and sharp pressure increase. This may produce a rapping or knocking noise that sounds almost as though the piston head had been struck a hard hammer blow. Actually, the sudden pressure increase does impose a sudden heavy load on the piston that is almost like a hammer blow. This can be very damaging to the engine, wearing moving parts rapidly and perhaps even causing parts to break. Also, some of

the energy in the gasoline is wasted since the sudden pressure increase does not permit best utilization of the fuel energy.

It has been found that some types of gasoline burn very rapidly in engine cylinders and thus knock very badly. Other types burn more slowly and thus have less tendency to knock. Also, certain chemicals have been found to re-

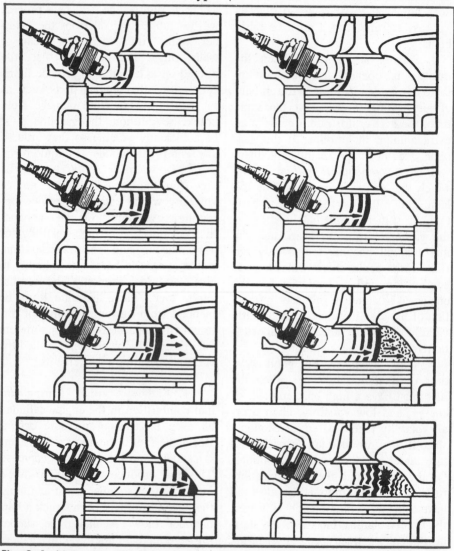

Fig. 9–1. Normal combustion without knocking is shown in the vertical row to the left. The fuel charge burns smoothly from beginning to end, providing an even, powerful thrust to the piston. Knocking is shown in the vertical row to the right. The last part of the fuel explodes, or burns almost instantaneously, to produce detonation, or knocking. (*General Motors Corporation*)

duce knocking tendency when added to the gasoline. The actual rating of the antiknock tendencies of gasolines are given in terms of *octane number*. This term is explained in the following articles.

§ 242. Heat of compression   To understand why knocking occurs, we should remember what happens to air or any other gas when it is compressed. We noted (§101) that the diesel engine compresses air to about one-fifteenth of its original volume and that this increases air temperature to about 1000°F. Article 59 contains an explanation of why this temperature increase occurs (it is due to crowding the air molecules closely together). The temperature rise is called *heat of compression*. Let us see how heat of compression affects knocking.

§ 243. Cause of knocking   During normal burning of fuel in the combustion chamber, the spark at the spark plug starts the burning process. A wall of flame spreads out in all directions from the spark (moving outward almost like a rubber balloon being blown up). The wall of flame travels rapidly outward through the compressed mixture until all the charge is burned. The speed with which the flame travels is called the *rate of flame propagation*. The movement of the flame wall through the combustion chamber during normal combustion is shown in the row of pictures to the left in Fig. 9–1. During combustion, the pressure increases to several hundred psi (pounds per square inch). It may exceed 700 psi in modern high-compression engines.

If the flame travels too rapidly through the mixture (rate of flame propagation is too high), the pressure will increase too rapidly. The effect will be as shown to the right in Fig. 9–1. The rapid increase, the excessive pressure reached causes the last of the charge to detonate, or explode, with hammer-like suddenness. The effect is almost the same as if the piston head had been struck a heavy hammer blow. In fact, it sounds as though this had happened. The sudden shock load due to detonation of the last part of the charge increases wear on bearings and may actually break engine parts if the knocking is severe enough.

Now, let's see why the last of the charge detonates. The rapid pressure increase, the excessive pressures reached raise the temperature of the unburned part of the charge. This is due to heat of compression. The high pressures reached, and the high temperatures resulting from the consequent heat of compression, cause the last of the charge to explode.

To sum up, the knocking process is about as follows: The spark occurs, and combustion starts. But the charge begins to burn too rapidly (rate of flame propagation is too high). Pressures go up excessively, and this produces excessive heat of compression in the remaining unburned charge. Then, before the flame wall can reach this unburned charge, it is set off by the heat of compression.

§ 244. Compression ratio vs. knocking   As compression ratios of engines have gone up (see §§ 81 and 82), so also has the tendency for engines to knock. Here is the reason. With a

229

higher compression ratio, the mixture, at TDC (top dead center), is more highly compressed and *is at a higher initial temperature.* With higher initial pressure and temperature, the temperature at which detonation occurs is sooner reached. Thus, high-compression engines have a greater tendency to knock. However, special fuels have been developed for use with the higher-compression engines, as explained below. These special fuels have a greater resistance to being set off suddenly by heat of compression. They are less apt to explode suddenly, and they depend for their ignition upon the wall of flame traveling through the air-fuel mixture.

§ 245. Measuring antiknock values
There are several methods of measuring the antiknock value of fuels. The rating is made in terms of octane number. A high-octane gasoline is highly resistant to knock. A low-octane fuel knocks rather easily. For example, there is one fuel called iso-octane that is very resistant to knocking; it is given an octane rating of 100. Another fuel, called heptane, knocks very easily; it is given a rating of zero. A mixture of half iso-octane and half heptane (by volume) would have a 50-octane rating. A mixture of 75 percent iso-octane and 25 percent heptane would have a rating of 75 octane.

Actually, iso-octane and heptane are reference fuels, used only to test and rate unknown fuels. The test is made approximately as follows: The fuel to be tested is used in an engine under various conditions and compression ratios and its tolerance to knocking noted. Then the two reference fuels are mixed in varying proportions and

used to run the engine under identical conditions. For example, suppose that a mixture of 68 percent iso-octane and 32 percent heptane is found to produce the same knocking characteristics as the fuel being tested. Then the reference fuel, as well as the fuel being tested, are considered to have the same 68-octane rating. There are two basic methods, laboratory and road.

1. Laboratory method. A special test engine is used which has an adjustable head. With this engine, the compression ratio can be changed. The fuel to be tested is used to operate the engine, and the compression ratio is increased until a certain intensity of knocking is obtained. Then, without changing the compression ratio, the engine is switched to a mixture of iso-octane and heptane. The proportion of iso-octane is decreased until the same intensity of knocking is noted. Now, since the proportion of iso-octane (and thus octane rating) of the reference-fuel mixture is known, the octane rating of the fuel being rated is also known.

2. Road-test methods. Road testing of fuels gives results that are more closely related with actual highway operation. One road test, the Cooperative Fuel Research (CFR) Uniontown road test, rates fuels for knock intensity at wide-open throttle at various speeds. Octane is assigned by comparing knocking of the fuel being tested to reference fuels (iso-octane and heptane) of known octane values.

Another road test, called the *borderline knock test,* rates the fuel at various speeds and is considered to give more information on fuel performance. This test is made by running the car at var-

230

ious speeds and then determining the amount of ignition spark advance the fuel can tolerate at each speed without knocking. If the spark is advanced too much at any particular speed, knocking will occur. Thus, the test results give a curve that shows, at every speed, the knock characteristics of the fuel being tested (Fig. 9–2). Any spark advance above the curve causes knock.

It must be noted, however, that some fuels will knock at high speeds, while others knock at low speeds. For example, refer to Fig. 9–3. This shows the curves of two fuels, *A* and *B*. Curve *C* is the amount of spark advance the distributor provides on the engine used in the test (see § 192 for a discussion of spark-advance mechanisms). If, at any particular speed, the distributor advances the spark more than the fuel can tolerate, the fuel will knock. Thus, at low speed, fuel *A* will knock since the spark advance is more than the fuel can tolerate (that is, curve *C* is above curve *A* at low speed). On the other hand, fuel *A* will not knock at high speed since the spark advance is not up to the amount the fuel can tolerate at high speed. But fuel *B* shows a different picture. It will not knock at low speed but will knock at high speed with the spark-advance curve shown. These curves, which apply only to fuels *A* and *B,* emphasize the fact that different fuels act differently at different speeds and in different engines.

§ 246. Detonation vs. preignition

Thus far, we have discussed the type of knocking that results from detonation, or sudden explosion, of the last part of the fuel charge. This type of knocking is usually regular in character

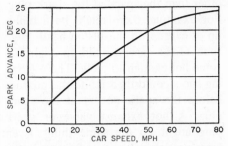

Fig. 9–2. Borderline knock curve. The fuel being tested will knock if the ignition spark is advanced to any value above the curve at any speed.

and is most noticeable when the engine is accelerated or is under heavy load, as when climbing a hill. Under these conditions, the accelerator is nearly or fully wide-open, and the engine is taking in a full air-fuel charge on every intake stroke. This means the compression pressures reached are at the maximum; detonation pressures are more likely to be reached after the mixture is ignited.

There is another type of knocking which has a different cause—preignition. Preignition occurs whenever the air-fuel mixture is ignited by any means

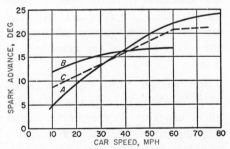

Fig. 9–3. Comparison of borderline knock curves of two fuels, A and B. Curve C is the spark advance actually provided by the ignition distributor on the engine.

231

other than the spark at the spark plug. For example, there might be a build-up of carbon on the piston head. High spots of the carbon build-up might become hot enough to glow. These glowing spots could then ignite the mixture before the spark occurs at the spark plug. A hot exhaust valve or spark plug might do the same thing. Even loose particles of carbon floating in the combustion chamber could cause preignition. The knocking that results from preignition is irregular; it is often called *wild* knocking since it can occur almost any time after the intake valve opens to start admitting the air-fuel charge.

§ **247. Chemical control of knocking**
Several chemicals have been found that, added to gasoline, tend to prevent detonation of the last part of the fuel charge during combustion. One theory regarding this is that the chemical tends to slow down the rate of flame propagation; this prevents the rapid pressure rise and "squeezing" of the last part of the compressed charge. One of the compounds most successful in preventing knocking is tetraethyllead, commonly called *ethyl* or *tel*. A small amount added to gasoline thus raises the octane rating of the gasoline.

§ **248. Factors affecting knocking**
Many mechanical factors in an engine affect knocking. For example, higher air temperatures increase the tendency to knock, higher humidity (or damper air) reduces the tendency to knock, engine deposits (carbon in combustion chamber) increase knock tendency, advancing the spark increases the

tendency to knock, and leaning the mixture increases the tendency to knock.

All these factors point up the need for good maintenance of the modern high-compression engine. Accumulations of scale in the cooling system, which reduces cooling efficiency; clogged fuel lines or nozzles in the carburetor, which lean out the mixture; improper ignition timing; engine deposits—all these increase knocking tendencies of the engine.

§ **249. Harmful chemicals and gum**
In addition to having the proper volatility and antiknock properties, gasoline must have minimum amounts of harmful chemicals and gum-forming substances. For instance, sulfur compounds are sometimes found in gasoline. When present in excessive quantities, they tend to form sulfur acids. These acids are very corrosive and will damage metal parts and bearings. Gum-forming substances, if in excessive quantities, tend to form deposits in the carburetor circuits and intake manifold and on valves, piston rings, and pistons. Gasoline manufacturers must maintain rigid controls in their refineries so as to keep these harmful chemicals to a minimum.

§ **250. Chemistry of combustion** We have already noted (in § 52) that gasoline, in burning, forms water, or H_2O, and carbon dioxide, or CO_2. This occurs *when enough oxygen is present* to take care of all the hydrogen and carbon atoms. However, in the gasoline engine, sufficient amounts of oxygen are not usually present. As a result, the carbon does not usually attain com-

plete combustion. Some atoms of carbon are able to unite with only one atom of oxygen (instead of two). This produces carbon monoxide, or CO. Carbon monoxide is a dangerously poisonous gas. It has no color, is tasteless, and has practically no odor. But 15 parts of carbon monoxide in 10,000 parts of air makes the air dangerous to breathe. Higher concentrations may cause quick paralysis and death. For this reason, an engine should never be operated in a closed space, such as a garage, without some means of exhausting the gas into the outside air. Remember this fact:

Enough carbon monoxide can be produced in 3 minutes by an automobile engine running in a closed one-car garage to cause paralysis and death! *Never operate an engine with the garage doors closed!*

§ 251. Diesel-engine fuels Diesel engines use fuel oil. The fuel oil is sprayed into the compressed air in the combustion chamber at the end of the compression stroke. Heat of compression ignites the fuel oil, and the combustion stroke follows (see § 101). Diesel oil is relatively light, with a rather low viscosity and proper cetane number (see § 253).

§ 252. Diesel-fuel viscosity Viscosity refers to the tendency of a liquid to resist flowing. Water has a low viscosity; it flows easily. A light oil is more viscous than water, but it still flows easily and has a relatively low viscosity. Heavy oil has a high viscosity; it flows slowly. The fuel oil used in diesel engines must have a relatively low viscos-

ity so that it flows easily through the fuel-pumping system. But it must have sufficient viscosity to provide lubrication for the moving parts in the pumping system. However, if the viscosity is too high, the fuel will not spray, or atomize, easily and thus will not burn well.

§ 253. Cetane number of diesel fuel The cetane number of diesel fuel refers to the ease with which the fuel ignites. With a high cetane number, the fuel ignites with relative ease (or at a relatively low temperature). The lower the cetane number, the higher the temperature must go to ignite the fuel. The lower the cetane number, the more likely the fuel is to knock. The fuel being sprayed into the cylinder will not ignite quickly so that it tends to accumulate. Then, when ignition does take place, there will be a combustion knock as the fuel present suddenly burns. On the other hand, if the cetane number is sufficiently high, the fuel will ignite and begin to burn as soon as the injection spray starts. There will thus be an even combustion-pressure rise and no knock.

§ 254. Liquefied petroleum gas (LPG) This fuel requires a special fuel system (§ 237). There are actually two types of LPG that have been used for automotive-engine fuel, *propane* and *butane*. Of these, propane is the more widely used. Sometimes, small amounts of butane are added. Propane boils at −44°F (at atmospheric pressure). Thus, it can be used in any climate where temperatures below this are not reached. Butane cannot

be used in any place where temperatures below 32°F are reached since it is liquid below that temperature. If it remained liquid, it would not vaporize in the fuel system and would thus never reach the engine.

REVIEW QUESTIONS

1. What does the term "hydrocarbon" mean?
2. Define volatility.
3. What is meant by volatility blend?
4. Define heat of compression.
5. Explain what causes knocking in an engine cylinder.
6. Explain how the antiknock values of gasolines are determined.
7. What is the difference between detonation and preignition?
8. What is "wild" knocking?

9. What factors affect knocking in an engine cylinder?
10. Can you tell by the odor whether or not carbon monoxide is present in a room? Is there any danger in breathing carbon monoxide? Why?
11. What does cetane number in diesel fuel mean?

STUDY QUESTIONS

1. Write an essay on the volatility blend in gasoline, explaining why the blend must be made from fuels of different volatilities.
2. Describe in detail the actions that produce knocking in the engine cylinder.
3. Describe the different tests used to octane-rate gasolines.

ORGANIZING YOUR NOTEBOOK

When you write something down in your notebook, you "write it down in your brain," too. This means you can remember it more easily. But if it does become hazy in your mind, you can always refresh your memory by looking it up in your notebook.

The better you keep your notebook, the easier it will be to find the facts you have written down. For example, you can organize your notebook into sections (engines, electric systems, steering, and so on) or even keep separate notebooks on each topic. With a loose-leaf notebook, you can remove old pages and insert new ones. You can rearrange the pages to suit yourself. If you get a page dirty, you can redo it and throw the dirty page away.

As you develop your notebook, you will find that it becomes increasingly valuable as a storehouse of information. If it is properly organized, you will refer again and again to the material you have compiled in it. You will be proud of your notebook.

THIS CHAPTER DESCRIBES VARIOUS types of engine lubricating systems and discusses the operation of their component parts. In addition, the purpose and properties of lubricating oil are described. We have already discussed friction (§ 78), engine bearings (§§ 116–121), and the action of the piston rings in controlling oil on the cylinder walls (§§ 124–128). If the facts outlined in these sections are not clear in your mind, we suggest that you reread them. They are closely related to the material (on lubricating systems) contained in the following pages.

§ 255. Purpose of lubricating system

We normally think of lubricating oil as a substance that makes possible minimum wear or low frictional loss between adjacent moving surfaces. However, the lubricating oil circulating through the engine to all moving parts requiring lubrication performs other jobs. The lubricating oil must:

1. Lubricate moving parts to minimize wear.
2. Lubricate moving parts to minimize power loss from friction.
3. Remove heat from engine parts by acting as a cooling agent.
4. Absorb shocks between bearings and other engine parts, thus reducing engine noise and extending engine life.
5. Form a good seal between piston rings and cylinder walls.
6. Act as a cleaning agent.

1 and 2. Minimizing wear and power loss from friction. Friction has been discussed in some detail (§ 78). The type of friction encountered in the engine is normally viscous friction, that is, the friction between adjacent moving layers of oil. If the lubricating system does not function properly, sufficient oil will not be supplied to moving parts and greasy or even dry friction will result between moving surfaces. This would cause, at the least, considerable power loss, since power would be used in overcoming these types of friction. At the worst, major damage would occur to engine parts as greasy or dry friction developed. Bearings would wear with extreme rapidity; the heat resulting from dry or greasy friction would cause bearing disintegration and failure, so that connecting rods and other parts would be broken. Insufficient lubrication of cylinder walls would cause rapid wear and scoring of walls, rings, and pistons. A properly operating engine lubricating system

supplies all moving parts with sufficient oil so that only viscous friction is obtained.

3. Removing heat from engine parts. The engine oil is in rapid circulation throughout the engine lubrication system. All bearings and moving parts are bathed in streams of oil. In addition to providing lubrication, the oil absorbs heat from engine parts and carries it back into the oil pan. The oil pan in turn absorbs heat from the oil, transferring it to the surrounding air. The oil thus acts as a cooling agent.

4. Absorbing shocks between bearings and other engine parts. As the piston approaches the end of the compression stroke and the mixture in the cylinder is ignited, pressure in the cylinder suddenly increases many times. A load of as much as 2½ tons is suddenly imposed on the top of a 3-inch piston as combustion takes place. This sudden increase in pressure causes the piston to thrust down hard through the piston-pin bearing, connecting rod, and connecting-rod bearing. There is always some space or clearance between bearings and journals; this space is filled with oil. When the load suddenly increases as described above, the layers of oil between bearings and journals must act as cushions, resisting penetration or "squeezing out," and must continue to interpose a film of oil between the adjacent metal surfaces. In thus absorbing and cushioning the hammerlike effect of the suddenly imposed loads, the oil quiets the engine and reduces wear of parts.

5. Forming a seal between piston rings and cylinder walls. Piston rings must form a gastight seal with the cylinder walls, and the lubricating oil that is delivered to the cylinder walls helps the piston rings to accomplish this. The oil film on the cylinder walls compensates for microscopic irregularities in the fit between the rings and walls and fills in any gaps through which gas might escape. The oil film also provides lubrication of the rings, so that they can move easily in the piston-ring grooves and on the cylinder walls.

6. Acting as a cleaning agent. The oil, as it circulates through the engine, tends to wash off and carry away dirt, particles of carbon, and other foreign matter. As the oil picks up this material, it carries it back to the crankcase. There, larger particles drop to the bottom of the oil pan. Many of the smaller particles are removed from the oil by oil-filter action.

§ 256. Properties of oil A satisfactory engine lubricating oil must have certain characteristics. It must have proper (1) body and fluidity, or viscosity; (2) resistance to carbon formation; and (3) resistance to oxidation.

1. Viscosity (body and fluidity). Primarily, viscosity is the most important characteristic of lubricating oil. Viscosity refers to the tendency of oil to resist flowing. In a bearing and journal, layers of oil adhere to the bearing and journal surfaces. These layers must move, or slip, with respect to each other, and the viscosity of the oil determines the ease with which this slipping can take place. Viscosity may be divided for discussion into two parts, body and fluidity. Body has to do with the resistance to oil-film puncture, or penetration, during the application of heavy loads. When the power stroke

236

begins, for example, bearing loads sharply increase. Oil body prevents the load from squeezing out the film of oil between the journal and the bearing. This property cushions shock loads, helps maintain a good seal between piston rings and cylinder walls, and maintains an adequate oil film on all bearing surfaces under load.

Fluidity has to do with the ease with which the oil flows through oil lines and spreads over bearing surfaces. In some respects, fluidity and body are opposing characteristics, since the more fluid an oil is, the less body it has. The oil used in any particular engine must have sufficient body to perform as explained in the previous paragraph and yet must have sufficient fluidity to flow freely through all oil lines and spread effectively over all bearing surfaces. Late types of engines have more closely fitted bearings with smaller clearances and consequently require oils of greater fluidity that will flow readily into the spaces between bearings and journals. Such engines use oils of lower viscosity.

Temperature influences viscosity. Increasing temperature reduces viscosity. That is, it causes oil to lose body and gain fluidity. Decreasing temperature causes oil viscosity to increase. The oil gains body and loses fluidity. Since engine temperatures range several hundred degrees from cold-weather starting to operating temperature, a lubricating oil must have adequate fluidity at low temperatures so that it will flow. At the same time, it must have sufficient body for high-temperature operation.

2. *Viscosity ratings.* Viscosity of oil is determined by use of a viscosimeter, a device that determines the length of time required for a definite amount of oil to flow through an opening of a definite diameter. Temperature is taken into consideration during this test, since high temperature decreases viscosity, while low temperature increases viscosity. In referring to viscosity, the lower numbers refer to oils of lower viscosity. SAE 10 oil is less viscous (thinner) than SAE 20 oil, for example.

3. *Resistance to carbon formation.* Cylinder walls, pistons, and rings operate at temperatures of several hundred degrees. This temperature acting on the oil films covering walls, rings, and pistons tends to cause the oil to break down or burn so that carbon is produced. Carbon formation can cause poor engine performance and damage to the engine. Carbon may pack in around the piston rings, causing them to stick in the ring grooves. This prevents proper piston-ring operation, so that blow-by, poor compression, excessive oil consumption, and scoring of cylinder walls may result. Carbon may build up on the piston head and in the cylinder head. This fouls spark plugs, excessively increases compression so that knocking occurs, and reduces engine performance. Carbon may form on the underside of the piston to such an extent that heat transfer will be hindered and the piston will overheat. Pieces of carbon may break off and drop into the oil pan, where they may be picked up by the lubrication system. They could then clog oil channels and lines so that the flow of lubricating oil to engine parts would be dangerously reduced. A good lubricating oil must be sufficiently resistant to the heat and

237

operating conditions in the engine to exhibit a minimum amount of carbon formation.

4. Resistance to oxidation. When oil is heated to fairly high temperatures and then agitated so that considerable air is mixed with it, the oxygen in the air tends to combine with oil, oxidizing it. Since this is the treatment that engine oil undergoes (that is, it is heated and agitated with or sprayed into the air in the crankcase), some oil oxidation is bound to occur. A slight amount of oxidation will do no particular harm; but if oxidation becomes excessive, serious troubles may occur in the engine. As the oil is oxidized, it breaks down to form various harmful substances. Some of the products of oil oxidation will coat engine parts with an extremely sticky, tarlike material. This material may clog oil channels and tend to restrict the action of piston rings and valves. A somewhat different form of oil oxidation coats engine parts with a varnishlike substance that has a similar damaging effect on the engine. Even if these substances do not form, oil oxidation may produce corrosive materials in the oil that will corrode bearings and other surfaces, causing bearing failures and damage to other parts. Oil chemists and refineries control the refining processes and may add certain chemicals known as *oxidation inhibitors* so that engine lubricating oils resist oxidation. (Any substance added to the oil is known as an *additive*.)

5. Foaming resistance. The churning action in the engine crankcase also tends to cause the engine oil to foam, just as an egg beater causes an egg white to form a frothy foam. As the oil foams up, it tends to overflow or to be lost through the crankcase ventilator (§ 266). In addition, the foaming oil is not able to provide normal lubrication of bearings and other moving parts. To prevent foaming, antifoaming additives are mixed with the oil.

6. Detergents. Despite the filters and screens at the carburetor and crankcase ventilator (§ 266), dirt does get into the engine. In addition, as the engine runs, the combustion processes leave deposits of carbon on piston rings, valves, and other parts. Also, some oil oxidation may take place, resulting in still other deposits. As a result of these various conditions, deposits tend to build up on and in engine parts. The deposits gradually reduce the performance of the engine and speed up wear of parts. To prevent or slow down the formation of these deposits, some engine oils contain a detergent additive.

The detergent acts much like ordinary hand soap. When you wash your hands with soap, the soap surrounds the particles of dirt on your hands, causing them to become detached so that the water can rinse them away. In a similar manner, the detergent in the oil loosens and detaches the deposits of carbon, gum, and dirt. The oil then carries the loosened material away. The larger particles drop to the bottom of the crankcase, but smaller particles tend to remain suspended in the oil. These impurities, or contaminants, are flushed out when the oil is changed.

7. Viscosity index. When oil is cold, it is thicker and runs more slowly than when it is hot. In other words, it becomes more viscous when it is cooled. On the other hand, it becomes less viscous when it is heated. In normal

238

automotive-engine operation, we do not have to be too concerned about this change of oil viscosity with changing temperature. We recognize that the engine is harder to start at low temperature because the oil is thicker, or more viscous. But until the engine is cooled to many degrees below zero, we do not have to take any special steps to start it.

Some oils change viscosity a great deal with temperature change. Other oils show a much smaller change of viscosity with temperature change. In order to have an accurate measure of how much any particular oil will change in viscosity with temperature change, the viscosity-index scale was adopted. Originally, the scale ran from 0 to 100. The higher the number, the less the oil viscosity changes with temperature changes. Thus, an oil with a VI (viscosity index) of 100 will change less in viscosity with temperature changes than an oil with a VI of 10. In recent years, special VI-improving additives have been developed which step up viscosity indexes to as much as 300. Such an oil shows relatively little change in viscosity from very low to relatively high temperature.

You could especially appreciate the significance of VI if you were operating automotive equipment in a very cold climate (say, in northern Alaska). You would have to start engines at temperatures of as much as 60° below zero (92° below freezing). But, once started, the engines would soon reach operating temperatures that heat the oil to several hundred degrees. If you could select an oil of a relatively high VI, then it would be fluid enough to permit starting but would not thin out (or lose viscosity) so much that lubricating effectiveness would be lost. On the other hand, an oil with a low VI would probably be so thick at low temperatures that it might actually prevent starting. But if you could start, it might then thin out too much as it warmed up.

Actually, VI is of relatively little importance in most parts of the country. Oil companies make sure that their oils have a sufficiently high VI to operate satisfactorily in the variations of temperatures they will meet.

§ 257. Water-sludge formation Water sludge is a thick, creamy, black substance that often forms in the crankcase. It clogs oil screens and oil lines, preventing normal circulation of lubricating oil to engine parts. This can result in engine failure from oil starvation.

1. How sludge forms. Water collects in the crankcase in two ways. First, water is formed as a product of combustion (§ 52). Second, the crankcase ventilating system (described in § 266) carries air, with moisture in it, through the crankcase. If the engine parts are cold, the water condenses and drops into the crankcase. There, it is churned up with the lubricating oil by the action of the crankshaft. The crankshaft acts much like a giant egg beater and whips the oil and water into the thick, black, mayonnaiselike "goo" known as water sludge. The black color comes from dirt and carbon.

2. Why sludge forms. If a car is driven for long distances each time it is started, the water that collects in the crankcase while the engine is cold quickly evaporates. The crankcase ven-

tilating system then removes the water vapor. Thus, no sludge will form. However, if the engine is operated when cold most of the time, then sludge will form. For example, the home-to-shop-to-home sort of driving, each trip being only a few miles, is sludge-forming. When a car is used for short-trip start-and-stop driving, the engine never has a chance to warm up enough to get rid of the water. The water accumulates and forms sludge.

3. Preventing sludge. To prevent sludge, the car must be driven long enough, when started, for the engine to heat up and get rid of the water in the crankcase. If this is impractical, then the oil must be changed frequently. Naturally, during cold weather, it takes longer for the engine to warm up. Thus, in cold weather, the trips must be still longer, or oil must be changed still more frequently, to prevent water accumulation and sludge formation.

§ 258. Service ratings of oil We have already mentioned that lubricating oil is rated as to its viscosity by number. An SAE 10 oil is less viscous (lighter) than an SAE 20 oil. An SAE 30 oil has a comparatively high viscosity. Lubricating oil is also rated in another way, by what is called *service* designation. That is, it is rated according to the type of service for which it is best suited. There are five service ratings: MS, MM, and ML for gasoline or other spark-ignition engines, and DG and DS for diesel engines. The oils differ in their characteristics and in the additives they contain.

1. MS oil. This oil is for severe service and unfavorable operating con-

ditions. It is to be used where there are special lubricating requirements for bearing-corrosion and engine-deposit control because of operating conditions or engine design. This includes:

a. Low operating temperature and short-trip start-stop driving conditions, as found in city operation.

b. High-speed highway driving, where oil will become unusually hot, as during a summer-vacation trip.

c. Heavy-load operation, such as is typical of highway truck service.

2. MM oil. This oil is for medium service such as:

a. High-speed but fairly short trips.

b. Long trips at moderate speeds and summer temperatures.

c. Operation at moderate cold-air temperatures where the car is used for both long and short trips.

3. ML oil. This oil is for comparatively light service where most of the trips are longer than. 10 miles and where no extremes of air temperature are encountered.

▶ *CAUTION:* Do not confuse *viscosity* and *service* ratings of oil. Some people think that a high-viscosity oil is a "heavy-duty" oil. This is not necessarily so. Viscosity ratings refer to the thickness of the oil; thickness is not a measure of heavy-duty quality. Remember that there are two ratings, viscosity and service. Thus, an SAE 10 oil can be an MS, MM, or ML oil. Likewise, an oil of any other viscosity rating can have any one of the three service ratings (MS, MM, or ML).

4. DS oil. This is an oil for lubricating diesel engines operating under the most severe service conditions such as:

a. Continuous low temperatures and light loads.

b. Continuous high-temperature and heavy-load conditions.

c. Operation on fuels of high sulfur content or abnormal volatility.

5. *DG oil.* This is an oil for lubricating diesel engines operating under comparatively light to normal conditions such as are typical of most trucking and farm-tractor operations.

§ 259. **Oil changes** From the day that fresh oil is put into the engine crankcase, it begins to lose its effectiveness as an engine lubricant. This gradual loss of effectiveness is largely due to the accumulation of various contaminating substances. For instance, water sludge may accumulate, as already noted (§ 257). In addition, during engine operation, carbon tends to form in the combustion chamber. Some of this carbon gets into the oil. Gum, acids, and certain lacquerlike substances may also be left by the combustion of the fuel or may be produced in the oil itself by the high engine temperatures. In addition, the air that enters the engine (in the air-fuel mixture) carries with it a certain amount of dust. Even though the air filter is operating efficiently, it will not remove all the dust. Then, too, the engine releases fine metal particles as it wears. All these substances tend to circulate with the oil. As the mileage piles up, the oil accumulates more and more of these contaminants. Even though the engine has an oil filter, some of these contaminants will remain in the oil. Finally, after so many miles of operation, the oil will be so loaded with contaminants that it is not safe to use. Unless it is drained and clean oil put in, engine wear will increase rapidly.

Modern engine oils are compounded to fight contamination. They contain certain chemicals (called *additives*) which deter corrosion and foaming and help to keep the engine clean by detergent action. Yet they cannot keep the oil in good condition indefinitely. As mentioned in the previous paragraph, after so many miles of service, the oil is bound to become contaminated, and it should be changed. The actual mileage varies with the type of operation. For dusty or cold-weather start-and-stop driving, the oil should be changed every 500 miles or 60 days. For "average" operation, that is, short-run start-and-stop service on paved roads with moderate temperatures, mixed with longer trips, the oil should be changed every 1,000 miles. For open-highway driving on paved roads, oil should be changed every 2,000 miles.

NOTE: Automobile manufacturers recommend that the oil be changed (along with the oil filter) and the air filter cleaned whenever the car has been subjected to a spell of dusty driving or has encountered a dust storm. When dusty conditions are encountered in driving, the air and oil filters are likely to become clogged with dust rather quickly. This means that the oil takes on an excessive amount of dust. This dust must be removed from the engine by draining the oil, cleaning the air filters, and replacing the oil filter.

§ 260. **Oil consumption** Oil is lost from the engine in three ways: by burn-

241

ing in the combustion chamber, by leakage in liquid form, and by passing out of the crankcase in the form of a mist. Two main factors affect oil consumption, *engine speed* and *the amount that engine parts have worn.* High speed produces high temperature. This, in turn, lowers the viscosity of the oil so that it can more readily work past the piston rings into the combustion chamber, where it is burned. In addition, the high speed exerts a centrifugal effect on the oil that is feeding through the oil lines drilled in the crankshaft to the connecting-rod journals. Thus, more oil is fed to the bearings and subsequently thrown on the cylinder walls. Also, high speed tends to cause "ring shimmy." With this condition, the oil-control rings cannot function quite so effectively and will allow more oil to get into the combustion chamber. Then, too, crankcase ventilation (§ 266) causes more air to pass through the crankcase at high speed. This increases the tendency for oil to be lost in the form of mist.

As engine parts wear, oil consumption increases. Worn bearings tend to throw more oil onto the cylinder walls. Tapered and worn cylinder walls prevent normal oil-control-ring action. The rings cannot change shape rapidly enough to conform with the worn cylinder walls as they move up and down. More oil consequently gets into the combustion chamber, where it burns and fouls spark plugs, valves, rings, and pistons. Carbon formation aggravates the condition, since it further reduces the effectiveness of the oil-control rings. Where cylinder-wall wear is not excessive, installation of special oil-control rings reduces oil consumption

by improving the wiping action so that less oil can move past the rings. After cylinder-wall wear has progressed beyond a certain point, the cylinders must be machined and new rings installed to bring oil consumption down.

Another cause of excessive oil consumption is a cracked vacuum-pump diaphragm which passes oil into the intake manifold and from there into the engine cylinders, where it is burned (see § 300).

§ 261. Types of lubricating systems
Three types of lubricating systems have been used. These are (1) splash, (2) pressure-feed, and (3) combination splash and pressure-feed. The latter two types predominate in modern engines.

1. Splash. In the splash lubricating system, dippers on the connecting-rod bearing caps enter oil trays in the oil pan with each crankshaft revolution (Fig. 10–1). The dippers pick up oil for the connecting-rod bearings and splash oil to the upper parts of the engine. The oil is thrown up as droplets and fine mist and provides adequate lubrication to valve mechanisms, piston pins, cylinder walls, and piston rings. In the engine shown in Fig. 10–1, an oil pump is used to deliver oil to the trays beneath the connecting rods.

2. Pressure-feed. In the pressure-feed lubricating system (Figs. 10–2 and 10–3), the oil is forced by an oil pump to the various parts of the engine requiring lubrication. The oil from the pump enters an oil line (or a drilled header, or channel, or gallery, as it is variously called). From the oil

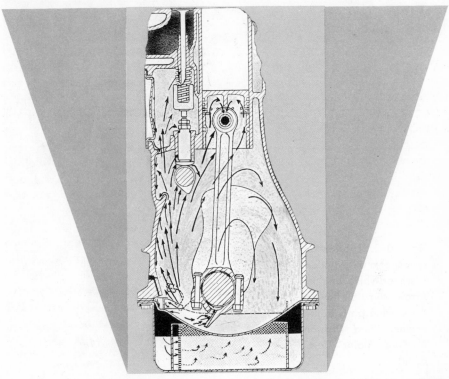

Fig. 10–1. Splash lubricating system used on an in-line engine. An oil pump maintains the proper level of oil in the tray under the connecting rods.

line, it flows to the main bearings and camshaft bearings. The main bearings have oil-feed holes or grooves that feed oil into drilled passages in the crankshaft. The oil flows through these passages to the connecting-rod bearings. From there, on many engines, it flows through holes drilled in the connecting rods to the piston-pin bearings. Cylinder walls are lubricated by oil thrown off from the connecting-rod and piston-pin bearings. Some engines have oil-spit holes in the connecting rods that index with drilled holes in the crankpin journals with each revolution. As this happens, a stream of oil is thrown onto the cylinder walls. On many overhead-valve engines, the rocker arms and other valve-mechanism parts are lubricated by an oil line that feeds into the hollow rocker-arm shaft. On overhead-valve engines that have independently mounted rocker arms (Fig. 6–58), the mounting studs are hollow and feed oil from an oil gallery in the head to the rocker-arm ball pivot. Also, the push rod is hollow and feeds oil from the valve lifter to the contact area between the push rod and the rocker arm. Sufficient oil is thus fed to the valve mechanisms to assure adequate lubrication.

3. *Combination splash and pressure-feed system.* The combination splash and pressure-feed lubricating system depends on oil splash to lubricate some

243

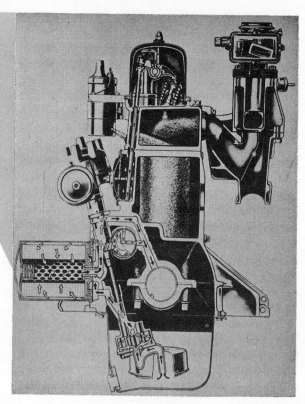

Fig. 10–2. Lubrication system of a six-cylinder, overhead-valve engine. Arrows show oil flow to the moving parts in the engine. (Ford Division of Ford Motor Company)

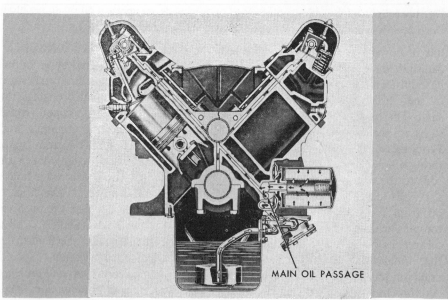

MAIN OIL PASSAGE

Fig. 10–3. Lubrication system of a V-8, overhead-valve engine. Arrows show oil flow to moving parts in engine. (Mercury Division of Ford Motor Company)

244

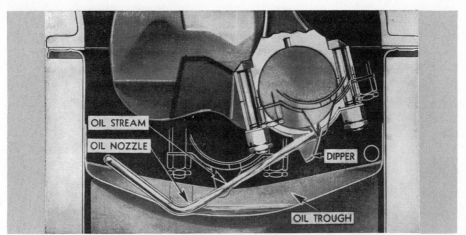

Fig. 10–4. Oil streams from the oil nozzles in the oil pan strike dippers on the connecting rods for rod-bearing lubrication. *(Chevrolet Motor Division of General Motors Corporation)*

engine parts and on pressure feed to lubricate other engine parts. In this engine, the oil is supplied under pressure to the main bearings, the camshaft bearings, and the valve mechanisms. The connecting-rod bearings are lubricated by means of dippers on the rod-bearing caps that dip into troughs in the oil pan. At high speed, oil streams are thrown up from the oil troughs through oil nozzles (Fig. 10–4), and these strike the dippers on the rod-bearing caps to provide adequate lubrication for the connecting-rod bearings. Cylinder walls, piston-pin bearings, and piston rings are lubricated by oil spray thrown off by the connecting rods.

§ 262. Oil pumps The two general types of oil pumps used in pressure-feed lubricating systems are shown in Figs. 10–5 to 10–7. The gear-type pump uses a pair of meshing gears. As the gears rotate, the spaces between the gear teeth are filled with oil from the oil inlet. Then, as the teeth mesh, the oil is forced out through the oil outlet. The rotor-type pump uses an inner rotor and an outer rotor. The inner rotor is driven and causes the outer rotor to turn with it. As this happens, the spaces between the rotor lobes become filled with oil. Then, when the lobes of the inner rotor move into the spaces in the outer rotor, the oil is squeezed out through the outlet. Oil pumps are usually driven from the

Fig. 10–5. Gear-type oil pump with built-in oil-pressure relief valve. Arrows indicate direction of oil through pump.

245

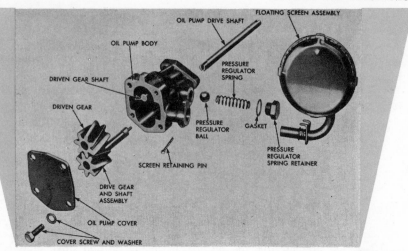

Fig. 10–6. Disassembled view of a gear-type oil pump. (*Pontiac Motor Division of General Motors Corporation*)

engine camshaft, from the same spiral gear that drives the ignition distributor. The oil intake for the oil pump is attached to a float in many engines. This floating intake then takes oil from the top of the oil in the oil pan. Since dirt particles sink, the top oil is cleanest.

§ 263. **Relief valve**   To keep the oil pump from building up excessive pressures, a relief valve is included in the lubricating system (Fig. 10–8). The valve consists of a spring-loaded ball (as in Fig. 10–5) or a spring-loaded plunger (Fig. 10–8). When the pres-

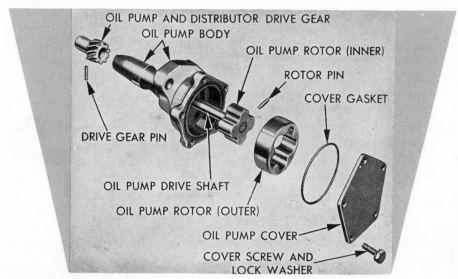

Fig. 10–7. Disassembled view of a rotor-type oil pump. (*Dodge Division of Chrysler Corporation*)

246

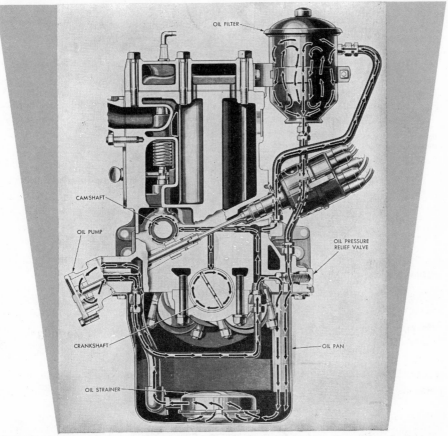

Fig. 10–8. End sectional view of an L-head engine, showing location of oil pump, oil filter, and oil-pressure relief valve. Direction of oil flow is shown by arrows. *(Dodge Division of Chrysler Corporation)*

sure reaches the preset value, the ball or plunger is moved against its spring to open a port through which oil can flow back to the oil pan. Thus, enough of the oil flows past the relief valve to prevent excessive pressure. The oil pump can normally deliver much more oil than the engine requires. This is a safety factor that assures delivery of adequate oil under extreme operating conditions.

§ 264. Oil filters   Many lubricating systems have an oil filter. Some or all of the oil from the oil pump circulates through this filter. In the filter is a mass of filtering material that traps particles of foreign matter. The filter thus helps to keep the oil clean and prevents the particles from entering the engine where they might damage bearings or other engine parts. Filters are of two types, those which filter part of the oil from the oil pump (called *by-pass* filters), and those which filter all the oil in circulation through the

247

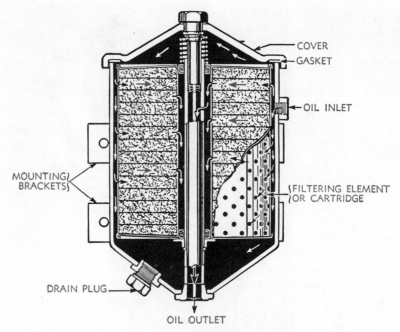

Fig. 10–9. Oil filter with replaceable filtering element (or cartridge).

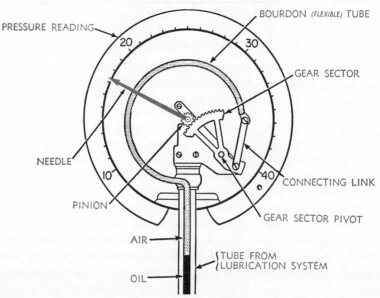

Fig. 10–10. Bourdon tube and linkage to indicating needle used in pressure-expansion oil-pressure indicator.

248

system (called *full-flow* filters). The full-flow filter includes a spring-loaded valve that serves as a protection against oil starvation in case the filter becomes clogged with contaminants. When this happens, the valve opens to bypass oil around the filter; the engine is thus assured of sufficient oil. However, the filter element should be replaced periodically so that the filter will maintain filtering efficiency. Figure 10–9 is a sectional view of a filter.

§ 265. Oil-pressure indicators The oil-pressure indicator tells the driver what the oil pressure is in the engine. This gives warning if some stoppage occurs in the lubrication system that prevents delivery of oil to vital parts. Oil-pressure indicators are of two general types, pressure-expansion and electric-resistance. The latter is the more commonly used.

1. Pressure-expansion. The pressure-expansion indicator uses a hollow Bourdon (curved) tube that is fastened at one end and free at the other. The oil pressure is applied to the curved tube through an oil line from the engine and causes the tube to straighten out somewhat as pressure increases (Fig. 10–10). This movement is transmitted to a needle by linkage and gears from the end of the tube. The needle moves across the face of a dial and registers the amount of oil pressure.

2. Electric. Electrically operated oil-pressure indicators are of two types, the balancing-coil type and the bimetal-thermostat type. The balancing-coil type makes use of two separate units, the engine unit and the indicating unit (Fig. 10–11). The engine unit consists of a variable resistance and a movable

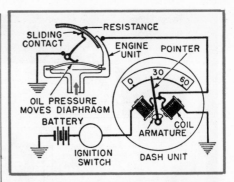

Fig. 10–11. Electric circuit of electric-resistance oil-pressure indicator.

contact that moves from one end of the resistance to the other in accordance with varying oil pressure against a diaphragm. As pressure increases, the diaphragm moves inward, causing the contact to move along the resistance so that more resistance is placed in the circuit between the engine and indicating units. This reduces the amount of current that can flow in the circuit. The indicating unit consists of two coils that balance each other in a manner similar to electrically operated fuel gauges (§ 200). In fact, this type of indicator operates in the same manner as the fuel indicator, the only difference being that the fuel indicator uses a float that moves up or down as the gasoline level changes in the gasoline tank, while in the oil-pressure indicator changing oil pressure operates a diaphragm that causes the resistance change. [Refer to the discussion on the operation of the fuel-indicator gauge (§ 200).]

The bimetal-thermostat type of all oil-pressure indicators is similar to the bimetal-thermostat fuel gauge (§ 200). The dash units are practically identical. The engine unit of the oil-pressure indicator, while somewhat different in

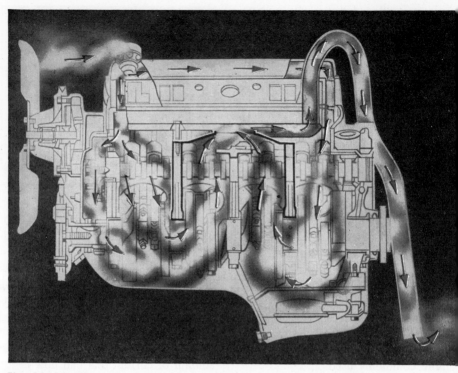

Fig. 10–12. Flow of ventilating air through crankcase of a V-8 engine. (Pontiac Motor Division of General Motors Corporation)

appearance from the tank unit of the fuel gauge, operates in a similar manner. Varying oil pressure on a diaphragm distorts the engine-unit thermostat blade varying amounts, and this distortion produces a like distortion in the dash-unit thermostat blade, causing the oil pressure to be registered on the dash unit.

§ 266. Crankcase ventilation   Water appears in the crankcase as a result of normal engine operation (§ 257). In addition, gasoline may seep down into the crankcase (§ 240, 6) and dilute the oil. After the engine reaches operating temperature, the water and gasoline evaporate. Then, crankcase ventilation removes the vapors. Crankcase ventilation is achieved by utilizing the natural whirling motion of the air in the crankcase caused by crankshaft rotation (Fig. 10–12). Outside air enters the crankcase somewhere toward the front (usually through the oil filler tube). It then passes through the crankcase, carrying with it water and gasoline vapors.

§ 267. Oil-level indicators   To determine the level of the oil in the oil pan, an oil-level stick, or "dip" stick, is used. The dip stick is so placed that it protrudes down into the oil. It can be withdrawn to determine the oil level by noting its height on the dip stick.

REVIEW QUESTIONS

1. Name the six jobs that the engine lubrication oil must perform.
2. How does the engine oil remove heat from the engine?
3. What are the main characteristics that a satisfactory engine lubricating oil must have?
4. What is viscosity?
5. What are the two properties into which viscosity may be divided?
6. What is oil body?
7. What is oil fluidity?
8. Does temperature influence the viscosity of oil? In what way?
9. Why must engine oil be resistant to carbon formation?
10. Why is oil oxidation harmful to the engine?
11. What is viscosity index?
12. What is water-sludge formation? Is this most likely to form during long drives or during short drives with frequent stops during which the engine is turned off?
13. In what three principal ways is oil lost from the engine?
14. What are the three main types of lubrication system?
15. Describe the actions that produce lubrication of engine parts in a splash lubrication system.
16. Describe the actions that produce lubrication of engine parts in a pressure-feed lubrication system.
17. What is the purpose of an oil pump?
18. What is the purpose of the relief valve in a pressure-feed lubrication system? How does the relief valve operate?
19. What are the two types of oil filters? Describe briefly how each operates.
20. What is a floating oil intake? How does it operate?
21. Name two types of oil-pressure indicators.
22. What is crankcase ventilation, and why is it desirable on the gasoline engine?
23. How can you determine the oil level in the oil pan of an engine?

STUDY QUESTIONS

1. In modern engines, the tendency has been to provide closer fits of bearings. On such engines, must the oil viscosity be greater or less? Explain the reason for your answer.
2. If you were driving a car, would you rather have the fuel gauge or the oil-pressure gauge stick?
3. Can you think of a design for an automatic gauge that would automatically indicate the level of the oil in the engine oil pan?
4. As engine bearings and cylinder walls wear, it is sometimes the practice to use a lubricating oil of a different viscosity. Is the viscosity less or greater than the viscosity of the oil used in a new engine? Explain your reasoning.
5. Make a sketch of a pressure-expansion type of oil-pressure indi-cator, and write a brief explanation of how it operates.
6. Make a sketch of a balancing-coil type of oil-pressure indicator, and write a brief explanation of how it operates.
7. Make a sketch of a bimetal-thermostat type of oil-pressure indicator, and write a brief explanation of how it operates.

251

THIS CHAPTER DISCUSSES the construction and operation of automotive-engine cooling systems. As previously noted, the cylinder block and cylinder head have water jackets (§§ 105 and 106) through which cooling water can circulate. It is this circulation of water between the water jackets and the radiator that makes the cooling system effective.

§ 268. Purpose of cooling system
The purpose of the cooling system is to keep the engine at its most efficient operating temperature at all engine speeds and all driving conditions. During the combustion of the air-fuel mixture in the engine cylinders, temperatures as high as 4500°F may be reached by the burning gases. Some of this heat is absorbed by the cylinder walls, cylinder head, and pistons. They, in turn, must be provided with some means of cooling, so that their temperatures will not reach excessive values. Cylinder-wall temperature must not increase beyond about 400 or 500°F. Temperatures higher than this will cause the lubricating-oil film to break down and lose its lubricating properties. But it is desirable to operate the engine at temperatures as close to the limits imposed by oil properties as possible. Removing too much heat through the cylinder walls and head would lower engine thermal efficiency (§ 94). Cooling systems are designed to re-

move about 30 to 35 percent of the heat produced in the combustion chambers by the burning of the air-fuel mixture.

Since the engine is quite inefficient when cold, the cooling system includes devices that prevent normal cooling action during engine warm-up. These devices allow the working parts to reach operating temperatures more quickly and shorten the inefficient cold-operating time. Then, when the engine reaches operating temperatures, the cooling system begins to function. Thus, the cooling system cools rapidly when the engine is hot, and it cools slowly or not at all when the engine is warming up or cold.

Two general types of cooling systems are used, air cooling and liquid cooling. Automotive engines now employ liquid cooling, although some special engines for airplanes, motorcycles, power lawn mowers, and so forth, are air-cooled. Only the liquid-cooled-engine cooling systems will be considered here. These generally employ a water pump to maintain circulation in the system. Figure 2–7 shows the cooling system for an L-head engine. Figure 11–1 shows the cooling system for an I-head engine. The water pump, driven by a belt from the engine crankshaft, circulates the cooling liquid between the radiator and engine water jackets, as shown. The cooling liquid is water. Antifreeze compounds are added to the

Fig. 11–1. Cooling system used in overhead-valve engine. (*Chevrolet Motor Division of General Motors Corporation*)

water during the winter. Following articles describe the cooling-system components in detail.

§ 269. Water jackets Just as we might put on a sweater or a jacket to keep warm on a cool day, so are water jackets placed around the engine cylinders. There is this difference: water jackets are designed to keep the cylinders cool. The water jackets are cast into the cylinder blocks and heads (§§ 105 and 106). Since the valve seats and valve guides may need additional cooling (as noted in § 135), it is often the practice to install water-distributing tubes and nozzles in the water jackets (Figs. 6–51 and 11–2). The

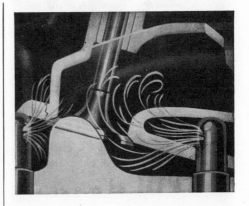

Fig. 11–2. Water nozzles used in cylinder head of overhead-valve engine to provide valve-seat cooling. (*Chevrolet Motor Division of General Motors Corporation*)

253

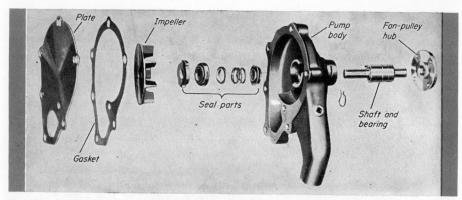

Fig. 11–3. Disassembled view of water pump. (Pontiac Motor Division of General Motors Corporation)

tubes direct additional cooling water to the critical areas for adequate cooling.

§ 270. Water pumps   Water pumps are usually of the impeller type and are mounted at the front end of the cylinder block between the block and the

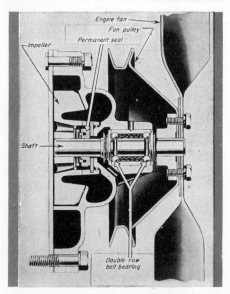

Fig. 11–4. Sectional view of water pump, showing manner of supporting shaft on double-row ball bearing and method of mounting fan and pulley on shaft. (Studebaker-Packard Corporation)

radiator (Figs. 2–7 and 6–5). The pump (Figs. 11–3 and 11–4) consists of a housing, with a water inlet and outlet, and an impeller. The impeller is a flat plate mounted on the pump shaft with a series of flat or curved blades, or vanes. When the impeller rotates, the water between the blades is thrown outward by centrifugal force and is forced through the pump outlet and into the cylinder block. The pump inlet is connected by a hose to the bottom of the radiator, and water from the radiator is drawn into the pump to replace the water forced through the outlet.

The impeller shaft is supported on one or more bearings; a seal prevents water from leaking out around the bearing. The pump is driven by a belt to the drive pulley mounted on the front end of the engine crankshaft.

§ 271. Engine fan   The engine fan usually mounts on the water-pump shaft and is driven by the same belt that drives the pump and the generator (Fig. 11–4). The purpose of the fan is to provide a powerful draft of air through the radiator. Some applica-

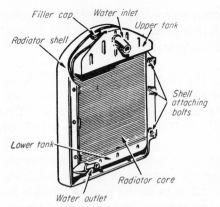

Fig. 11–5. Radiator assembly.

tions are equipped with a fan shroud that improves fan performance. The shroud increases the efficiency of the fan, since it assures that all air pulled back by the fan must first pass through the radiator.

Most of the belts are of the V type. Friction between the sides of the belt and the sides of the grooves in the pulleys causes the driving power to be transmitted through the belt from one pulley to the other. The V-type belt provides a substantial area of contact, so that considerable power may be transmitted; the wedging action of the belt as it curves into the pulley grooves

aids in preventing belt slippage. Figure 2–1 shows a V belt in place on the generator, engine fan, and crankshaft pulley of an engine.

§ 272. Radiator The radiator (Fig. 11–5) is a device for holding a large volume of water in close contact with a large volume of air so that heat will transfer from the water to the air. The radiator core is divided into two separate and intricate compartments; water passes through one, and air passes through the other. There are several types of radiator core. Two of the more commonly used types are the tube-and-fin (Fig 11–6) and the ribbon-cellular (Fig. 11–7). The tube-and-fin type consists of a series of long tubes extending from the top to the bottom of the radiator (or from upper to lower tank). Fins are placed around the tubes to improve heat transfer. Air passes around the outside of the tubes, between the fins, absorbing heat from the water in passing.

The ribbon-cellular radiator core (Fig. 11–7) is made up of a large number of narrow water passages formed by pairs of thin metal ribbons soldered

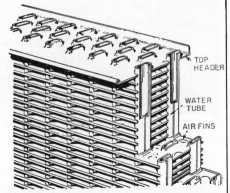

Fig. 11–6. Construction of tube-and-fin radiator core.

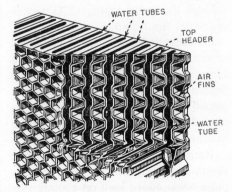

Fig. 11–7. Construction of ribbon-cellular radiator core.

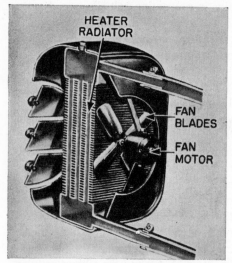

Fig. 11–8. Hot-water car heater. (*E. I. du Pont de Nemours & Company, Inc.*)

together along their edges, running from the upper to the lower tank. The edges of the water passages, which are soldered together, form the front and back surfaces of the radiator core. The water passages are separated by air fins of metal ribbon, which provide air passages between the water passages. Air moves through these passages from front to back, absorbing heat from the fins. The fins, in turn, absorb heat from the water moving downward through the water passages. As a consequence, the water is cooled.

On every radiator, a water chamber, or tank, is provided at the top of the radiator, into which hot water is delivered from the engine. A filler cap placed on the water chamber can be removed in order to add water to replace that lost by evaporation or leakage.

Radiator grills, which add to the streamlined appearance of the car, place some added load on cooling systems, since they tend to restrict the flow of air through the radiator. How-

ever, where they are used, the cooling system is designed to meet all cooling requirements adequately.

§ **273. Hot-water car heater** Many automobiles are equipped with car heaters of the hot-water type (Fig. 11–8). This device might be considered a secondary radiator that transfers heat from the cooling system to the passenger compartment of the automobile instead of to the air passing through the main radiator. Hot water from the engine is circulated through the heater radiator, and a small electric motor drives a fan that forces air through the radiator section of the heater. The air absorbs heat from the heater radiator.

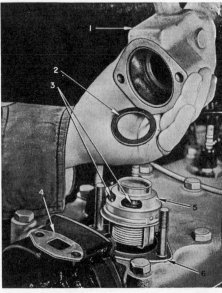

Fig. 11–9. Thermostat, used to restrict water circulation with engine cold, shown in place in cylinder head: 1, elbow; 2, gasket; 3, thermostat openings; 4, gasket; 5, thermostat; 6, gasket. (*Plymouth Division of Chrysler Corporation*)

Fig. 11–10. Thermostat in place in cylinder head, showing water circulation through thermostat when thermostat is opened. (*Studebaker-Packard Corporation*)

§ 274. **Thermostat** The thermostat is placed in the water passage between the cylinder head and the top of the radiator (Fig. 2–7). Its purpose is to close off this passage when the engine is cold, so that water circulation is restricted, causing the engine to reach operating temperature more quickly. The thermostat consists of a thermostatic bellows and a valve (Figs. 11–9 and 11–10). When the bellows is cold, the valve is closed. When the bellows expands with increasing temperature, the valve opens. Thermostats are designed to open at specific temperature. For example, a thermostat stamped "151" should start to open at around that temperature (or 148 to 155°F) and should be fully opened at 173°F. A thermostat stamped "170" should start to open at 166 to 174°F and should be fully opened at 194°F.

Thermostats of the proper characteristics are selected to suit the operating requirements of engines on which they are used.

With the engine cold and the thermostatic valve consequently closed, the water pump circulates the water as shown in Fig. 11–11. The water is merely recirculated through the cylinder block and head. A small spring-loaded bypass valve is forced open by the water pressure from the pump so that the water can circulate as shown by the arrows. Restriction of water circulation in this manner prevents the removal of any appreciable amount of heat from the engine by the cooling system. The engine consequently reaches operating temperatures more rapidly. When the engine reaches operating temperature, the thermostatic valve begins to open. Then, water can

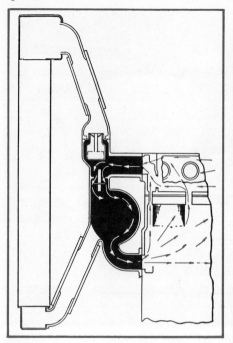

Fig. 11–11. Location of thermostat in water passage between cylinder head and radiator. Engine is cold, thermostat closed, and bypass valve open. Water circulates as shown by arrows. (*Buick Motor Division of General Motors Corporation*)

evaporation and surge losses, many late automobiles use a pressure cap on the radiator (Fig. 11–13). At sea level, where atmospheric pressure is about 15 psi (pounds per square inch), water boils at 212°F. At higher altitudes, where atmospheric pressure is less (§ 63), water will boil at lower temperatures. Higher pressures increase the temperature required to boil water. Each added pound per square inch increases the boiling point of water about $3\frac{1}{4}$°F. The use of a pressure cap on the radiator increases the air pressure within the cooling system several pounds per square inch. Thus, the water may be circulated at higher temperatures without boiling. The

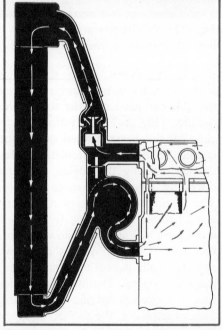

circulate through the radiator as shown in Fig. 11–12. Figure 11–10 shows the water circulation through the thermostat when the thermostat is open. Operation of the cooling system then proceeds in a normal manner as already described.

Instead of the spring-loaded-valve type of bypass for water recirculation with the thermostatic valve closed, shown in Fig. 11–11, some engines use a small bypass passage from the cylinder head through the engine block to the pump inlet.

§ 275. **Radiator pressure cap** To improve cooling efficiency and prevent

Fig. 11–12. Circulation of water with thermostat open. Some systems incorporate a bypass valve as shown here and in Fig. 11–11. Other systems use a bypass port. (*Buick Motor Division of General Motors Corporation*)

water therefore enters the radiator at a higher temperature, and the difference in temperature between the air and the water is greater. Heat then is more quickly transferred from the water to the air, improving cooling efficiency. Evaporation of water is reduced by the higher pressure, inasmuch as the boiling point of the water is higher. The pressure cap also prevents loss of water due to surging when the car is quickly braked to a stop.

The pressure cap fits over the radiator filler tube and seals tightly around the edges. The cap contains two valves, the blowoff valve and the vacuum valve. The blowoff valve consists of a valve held against a valve seat by a calibrated spring. The spring holds the valve closed so that pressure is produced in the cooling system. If pressure is obtained above that for which the system is designed, the blowoff valve is raised off its seat, relieving the excessive pressure. Pressure caps are designed to provide as much as 12 pounds of pressure per square inch in the cooling system; this increases the boiling point of the water to as much as 250°F.

The vacuum valve is designed to prevent the formation of a vacuum in the cooling system when the engine has been shut off and begins to cool. If a vacuum forms, atmospheric pressure from the outside causes the small vacuum valve to open, admitting air into the radiator. Without a vacuum valve, the pressure within the radiator might drop so low that atmospheric pressure would collapse it.

§ 276. Antifreeze solutions Antifreeze solutions are required to prevent freezing of the water when tempera-

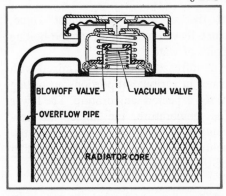

Fig. 11–13. Radiator pressure cap. (AC Spark Plug Division of General Motors Corporation)

tures drop below 32°F. When water freezes in the engine, the resulting expanding force is often sufficient to crack the cylinder block and the radiator. Antifreeze solutions added to and mixed with the water prevent freezing of the mixture. A good antifreeze material must mix readily with water, prevent freezing of the mixture at the lowest temperatures encountered, and circulate freely. It must not damage the cooling system by corrosive action or lose its antifreezing properties after extended use. In the past, a number of different materials have been tried, including salt and sugar solutions, oil, kerosene, and glycerine, but their use has been generally abandoned because of harmful or dangerous effects. The most commonly used antifreeze materials are now either alcohol or alcohol-base or ethylene glycol. The alcohol-base materials make only temporary antifreeze solutions, since they evaporate at temperatures below the boiling point of water and thus are gradually lost. Such materials may require periodic additions to maintain an antifreeze solution of adequate strength. The ethylene glycol antifreeze materials are

of the so-called "permanent" type, since they remain liquid at the boiling point of water.

Antifreeze materials are mixed with water in various proportions according to the expected temperature. The lower the temperature, the higher the percentage of antifreeze material in the solution necessary to prevent freezing of the mixture.

§ 277. **Temperature indicators** In order that the operator will know at all times the water temperature in the cooling system, a temperature indicator is installed in the car. An abnormal heat rise is a warning of abnormal conditions in the engine. The indicator thus warns the operator to stop the engine before serious damage is done. Temperature indicators are of two general types, vapor-pressure and electric.

1. Vapor-pressure. The vapor-pressure temperature indicator (Fig. 11–14) consists of an indicator bulb and a tube connecting the bulb to the indicator unit. The indicator unit contains a curved, or Bourdon, tube, one end of which is linked to the indicator needle. The other end is open and is connected through a tube to the bulb. The indicator bulb, usually placed in the water jacket of the engine, is filled with a liquid that evaporates at fairly low temperature. As the engine temperature increases, the liquid in the bulb begins to evaporate, creating pressure that is conveyed through the connecting tube to the Bourdon tube in the indicating unit. The pressure tends to straighten out the tube; the resulting movement causes the indicating needle to move across the dial face and indicate the temperature in the water jacket. This unit is much like the oil-pressure indicator illustrated in Fig. 10–10.

2. Electric indicators. Electrically operated temperature indicators are of two types, the balancing-coil type and

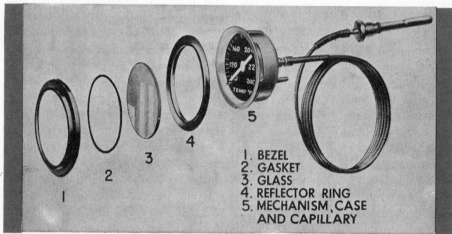

1. BEZEL
2. GASKET
3. GLASS
4. REFLECTOR RING
5. MECHANISM, CASE
   AND CAPILLARY

Fig. 11–14. Vapor-pressure temperature indicator. (AC *Spark Plug Division* of *General Motors Corporation*)

the bimetal-thermostat type. The balancing-coil-type oil-pressure indicator (§ 265), fuel gauge (§ 200), and temperature indicator all operate in a similar manner. The dash indicating units are, in fact, practically identical, consisting of two coils and an armature to which a needle is attached (Fig. 11–15). The engine unit changes resistance with temperature in such a way that at higher temperatures it has less resistance and will thus pass more current. When this happens, more current passes through the right-hand coil in the indicating unit, so that the armature to which the needle is attached is attracted by the increased magnetic field. The armature and the needle move around so that the needle indicates a higher temperature.

The bimetal-thermostat-type temperature indicator is similar to the bimetal-thermostat fuel gauge (§ 200). The dash units are practically identical. The engine unit of the temperature indicator, while slightly different in appearance from the tank unit of the fuel gauge, operates in a somewhat similar manner. In the temperature indicator, the temperature of the cool-

ing liquid is directly imposed on the engine-unit thermostatic blade. When the temperature is low, most of the blade heating must come from electric current. More current flows, and the dash unit distorts a considerable amount to indicate a low temperature. As temperature increases, less heat from current flow is required to bring the engine-unit blade up to operating temperature. Less current flows, and the dash unit indicates a higher temperature.

STUDY QUESTIONS

1. What is the purpose of the engine cooling system?
2. What are the two general types of cooling systems?
3. Give three examples of air-cooled engines.
4. What are water jackets?
5. What is the purpose of water-distributing tubes?
6. What function does the water pump perform?
7. Where are water pumps usually mounted? How are they usually driven?
8. What is the purpose of the engine fan? Where is it located, and how is it usually driven?
9. What is a V belt?
10. Describe a radiator, and explain how it operates.
11. What is the purpose of the thermostat? How does it operate?
12. What is the purpose of the pressure-type radiator cap? How does it operate?
13. Why are antifreeze solutions used? Give the characteristics of a good antifreeze solution.

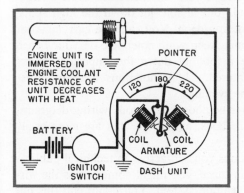

Fig. 11–15. Circuit diagram of electric-resistance temperature-indicator system.

14. Into what two classifications are the most commonly used anti-freeze solutions divided?
15. In what way is the strength of anti-freeze solution tested?
16. Name the two general types of engine temperature indicator.
17. Describe how the vapor-pressure temperature indicator operates.
18. Describe how the balancing-coil type of temperature indicator operates. The bimetal-thermostat type.

STUDY QUESTIONS

1. What advantages might an air-cooled engine have over a liquid-cooled engine? What disadvantages?
2. What might happen if the water-distributing tubes were accidentally left out of an engine?
3. Would a forced-circulation cooling system completely stop functioning if the water pump stopped operating?
4. Can you think of any reasons for not using a flat belt in place of the V belt?
5. Make a sketch of a vapor-pressure temperature-indicator system, and write a brief explanation of how it operates.
6. Make a sketch of a balancing-coil type of temperature-indicator system, and write a brief explanation of how it operates.
7. Make a sketch of a bimetal-thermostat type of temperature-indicator system and write a brief explanation of how it operates.

MAKING NOTES IN YOUR NOTEBOOK

You will normally make notes in your notebook on two occasions: when you are studying and when you are working in the shop.

When you are studying your lesson in the textbook, have your notebook open. Start with a fresh notebook page at the beginning of the lesson. Write the lesson number or page numbers of your textbook at the top of the notebook page, along with the date (or perhaps your instructor has some instructions for you to follow). As you read your lesson, jot down the high spots.

In the shop you will use a different approach. You can't be carrying your notebook around with you all the time. Keep your notebook on your bench or in a drawer. After you complete a job, jot down the important points covered or special problems encountered. These notations are simply reminders. You can redo the page in the evening.

You can also make sketches in your notebook of various wiring diagrams, structural arrangements, machining methods, and so on, that are more easily drawn than described in words.

You can insert articles and illustrations you run across in technical publications that relate to your studies. For instance, you might come across the wiring circuit and description of a new ignition system. You could clip this out and insert it in the electrical section of your notebook.

THIS CHAPTER DESCRIBES different engine-testing procedures and the tools used to make the tests. The next chapter describes engine trouble-shooting procedures, that is, the procedures used to track down specific troubles in the engine. Later chapters then supply details of various servicing procedures on the engine, the fuel, lubricating, cooling, and electric systems, and their components.

§ 278. Engine-testing instruments A considerable number of instruments are available to test the engine and its component parts. Those relating directly to the engine are described in this chapter; those relating to such components as generators, ignition distributors, and so on, are discussed in following chapters.

§ 279. Tachometer Since many tests must be made at specified engine speeds, a speed-measuring device is required. This device, called a tachometer, or rpm (revolutions per minute) indicator, is shown in use in Fig. 12–1. It is connected to the ignition primary circuit and measures the number of times per minute the primary circuit is interrupted. It then translates this information into engine rpm.

§ 280. Cylinder compression tester This instrument (Fig. 12–2) is one of the most important engine-testing devices. It measures cylinder pressure, in psi (pounds per square inch), as the piston moves up to TDC (top dead center). This pressure is an indication of engine condition. If the pressure is low, then the cylinder cannot hold compression (possibly owing to worn rings, piston or cylinder walls or to poor valve seating, and so on).

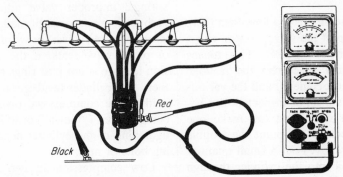

Fig. 12–1. Electric connections to check engine rpm with tachometer. Selector knob must be turned to four-, six-, or eight-lobe position, according to number of engine cylinders (or number of lobes on distributor cam). (*Sun Electric Corporation*)

Fig. 12–2. Using cylinder compression tester. (*Allen Electric and Equipment Company*)

To use the compression tester, remove all spark plugs, hold the tester fitting tightly in the spark-plug hole of a cylinder, and crank the engine with the cranking motor. Be sure to hold the throttle valve wide open so that the fuel system does not deliver fuel to engine during the test. Note the maximum compression as indicated by the needle on the compression-tester dial.

If compression is too low, then there is leakage past the valves, piston rings, or cylinder-head gasket. This means that, in order to correct the trouble, the head must come off and the various engine parts must be inspected. But before this is done, you can make one further check to pin-point the trouble more accurately. Pour a small quantity of heavy oil into the cylinder through the spark-plug hole, and then retest the compression pressure. If the compression pressure increases to a more normal figure, this means that the loss of compression is due to leakage past the piston rings. This can result from worn or scored piston rings, pistons, or cylinder walls or from piston rings being weak, broken, or stuck in their grooves. If adding oil does not help the compression pressure, the chances are that the leakage is past the valves. This could be due to weak or broken valve springs; improper valve adjustments; carboned valve stems; burned, warped, worn, or pitted valves; or worn, burned, or pitted valve seats. If the compression leakage is not past rings or valves, then the cylinder-head gasket is not holding the compression, owing to its being burned ("blown") or to improper tightening of the cylinder-head attaching bolts or nuts.

Low compression in two adjacent cylinders indicates that there is a blown gasket between the cylinders that allows leakage between them.

§ 281. Engine vacuum gauge This is another very important engine tester. It measures intake-manifold vacuum. The intake-manifold vacuum varies with different operating conditions, and also with different engine defects. The manner in which the vacuum varies from normal indicates the type of engine trouble. Figures 12–3 and 12–4 show two types of vacuum gauge. The gauge is connected to the intake manifold at the point where the windshield wiper (or vacuum pump) is normally connected. Then, the engine is operated at idle speed (after it has been warmed up) and the vacuum-gauge reading noted. Meanings of various readings are as follows:

1. A steady and fairly high reading (17 to 22 inches, depending on altitude and engine) indicates normal performance. The reading will be lower at higher altitudes because of the lowered atmospheric pressure. For every 1,000 feet above sea level, the reading will be reduced about 1 inch.

2. A steady and low reading indi-

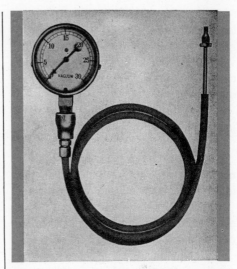

Fig. 12–3. Vacuum gauge for measuring intake-manifold vacuum. (*Kent-Moore Organization, Inc.*)

cates late ignition or valve timing, or possibly leakage around pistons owing to stuck piston rings or to worn or scored rings, pistons, or cylinder walls. Any of these reduce power output. With reduced power, the engine does not "pull" as much vacuum.

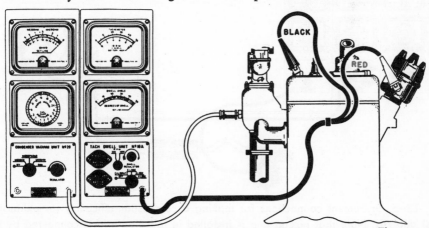

Fig. 12–4. Instrument connections for making manifold-vacuum test. The vacuum gauge shown here is built into a panel as part of a test stand. (*Sun Electric Corporation*)

3. A very low reading indicates a leaky intake manifold or carburetor gasket or leaks around the throttle-valve shaft. Air leaks into the manifold cause loss of vacuum and low engine output.

4. Oscillations of the needle increasing with engine speed indicate weak valve springs.

5. A gradual falling back of the needle toward zero with the engine idling indicates a clogged exhaust line.

6. Regular dropping back of the needle indicates a valve sticking open or a plug not firing.

7. Irregular dropping back of the needle indicates sticking valves that stick irregularly.

8. Floating motion or slow oscillation of the needle indicates an excessively rich air-fuel mixture. (See item 18, "Excessive fuel consumption," in the Engine Trouble-shooting Chart, in § 290 and see § 302 for troubles in the fuel system that could cause an excessively rich mixture.)

9. A test for loss of compression due to leakage around pistons as a result of stuck piston rings or of worn or scored rings, pistons, or cylinder walls can be made as follows: Race the engine momentarily, and then quickly close the throttle. If the needle swings around momentarily to 23 to 25 inches as the throttle is closed, the compression is probably satisfactory. If the needle fails to swing this far around, there is loss of compression.

§ 282. Exhaust-gas analyzer The exhaust-gas analyzer, or combustion tester, checks the exhaust gas to determine what percentage of the gasoline has not been burned. When mixture ratios are not correct, or when there is a fouled plug or sticky valves (among other things), not all the gas-

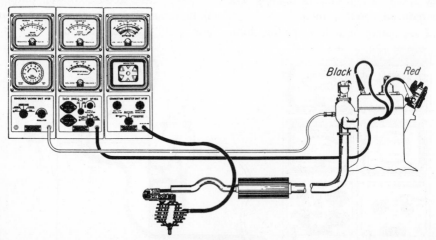

Fig. 12–5. Instrument connections for making a combustion-efficiency (or exhaust-gas) analysis. Note that pickup gun is installed in tail pipe and is connected by a hose to the analyzer. A small pump, or booster, draws exhaust gas through the hose to the analyzer. (*Sun Electric Corporation*)

oline burns. Combustion efficiency is low, and gasoline is being wasted. The exhaust-gas analyzer draws a small part of the exhaust gas from the tail pipe and runs it through an analyzing device which then reports, by an indicating needle on a dial, the fuel ratio (mixture richness) or combustion efficiency (see Fig. 12–5). When not influenced by abnormal engine factors, the combustion efficiency and fuel ratio can be said to be directly related. The richer the ratio, the lower the efficiency (that is, a smaller percentage of the gasoline burns).

§ 283. Fuel-mileage testers An accurate measurement of fuel mileage can be obtained by using a special measuring device that measures the exact amount of fuel being used during a trial run (Fig. 12–6). In the tester shown, tubes are connected to the carburetor so that a measured amount of fuel can be fed to the carburetor. The distance the car runs is accurately measured while the measured amount of fuel is being used up.

§ 284. Fuel-pump testers Occasionally, a test of the fuel pump may be made to determine whether its capac-

ity and developed pressure are within limits. Low pump pressure will cause gas starvation and poor engine performance. High pressure will cause an overrich mixture, excessive fuel consumption, and probably such engine troubles as fouled spark plugs and clogged rings and valves (from excessive carbon deposits). Fuel-pump testers are connected into the line at the pump and measure any one of three factors (according to type of tester): the pressure the pump can develop; the amount of fuel the pump can deliver in a given time; the vacuum that the pump can develop.

§ 285. Ignition timing The ignition must be timed correctly when the engine is idling so that the compressed air-fuel mixture will be ignited at the proper instant at the end of the compression stroke. In order to time the ignition, most engines have markings on the flywheel or crankshaft pulley (or vibration damper). When correctly timed, these markings align with stationary pointers at the instant that the plug in cylinder 1 fires. This alignment can be observed with a device called a stroboscopic light (also referred to as a timing light) as shown in Fig.

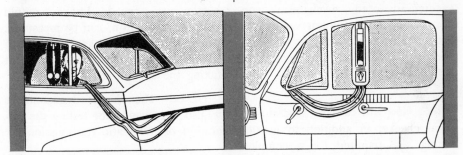

Fig. 12–6. Fuel-mileage tester as it looks from outside and inside of car when mounted in place ready for test. (*Kent-Moore Organization, Inc.*)

267

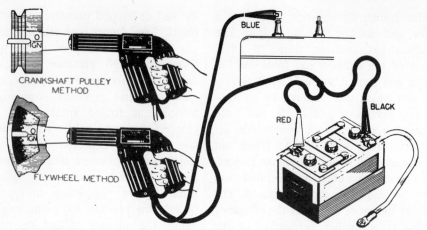

Fig. 12–7. Using stroboscopic, or ignition-timing, light to check ignition timing. Light flashes with each firing of plug 1. Timing is correct when pointer and marking on flywheel or pulley align. (*Sun Electric Corporation*)

12–7. Power for the light is obtained from the battery. The light flashes are triggered by the firing of plug 1. At the instant that plug 1 fires, the light flashes on. It goes off again almost at once. Thus the repeated flashes make the flywheel or pulley seem to stand still. (This is the stroboscopic effect.) The timing of the ignition can therefore be observed. Correction is made by loosening and turning the distributor in its mounting. Earlier-model Fords have the timing set with the distributor off the car. Also, in checking timing of Fords which have the vacuum-advanced mechanism connected into the carburetor venturi, the vacuum line should be disconnected. (See § 372 for more information on ignition timing.)

§ 286. Electrical checks Several electrical checks, in addition to ignition timing, are required for a complete diagnosis of the car electrical system. These include tests of the battery, gen-

erator, regulator, cranking motor, and ignition system (see Chap. 15).

§ 287. Chassis dynamometer Article 87 describes engine and chassis dynamometers for testing engine performance. The chassis dynamometer is coming into widespread use. It tests engines in cars (see § 87). This device is very handy since it can be adjusted to simulate different driving conditions (low-speed, accelerating, high-speed, hill climbing, and so on). Various instruments can be used at the same time so that the engine horsepower, speed, intake-manifold vacuum, and so on, can be measured. Thus, a rather complete analysis of engine operation can be made without taking the car out of the shop.

NOTE: The chassis dynamometer is also very handy for testing the operation of automatic transmissions.

§ 288. Engine tune-up Engine tune-up is a procedure for checking the

268

various operating characteristics of an engine and its accessories. In this procedure, not only are operating faults detected, but they also are corrected. Thus, the engine is "tuned up"; its performance is improved.

A typical tune-up procedure follows. Explanations of how to make various checks are detailed in following chapters.

1. Check the battery. Visually inspect for signs of damage, and make sure that cables are good and connections are tight. Check specific gravity, and, if above 1.225, make a load test.

2. Check cranking system. A battery load test using the cranking motor is also a test of the cranking motor. But voltage drop in circuit, as well as amperage draw, should be checked.

3. Check engine idle speed with engine at operating temperature, and adjust if necessary.

4. Check generator-regulator system, including regulator settings, generator output, relay closing and opening settings, voltage drop in charging circuit, and condition of generator and fan belt.

5. Check ignition timing (§ 285), and adjust if necessary.

6. Check intake-manifold vacuum (§ 281).

7. Check for cylinder balance to determine whether any cylinders are weak or missing. This is done by running the engine on only two cylinders at a time. Two cylinders are used because running the engine on only one cylinder at a time is not conclusive. The procedure is as follows:

a. Connect tachometer and vacuum gauge (Fig. 12–8), start engine, and run it until it reaches operating temperature. Then operate it at 1,000 rpm if it is a six-cylinder engine or 1,500 rpm if it is an eight-cylinder engine.

b. Ground out (or disconnect spark-plug leads from) all but two cylinders so that engine will run on two cylinders only. Determine which cylinders to use by taking engine firing order and

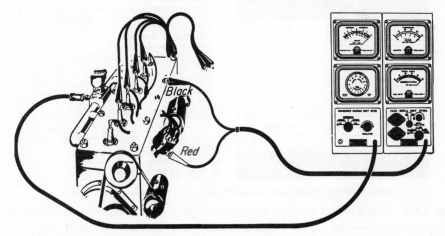

Fig. 12–8. Tachometer and vacuum-gauge connections to make cylinder balance test. Multiple-lead plug-grounding lead assembly can be used to ground plugs as shown, or plug leads can be disconnected. (*Sun Electric Corporation*)

269

scientific test report

COL. 1 Contains Specifications for your Car
COL. 2 Contains Numerical Test Readings from Your Car
COL. 3 An X Here Indicates a Satisfactory Condition
COL. 4 An X Here Indicates An Unsatisfactory Condition Further Explained at the right.
A Circled ⓧ Indicates an Unsatisfactory Condition Corrected During Diagnosis.

	1.	2.	3.	4.
1. BATTERY Visual Inspection — Carrier, Cables, Connections, Water, Case, Cell Covers, Electrical Leakage			X	
Specific Gravity — Pos. Cell 1. 1.220, 2. 1.220, 3. 1.215 — Should be 1.250 or more and even within .025				X
Battery Capacity @3xAH Load	Min. 4.8 for 6V, Min. 9.6 for 12V	4.7 Volts		X
★ Three Minute Test Charge Cell Voltage — Should be even within .1 volt and not exceed: 7.75V for 6V - 15.5V for 12V				
Pos. Cell 1: 2.5, 2: 2.5, 3: 2.5, 4: , 5: , 6:		Total Volts 7.5	X	
2. STARTING SYSTEM Visual Inspection — Brushes, Commutator, Mounting bolts			X	
Starter Amperage Draw	170-240 Amps	180 Amps	X	
Insulated Cables & Switches	.2 Volt	.2 Volt	X	
Starter Ground Circuit	.2 Volt	.1 Volt	X	
Cranking Voltage	5.0 Volts	5.6 Volts	X	
3. DISTRIBUTOR				
Distributor Resistance	Must be in black bar on meter		X	
Dwell at Idle	28-34 Deg.	34 Deg.	X	
Dwell Variation	2° Max. Variation Idle to 2000 RPM	4° Deg.		X
4. ENGINE IDLE R.P.M.	375 RPM	375 RPM	X	
5. CHARGING SYSTEM Visual Inspection — Belt, Brushes, Commutator, Wiring, Mounting Bolts			X	
Insulated Circuit Resistance	Max. .8 Volt @20 Amps	.6 Volt	X	
Ground Circuit Resistance	Max. .1 Volt @20 Amps	.05 Volt	X	
Regulator Ground Resistance	Max. .1 Volt	.0 Volt	X	
Generator Output	45 Amps	45 Amps	X	
Cutout Relay—Closes	5.9-6.8 Volts	6.4 Volts	X	
Opens	0-4 Amps	-3 Amps	X	
Voltage Regulator (Hot)	7.0-7.7 Volts	6.8 Volts		X
Current Regulator (Hot)	45-51 Amps	49 Amps	X	
6. SPARK TIMING	5° BTDC	5° BTDC	X	
7. MANIFOLD VACUUM Idle Speed	20-21 In.	19 In.		X
8. SECONDARY EFFICIENCY Reading Should Be In Good Band And Even — 1: 3.9, 2: 3.9, 3: 4.0, 4: 4.0, 5: 3.9, 6: 3.9, 7: 4.0, 8: 3.9			X	
9 CYLINDER BALANCE Maximum Variation—1 inch Vacuum And/or 40 R.P.M. — Cyl. No's. 1-6, 8-5, 4-7, 3-2; Vacuum 11¾, 11¾, 11¾, 11¾; R.P.M. 530, 530, 530, 530			X	
10. FUEL SYSTEM Visual Inspection — Tank, Venting, Fuel Lines, Pump Mounting, Fuel Filter, Carburetor Linkage			X	
Manifold Heat Control Valve — Free and Operating			X	
Idle Speed Circuit @Specified Idle Speed	70±3%	83 %		X
Intermediate Speed Test — Should Lean Out Progressively As Speed Is Increased To 2000 R.P.M.			X	

	1.	2.	3.	4.
High Speed Circuit	75-85%	82 %	X	
Air Cleaner Restriction	5 %	3 %	X	
Choke — Visual Inspection of Adjustment And Condition			X	
Accelerating Pump — Minimum 8% Summer—10% Winter		14 %	X	
Intake Manifold Leak	Maximum 3%	2 %	X	
11. FUEL PUMP				
Volume @ Idle	1PT. 45 SEC.	30 SEC.	X	
Pressure @ 1000 Engine R.P.M.	4-5¼ Lbs.	4¼ Lbs.	X	
★ Vacuum — Minimum Vacuum @ Idle	11 Inches	11½ In.	X	
Vacuum Booster @ 1000 R.P.M.	8½ Inches or more	9 In.	X	
12. SPARK PLUGS Gap and Condition	.033-.038 In.	.045 In.		X
Heat Range	AC 48X	AC 48X	X	
13. COMPRESSION First Stroke Reading / Fourth Stroke Reading — 1. 124/149 2. 125/143 3. 129/150 4. 124/148 5. 124/150 6. 124/150 7. 124/145 8. 126/152			X	
★ Compression—Auxiliary Test — 1. / 2. / 3. / 4. / 5. / 6. / 7. / 8. /				
14. IGNITION PRIMARY CIRCUIT Resistance Test	.2 Volt	.1 Volt	X	
15. COIL Secondary Continuity	Less than 20,000 Ohms	4,800 Ohms	X	
Coil Capacity — Must read steady in Good Band			X	
16. SECONDARY CIRCUIT INSULATION				
Distributor Cap — Must read steady in Good Band			X	
Rotor — Must read steady in Good Band			X	
Ignition Cables — Must read steady in Good Band			X	
17. CONDENSER				
Resistance (Microhm) — Must be within Microhm Bar			X	
Capacity (Microfarad)	.18-.23 Mfd	.21 Mfd	X	
Insulation (Megohm) — Must be within Megohm Bar			X	
18. DISTRIBUTOR (Removed)				
Contact Point Condition (Visual)			X	
Contact Point Resistance — Must be within Black Bar			X	
Point Spring Tension	19-23 Oz.	21 Oz.	X	
Contact Point Gap	.013 In.	.013 In.	X	
Contact Point Dwell	28-34 Deg.	34 Deg.	X	
Shaft and Bushings	Max. Variation 2 Deg.	1 Deg.	X	
Cam Lobe Accuracy	Max. Variation 1 Deg.	½ Deg.	X	
Breaker Plate Test	Max. Variation 2 Deg.	3 Deg.		X
Mechanical Advance Test	See Scroll Chart	1° LATE	X	
Vacuum Advance Test	See Scroll Chart	1° EARLY	X	
19. SPEEDOMETER	See Manufacturers Specifications	2 MPH FAST AT 60	X	
20. RADIATOR, PUMPS, HOSES, Other (Visual)			X	
21. EXHAUST SYSTEM (Visual)			X	
22. OTHER ELECTRICAL SYSTEMS (Operational Tests)			X	

★ AUXILIARY TESTS TO BE MADE ONLY WHEN PREVIOUS TESTS OF SECTION ARE UNSATISFACTORY

Fig. 12–9. A test report supplied by a test-instrument manufacturer as a guide to the engine serviceman. By following the report step by step, the tester will avoid overlooking any important check. (*Sun Electric Corporation*)

putting the first half over the second, as:

$$1\text{-}2\text{-}7\text{-}8\text{-}4\text{-}5\text{-}6\text{-}3 \text{ would be } \frac{1\text{-}2\text{-}7\text{-}8}{4\text{-}5\text{-}6\text{-}3}$$

Then select the cylinders whose numbers are directly above and below each other, as 1 and 4. After running on 1 and 4, run engine on 2 and 5, then 7 and 6, then 8 and 3.

c. Note engine rpm and intake-manifold vacuum for each pair of cylinders. If one pair shows definitely lower readings, one of the two cylinders is weak or missing. To determine which one it is, short out half the cylinders (front or rear half in an in-line engine, one bank in a V-8). The half, or bank, giving the lower readings will contain the weak cylinder.

8. Check fuel system visually and by use of exhaust-gas analyzer (§ 282). The fuel-pump action can be tested to note whether it develops specified pressure and vacuum and can deliver specified amounts of gasoline.

9. Spark plugs should be removed, tested, cleaned, and regapped.

10. With the plugs out, check compression (§ 280).

11. Ignition system should then be checked. This includes tests of distributor-point setting, condition of points, rotor, cap, advance mechanisms, coil, condenser, and wiring.

12. During the above procedure, various other automotive components should be checked. For instance, radiator hose should be checked for wear and tightness of fastenings. Block, radiator, and hose should be examined for evidence of leaks. Mounting nuts, bolts, clamps, and so forth, should be checked for tightness on all accessory parts such as generator, carburetor, manifolds, regulator, cranking motor, and so on. Oil level in oil pan, water level in radiator, and air pressure in tires should be checked. In addition, the need for lubrication (oil change, oil-filter change, cleaning and reoiling air cleaner, chassis lubrication, and so forth) should be checked. Note mileages marked on the doorjamb sticker, and advise driver if any lubrication service is needed.

§ **289. Test reports** Test-instrument manufacturers may supply test-report sheets, such as the one shown in Fig. 12–9, to assist the engine serviceman in making the necessary tests on the car that is being diagnosed. The test report lists step by step the procedure to follow and the tests to be made. If the serviceman follows the procedure listed, he will not overlook any important check and will therefore arrive at a complete analysis of the engine condition. Since different testing instruments may operate in somewhat different ways, the test-report sheets issued by different companies will not be identical. Essentially, however, all are designed to give the same over-all information and to disclose any condition in the engine that could cause trouble.

The advantage of the test-report sheets from the standpoint of customer relations is that they nearly always make a very favorable impression on the customer. The customer is convinced that his car is getting a thorough check and that no important point will be overlooked.

REVIEW QUESTIONS

1. What is the purpose of the tachometer?
2. What is the purpose of the cylinder compression tester? How is it used?
3. What might cause low compression?
4. If pouring heavy oil into the cylinder increases compression, what has caused compression loss?
5. What is the purpose of the engine vacuum gauge, and how is it used?
6. Explain what the various readings on the vacuum gauge mean.
7. Explain how to use the exhaust-gas analyzer.

8. Explain how to use the timing light to time ignition.
9. What is engine tune-up? Name the major steps in a tune-up procedure.

STUDY QUESTIONS

1. Make a list of possible causes of compression loss.
2. List the different possible readings the vacuum gauge might give, and explain what would cause each.
3. List the major steps in a tune-up procedure.
4. How do you check for cylinder balance to find out whether any cylinder is missing or weak? Explain the procedure.

HOW TO STUDY

Most young men and women graduating from high school are convinced that they know at least something about how to study. Yet experiments and tests by psychologists show that many of these graduates could have done much better, made better grades, if they had improved their study habits.

There are certain fundamental habits that, once set up, will help you tremendously in your studies. In the first place, you should have a regular time and place to do your homework. It might be an hour and a half or two hours every evening, starting at seven. The study period might be split up, an hour in the morning before going to work and an hour in the evening. The important thing is to set this time aside each day and to use it for studying.

If possible, the place to study should be quiet, away from other family members. This well help you to concentrate.

Once you form the study habit, you will find it becomes increasingly easy to settle down to studying each day. You know you are studying for a good cause —to better yourself—and this knowledge will make studying all the more worthwhile.

And when you start to study, don't dawdle. As soon as you sit down, pick up your book or study materials and begin. Tell yourself, "Now, I am going to study!" and start in. This takes will power, but again, you know you must do it to get ahead. This is part of maturing, of getting ahead, of making the most of your opportunities.

THIS CHAPTER DISCUSSES VARIOUS engine troubles and explains what may cause these troubles. Further, it indicates how those troubles may be cured. In other words, the chapter covers engine trouble-shooting. Following chapters describe servicing and repair procedures to be used after a trouble has been tracked down to its cause.

§ 290. **Trouble-shooting chart** The chart that follows lists various engine complaints, their possible causes, and checks or corrections to be made. Use of the information in this chart will often greatly shorten the time required to correct a trouble. For, by following a logical procedure, the cause of trouble usually can be located quickly. On the other hand, haphazard guesswork wastes time and effort.

NOTE: The troubles and possible causes are not listed in the chart in the order of frequency of occurrence. That is, item 1 (or item *a* under "Possible Cause") does not necessarily occur more frequently than item 2 (or item *b*).

ENGINE TROUBLE-SHOOTING CHART

(See §§ 291–303 for detailed explanations of trouble causes and corrections listed below.)

Complaint	Possible Cause	Check or Correction
1. Engine will not turn over (§ 291)	a. Run-down battery	Recharge or replace
	b. Starting circuit open	Locate and eliminate open
	c. Bendix drive jammed	Free drive
	d. Cranking motor jammed	Remove for teardown and correction
	e. Engine jammed	Check engine to find trouble
	f. Also causes listed under item 3, "Engine turns over at normal speed but does not start," below. Driver may have run battery down trying to start	
2. Engine turns over slowly but does not start (§ 292)	a. Run-down battery	Recharge or replace
	b. Defective cranking motor	Replace or repair

Complaint	Possible Cause	Check or Correction
	c. Bad connections in starting circuit	Clean and tighten
	d. Undersized battery cables	Replace
	e. Also causes listed under item 3, "Engine turns over at normal speed but does not start," below. Driver may have run battery down trying to start	
3. Engine turns over at normal speed but does not start (§ 293)	a. Ignition system defective	Try spark test; check timing, ignition system
	b. Fuel system defective	Prime engine; check fuel pump, line, choke, carburetor
	c. Air leaks in intake manifold or carburetor	Tighten mounting; replace gasket as needed
	d. Engine defective	Check compression (see § 280), valve action, timing, etc.
4. Engine runs but misses—one cylinder (§ 294)	a. Defective spark plug	Clean or replace
	b. Distributor cap or lead defective	Replace
	c. Stuck valve	Free valve; service stem and guide
	d. Defective rings or piston	Replace; service piston, cylinder wall, as needed
	e. Defective head gasket	Replace
5. Engine runs but misses—different cylinders (§ 294)	a. Defective ignition	Check timing and ignition
	b. Defective fuel system	Check fuel pump, carburetor
	c. Loss of compression	Check compression (see § 280)
	d. Defective valve action	Check valve action with compression or vacuum test (see §§ 280 and 281)
	e. Defective rings	Check compression and vacuum; replace rings, service pistons, cylinder walls as needed
	f. Overheated engine	Check cooling system

Complaint	Possible Cause	Check or Correction
	g. Manifold heat-control valve sticking	Free valve
	h. Clogged exhaust	Check tail pipe, muffler; eliminate clogging
6. Engine lacks power, acceleration, or high-speed performance, hot or cold (§ 295)	a. Ignition defective	Check timing, distributor, wiring, condenser, coil, plugs
	b. Fuel system defective	Check carburetor, air cleaner, fuel pump
	c. Throttle valve not fully opening	Adjust linkage
	d. Clogged exhaust	Check tail pipe, muffler; eliminate clogging
	e. Loss of compression	Check compression (see § 280)
	f. Excessive carbon in engine	Remove carbon
	g. Defective valve action	Check with compression or vacuum tester (see §§ 280 and 281)
	h. Excessive rolling resistance from low tires, dragging brakes, wheel misalignment, etc.	Correct the defect causing rolling resistance
	i. Heavy oil	Use lighter oil
	j. Wrong or bad fuel	Use good fuel of correct octane
7. Engine lacks power, acceleration, or high-speed performance, hot only (§ 295)	a. Engine overheats	Check cooling system (see item 9 below)
	b. Defective choke	Repair or replace
	c. Sticking manifold heat-control valve	Free valve
	d. Vapor lock	Use different fuel, or shield fuel line
8. Engine lacks power, acceleration, or high-speed performance, cold only (§ 295)	a. Automatic choke stuck	Repair or replace
	b. Manifold heat-control valve stuck	Free valve
	c. Cooling-system thermostat stuck	Repair or replace
	d. Stuck engine valves	Free valves; service valve stems and guides as needed

Complaint	Possible Cause	Check or Correction
9. Engine overheats (§ 295)	a. Lack of water	Add water
	b. Ignition timing late	Retime
	c. Loose or broken fan	Tighten or replace
	d. Defective thermostat	Replace
	e. Clogged water jackets	Clean out
	f. Defective radiator hose	Replace
	g. Defective water pump	Repair or replace
	h. Insufficient engine oil	Add oil
	i. High-altitude, hot-climate operation	Drive more slowly; keep radiator filled
	j. Valve timing late	Retime
10. Rough idle (§ 297)	a. Carburetor idle adjustment incorrect	Readjust idle mixture and speed
	b. Other causes, which are listed under "Engine lacks power, etc." (items 6, 7, and 8 above)	
11. Engine stalls as it warms up (§ 298)	a. Choke valve closed	Open choke valve; free or repair automatic choke
	b. Manifold heat-control valve stuck	Free valve
	c. Engine overheats	See item 9, "Engine overheats," above
	d. Engine idling speed set too low	Increase idling speed to specified value
12. Engine stalls after idling or slow-speed drive (§ 298)	a. Defective fuel pump	Repair or replace fuel pump
	b. Overheating	See item 9, "Engine overheats," above
	c. High float level	Adjust
	d. Idling adjustment incorrect	Adjust
13. Engine stalls after high-speed drive (§ 298)	a. Vapor lock	Use different fuel, or shield fuel line
	b. Carburetor antipercolator defective	Check and repair
	c. Engine overheats	See item 9, above
14. Engine backfires (§ 299)	a. Ignition timing off	Retime
	b. Spark plugs of wrong heat range	Install correct plugs

276

Complaint	Possible Cause	Check or Correction
	c. Excessively rich or lean mixture	Repair or readjust fuel pump or carburetor
	d. Overheating of engine	See item 9, "Engine overheats," above
	e. Carbon in engine	Clean out
	f. Valves hot or sticking	Adjust; free; clean; replace if bad
	g. Cracked distributor cap	Replace cap
15. Smoky exhaust		
1) Blue smoke	Excessive oil consumption	See item 16 below and § 300
2) Black smoke	Excessively rich mixture	See item 18 below and § 302
16. Excessive oil consumption (§ 300)	a. External leaks	Correct seals; replace gaskets
	b. Burning oil in combustion chamber	Check valve-stem clearance, piston rings, cylinder walls, rod bearings, vacuum-pump diaphragm
	c. High-speed driving	Drive more slowly
17. Low oil pressure (§ 301)	a. Worn engine bearings	Replace
	b. Engine overheating	See item 9, above
	c. Oil dilution	Replace oil
	d. Lubricating-system defects	Check oil lines, oil pump, relief valve
18. Excessive fuel consumption (§ 302)	a. "Nervous" or "jack-rabbit" driver	Drive more reasonably
	b. High speed	Drive more slowly
	c. Short-run operation	Make longer runs
	d. Excessive fuel-pump pressure or pump leakage	Reduce pressure; repair pump
	e. Choke closed	Open; repair or replace automatic choke
	f. Clogged air cleaner	Clean
	g. High carburetor float level	Adjust
	h. Stuck or dirty float needle valve	Free and clean

Complaint	Possible Cause	Check or Correction
	i. Worn carburetor jets	Replace
	j. Stuck metering rod or full-power piston	Free
	k. Idle too rich or too fast	Adjust
	l. Stuck accelerator-pump check valve	Free
	m. Carburetor leaks	Replace gaskets, tighten screws, etc
	n. Faulty ignition	Check coil, condenser, timing, plugs, contact points, wiring
	o. Loss of engine compression	Check compression (see § 280)
	p. Defective valve action	Check with compression or vacuum tester (see §§ 280 and 281)
	q. Excessive rolling resistance from low tires, dragging brakes, wheel misalignment, etc.	Correct the defects causing rolling resistance
	r. Clutch slippage	Adjust or repair
19. Engine is noisy (see § 303)		
1) Regular clicking	Valve and tappet	Readjust valve clearance
2) Ping or chatter on load or acceleration	Spark knock due to low-octane fuel, carbon, advanced ignition timing, or causes listed under item 14, "Engine backfires," above	Use higher-octane fuel; remove carbon; retime ignition
3) Light knock or pound with engine floating	Worn connecting-rod bearing or crankpin, misaligned rod, lack of oil	Replace or adjust bearings; service crankpins; realign rod; correct lack of oil
4) Light double knock during idle	Worn or loose piston pin or bushing or lack of oil	Service pin and bushing; correct lack of oil
5) Chattering or rattling during acceleration	Worn rings, cylinder walls, low ring tension, broken rings	Service walls; replace rings

278

Complaint	Possible Cause	Check or Correction
6) Hollow, muffled bell-like sound, engine cold	Piston slap due to worn pistons, walls, collapsed piston skirts, excessive clearance, lack of oil, misaligned rods	Replace or resize pistons; service walls; align rods; correct lack of oil
7) Dull, heavy knock under load or acceleration, especially when cold	Regular noise, worn main bearings; irregular, worn end-thrust bearings	Replace or service bearings and crankshaft
8) Miscellaneous noises	Rattles, etc., from loosely mounted accessories; generator, horn, oil pan, etc.	Tighten mounting

§ 291. Engine will not turn over If the engine will not turn over when starting is attempted, turn on the headlights or dome light and try to start. The lights will (1) stay bright, (2) dim considerably, (3) dim slightly, (4) go out, (5) not burn at all.

1. If the lights stay bright, there is an open circuit in the cranking motor, switch, or main or control circuit. Check as outlined in § 364.

2. If the lights dim considerably, the battery may be run down, or there is mechanical trouble in the cranking motor or engine. If the battery checks O.K. with a hydrometer, remove the cranking-motor cover band and try to turn the armature by hand (do not use a screw driver since this could damage the armature). If the armature is jammed, remove the cranking motor for further analysis. On the Bendix-type cranking motor (which does not use a shift lever), the drive pinion may be jammed. If the armature turns readily, the trouble is probably in the engine.

3. If the lights dim only slightly, listen for cranking-motor action (sound of an electric motor running). If it runs, the pinion is not engaging the engine flywheel (this trouble could happen only on Bendix-type units and would be due to a stuck pinion). If the armature does not rotate, the pinion may be engaging the flywheel but excessive resistance or an open circuit in the cranking motor is preventing formal action.

4. If the lights go out as cranking is attempted, chances are there is a bad connection in the main circuit, probably at a battery terminal.

5. If the lights burn dimly or not at all when they are turned on, even before cranking is attempted, the battery is probably run down.

§ 292. Engine turns over slowly but does not start Causes of this condition could be a run-down battery, a defective cranking motor, undersized battery cables, or mechanical trouble in the engine. Check the battery, cranking motor, and circuit as outlined in Chap. 15. If they are normal, the

trouble probably is in the engine (defective bearings, rings, and so on, that could produce high friction). Remember that, in cold weather, cranking speed is reduced by thickening of the engine oil and reduction of battery efficiency.

NOTE: If the battery is run down, it could be that the driver has discharged the battery in a vain attempt to start. In such a case, the cause of starting failure could be as noted in the following paragraphs.

§ 293. Engine turns over at normal cranking speed but does not start

This means the battery and cranking motor are in normal condition. The cause of trouble is probably in the ignition or fuel system. Disconnect the lead from one spark plug (or from center distributor-cap terminal), and hold it about three-sixteenths inch from the engine block. Crank the engine to see if a good spark occurs. If no spark occurs, check the ignition system. If a spark does occur, the ignition system is probably O.K. (timing could be off, however).

If the ignition system seems to be operating normally, the fuel system should be analyzed. First, prime the engine by operating the carburetor accelerator pump several times. Or remove the air cleaner, and squirt a small amount of gasoline from an oil can into the carburetor air horn.

▶*CAUTION:* Gasoline is highly explosive! Keep back out of the way while priming the engine; the engine might backfire through the carburetor.

If the engine now starts and runs

for a few seconds, the fuel system is probably faulty; it is not delivering fuel to the engine. Loosen or disconnect the fuel inlet to the carburetor temporarily, hold cloths around the fuel line, and crank the engine to see whether fuel is delivered. If it is not, the fuel pump is defective or the fuel line is clogged. If fuel is delivered, the carburetor is probably at fault (jets or circuits clogged), the automatic choke is not working correctly, or possibly there are air leaks into the intake manifold or carburetor.

NOTE: The above analysis applies to a cold engine. Failure to start with a hot engine may be due to a defective choke that fails to open properly as the engine warms up. This would cause flooding of the engine (delivery of too much gasoline). Open throttle wide while cranking (this dechokes engine), or open choke valve by hand while cranking.

§ 294. Engine runs but misses

A missing engine is a rough engine; failure of cylinders to fire throws the engine out of balance so that roughness and loss of power are evident. It is sometimes hard to track down a miss since it might occur at some speeds or throttle openings and not others. Also, a miss may skip around from cylinder to cylinder.

1. One method of tracking down a miss is to short out each cylinder spark plug in turn with a screw driver. The screw driver should have an insulated handle so that you do not get shocked. Put the screw-driver shank between the spark-plug terminal and the engine block. This prevents a spark from oc-

curing so the cylinder will miss. If the engine rhythm or speed changes, then that cylinder was delivering power. If no change occurs, the cylinder was missing before the plug was shorted out. All cylinders can be tested in this way very quickly.

2. A more accurate method of checking for missing cylinders is outlined in §288.

3. Check a missing cylinder further by removing the spark-plug lead and holding it close to the engine block while the engine is running. If no spark occurs, there is probably a high-tension leak due to a bad lead or a cracked or burned distributor cap. If a good spark occurs, install a new spark plug in the cylinder, reconnect the lead, and see whether the cylinder still misses. If it does, the cause of the trouble is probably defective engine parts such as valves or rings.

4. If the miss is hard to locate, perform a general tune-up (§288). This will disclose and may eliminate various causes of missing, including defects in ignition system, defects in fuel system, loss of engine compression, sticky or damaged engine valves, overheated engine, manifold heat control sticking, a clogged exhaust, and so on.

§ 295. Engine lacks power This is a rather general complaint that is often difficult to analyze. The best procedure is to perform a tune-up (§288) since this will disclose various engine conditions that could cause loss of power. Some idea of the cause of trouble can be gained by determining whether the engine lacks power only when cold, only when hot, or either hot or cold.

NOTE: The chassis dynamometer accurately measures engine horsepower (§ 287) and is very useful in analyzing this type of complaint.

1. If the engine lacks power and acceleration either hot or cold, the fuel system may not be enriching the mixture as the throttle is opened. This could be due to a faulty accelerator pump or defective high-speed or full-power circuit in the carburetor. Also, the fuel system could be supplying an excessively lean or rich mixture (fuel pump defective, lines clogged, filter clogged, carburetor jets or lines worn, air leaks at carburetor or manifold joints, and so on). The throttle linkage may be preventing full throttle opening. The ignition system may be causing trouble owing to incorrect timing, a "weak" coil, wrong spark-plug heat range, and so on. The wrong fuel or oil for the engine could reduce performance. In the engine, numerous conditions could cause loss of power, including engine deposits (carbon), lack of compression (faulty valves, rings, worn cylinder walls, pistons, and so on), and defective bearings. A clogged exhaust (bent tail pipe or clogged muffler) could create back pressure that would cause poor engine performance. Also, any sort of excessive rolling resistance would absorb engine power and hold down engine acceleration and speed. This would include dragging brakes, underinflated tires, misaligned wheels, and excessive friction in the transmission or power train.

2. If the engine lacks power only when hot, the engine may be overheating (§ 296), the automatic choke may not be opening normally as the engine

warms up, the manifold heat-control valve may be stuck, or there may be a vapor lock in the fuel pump or line (§ 240).

3. If the engine lacks power when cold or reaches operating temperature too slowly, the automatic choke may be leaning out the mixture too soon (before the engine warms up), the manifold heat-control valve may not be closed (so that insufficient heat reaches the intake manifold), or the cooling-system thermostat may be stuck open. In this case, water circulation goes on between the engine and radiator even with the engine cold, and so warm-up is delayed. Occasionally engine valves may stick when the engine is cold, but as the engine warms up, the valves become free and work normally.

§ 296. Engine overheats   The first thought that comes to mind when an engine overheats is that the cooling system is not functioning properly. Such faults in the cooling system as lack of water, loose or broken fan belt, defective water pump, clogged water jackets, defective radiator hose, or defective thermostat could cause engine overheating. However, late ignition or valve timing, lack of engine oil, or high-altitude or hot-climate operation may cause overheating. Also, freezing of the cooling water could cause lack of water circulation so that local hot spots and boiling would take place.

§ 297. Rough idle   If the engine idles roughly but runs normally above idle, the chances are that the idle speed and mixture are incorrectly adjusted. But the rough idle could be due to other causes (see § 295).

§ 298. Engine stalls   If the engine starts and then stalls, note whether the stalling takes place as the engine warms up, or after idling or slow-speed driving, or after high-speed or full-load driving.

1. *Engine stalls as it warms up.* This could result if the choke valve is stuck closed; the mixture becomes too rich for a hot engine, and so the engine stalls. If the manifold heat-control valve sticks, the air-fuel mixture might become overheated and too lean, causing the engine to stall. If the hot-idle speed is too low, the engine may stall as it warms up because the idling speed drops too low. Also, stalling may be caused by overheating of the engine (see § 296).

2. *Engine stalls after idling or slow-speed driving.* This could occur if the fuel pump has a cracked diaphragm, weak spring, or defective valve. The pump fails to deliver enough fuel for idling or slow-speed operation (although it could deliver enough for high-speed operation). If the carburetor float level is set too high or the idle adjustment is too rich, the engine may "load up" and stall. A lean idle adjustment may also cause stalling. The engine may overheat during sustained idling or slow-speed driving; with this condition, the air movement through the radiator may not be sufficient to keep the engine cool. Overheating, in turn, could cause the engine to stall. (See § 296 for other causes of overheating).

3. *Engine stalls after high-speed*

driving. This could occur if enough heat accumulates to cause a vapor lock (§ 240). The remedy here would be to shield the fuel line and pump or use a less volatile fuel. Failure of the antipercolator in the carburetor may also cause stalling after high-speed operation. And, of course, overheating of the engine could cause stalling (§ 296).

§ 299. **Engine backfires** This could be due to late ignition timing, ignition cross-firing (due to spark jumping across distributor cap or through cable insulation), spark plugs of the wrong heat range (which overheat and cause preignition), excessively rich or lean mixtures (due to· fuel-pump or carburetor troubles), overheating of the engine (§ 296), carbon in the engine, hot valves, or intake valves that stick or seat poorly. Carbon in the engine, if ·excessive, may retain enough heat to cause the air-fuel mixture to preignite as it enters the cylinder so that back-firing occurs. Carbon also increases the compression ratio and thus the tendency for knocking and preignition. Hot plugs may cause preignition; cooler plugs should be installed. If intake valves hang open, combustion may be carried back into the carburetor. Also, valves which have been ground excessively so that they have sharp edges or those which seat poorly, or are carboned so that they overheat, will often produce backfiring.

§ 300. **Excessive oil consumption** Oil is lost from the engine in three ways: by burning in the combustion chamber, by leakage in liquid form, and by pass-ing out of the crankcase through the crankcase ventilating system in the form of mist or vapor.

External leakage can often be ·detected by inspecting the seals around the oil pan, valve cover plate, timing-gear housing, or at oil-line and filter connections.

Burning of oil in the combustion chamber gives the exhaust gas a bluish tinge. Oil can enter the combustion chamber in three ways: through a cracked vacuum-pump diaphragm, through clearance between. intake-valve stems and valve guides, and past piston rings. The vacuum pump can be quickly checked by operating the windshield wipers and then quickly accelerating the engine. If the wipers stop, this means that the vacuum-pump diaphragm is cracked. Oil can pass through this crack into the combustion chamber. This check · applies only to cars equipped with a combination fuel and vacuum pump.

If intake-valve-stem clearance is excessive, oil will be "pulled" through this clearance and into the combustion chamber on each intake stroke. The appearance of the intake-valve stem often indicates that this is occurring; some of the oil remains on the underside of the valve and stem to form carbon. The remedy is to install valve packing or a new valve guide and possibly valve.

Probably the most common cause of excessive oil consumption is passage of oil into the combustion chamber between the piston rings and cylinder walls. This is often called "oil pumping" and is due to worn, tapered, or out-of-round cylinder walls or to worn or carboned rings. In addition, when

engine bearings are worn, excessive oil will be thrown on the cylinder walls. The rings will not be able to control all of it, and too much will work up into the combustion chamber.

High speed must also be considered in any analysis of excessive oil consumption. High speed means high temperatures and thus thin oil. More oil, and thinner oil, is thrown on the cylinder walls at high speed. The piston rings, moving at high speed, cannot function so effectively, and more oil works up into the combustion chamber. In addition, the churning effect on the oil in the crankcase creates more oil vapor and mist at high speed. More oil is thus lost through the crankcase ventilating system. Tests have shown that an engine will use several times as much oil at 60 mph (miles per hour) as at 30 mph.

§ 301. **Low oil pressure** Low oil pressure is often a warning of worn engine bearings. The bearings can pass so much oil that the oil pump cannot maintain oil pressure. Further, the end bearings will probably be oil-starved and may fail. Other causes of low oil pressure are a weak relief-valve spring, worn oil pump, broken or cracked oil line, or a clogged oil line. Oil dilution, sludge, insufficient oil, or oil made too thin by engine overheating will cause low oil pressure.

§ 302. **Excessive fuel consumption** This condition can be caused by almost anything in the car, from the driver to underinflated tires or a defective choke. A fuel-milage tester can be used to accurately check fuel con-

sumption (§ 283). The compression tester (§ 280) and vacuum gauge (§ 281) will help determine whether the trouble is in the engine, fuel system, ignition system or elsewhere.*

If the trouble seems to be in the fuel system, consider the following:

1. A "nervous" driver who pumps the accelerator when idling and insists on being the first to get away when the stop light changes will use excessive amounts of fuel.

2. Operation with the choke partly closed after warm-up will use excessive amounts of fuel.

3. Short-run operation means the engine will be operating on warm-up most of the time. This means fuel consumption will be high.

These three conditions are due to the type of operation; changing operating conditions is the only cure. If the excessive fuel consumption is not due to any of these, then check the fuel pump for excessive pressure. High fuel-pump pressure will cause a high float-bowl level and a rich mixture.

4. If excessive fuel consumption is not due to high fuel-pump pressure or to operating conditions, the trouble is

* A rough test of mixture richness that does not require any testing instruments is to install a set of new or cleaned spark plugs of the correct heat range for the engine and to operate the car for 15 or 20 minutes, then stop the car, and remove and examine the plugs. If they are coated with a black carbon deposit, the indication is that the mixture is too rich. (See points *a* to *g* under item 4 below.) Black exhaust smoke is another indication of an excessively rich mixture: the mixture is too rich to burn fully, and so the exhaust gas contains "soot," or unburned fuel.

likely to be in the carburetor and could be any of the following:

a. If the car is equipped with an automatic choke, the choke may not be opening rapidly enough during warm-up or may not fully open. This can be checked by removing the air cleaner and observing the choke operation during warm-up.

b. A clogged air cleaner that does not admit sufficient air will act somewhat like a partly closed choke valve. The cleaner element should be cleaned or replaced.

c. If the float level is high in the float bowl, it will cause flooding and delivery of excessive fuel to the carburetor air horn. The needle valve may be stuck open or may not be seating fully. The float level should be checked and adjusted.

d. If the idle is set too rich or the idle speed too high, excessive fuel consumption will result. These should be checked and adjusted as necessary.

e. Where the accelerator-pump circuit has a check valve, failure of the check valve to close properly may allow fuel to feed through into the carburetor air horn. The carburetor will require disassembly for repair.

f. If the metering rod is stuck in the high-speed full-throttle position or the economizer valve holds open, it will permit the high-speed full-power circuit to function, supplying an excessively rich mixture. The carburetor will require disassembly for repair.

g. Worn jets, permitting the discharge of too much fuel, require replacement during carburetor rebuilding.

5. Faulty ignition can also cause excessive fuel consumption; the ignition system could cause engine miss and thus failure of the engine to utilize all the fuel. This sort of trouble would also be associated with loss of power, acceleration, or high-speed performance (§ 295). Conditions in the ignition system that might contribute to the trouble include a "weak" coil or condenser, incorrect timing, faulty advance-mechanism action, dirty or worn plugs or contact points, or defective wiring.

6. Inferior engine action can produce excessive fuel consumption; for example, loss of engine compression from worn or stuck rings, worn or stuck valves, or a loose or burned cylinder-head gasket cause loss of power; more fuel must be burned to achieve the same speed. (Refer to § 280 for compression checking procedure.)

7. Excessive fuel consumption can also result from conditions that make it hard for the engine to move the car along the road. Such factors as low tires, dragging brakes, and misalignment of wheels increase the rolling resistance of the car. The engine must use up more fuel to overcome this excessive rolling resistance.

§ 303. **Engine noises** Various types of engine noises may be found, some of which have little significance. Other noises may indicate serious engine trouble that will require prompt attention to prevent major damage to the engine. Characteristics of various noises and their causes are described below, along with tests that may be necessary to confirm a diagnosis. Following chapters describe corrections of these causes.

A listening rod will be of help in locating the source of a noise. The rod acts somewhat like the stethoscope that a doctor uses to listen to a patient's heartbeat or breathing. When one end is placed at the ear and the other end at some particular part of the engine, noises from that part of the engine will be carried along the rod to the ear. A long screw driver or one of the engine stethoscopes now available can be used. When using the listening rod to locate the source of a noise, put the engine end at various places on the engine until the noise is the loudest. You can also use a piece of garden hose (about 4 feet long) to localize engine noises. Hold one end of the hose to your ear, and move the other end of the hose around the engine until the noise is the loudest. By determining the approximate source of the noise, you can, for example, locate a broken and noisy ring in a particular cylinder or a main-bearing knock.

▶ CAUTION: Keep away from the moving fan belt and fan when using the listening rod.

1. *Valve and tappet noise.* This is a regular clicking noise that increases in intensity as engine speed increases. The cause is usually excessive valve clearance. A feeler gauge inserted between the valve stem and lifter or rocker arm will reduce clearance. If the noise also is reduced, then the cause is excessive clearance; clearance should be readjusted. If inserting the feeler gauge does not reduce noise, the noise is resulting from such conditions in the valve mechanism as weak springs, worn lifter faces, lifters loose in block, rough adjustment-screw face,

or rough cams, or else the noise is not from the valves at all. (See other conditions listed below.)

2. *Spark knock.* Spark knock, or rap, is a pinging or chattering sound most noticeable during acceleration or when the car is climbing a hill. Some spark knock is normal, but when it becomes excessive, it is due to any of several conditions such as use of fuel of excessive low-octane rating for the engine, carbon deposits in engine which increase compression ratio, advanced ignition timing, or conditions described in § 299.

3. *Connecting-rod noises.* Connecting-rod noises usually have a light knocking or pounding character. The sound is most noticeable when the engine is "floating" (not accelerating or decelerating). The sound becomes more noticeable as the accelerator is eased off with the car running at medium speed. To locate connecting-rod noise, short out spark plugs one at a time. The noise will be considerably reduced when the cylinder that is responsible is not delivering power. A worn bearing or crankpin, a misaligned connecting rod, inadequate oil, or excessive bearing clearances cause connecting-rod noise.

4. *Piston-pin noise.* Piston-pin noise is somewhat similar to valve and tappet noise, but it has a metallic double-knock characteristic. In addition, it is usually most audible during idle with the spark advanced. However, on some engines, the noise becomes most audible at car speeds of around thirty miles per hour. A check can be made by running the engine at idle with the spark advanced and then shorting out spark plugs. Piston-pin noise will be

reduced somewhat when a plug in a noisy cylinder is shorted out. Causes of this noise are a worn or loose piston pin, worn bushing, or lack of oil.

5. *Piston-ring noise.* Piston-ring noise is also somewhat similar to valve and tappet noise since it is characterized by a clicking, snapping, or rattling noise. This noise, however, is most evident on acceleration. Low ring tension, broken rings, or worn rings or cylinder walls produce this noise. Since the noise can sometimes be confused with other engine noises, a test can be made as follows: Remove the spark plugs, and add an ounce or two of heavy engine oil in each cylinder. Crank the engine for several revolutions to work the oil down past the rings. Then replace the plugs, and start the engine. If the noise has been reduced, it is probable that the rings are at fault.

6. *Piston slap.* Piston slap is characterized by a muffled, hollow, bell-like sound and is due to the rocking back and forth of the piston in the cylinder. If it occurs only with the engine cold, it should not be considered serious. When it occurs under all operating conditions, further investigation is in order. It is caused by inadequate oil, worn cylinder walls or pistons, collapsed piston skirts, excessive piston clearances, or misaligned connecting rods.

7. *Crankshaft knock.* This noise is a heavy and dull metallic knock most noticeable when the engine is under a heavy load or accelerating, particularly when cold. When the noise is regular, it probably results from worn main bearings. When the noise is irregular and sharp, it is probably due to worn end-thrust bearing. This latter condi-

tion, when unusually bad, will cause the noise to be produced each time the clutch is released and engaged.

8. *Miscellaneous noises.* Other noises result from loosely mounted accessory parts, such as generator, cranking motor, horn, water pump, manifolds, flywheel, crankshaft pulley, oil pan, and so forth. In addition, other automotive components such as the clutch, transmission, and differential may develop various noises.

REVIEW QUESTIONS

1. What could be possible causes if the engine will not turn over? How do you use the lights to check for the cause?
2. What could be the cause if the engine turns over slowly but does not start?
3. What could be the cause if the engine turns over at normal cranking speed but does not start? How do you check the ignition system with this condition? The fuel system?
4. What could cause the engine to miss?
5. What could cause the engine to lack power, acceleration, or high-speed performance?
6. What could cause the engine to overheat?
7. What could cause the engine to stall as it warms up? After prolonged idling? After high-speed driving?
8. What could cause the engine to backfire?
9. What could cause excessive oil consumption?
10. What could cause excessive fuel consumption?

11. Describe various engine noises, and explain what could cause them.

STUDY QUESTIONS

1. Make lists of various engine troubles, their causes, and their corrections. Study these lists to learn them thoroughly.
2. Write down the procedure for using the lights to find the cause if the engine fails to turn over.
3. Write down the procedure for checking the ignition system by the spark test.
4. Write down the procedure for priming the engine to check the fuel system.
5. Write down the procedure for using a screw driver to track down a miss.

REMEMBERING WHAT YOU READ

When you are reading relatively unfamiliar subject matter, it is hard to remember what you read. We have all had the experience of reading a page with wandering mind, half convinced that everything is clear, and then suddenly realizing that nothing on that page has stuck with us. This is almost worse than not trying to read at all. For if you continue to do this, you form a bad habit that is hard to break. However, there is a way to break such a habit and to improve your reading skills so that you do remember what you read.

First, pause after every paragraph or even after every sentence and tell yourself just what you have read. Repeat the sense of it. That is, try to pick out the basic facts in the sentence or paragraph and tell yourself—out loud if you want to—what the facts are.

For example, suppose you read, while studying about the engine, that "There are two openings, or ports, in the enclosed end of the engine cylinder." Now, what have you just read? Tell yourself the facts, but in your own words. You might say, for instance, "One end of the cylinder is closed except for two openings called ports."

See what you've done? You have taken the sentence and repeated the sense of it to yourself in your own words. You have intelligently thought about it. You have learned an important fact about engine cylinders. By now you will find it hard to forget that the enclosed end of the engine cylinder has two ports.

To learn a fact, therefore, think about it intelligently. Phrase it in your own words. That is the essence of studying. Just remember—and use—the procedure. It will be hard at first, but as you progress, it will become increasingly easier. Soon, if you continue to use the procedure, you will find it has become second nature to you. Furthermore, the facts will stick with you. Your memory will improve.

THIS CHAPTER DESCRIBES VARIOUS engine services and explains how various troubles mentioned in previous chapters are corrected. Following chapters discuss servicing of the electric, fuel, lubricating, and cooling systems. You will notice, in the discussions of various engine-servicing jobs, that the time to do the job is often given. These figures are included to give you some idea of the size of the job and should not be considered to be accurate enough for cost-estimating service jobs.

§ 304. Cleanliness   The major enemy of good service work is dirt. A trace of dirt left on a bearing or cylinder wall could ruin an otherwise good service job. Thus, you must be absolutely sure that you do not leave dirt or abrasive in the engine or on engine parts when you finish a service job.

Before any major service job, the block should be cleaned. Electrical units should be removed or covered if the engine is steam-cleaned so that moisture does not get into them.

VALVES AND VALVE TRAINS

§ 305. Valve troubles   Valves must be properly timed. They must seat tightly and operate without lag. Valve-tappet clearance, as well as the clearance between the valve stems and guides, must be correct. Failure to meet any of these requirements means valve and engine trouble.

As an example, suppose the clear-ance between valve stems and guides is excessive. This means that, on every intake stroke, oil will be pulled past the intake-valve stem and into the combustion chamber, where it will be burned. This, in turn, can lead to excessive oil consumption, engine deposits, preignition, clogged piston rings, and fouled spark plugs. Valve action may be hindered by carbon build-up on the valves and stems. This further reduces engine performance and may lead to valve burning. Thus, it can be seen that an apparently minor fault like excessive valve-stem clearance can cause serious engine trouble. This emphasizes the importance of performing every engine service correctly. Being slightly "off" on one measurement could cause serious engine trouble.

§ 306. Types of trouble   Valve troubles include sticking, burning, breakage, wear, and deposits. Following articles supply information on the various valve services.

§ 307. Valve sticking   Gum or carbon deposits on the valve stem (§ 311) will cause valve sticking. Excessive valve-stem clearance speeds up valve deposits. Another cause of valve sticking is warped stems. This could result from overheating, an eccentric seat (which throws side pressure on valve), or from a cocked spring or retainer (which tends to bend stem). Insufficient oil would also cause valve stick-

ing. Sometimes valves will stick when cold but will work free as the engine warms up.

NOTE: When valves and piston rings are badly clogged with deposits, an engine overhaul is usually required. However, there are certain compounds that can be put in the fuel or oil which will help to free rings and valves. When parts are not too badly worn, and the major trouble seems to be from deposits, use of these compounds often postpones engine overhaul.

§ 308. Valve burning This is usually an exhaust-valve problem. Any condition that prevents normal exhaust-valve seating may lead to valve burning. The poor seating prevents normal valve cooling through the valve seat. It also allows hot gases to blow by, further heating the valve. A worn guide also prevents normal valve cooling. If water circulation around the valve seat is impeded—by clogged distribution tubes or jackets, for example—local hot spots may develop. This could cause seat distortion, poor seating, and overheated valves. Seat dis-

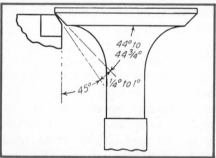

Fig. 14–1. Interference angle between valve face and seat. The seat and interference angles have been exaggerated to show how sealing pressure is applied mostly at upper edge of seat.

290

tortion can also result from improper cylinder-head-bolt tightening. Other conditions that could prevent normal seating include a weak or cocked valve spring and insufficient valve-tappet clearance.

Engine overloading or overheating will cause hot valves. A lean air-fuel mixture may cause valve burning; in this case, the fuel system should be serviced. Preignition or detonation, which produce high combustion pressures and temperatures, are hard on valves as well as other engine parts. Correction is to clean out carbon, re-time the ignition, and use higher-octane fuel.

In some persistent cases of seat leakage (especially where deposits on the valve seat and face prevent normal seating), the use of an "interference angle" has proved helpful. The valve is faced at an angle $\frac{1}{4}$ to 1 degree flatter than the seat angle (Fig. 14–1). This produces greater pressure at the upper edge of the valve seat; the valve-seat edge thus tends to cut through any deposits that have formed and thereby establish a good seal.

Sometimes valve stems will stretch owing to overheating and to valve heavy springs. Lighter springs and elimination of overheating (§ 296) are the remedy here.

§ 309. Valve breakage Any condition that causes the valve to overheat (§ 308) or to be subjected to heavy pounding (as from excessive tappet clearance or from detonation) may cause valves to break. Excessive tappet clearance permits heavy impact seating. If the seat is eccentric to the stem or if the valve spring or retainer

is cocked, then the valve will be subjected to side movement or pressure every time it seats. Ultimately, this may cause it to fatigue and break. If the stem has been scratched during cleaning, the scratch may serve as a starting point for a crack and a break in the stem.

§ 310. **Valve-face wear** In addition to the conditions discussed in § 308 (Valve burning), excessive tappet clearance or dirt on the valve face or seat could cause valve-face wear. Excessive tappet clearance causes heavy impact seating that is wearing on the valve and may cause valve breakage (§ 309). Dirt may cause valve-face wear if the engine operates in dusty conditions or if the carburetor air cleaner is not functioning properly. The dust enters the engine with the air-fuel mixture, and some of it deposits on the valve seat. The dust will also cause bearing, cylinder-wall, and piston and ring wear.

§ 311. **Valve deposits** If the fuel has excessive amounts of gum in it, some of this gum may deposit on the intake valve as the air-fuel mixture passes the valve on the way to the engine cylinder. Carbon deposits may form from an excessively rich mixture or from oil passing a worn valve guide (intake valve). Improper combustion, due to a rich mixture, defective ignition system, loss of compression in the engine, a cold engine, and so forth, will result in carbon deposits on the exhaust valves. Dirty or improper oil will cause deposits to form on the valves.

§ 312. **Valve service** Valve service

includes adjusting valve-tappet clearances (also called *adjusting valve lash*), grinding valves and valve seats, installing new seat inserts, cleaning or replacing valve guides, servicing the camshaft and camshaft bearings, and timing the valves. A complete valve-service job, including grinding valves and seats, checking springs, cleaning guides, and tuning the engine, requires from about 5 hours (overhead-valve six-cylinder engine) to about 8 hours (eight-cylinder L-head engine). Replacing the camshaft requires about 8 hours; 4 additional hours is required for replacing camshaft bearings.

§ 313. **Valve-tappet clearance** Checking and adjusting valve-tappet clearance requires different procedures in different types and models of engines. Engines with hydraulic valve lifters normally require no tappet-clearance adjustment as noted below. Following are typical procedures.

▶*CAUTION:* Where a pressure-type radiator cap is used (§ 275), it should be removed during the adjusting procedure to prevent excessive engine temperatures.

1. L-head engine. Remove valve-cover plates, and use feeler gauges to

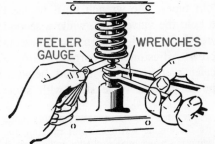

Fig. 14–2. Adjusting valve-tappet clearance (or valve lash) on L-head engine.

291

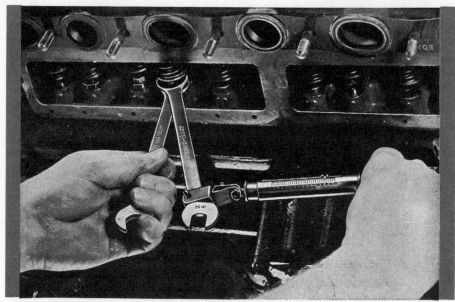

Fig. 14–3. Measuring force required to turn the self-locking adjustment screw in valve lifter. (*Studebaker-Packard Corporation*)

measure clearance between the valve stem and the adjusting screw in the valve lifter (Fig. 14–2). Engine should be warmed up and idling.* If clearance is not correct, the adjusting screw must be turned in or out as necessary to correct it. Some tappet-adjusting screws are self-locking; others have a locking nut. On the second type, the locking nut must be loosened. This requires two wrenches, one to hold the screw, the other to turn the nut. Then, on both types, one wrench must be used to hold the valve lifter, while a second wrench is used to turn the adjusting screw. Adjustment is correct when the feeler gauge can be moved between the screw and valve stem with some

* On a few engines, measurement is made with the engine warm and not running; the engine is turned over until the valve lifter is on the low point of the cam, and the clearance is then checked.

292

drag when the valve is closed. When a locking nut is used, it should be tightened after the adjustment is made and the clearance again checked. On the self-locking type of adjusting screw, find out how much force is required to turn the screw by using a spring gauge hooked to a wrench (Fig. 14–3). If the screw turns too easily, the self-locking feature is worn and a new valve-lifter-and-screw assembly should be installed. After the adjustment is completed, replace the cover plates, using new gaskets.

2. *I-head engine.* On the overhead-valve engine, the valve cover must be removed and the clearance measured with a feeler gauge between the valve stem and the rocker arm. The engine must be warmed up and running at fast idle. Adjustment varies according to engine construction. Many rocker arms have an adjusting screw and locking

nut. This type of rocker arm is mounted on a rocker-arm shaft (Fig. 6–56). Adjustment is made on these by loosening the locking nut and turning the adjusting screw (Fig. 14–4a). On other engines, the rocker arms are individually supported by studs, ball seats, and nuts (Fig. 6–58). On these, adjustment is made by turning the self-locking rocker-arm-stud nut until the specified clearance between the valve stem and rocker arm is attained (Fig. 14–4b).

3. *F-head engine.* This engine (Fig. 5–7) requires a combined L-head and I-head adjusting procedure. In-block valves are checked and adjusted as in an L-head engine. In-head valves are checked and adjusted as in an I-head

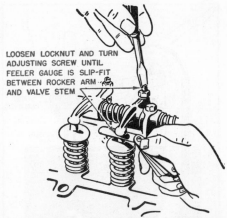

Fig. 14–4a. Adjustment of valve-tappet clearance (or valve lash) on overhead-valve engine.

engine. Valves of the free type (§ 143) have the clearance check made between

Fig. 14–4b. Adjusting valve-tappet clearance on engine with rocker arms independently mounted on ball studs. Backing stud nut out increases clearance. (*Chevrolet Motor Division of General Motors Corporation*)

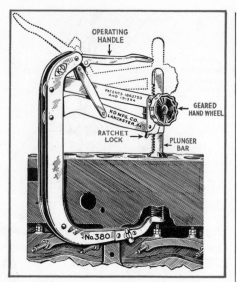

Fig. 14–5. Valve-spring compressor in place on engine. Geared hand wheel provides initial adjustment. Operation of handle (from position shown dotted) then compresses the spring. (*K-D Manufacturing Company*)

the tip cup on the valve stem and the adjusting screw in the valve lifter (not between the valve stem and screw).

4. *Ford engines.* Some Ford engines are L-head, others are I-head. Adjustment on these is basically as described in previous paragraphs. On the type of Ford engine using the valve design shown in Figs. 14–7 or 14–9, the only provision for adjustment is this: grind off the valve stem to increase clearance; grind the valve to reduce clearance. Clearance is checked between the lifter and valve stem with a "go, no-go," or stepped, feeler gauge (Fig. 1–53). The go part of the gauge should fit the clearance between the lifter and valve stem (engine stopped and valve closed). If the go part does not enter, the clearance is too small and the valve stem must be ground off.

294

If the no-go part enters, the clearance is excessive and refacing of the valve or valve seat is required. Clearances must then be rechecked and the valve stem ground if necessary.

5. *Hydraulic valve lifters.* Engines with hydraulic valve lifters normally require no valve-tappet-clearance checks or adjustments. However, on some engines, there is provision for an initial adjustment. Such an adjustment is normally required on these engines only after valve work has been done. Refer to the manufacturer's shop manual, and follow the specifications given there.

§ 314. **Valve removal** Before removing the valves, the cylinder head must be taken off (§ 317) and carbon removed from the head and block (§ 320). Valves and valve parts must not be interchanged; each valve, with its own spring, retainer, and lock, must be replaced in the same valve port from which it was removed. Different valve-removing procedures are outlined below.

1. *L-head engines.* If manifolds interfere with valve removal, they must be taken off the engine (§ 319). Then, a valve-spring compressor or lifter (Figs. 14–5 and 14–6) can be used to compress the valve spring. This releases the retainer lock, or keeper, so that it can be removed from the valve stem. Various types of locks are shown in Fig. 6–54. Do not allow the lock to fall down into the crankcase; it could jam into moving parts and cause serious damage. Close openings through which the lock could drop with clean cloths, or use a magnet to hold the lock as it is released (Fig. 14–6). With

Fig. 14–6. Removing retainer lock with magnet. Magnet attracts lock as it is loosened so that it does not fall down into crankcase. Note that, with the spring lifter being used, the manifolds do not have to be removed from this engine. (*Studebaker-Packard Corporation*)

the lock off, the valve may be removed from the top of the block. Then, the spring can be taken out.

　　2. Ford L-head engines. Ford L-

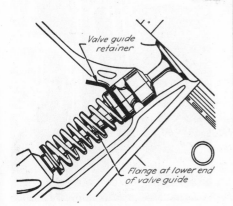

Fig. 14–7. Valve, split valve guide, and retainer arrangement used in Ford engine. (*K-D Manufacturing Company*)

head engines use the valve, valve guide, and retainer arrangements shown in Figs. 14–7 to 14–9. On the earlier type, the valve guide is split and the lower end of the valve stem is enlarged so as to hold the spring retainer in place. The retainer has a slot on one side so that it can slip onto the upper valve stem. Then, it anchors on the enlarged lower end to hold the valve spring in position. On the later type, the valve guide is in one piece. The valve stem is straight and has an undercut to hold the valve-spring-retainer locks in position. With both types, the valve guide, spring, and valve are removed as a unit from the engine and separated after they are out. Both types have a valve-guide retainer to hold the guide in place.

295

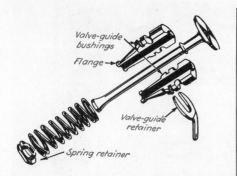

Fig. 14–8. Valve, spring, split valve guide, and retainers used in Ford engines in disassembled view. (K-D Manufacturing Company)

The valve-guide retainer must be removed as a first step in valve removal. This is done in either of two ways. One method is to insert a bar-type lifter through the valve springs and above the flange on the valve guide (see Fig. 14–7). Then, prying on the flange will move the guide down far enough to permit the retainer to be pulled out. The second method uses a driver which is hooked into the retainer. Driving against the retainer pulls the retainer.

The valve-spring-and-guide assembly can be removed after the retainers are

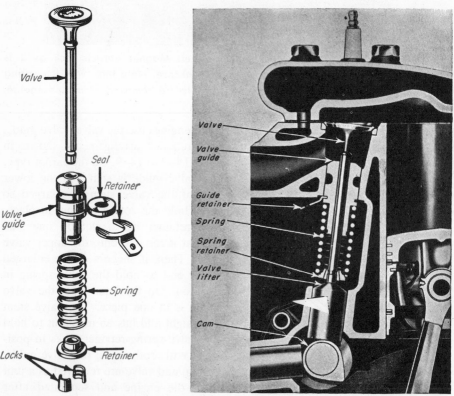

Fig. 14–9. Left, disassembled and right, sectional views of valve mechanism using one-piece valve guide. The disassembled view shows a seal not shown in the sectional view. (Ford Motor Company)

off. If the guide sticks, a guide puller may be required (Fig. 14–10). Turning the screw handle forces the guide up and out. Penetrating oil squirted around the guide may help to loosen it if it is "frozen" in place. With the assembly out, the spring is compressed so that the spring retainer, spring, and guide can be removed from the valve stem.

3. *Overhead-valve engines.* On these engines, the cylinder-head assembly, with valves and rocker arms, is removed as a unit. Then, the valves and other parts are taken off the cylinder head. Figure 14–12 shows the cylinder head in a special fixture with the spring compressor being used so that a valve-retainer lock can be removed. Valve-stem seals, where used (Fig. 14–11), should be replaced if worn or damaged. Removal of snap rings (in model shown) permits seal to be taken off guide. Article 318 explains how to remove and replace the rocker-arm assemblies.

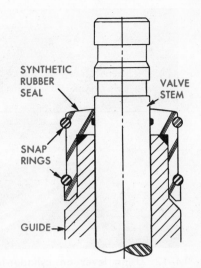

Fig. 14–11. Seal around intake-valve stem. (*Chevrolet Motor Division of General Motors Corporation*)

§ 315. **Testing valve springs** Valve springs should be tested for proper tension (Fig. 14–13). Also, they should be lined up on a flat surface, side by side, to detect warped, cocked, short, or crooked springs. Springs defective in any way should be discarded.

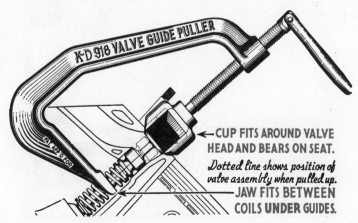

←CUP FITS AROUND VALVE HEAD AND BEARS ON SEAT.
Dotted line shows position of valve assembly when pulled up.
JAW FITS BETWEEN COILS UNDER GUIDES.

Fig. 14–10. Using guide puller to remove valve and guide assembly from Ford engine. (*K-D Manufacturing Company*)

Fig. 14–12. Using lever on cylinder-head holding fixture to compress a valve spring and remove a valve-spring retainer and lock. (*Chevrolet Motor Division of General Motors Corporation*)

§ 316. **Valve reassembly**   After valves, valve seats, and valve guides have been serviced as noted in following articles, they should be reinstalled in the block or head. The installation procedure is just the reverse of removal. The valve-assembly sequence for an overhead-valve engine is shown

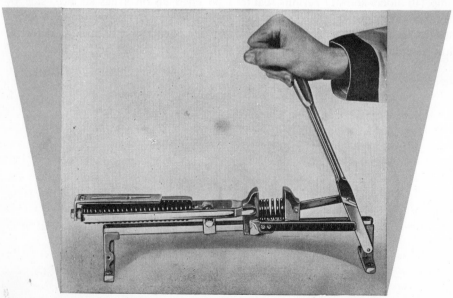

Fig. 14–13. Using a valve-spring-tension tester to measure valve-spring tension. (*Chevrolet Motor Division of General Motors Corporation*)

in Fig. 14–14. Note that the intake valves use stem oil seals in this engine.

When installing free valves (§ 143), put tip cups and retainer locks back on the same valves from which they were removed. Worn sides of the locks should contact the tip cups. If the locks are badly worn, replace locks and tip cups. After free valves are installed, check them for freeness. Turn engine over to open valve, and then see if valve can be turned. If valve cannot be turned easily, it is probably binding against the tip cup. Grind a few thousandths off the valve stem. There should be a clearance of less than 0.004 inch between the valve stem and tip cup with the valve open. This clearance can be checked by mounting a dial indicator on the block so that the up-and-down movement of the valve can be measured as it is moved by hand. If clearance is too great, grind a few thousandths off the upper edge of the tip cup. This is done by laying a piece of fine emery cloth on a flat surface; then move the tip cup back and forth on the emery cloth in a figure 8 pattern.

§ 317. Removing and replacing heads

On some cars, the manifolds must be removed before the cylinder heads can be taken off. On other cars, the manifolds can be left in place.

1. Removing cylinder heads. Drain the radiator and block; remove the thermostat housing and thermostat. Other parts attached to the head must also be removed; these include spark-plug wires, ignition coil, oil filter, distributor, temperature gauge, and so on. Remove rocker-arm assemblies by taking out bracket-attaching bolts or nuts

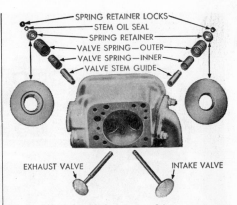

Fig. 14–14. Valve-assembly sequence in an overhead-valve V-8 engine. (*Chrysler Sales Division of Chrysler Corporation*)

(shaft-mounted type), or taking off adjusting nuts (individually mounted type as on Chevrolet V-8).

On many I-head engines, the manifolds must be removed before the head can be taken off. On others, manifolds can be left in place by detaching them and moving them to one side. Manifolds do not require removal on L-head engines.

▶*CAUTION:* Cover carburetor with a clean cloth to protect it from dirt if it is left on the manifold.

After the above preliminary work, take off the head bolts or nuts, and remove head. If it sticks, use pry bars to loosen it. But be careful that you do not damage the head or block. Clean head and block of carbon and gasket particles (§ 320), and inspect head.

2. Inspecting cylinder heads. Cylinder heads should be checked for cracks, warpage, or rough gasket surfaces. To check for cracks, moisten the surface with kerosene, tap the head with a

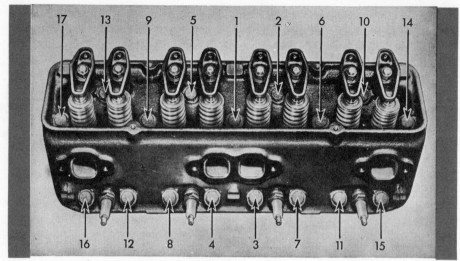

Fig. 14–15a. Sequence chart for tightening cylinder-head bolts on a V-8 engine. (*Chevrolet Motor Division of General Motors Corporation*)

hammer, wipe the surface, and tap the head again. Cracks will be shown up by lines of kerosene appearing along the cracks. Warpage can be detected by laying a long straightedge against the sealing surfaces of the head.

3. Replacing cylinder heads. After gasket surfaces on the head and block have been cleaned (§ 320), inspect them for roughness. File off any rough spots with a fine-cut mill file. Use a new gasket. If it is the lacquered type, handle it carefully to avoid chipping the lacquer. When the block has stud bolts, put the gasket into position, right side up. Use gasket sealer only if specified by manufacturer. If block does not have stud bolts, use two pilot pins screwed into two boltholes to assure gasket alignment. Then lower the head into position, and run on the nuts or bolts finger-tight. Substitute bolts for pilot pins (if used).

▶*CAUTION:* Make sure that all boltholes have been cleaned out. If they

are not, the bolts may bottom against the foreign material and the head will not be tight.

Use a torque wrench (§ 15) to tighten the nuts or bolts. They must be tightened in the proper sequence and to the proper tension; if they are not, head or block distortion, gasket leakage, or bolt failure may occur. Refer to the sequence chart of the engine being serviced, and note the torque called for. Figure 14–15a shows the sequence for one head of a V-8 engine. Each nut or bolt should be tightened in several steps; that is, the complete circuit of all should be made several times, with each bolt or nut being drawn down little by little. When all are tightened to the correct tension, the engine should be run until it warms up and the tensions checked once again. Specifications for some engines using aluminum heads call for rechecking tension after the engine has been turned off and has cooled.

§ **318. Servicing rocker-arm assemblies** On many engines, the rocker arms are assembled on a shaft. The shaft is supported on the head by a series of brackets. After the rocker-arm assembly has been removed from the head, it is disassembled by loosening the pilot screw in the bracket that locks the shaft, removing the cotter pin, and sliding the brackets, rocker arms, and springs from the shaft. On some engines, the shaft is doweled to the bracket instead of being locked with a screw. On these, the bracket and shaft are handled as a unit. Rocker arms with worn bushings can be rebushed. When the valve ends of the arms are worn, they can be refaced on the valve-refacing machine. On reassembly, be sure that all springs and arms are restored to the shaft in their proper positions. Make sure that the oilholes in the shaft are on the underside so that they will feed oil to the rocker-arm bushings.

On engines with independently mounted rocker arms (Fig. 6–58), the rocker arms are removed by taking off the adjusting nuts. On these engines, be sure to replace push rods with the same ends up as on the original installation. The rocker-arm studs may be replaced if studs are loose in the head or if stud threads are damaged. This is done by using a stud puller to remove the old stud and then pressing or driving in the new stud. If the old stud was loose, the stud hole in the head should be reamed oversize and an oversize stud installed.

§ **319. Removing and replacing manifolds** Take off carburetor. Handle it with care to avoid damaging it or spilling gasoline from the float bowl. Disconnect vacuum line and exhaust pipe. Remove nuts or bolts, and take manifolds off.

When reinstalling manifolds, use new gaskets. Make sure all trace of the old gaskets has been removed from the head or block and manifolds. Tighten attaching nuts or bolts to the proper tension, using a torque wrench (see Fig. 14–15*b*).

§ **320. Cleaning carbon from head and block** Accumulations of carbon should be scraped from the combustion-chamber surfaces of both the head and the block. To remove carbon from the cylinder head, place it upside down on the bench or in the head-holding fixture, and use a carbon scraper to take off heavy accumulations of carbon. On I heads with valves still in place, take carbon off the valve surfaces as well. Do not scrape on flat finished surfaces of the cylinder head, since this might scratch the surfaces and prevent normal sealing. Particles of gasket and gasket cement should be scraped off with a flat scraper. To finish the carbon-removing job, a carbon-removing brush driven by an electric drill may be used. All traces of dirt and dust should then be blown away with compressed air.

To remove carbon from an engine block, cover all cylinders with cloths except the one being worked on (Fig. 14–16). Crank the engine until the piston of the cylinder to be cleaned is at TDC (top dead center) and (on L-head engines) both valves of the cylinder are closed. If the carburetor has not been removed, cover it with cloths. Then use a carbon scraper to

Fig. 14–15b. Sequence chart for tightening intake-manifold attaching bolts on a V-8 engine. (*Chevrolet Motor Division of General Motors Corporation*)

Fig. 14–16. Preparation of engine block for removal of carbon. Piston should be at TDC, and valves should be closed (on L-head engines). Other cylinders should be covered with cloths.

remove carbon from the block surfaces, piston, and valves (L-head engine) of the exposed cylinder. Put a carbon-removing brush into an electric drill, and complete the job. Then use compressed air to blow all dust from the work. Be sure that boltholes are cleaned out, because dirt in the boltholes may cause the bolts to bottom so that they cannot be tightened to provide a good seal of the head of the block. Bottoming of the bolts due to dirt in the boltholes may also cause the bolts to be twisted off before they are tightened to the specified tension.

▶ *CAUTION:* Goggles should be worn when a carbon brush or compressed air is used, to prevent particles of dust from being blown into the eyes.

Be very careful to avoid getting dirt or dust into open valve ports or into cylinders where the piston is not at TDC. Do not scrape flat finished surfaces with the carbon scraper, but use a flat scraper to remove traces of gasket or gasket cement.

§ **321. Servicing valves** First, clean carbon off the valves. This may be done with a wire brush or buffing wheel (wear goggles when using the wheel so that particles of wire will not fly into your eyes). Valve stems should be cleaned with fine abrasive cloth. One method of doing this is to rotate the valve in a lathe or an electric drill while a strip of abrasive cloth is held wrapped partly around the stem. The valve can also be clamped in the soft jaws of a vise while the abrasive cloth, wrapped around the stem, is pulled back and forth. Do not cut metal from

the valve stem since this would cause excessive clearance at the valve guide.

Examine the valves while you clean them, discarding valves that are cracked, badly pitted or worn, and bent. Small pits or burns in the valve face can be removed as noted below. Do not mix the valves. Each valve must be returned to the valve port from which it was removed after it is serviced.

*1. Refacing or grinding valves.** The valve stem is clamped in the chuck of the valve-refacing machine (Fig. 14–17). Then, the seating face of the valve is brought into contact with the rotating grinding wheel. The chuck is set at the proper angle to give the correct angle to the seating face. This angle must just match the valve-seat angle, or else there should be an interference angle of $\frac{1}{4}$ to 1 degree (see Fig. 14–1).

At the start of the operation, the first cut should be a light one. If this cut removes metal from only one-third or one-half of the face, the valve may not be centered in the chuck or else the valve stem is bent. If bent, the valve should be discarded. On subsequent cuts, only sufficient metal should be removed to true up the surface and remove pits. Do not take heavy cuts. If so much metal must be removed that the margin is lost (see Fig. 6–

* At one time, it was common practice to lap valves instead of grinding them. In lapping, the valve and seat are covered with abrasive compound, and the valve is turned back and forth on the valve seat. This method is no longer recommended. However, some engine manufacturers recommend a light final lapping after valve grinding to perfect the valve-to-seat fit.

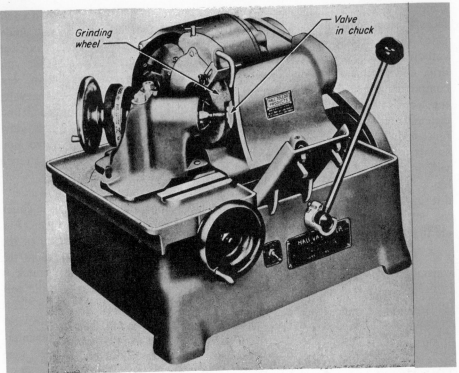

Fig. 14–17. Valve-refacing machine. (Hall Manufacturing Company)

49), the outer edge will be sharp. This would cause the valve to run hot in the engine; it should be discarded. If new valves are required, reface them lightly to assure proper seating angles.

NOTE: Follow the operating instructions issued by the refacer manufacturer. In particular, dress the grinding wheel as necessary with the diamond-tipped dressing tool. As the diamond is moved across the rotating face of the wheel, it cleans and aligns the grinding face.

2. Valve-stem-tip refacing. If the tip ends of the valve stems are rough or worn unevenly, they can be ground lightly with the special attachment furnished with the valve-refacing machine.

§ 322. Valve seats For effective valve seating and sealing, the valve face must be concentric with the valve stem, and the valve guide must be concentric with the valve face. Also, the valve-face angle must match the valve-seat angle (or have an interference angle). Thus, as a first step in valve-seat service, the valve guides must be cleaned or serviced (§ 323).

Valve seats are of two types, the integral type, which is actually the cylinder block or head, and the insert type, which is a ring of special metal set into the block or head (Fig. 6–53). Replacing seat inserts and grinding seats are described below.

1. Replacing valve-seat inserts. When a valve-seat insert is badly worn

or has been ground down on previous occasions so that there is insufficient metal for another grind, it must be replaced. The old seat must be removed with a special puller. If a puller is not available, the insert should be punchmarked on two opposite sides and an electric drill used to drill holes almost through the insert. Then, a chisel and hammer can be used to break the insert into halves so that it can be removed. Care must be used so that the counterbore is not damaged. If the new insert fits too loosely, the counterbore must be rebored oversize and an oversize insert installed. The new in-

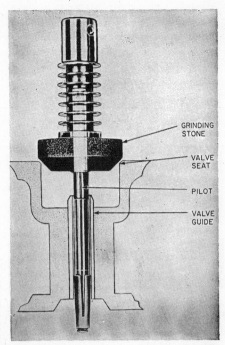

GRINDING STONE

VALVE SEAT

PILOT

VALVE GUIDE

Fig. 14–19. Pilot on which grinding stone rotates. The pilot keeps the stone concentric with the valve seat. (*Black and Decker Manufacturing Company*)

sert should be chilled in dry ice for 15 minutes to shrink it so that it can be driven into place. Then, the valve seat should be ground.

*2. Grinding valve seats.** Two general types of valve-seat grinders are used, the concentric grinder and the eccentric grinder. The concentric grinder rotates a grinding stone of the proper shape on the valve seat (Fig. 14–18). The stone is kept concentric with the valve seat by a pilot installed

Fig. 14–18. Concentric valve-seat grinder of type using the patented Vibrocentric principle. The stone is rotated at high speed, and, about once every revolution, it is automatically lifted off the valve seat so that it can throw off loosened grit and grindings. (*Black and Decker Manufacturing Company*)

* A method of servicing valve seats, no longer in wide use, requires valve-seat reamers or cutters. These tools have a series of teeth that cut material off the seat when they are turned on the seat. Use of a grinder is the preferred method for servicing valve seats.

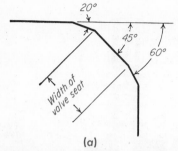

(a)

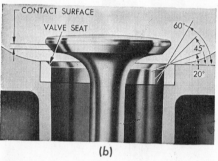

(b)

Fig. 14–20. (a) Diagram and (b) sectional view of valve seat, showing angles to which seat and upper and lower cuts must be ground on one engine. Dimensions and angles vary with different engines. (*Chrysler Sales Division of Chrysler Corporation*)

in the valve guide (Fig. 14–19). This means that the valve guide must be cleaned and serviced (§ 323) before the seat is ground. In the unit shown in Fig. 14–18, the stone is automatically lifted about once a revolution. This permits the stone to clear itself of grit and dust by centrifugal force. After the seat is ground, it will be too wide. It must be narrowed by using upper and lower grinding stones to grind away the upper and lower edges of the seat. A typical seat, with angles, is shown in Fig. 14–20.

The eccentric valve-seat grinder (Fig. 14–21) uses an eccentric grinding mechanism in which the grinding

stone is offset from the center of the valve seat. It makes only line contact with the valve seat. As the stone revolves, its center rotates slowly on an eccentric shaft. This permits the line contact at which grinding is taking place to progress evenly around the entire valve seat. This valve-seat grinder also pilots in the valve guide.

Fig. 14–21. Eccentric valve-seat grinder installed on cylinder block, ready to grind a valve seat. The micrometer feed permits accurate feeding of the grinding wheel into the valve seat. (*Hall Manufacturing Company*)

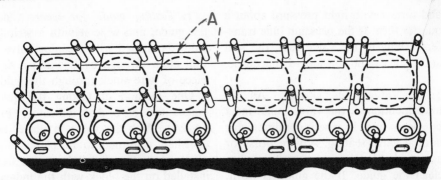

Fig. 14–22. Use of masking tape (A) to cover cylinders of L-head engine during valve-seat grinding. The masking tape prevents abrasive or grinding dust from getting into the cylinders, where it could cause serious trouble.

▶ CAUTION: Be sure to follow instructions furnished by the grinder manufacturer. Note that the grinding stone must be dressed frequently with the diamond-tipped dressing tool. Also, make sure that cuttings do not get into the block if the engine has not been completely torn down. To protect bearings and cylinders in L-head engines, cover cylinders with masking tape as shown in Fig. 14–22.

3. Checking valve seats for concentricity. After the valve guides are serviced and valve seats ground, the concentricity of the two can be checked with a valve-seat dial gauge (Fig. 14–23). The gauge is mounted in the valve guide and is rotated so that the indicator finger sweeps round the valve seat. Any eccentricity of the seat is thus registered on the gauge dial.

4. Testing valve seating. Contact between the valve face and seat may be tested by marking lines with a soft pencil about ¼ inch apart around the entire valve face. Then the valve should be put into place and, with light pressure, rotated half a turn to the left and then half a turn to the

right. If this removes the pencil marks, the seating is good. The seating can also be checked with prussian blue. Coat the valve face lightly with prussian blue, put the valve on its seat,

Fig. 14–23. Valve-seat dial gauge. The unit shown is mounted on the valve-seat-grinder pilot. (Kent-Moore Organization, Inc.)

307

and turn it with light pressure about a quarter turn. If the prussian blue transfers evenly to the valve seat, the seat and guide can be considered concentric.

§ 323. Valve-guide service As we have mentioned, the valve guide must be clean and in good condition for normal valve seating. A wire brush or adjustable-blade cleaner can be used to clean the guide. If the guide is worn, it will require servicing. The servicing procedure required depends upon whether the valve guide is of the integral or the replaceable type. If the valve guide is of the integral type (that is, bored directly in the head), then it must be reamed to a larger size and a valve with an oversize stem installed. If the worn guide is of the replaceable type, it should be removed and a new guide installed. Checking valve guides for wear is discussed below. In addition, the removal and installation of the replaceable type of valve guide are described.

Fig. 14–24. Dial indicator set up to measure valve-guide wear. (*Plymouth Division of Chrysler Corporation*)

1. Testing guide for wear. Clean the guide, and wipe it with a strip of cloth dampened with cleaning solvent. Pull cloth through by hooking it to a piece of wire stuck through the guide.

One method of testing the guide makes use of a dial indicator (Fig. 14–24). With the valve in place, the camshaft is turned to raise the valve off its seat. The dial indicator is then installed on the block with the indicating button touching the edge of the valve head. Then, the valve can be moved sideways to determine the wear as indicated by the amount of movement.

A second checking method is to insert a tapered pilot into the guide until it is tight. Then, pencil-mark the pilot at the top of the guide, remove it, and measure the pilot diameter ½ inch below the pencil mark. This gives the guide diameter, which can then be compared with the valve-stem diameter.

Neither of the two above methods will accurately show up valve-guide eccentricity and bellmouthing. The valve guide is apt to wear oval-shaped or bellmouthed owing to the tendency for the valve to wobble as it opens and closes. The bellmouth shown in Fig. 14–25 is exaggerated. A small-hole gauge, shown in Fig. 14–25, will detect oval or bellmouth wear. It is used as shown: the split ball is adjusted until it is a light drag fit at the point being checked. Then, the split ball is measured with a micrometer. By checking the guide at various points, any eccentricity will be detected.

2. Removing valve guide (replaceable type). A guide puller (Fig. 14–26) is handy for removing the old

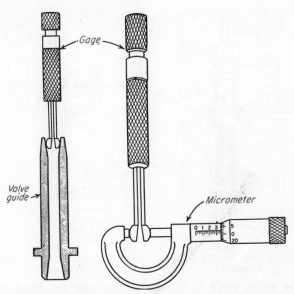

Fig. 14–25. A small-hole gauge is the most accurate device to check for valve-guide wear. The gauge is adjusted so that the split ball is a drag fit in the guide (*left*), and then the split ball can be measured with a micrometer as shown (*right*).

valve guide. As the nut is turned on the screw, the guide is pulled out. On some L-head engines, the guide can be driven down into the valve-spring compartment. On I-head engines, the valve guide can be pressed out of the head with an arbor press.

3. *Installing valve guide* (*replaceable type*). New valve guides should be installed with a special driver, or

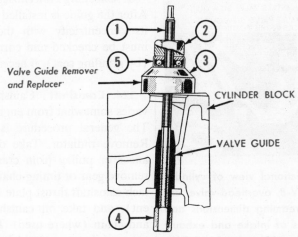

Fig. 14–26. The valve guide is removed from the cylinder block with a special puller: 1, screw; 2, nut; 3, spacer; 4, nut; 5, bearing. (*Willys Motors, Inc.*)

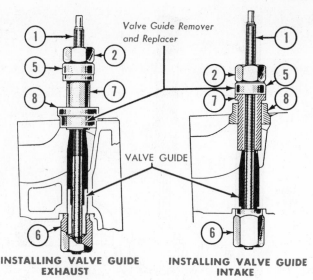

Fig. 14–27. The valve guide is installed in the cylinder block with a special replacer: 1, screw; 2, nut; 5, spacer; 6, recessed nut; 7, sleeve; 8, collar. (*Willys Motors, Inc.*)

replacer (Fig. 14–27). Guides can be installed in I heads with an arbor press. Guides must be installed to the proper depth in the block or head. Then, they must be reamed to size. This is usually

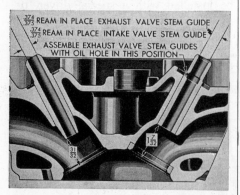

Fig. 14–28. Sectional view of cylinder head from a V-8 overhead-valve engine, showing reaming dimensions and correct locations of intake and exhaust valve-stem guides. (*Chrysler Sales Division of Chrysler Corporation*)

done in two steps, a rough ream and then a second, or final, finishing ream. Figure 14–28 illustrates both the depth of assembly of valve guides and the reaming dimensions on one engine.

4. *Checking concentricity with seat.* After the guide is installed and reamed, its concentricity with the valve seat must be checked and correction made (by grinding seat), if necessary (§322).

§ 324. Camshaft Camshaft removal varies somewhat from engine to engine. The general procedure is as follows: Remove radiator. Take dynamic balancer or pulley from crankshaft, and remove gear or timing-chain cover. Detach camshaft thrust plate (where present), and take off camshaft sprocket and chain (where used). The distributor or oil pump (whichever has the driven gear) must be removed so that

310

Fig. 14–29. Blocking up valves in L-head engine with small wood blocks preparatory to removing camshaft. (*Studebaker-Packard Corporation*)

Fig. 14–30. Using spring-type clothespins to hold valve lifters up so that they will clear the camshaft bearings and cams as camshaft is removed. (*Studebaker-Packard Corporation*)

311

Fig. 14–31. Check of camshaft alignment. (*Chevrolet Motor Division of General Motors Corporation*)

the gear will not interfere with the camshaft removal.

Next, on L-head engines, raise and block up the valves and valve lifters (Figs. 14–29 and 14–30). This keeps the lifters from falling down behind cams and jamming. On overhead-valve engines, the rocker-arm assemblies and push rods must be removed. Then the lifters must either be removed or else be lifted and held up out of the way by spring-type clothespins as on the L-head engine (Fig. 14–30). Now, the camshaft is free and can be pulled forward and out. Be very careful to keep journals and cams from scratching the camshaft bearings. Support the rear of the camshaft as it is pulled so that journals and cams do not hit the bearings.

1. Checking camshaft. Check for alignment by rotating the camshaft in V blocks and using a dial indicator to check for eccentricity (Fig. 14–31). A bent camshaft may sometimes be straightened in a hydraulic press. Journal diameters should be checked with a micrometer and the bearings with a telescope gauge. The two dimensions can then be compared to determine whether bearings are worn. If they are, they should be replaced.

2. Replacing camshaft bearings. With a special bearing remover, all bearings can be removed at one time on many engines. The remover bar is inserted through the bearings, puller sleeves being installed on the bar at each bearing. Then, when the remover handle is turned, all bearings are pulled. By a similar action, new bearings are installed. Oilholes in the new bearings should align with the oilholes in the block. Also, new bearings should be staked in place if the old bearings were staked. If the new bearings are not of the precision type, they will require reaming to establish the proper fit.

3. Timing the valves. The timing gears or sprockets and chain are marked to establish the proper positions and correct valve timing (Figs. 6–47 and 6–48). To get to these markings, however, the front of the car has to be partly torn down. Thus, many engines have another marking system for checking valve timing. This marking is on the flywheel or vibration damper, near the ignition-timing markings (Fig. 12–7). When this marking is visible or registers with a pointer, a certain designated valve should be just opening or should have opened a specified amount. Valve action is observed

by removing the valve cover. On L-head engines, you can tell when a valve is about to open by grasping the valve lifter and moving it up and down. At the instant after all clearance is taken up, the valve starts to open. The same thing can be done with the rocker arm on I-head engines. To measure the amount of opening, a dial indicator must be used.

When the flywheel or vibration damper is not marked, piston position can be measured with a special gauge inserted through a special hole in the head; the relationship of the piston with the valves can therefore be established.

4. Timing gear and chain. Gear run-out can be checked by mounting a dial indicator on the block, with the indicating finger resting on the side of the gear. Runout will then be indicated as the gear is rotated. Gear backlash is measured by inserting a narrow feeler gauge between the meshing teeth. Excessive runout or backlash requires gear replacement. Excessive slack in the timing chain indicates a worn chain, and possibly worn sprockets. Worn parts should be replaced.

§ 325. Valve lifters The plain-sleeve and the hydraulic valve lifters require different servicing procedures.

1. Plain-sleeve lifter. Plain-sleeve lifters are removed from the camshaft

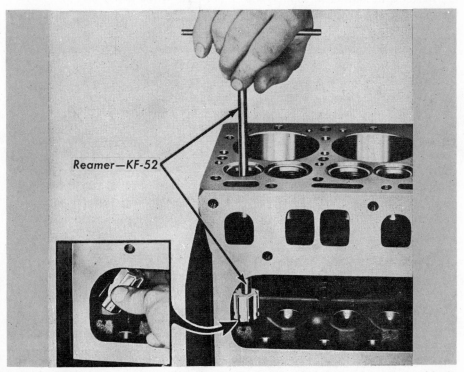

Reamer—KF-52

Fig. 14–32. Using special reamer to ream out the lifter bores in cylinder block. (*Willys Motors, Inc.*)

side on many engines. This requires camshaft removal as a first step (§ 324). Lifters should be kept in order so that they can be restored to the bores from which they were removed. If the face of the adjusting screw in the lifter is worn, it may be smoothed on the valve-refacing machine. Oversize valve lifters may be installed on many engines if the lifter bores have become worn. Before this is done, the lifter bores must be reamed oversize (Fig. 14–32).

2. Hydraulic valve lifter. On some engines, a "leak-down" test is used to determine the condition of the hydraulic valve lifters. This test is made by inserting a feeler gauge between the rocker arm and valve stem. Then, the time it takes for the valve lifter to

leak enough oil to allow the valve to seat is noted. As the valve seats, the feeler gauge becomes loose and this indicates the end of the test. If the leak-down time is too short, the valve lifter is defective.

To remove the type of hydraulic valve lifter shown in Fig. 6–62, remove the push-rod cover and rocker-arm assembly. Then take out push rods, and use a piece of stiff wire slightly hooked at one end to remove the lifters.

On some engines with shaft-mounted rocker arms, the rocker arm can be moved by compressing the spring so that the push rod can be removed. Thus, the rocker-arm assembly does not have to be taken off.

On engines where the valve lifter

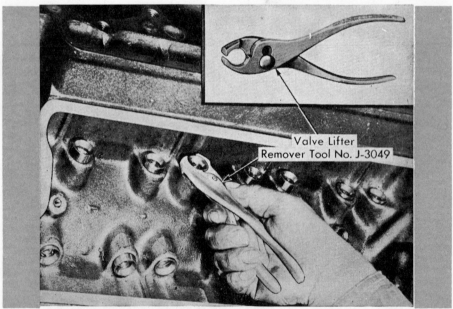

Fig. 14–33. Using special valve-lifter removing tool to remove hydraulic valve lifter from cylinder block. The tool has special jaws that fit the lifter so that the lifter body is not scratched. (*Cadillac Motor Car Division of General Motors Corporation*)

protrudes above the lifter bore in the block, a special removing tool can be used to take the lifters out (Fig. 14–33). Figure 14–34 shows a still different removal procedure. On this engine, a special tool is inserted into the push-rod hole so that the plunger unit of the lifter can be withdrawn. The body of the lifter remains in the lifter bore in the block.

3. *Servicing hydraulic valve lifters.* The lifters should be disassembled and all parts cleaned in solvent. If any part is defective, the lifter should be replaced. On reassembly, fill the lifter with clean, light engine oil.

Work on only one lifter at a time so that you do not mix parts between lifters. Also, make sure each lifter goes back in the bore from which it was removed.

▶ *CAUTION:* Be extremely careful to keep everything clean when servicing and handling hydraulic valve lifters. It takes only one tiny particle of dirt to cause a lifter to malfunction.

CONNECTING RODS AND ROD BEARINGS

§ 326. **Bearing oil-leak detector** On many engines, connecting-rod and main bearings (crankshaft bearings) can be checked for wear with an oil-leak detector (Fig. 14–35) before the engine

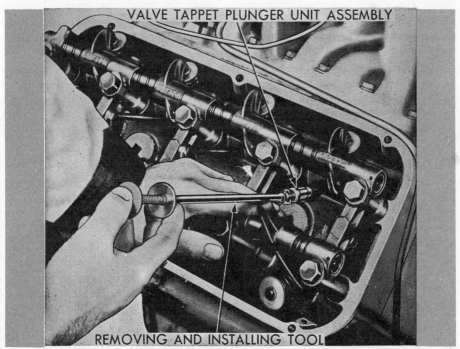

Fig. 14–34. Using special tool to remove valve-tappet–plunger-unit assembly from hydraulic valve lifter. Pressing and releasing the button with the thumb opens and closes the jaws on the end of the tool so that the tool can be inserted into the push-rod hole to grasp the plunger-unit assembly for removal. (*Chrysler Sales Division of Chrysler Corporation*)

is torn down. To use the detector, the oil pan is removed (§ 329), and the detector hose is connected to the pressure side of the engine lubricating system (at the oil filter, for example). Then, with the detector filled with SAE 30 oil, an air pressure of 25 psi (pounds per square inch) is applied to the detector tank. This pressure forces oil through the engine lubricating system. If bearings are worn, considerable oil will leak from them. The detector manufacturer states that a normal bearing will leak between 20 and 150 drops of oil a minute. If it leaks more, the bearing is worn. If it leaks less than 20 drops per minute, then either the bearing clearance is too small or else the oil line to the bearing is stopped up.

NOTE: When oil-passage holes in the crankshaft and bearing align, considerable oil will be forced through the bearing, giving the appearance of ex-

cessive wear. In such a case, the crankshaft should be rotated somewhat to move the oilholes out of register.

§ **327. Preparing to remove rods** Connecting rods and pistons are removed as an assembly from the engine. Removing, servicing, and replacing connecting rods requires about 5 to 8 hours, according to the type of engine. About 3 additional hours is required to install new piston rings. Additional time is needed for such services as piston-pin or bushing replacement. On most engines, the piston-and-rod assemblies are removed from the top of the engine (on a few from the crankcase end). Thus, the first step is to remove the cylinder head. Cylinders should be examined for wear. If wear has taken place, there will be a ridge at the top of the cylinder that marks the upper limit of the top-ring travel (Fig. 14–36). If this ridge is not removed, the top ring

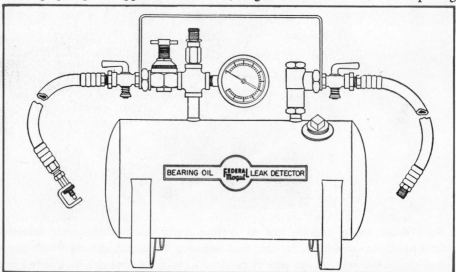

Fig. 14–35. Engine-bearing oil-leak detector to check main and connecting-rod bearings for wear. (*Federal-Mogul Corporation*)

could jam under it as the piston is moved upward. This might break the rings or the piston-ring-groove lands (Fig. 14–36). Thus, the ridge, if present, should be removed.

§ 328. **Removing ring ridge** To remove ring ridges, use a special remover, as shown in Fig. 14–37. With piston near the bottom of the stroke, stuff cloths into the cylinder, and install the ridge remover. Adjust cutters to take off just enough metal to remove the ridge. Cover other cylinders (and valves on L-head engines) to keep cuttings from getting into them. Rotate tool to cut ridge away. Remove tool, take cloth out, and wipe cylinder walls. Repeat for other cylinders.

§ 329. **Removing oil pan** The oil pan must be removed so that the connecting rods can be detached from the crankshaft. First, remove drain plug

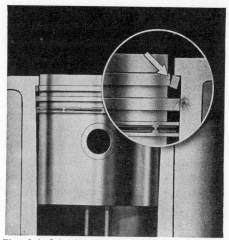

Fig. 14–36. Manner in which ring ridge caused by cylinder wear might break ring if piston is withdrawn without removal of ridge. (*Sealed Power Corporation*)

to drain crankcase oil. On many cars, the steering idler or other steering linkage must be removed. In such a case, note the manner in which the

Fig. 14–37. Ridge-removing tool in place in top of cylinder. Cutters remove the ridge as the tool is turned in the cylinder. (*Studebaker-Packard Corporation*)

linkage is attached and the number and location of shims (if used). On some Fords, the oil pan is more easily removed if the engine mounting bolts are removed and the engine is raised slightly. Other parts that may require removal before the oil pan can be taken off include the exhaust pipe, oil-level tube, brake-return spring, and cranking motor. Then, the nuts or bolts holding the oil pan to the engine block can be removed. Steady pan as the last two nuts or bolts are removed so that it does not drop. If the pan

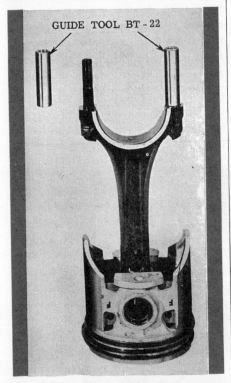

Fig. 14–38. Using guide sleeves over rod bolts to protect the crankshaft-bearing surfaces when rod is removed or replaced. (*Oldsmobile Division of General Motors Corporation*)

strikes the crankshaft so that it does not come free, turn the engine over a few degrees.

Clean oil pan, oil screen, and oil pump thoroughly before replacing pan. Make sure gasket material is scraped from the pan and block gasket surfaces. Apply new gasket cement (if specified); lay gasket (or gaskets) in place. Be sure boltholes in gasket and pan line up. Install pan, and tighten bolts or nuts to the proper tension.

§ 330. **Removing and replacing piston-and-rod assemblies** After the preliminaries are out of the way, as noted in previous sections, proceed as follows to remove and replace piston-and-rod assemblies.

1. Removal. With head and pan off, crank engine so that the piston of cylinder 1 is near bottom. Examine rod and rod cap for identifying marks. If none can be seen, mark them with metal numbering dies (do this before removing them, and tap dies lightly, to avoid distorting the rod or cap). Marks are needed to make sure parts go back into the same cylinders from which they were removed (piston should also be numbered if not already marked).

Remove rod nuts and cap. Slide rod and piston assembly up into the cylinder away from the crankshaft. Use guide sleeves on the rod bolts, if specified, to keep the bolt threads from scratching the crankshaft journals (see Fig. 14–38).

Turn crankshaft as you go from rod to rod so that you can reach the rod nuts. When all rods are detached and the piston-and-rod assemblies have

been pushed up in the cylinders, remove the assemblies from the top of the engine.

2. Separating rods and pistons. Lay the piston-and-rod assemblies out on the bench in order as they are removed from the engine. Detach the pistons from the rods by removing the piston pins. On the free-floating type, slip the pin out after removing snap rings. On other types, loosen the locking bolt in the rod or piston, or press the pin out with an arbor press. Never clamp the piston in an ordinary vise when it is necessary to hold the piston firmly; this could distort and ruin it. Instead, use a special piston vise which has curved jaws that will not distort the piston or damage its finish (Fig. 14–39). Check rods, pistons, pins, and rings as noted in following articles.

3. Reinstalling piston-and-rod assemblies. As the rods, pistons, and rings are assembled, make sure they are rematched. Parts should go back into the same cylinders from which they were removed. Rings should be positioned so that the gaps are uniformly spaced around the piston (except on pistons where rings are pinned). Then, the piston-ring-and-rod assembly should be dipped in heavy oil or castor oil to provide initial lubrication. Castor oil is considered better since it has greater film strength and will not wash out as easily as mineral oil. Install pistons in cylinders, using a ring compressor (see § 342). Use bolt guide sleeves, if specified, to keep the bolts from scratching the crankshaft journals. Attach rod cap with nuts, turned down lightly. Then

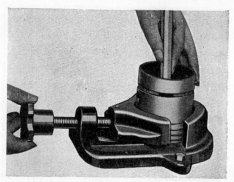

Fig. 14–39. Piston vise. The vise jaws fit the piston contour and prevent damage to the piston. (Kent-Moore Organization, Inc.)

tap bearing cap on its crown lightly with a brass hammer to help center it. Use torque wrench to final-tighten nuts.

▶*CAUTION:* Bearing clearances should be checked (§ 335).

§ 331. **Checking rod alignment** Figure 14–40 is an exaggerated view showing the effects of a misaligned connecting rod. Heavy loading at points *A* and *B* on the bearing would cause bearing failure at these points. The heavy-pressure spots *C* and *D* on the piston will cause heavy wear and possibly scoring of the piston and cylinder wall.

A rough check for rod alignment can be made by detaching the oil pan and watching the rod while the engine is cranked. If the rod moves back and forth on the piston pin, or is not centered, the rod is out of line. It should stay centered on the pin.

To check rod alignment out of the engine, reinstall the piston pin in the

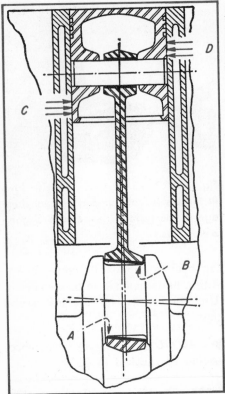

Fig. 14–40. Heavy - pressure areas caused by a bent rod. Bent condition is exaggerated. Areas of heavy pressure will wear rapidly so that early failure results. (*Federal-Mogul Corporation*)

crankpin causes the rod to be subjected to bending stresses.

Bent rods must be straightened or replaced. To straighten a rod, use a straightening bar inserted into the piston-pin hole. Bend the rod a little past straight and then back to straight again. This relieves stresses set up by the bending process.

NOTE: Some engine manufacturers call for replacement of bent connecting rods. Their experience has shown that their rods, if bent, tend to take on a permanènt set. Even if straight-

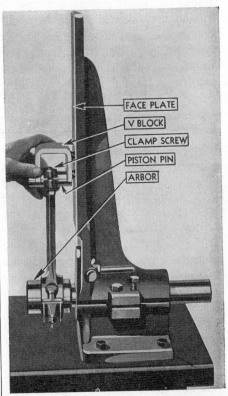

Fig. 14–41. Connecting-rod alignment fixture being used to check alignment of a connecting rod. (*Chevrolet Motor Division of General Motors Corporation*)

rod. Then mount the rod on the arbor of the special fixture by attaching the rod cap (Fig. 14–41). Put the V block over the piston pin, and move it in against the faceplate. If the V block does not fit squarely against the faceplate, the rod is out of line. This same fixture can be used to check alignment of the rod-and-piston assembly before the rings are installed (see Fig. 14–59).

If the rod is out of line, check the crankpin for taper (§ 336). A tapered

ened, they may drift back to the permanent-set or bent condition.

§ 332. Piston-pin bushings

When the rod has a piston-pin bushing, check the fit of the pin. If the fit is correct, the pin will not drop through the bushing of its own weight when held vertical. It will require a light push to force it through. If the fit is too loose, the bushing should be reamed or honed for an oversize pin or else replaced. On some rods, the bushing cannot be replaced; if the bushing is so worn that it cannot be reamed or honed for an oversize pin, the complete rod must be replaced. On other rods, the worn bushings can be replaced and the new bushings reamed or honed to fit the present pins (if they are in good condition) or new standard-sized pins. Pins that are worn, pitted, or otherwise defective should be discarded. To replace bushing, press out the old bushing in an arbor press. Burrs on the edges of the bushing bore in the rod should be removed with a hand scraper or tapered burring reamer. Then, a new bushing can be pressed in with an arbor press. A tapered mandrel should then be used to expand the edges of the bushing and thereby swage them firmly in the rod. Make sure the oilholes in the bushing and rod align. Ream or hone the new bushing to size.

Some rods have two piston-pin bushings, separated a fraction of an inch to form an oil groove. On these, each bushing must be swaged, or expanded, into place with a burnishing tool (Fig. 14-42). To do this, install one bushing flush with the edge of the bore. Put rod in arbor press, bushing

Fig. 14-42. Using a burnisher to burnish piston-pin bushings in connecting rod. (*Studebaker-Packard Corporation*)

side down. Push the burnisher through. Install second bushing, turn rod over, and pass burnisher through first bushing and then through the second bushing. Ream or hone bushings as necessary.

When reaming a set of bushings, proceed slowly on the first rod. Use an expansion reamer, and expand the reamer by easy stages, taking off a little metal each time. Try the pin fit after each reaming operation. This procedure guards against overreaming. Then, after the first rod is reamed, all others may be quickly reamed by reducing the reamer diameter about 0.0005 inch to rough-ream all rods. Then expand the reamer to take the final cut. At this stage, check pins with a micrometer so that any slight variation can be taken care of. Thus, if one pin is slightly larger than the others, the bushing into which it will fit can be reamed slightly larger to provide

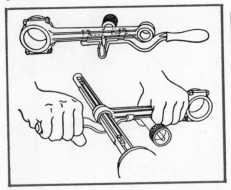

Fig. 14–43. Connecting rod in clamp, and method of holding rod and clamp while honing (grinding) the piston-pin bushing.

a good fit. This assures a good matching fit of pins to bushings.

To hone a set of bushings, follow the same two-step procedure. Rough-hone the bushings to within about 0.0005 inch of the proper size. Then change hone, and finish-hone to size. Check pins with a micrometer during finish-honing so that variations in pin size can be taken care of. Figure 14–43 shows a clamp to hold the connecting rod and the method of holding the rod and clamp during honing. The bushing should be moved from one end of the stone to the other and should not be held in one spot. However, the bushing should not be moved past the end of the stone since this would wear the edges of the bushing bell-shaped.

NOTE: If oversize pins are used, piston bearings or bushings must be reamed or honed oversize (§ 338).

§ 333. Connecting-rod bearings Connecting-rod big-end bearings are of two types, direct-bonded and precision-insert (§ 119). Some adjustment is pos-sible on the direct-bonded type (§ 335), but if this bearing is worn, the complete rod and cap must be replaced. The precision-insert type is not adjustable. However, this type bearing can be replaced without difficulty provided the rod, crankpin, and other engine components are in good condition. Whenever a rod bearing fails, an analysis should be made so that the cause can be determined. Then, the cause can be eliminated so that the failure will not be quickly repeated (see § 334).

§ 334. Analysis of bearing failures Types of bearing failure and their causes are discussed below.

1. Bearing failure due to lack of oil (A in Fig. 14–44). When insufficient oil flows to a bearing, actual metal-to-metal contact results. The bearing overheats, and the bearing metal melts or is wiped out of the bearing shell. Welds may form between the rotating journal and bearing shell. There is a chance that the engine will "throw a rod," that is, the rod will "freeze" to the crankpin and break, and parts of the rod will go through the engine block. Oil starvation of a bearing could result from clogged oil lines, a defective oil pump or pressure regulator, or insufficient oil in the crankcase. Also, if other bearings have excessive clearance, they may pass all the oil from the pump so that some bearings are starved and thus fail.

2. Fatigue failure of bearings (B in Fig. 14–44). Repeated application of loads on a bearing will ultimately fatigue the bearing metal so that it starts to crack and flake out. Craters, or pockets, form in the bearing. As

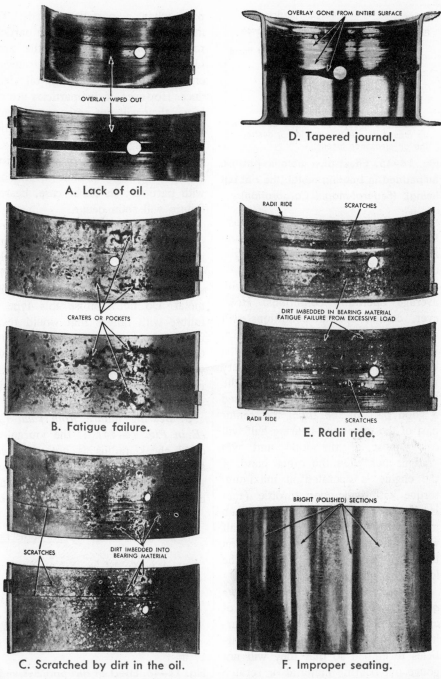

A. Lack of oil.

D. Tapered journal.

B. Fatigue failure.

E. Radii ride.

C. Scratched by dirt in the oil.

F. Improper seating.

Fig. 14–44. Types of engine-bearing failure. Appearance of bearing usually indicates cause of failure. (*Ford Motor Company*)

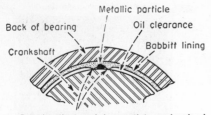

Fig. 14–45. Effect of a metallic particle embedded in bearing metal (the babbitt lining). (*Federal-Mogul Corporation*)

more and more of the metal is lost, the remainder is worked harder and fatigues at a faster rate. Ultimately, complete bearing failure occurs.

Fatigue failure seldom occurs with average operating conditions. However, certain special conditions will cause this type of failure. For instance, if a journal is worn out of round, the bearing will be overstressed with every crankshaft revolution. Also, if the engine is idled or operated at low speed a good part of the time, the center part of the upper rod-bearing half will carry most of the load and will "fatigue out." On the other hand, if the engine is operated at maximum torque with wide-open throttle (that is, if the engine is "lugged"), then most or all of the upper bearing half will fatigue out. High-speed operation tends to cause fatigue failure of the lower bearing half.

3. Bearing scratched by dirt in the oil (C in Fig. 14–44). The property of embeddability (§ 120) enables a bearing to protect itself by allowing particles to embed so that they will not gouge out bearing material or scratch the rotating journal. Figure 14–45 shows, in exaggerated view, what hap-

pens when a particle embeds. The metal is pushed up around the particle, reducing oil clearance in the area. Usually the metal can flow outward enough to restore adequate oil clearance. However, if dirt particles are too large, they will not embed completely and will be carried with the rotating journal, gouging out scratches in the bearing. Also, if the oil is very dirty, the bearing will become overloaded with particles. In either case, bearing failure will soon occur.

4. Bearing failure due to tapered journal (D in Fig. 14–44). If the journal is tapered, one side of the bearing will carry most or all of the load. This side will overheat and lose its bearing metal. Do not confuse this type of failure with failure that would result from a bent connecting rod. With a tapered journal, both bearing halves will fail on the same side. With a bent rod, failure will be on opposite sides (*A* and *B* in Fig. 14–40).

5. Bearing failure from radii ride (E in Fig. 14–44). If the journal-to-crank-cheek radius is not cut away sufficiently, the edge of the bearing will ride on this radius. This would cause cramming of the bearing, possibly

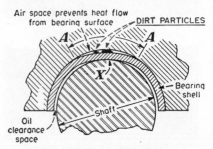

Fig. 14–46. Effect of dirt particles under the bearing shell due to poor installation. (*Federal-Mogul Corporation*)

poor seating, rapid fatigue, and early failure. This trouble would be most likely to occur after a crankshaft-grind job during which the radii were not sufficiently relieved.

6. Bearing failure from poor seating in bore (F in Fig. 14–44). Poor seating of the bearing shell in the bore will cause local high spots where oil clearances will be too low. Figure 14–46 shows, in exaggerated view, what happens when particles of dirt are left between the bearing shell and the counterbore. Not only does this reduce oil clearance (as at X), but, also, an air space exists which prevents proper cooling of the bearing. The combination can lead to quick bearing failure.

7. Bearing failure from ridging. Crankpin ridging, or "camming," may cause failure of a partial-oil-groove type of replacement bearing which has been installed without removal of the ridge. The ridge forms on the crankpin as a result of uneven wear between the part of the crankpin in contact with the partial oil groove and the part that runs on the solid bearing. The original bearing wears to conform to this ridge. However, when a new bearing is installed, the center zone may be overloaded (at the ridge) and may soon fail. A ridge so slight that it can scarcely be detected (except with a carefully used micrometer) may be sufficient to cause this sort of failure. Failures of this sort have been reported in engines having ridges of less than 0.001 inch.

§ 335. Checking connecting-rod-bearing fit Precision-insert bearings are checked in one way, the direct-bonded type in another, as noted below.

▶CAUTION: Before installing new bearings, the crankpins should always be checked for taper or out-of-roundness (§ 336).

1. Precision-insert bearings. Fit of these bearings can be checked in any of three ways, with Plastigage, feeler stock, or micrometer and telescope gauge. Also, the amount of bearing wear can be checked with a micrometer and a piece of round bar stock (Fig. 14–47).

a. Plastigage. Plastigage is a plastic material that comes in strips and flattens when pressure is applied to it. A strip of the material is put into the bearing cap, the cap is installed, and the rod nuts are tightened to the specified tension. Then, the cap is removed, and the amount of flattening is measured. If the Plastigage is flattened only a little, then oil clearances are large. If it is flattened considerably, oil clearances are small. Actual clearance is measured with a special scale supplied with the Plastigage (Fig. 14–48).

The bearing cap and crankpin should be wiped clean of oil before the Plastigage is used and the crankshaft turned so that the crankpin is about 30 degrees back of BDC (bottom dead center). Do not move the crankshaft while the cap nuts are tight. This would further flatten the Plastigage and throw off the clearance measurement.

b. Feeler stock. Lubricate a strip of feeler stock, and lay it lengthwise in the center of the bearing cap. Install cap, and tighten cap nuts lightly. Note ease with which rod may be moved endwise on the crankpin. If rod moves

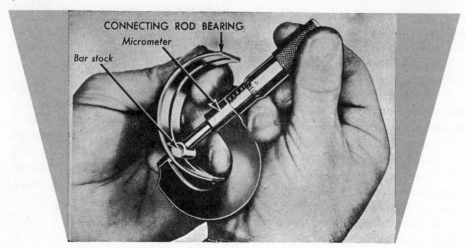

Fig. 14-47. Using micrometer and finished bar stock to measure thickness of bearing and thereby determine amount of wear. (*Willys Motors, Inc.*)

easily, tighten nuts a little more and recheck. Repeat the procedure until the nuts have been drawn down to the specified tightness or until the rod tightens up on the crankpin. If the rod tightens up, the clearance is less than the thickness of the feeler stock. If the rod does not tighten up, the clearance is greater than the thickness of the feeler stock. With the latter condition, lay an additional strip of feeler stock on top of the first and repeat the checking procedure. If the rod still does not tighten up, keep adding feeler stock until the actual bearing clearance is determined. Excessive

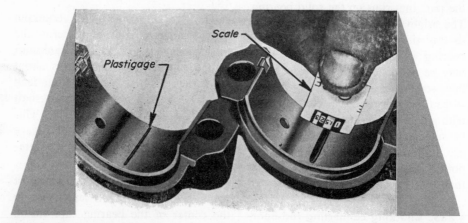

Fig. 14-48. Bearing clearance being checked with Plastigage. (*Left*) Plastigage in place before tightening cap. (*Right*) Measuring amount of flattening (or bearing clearance) with scale. (*Buick Motor Division of General Motors Corporation*)

clearance requires bearing replacement (§ 336).

c. Micrometer and telescope gauge. Check the crankpin diameter with a micrometer. Check the bearing diameter (cap in place) with a telescope gauge and micrometer (or an inside micrometer). The two diameters can then be compared to determine the difference, or bearing clearance. At the same time, the crankpin can be checked for taper or eccentric wear. Measure diameter at several places along the crankpin (to check for taper) and also around the crankpin (to check for eccentricity, or out-of-roundness).

2. Direct-bonded connecting-rod bearings. On these, adjustment is made by installation or removal of shims under the cap. Shims are thin strips of copper or similar metal. Shims placed between the cap and rod (at the bolt bosses) hold the cap away from the rod when the nuts are tightened. This increases the bearing clearance. Clearance can be checked with a micrometer and telescope gauge, as noted above. Or it can be checked by attempting to snap the rod back and forth on the crankpin with one hand (Fig. 14–49). If the rod moves easily, take off the rod cap and remove one shim only from each side of the cap. Replace cap and try to move rod. If rod still moves easily, take off another pair of shims. Repeat this procedure until the rod will not move. Then add one shim to each side of the cap, replace and tighten cap, and retest. Adjustment should now be correct.

If the bearing is worn, pitted, scored, chipped, or otherwise damaged, replace rod and cap as a unit.

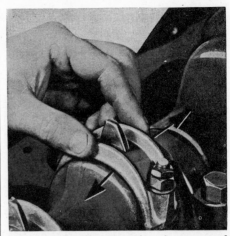

Fig. 14–49. Checking the clearance of the adjustable type of connecting-rod bearing. (*Chevrolet Motor Division of General Motors Corporation*)

Rebabbitting of this type of rod should not be attempted in the field since special equipment is required to do this job.

§ 336. Installing precision rod bearings New precision connecting-rod bearings are required if the old ones are defective (§ 334) or have worn so much that clearances are excessive. They are also required if the crankpins have worn out of round or tapered so much that they have to be reground. In this case, new undersized bearings are required. In addition, it is often the practice of engine rebuilders to replace the bearings in an engine when it is torn down, regardless of whether or not the old bearings are in bad condition. Their reasoning is that it costs little more to put in new bearings when the engine is torn down for rebuilding. However, if the engine had to be torn down especially for bearing installa-

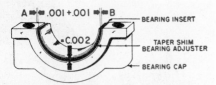

Fig. 14–50. Taper shim bearing adjuster. The thickness of the taper shim is exaggerated. (*Perfect Circle Company*)

tion, the cost would be high. They believe it is cheap insurance against failure to install new bearings during the engine-rebuilding job.

1. Checking crankpins. Crankpins should always be checked with a micrometer for taper or eccentricity. If crankpins are out of round or tapered more than 0.0015 inch, the crankshaft must be replaced or the crankpins reground (§ 351). Bearings working against taper or out-of-roundness of more than 0.0015 inch will not last long. And when bearings go, there is always the chance that the engine will be severely damaged. Measurements should be taken in several places along the crankpin to check for taper. Diameter should also be checked all the way around to check for out-of-roundness.

2. Taper shim bearing adjuster. If the crankpins are not excessively out of round or tapered, yet there is excessive clearance, new bearings should be installed. Sometimes, however, the new bearings will not reduce clearances to specified limits (because of crankpin wear). This calls for crankpin grinding and installation of new undersize bearings. There is, however, a compromise repair that can be made in case the value of the car does not warrant the more expensive but cor-

rect (from the engineering standpoint) crankpin-regrind and new-bearing job. This compromise involves the use of taper shim bearing adjusters (Fig. 14–50) under the bearing shells. The adjusters come in different thicknesses. The correct thickness must be selected for each bearing to provide the proper clearance at that bearing. Note that the adjuster is tapered from the center to half thickness at the ends. The adjuster shown, for example, is 0.002 inch thick at the center *(C)* but only 0.001 inch thick at the ends (*A* and *B*). This provides the same correction of clearance at the ends as at the center of the bearing shell (that is, $A + B = C$).

▶ *CAUTION:* This is not a recommended repair procedure but is a relatively inexpensive way to get some added mileage out of an old car. It should never be used in a late-model car since the small saving achieved is not worth the risk of subsequent bearing and engine failure.

3. Installing new bearings. When new bearings are to be installed, make sure that your hands, the workbench, tools, and all engine parts are clean. Keep the new bearings wrapped up until you are ready to install them. Then handle them carefully, wiping each with a fresh piece of cleaning tissue (such as Kleenex) just before installing it. Be very sure that the bores in the cap and rod are clean and not excessively out of round.* Then

* Some manufacturers recommend a check of bore symmetry with the bearing shells out. Cap should be attached with nuts drawn up to specified tension. Then a telescope gauge and micrometer or a special out-of-round gauge can be used to check the bore.

put the bearing shells in place. If they have locking tangs, make sure the tangs enter the notches provided in the rod and cap. Note comments about bearing spread and crush, below. Check clearance after installation (§ 335).

▶ *CAUTION:* Do not attempt to correct clearance by filing rod cap. This destroys the original relationship between cap and rod and will lead to early bearing failure.

4. Bearing spread. Bearing shells are usually manufactured with "spread," that is, with the shell diameter somewhat greater than the diameter of the rod cap or rod bore into which the shell will fit (Fig. 14–51). Then, when the shell is installed into the cap or rod, it will snap into place and will hold its seat during subsequent assembling operations.

5. Bearing crush. In order to make sure that the bearing shell will "snug down" into its bore in the rod cap or rod when the cap is installed, the bearings have crush (Fig. 14–52), that is, they are manufactured to have some additional height over a full half. This additional height must be crushed down when the cap is installed. Crushing down the additional amount forces the shells into the bores in the cap and rod, assuring firm seating and snug contact with the bores.

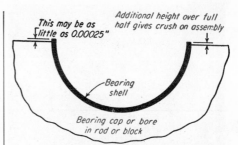

Fig. 14–52. Bearing crush.

▶ *CAUTION:* Never file off the edges of the bearing shells in an attempt to remove crush. When you select the proper bearings for an engine (as recommended by the engine manufacturer), you will find that they have the correct crush. Precision-insert bearings must not be tampered with in any way in an attempt to make them "fit better." This will usually lead only to rapid bearing failure.

PISTONS AND RINGS

§ **337. Piston service** After the piston-and-connecting-rod assemblies have been removed from the engine and the pistons and rods separated (§§ 327–330), the rings should be removed from the piston (Fig. 14–53). (The rings may be removed from the piston before the piston and rod are separated.) A special ring tool is required for ring removal. The tool has two small claws that catch under the ends of the ring. Then, when pressure is applied to the tool handles, the ring is sprung enough so that it can be lifted out of the ring groove and off the piston. Examine rings as explained in § 340.

1. Piston cleaning. With the rings off, the piston should be cleaned inside and out. A carbon scraper should

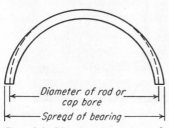

Fig. 14–51. Bearing spread.

Fig. 14–53. Ring-removing and replacing tool in use. (*Studebaker-Packard Corporation*)

be used to scrape the carbon from the head and from inside the piston. Do not scrape the piston skirts, since this could scratch the finish and thus lead to rapid cylinder-wall and piston wear. Clean out the ring grooves with a cleanout tool (Fig. 14–54). This tool pulls a cleanout device through the groove to remove accumulated carbon. Care must be used to avoid removing metal from the ring lands; this would cause an excessively loose ring fit. Oil-

holes in the oil-ring grooves should be cleaned out so that the oil can drain through them freely. A drill is handy for this job if the holes are badly carboned. The drill should just fit the holes but should not remove metal from the piston.

2. *Piston fit.* The piston must be in good condition if it is to be reinstalled in the engine. This means it must properly fit the cylinder and must be free of cracks, pits, scratches, and so on. To check the fit, the piston should first be measured with a micrometer (Fig. 14–55). Measurements should be made at various places around the piston and from top to bottom in order to find out whether or not the piston has "collapsed." A piston that has collapsed has suffered an excessive reduction in diameter at the lower end of the piston skirt; the piston is tapered. Piston measurements should be compared with cylinder measurements (taken as explained in § 354). The difference is the piston clearance. The engine manufacturer's shop man-

Fig. 14–54. Groove-cleanout tool in use on piston-ring grooves. (*Willys Motors, Inc.*)

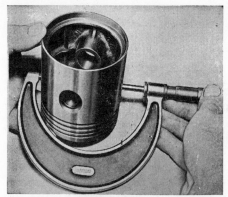

Fig. 14–55. Piston being measured with micrometer. *(Plymouth Division of Chrysler Corporation)*

ual should be consulted for details of measurements and allowable clearances as well as for maximum allowable piston and cylinder-wall taper.

On cam-ground pistons (Figs. 6–42 and 6–43), take measurements for taper at the larger diameter (or in the direction vertical to piston-pin holes). Take measurements close to the top and bottom of the piston.

Actual fit of the piston in the cylinder can be checked with feeler stock, as follows: Put the piston into the cylinder upside down with the feeler stock, lightly oiled, placed at right angles to and 90 degrees from the piston-pin holes. The fit is thus measured at the point of greatest piston diameter. Stock of different thicknesses can be tried to determine the clearance. A refinement of this procedure, which is more exact, requires the use of a spring scale. The amount of force required to pull the feeler stock out is measured (Fig. 14–56). As an example, on one engine, a ribbon of feeler stock ½ inch wide, 12 inches long, and 0.0015 inch thick should be

withdrawn from between the piston and cylinder wall with a pull of 7 to 9 pounds. If the feeler stock pulls out too easily, the fit is too loose. If it pulls out too hard, the fit is too tight.

If the fit is too loose, a new piston or piston resizing is necessary to reestablish the close fit required. Also, if the cylinder is so worn that it must be rebored or honed (§§ 355–357), then new pistons probably will be required. However, if the increase in cylinder size is not too great, the piston can be resized (made larger in diameter) so that it will fit the enlarged cylinder. Several piston-resizing methods are in use, all operating on similar principles. A simple piston resizer is shown in Fig. 14–57. It has a

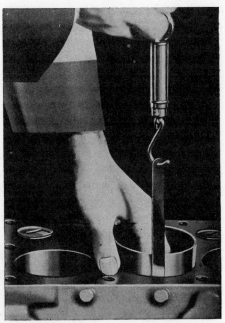

Fig. 14–56. A spring scale hooked to feeler stock being used to measure the fit of the piston in the cylinder. *(Plymouth Division of Chrysler Corporation)*

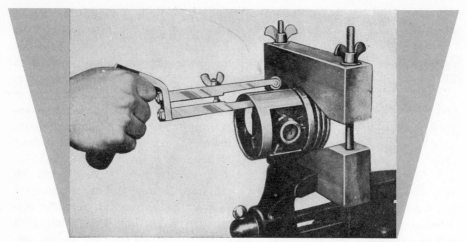

Fig. 14–57. Simple type of piston resizer. Pressure between inner and outer roller wheels squeezes metal and expands skirt. (*Sealed Power Corporation*)

Fig. 14–58. Piston-pin bushings being honed. (*Sunnen Products Company*)

pair of rollers that roll under pressure on the piston skirt as the tool is moved back and forth. This squeezes the metal and expands the skirt. In addition to this type of tool, there are piston-skirt expanders that can be inserted in the piston. These devices spring-load the skirt from the inside and thus increase the skirt diameter slightly.

3. New pistons. New pistons are supplied either finished or semifinished. The finished type, ready for installation, is available in a number of sizes. When these are used, the cylinders must be finished to fit the pistons. Semifinished pistons are oversize and must be finished down to size to fit the cylinders.

▶ *CAUTION:* Finished pistons usually have a special finish and should not be turned down or finished to a smaller size. This would remove the finish and possibly cause rapid piston wear after installation.

§ 338. **Fitting piston pins** If the piston-pin bushings are worn, they should be reamed or honed oversize (Fig. 14–58) and oversize pins installed. The pins should be replaced if they are worn or pitted. The reaming and honing procedures are very similar to those used on connecting-rod piston-pin bushings (§ 332). When the pin is of the type that is free in the bushing, fit is correct if the pin will pass through with light thumb pressure when both piston and pin are at room temperature. When the pin is a press fit, it is forced into place under pressure. Another method is to heat the piston and then install the pin with a pilot tool. Some pistons have a locking bolt for

locking the pin in the piston after it is installed.

§ 339. **Rod and piston alignment** After the rod and piston have been reassembled, but before the rings are installed on the piston, rod and piston alignment should be checked (Fig. 14–59). The alignment tool shown in Fig. 14–41 is used for this check. If the V block does not line up with the face plate as the piston is moved to various positions, the connecting rod is twisted. (See § 331 on checking and correcting rod alignment.)

§ 340. **Piston-ring service** If an engine is torn down for overhaul after considerable mileage, the chances are the rings will require replacement. Sometimes, all that is required is to free up the rings in the ring grooves by cleaning out carbon. Special compounds that can be introduced into the intake manifold and engine oil to help free the rings without tearing down the engine have already been mentioned (§ 307).

In examining rings to determine whether or not they should be reused, several conditions may be found. Conditions requiring ring replacement include loss of tension, irregular light and dark areas (showing uneven wear caused by warped or worn rings), and scores or scratches.

Proper selection of new rings depends upon the condition of the cylinder walls and whether or not they are to be reconditioned. Article 354 describes the checking of cylinder walls for wear and taper. If they are only slightly tapered or out of round (consult manufacturer's specifications for

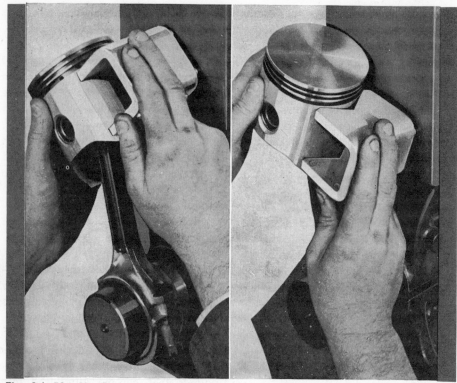

Fig. 14–59. Checking connecting-rod and piston alignment with alignment-checking tool. (*Chevrolet Motor Division of General Motors Corporation*)

maximum allowable), then standard-type rings can be installed. Where the walls have some taper, but not enough to warrant the extra expense of a rebore or hone job, special "severe," or "drastic," rings should be used. These rings have greater tension and are more flexible. This enables them to expand and contract as they move up and down in the cylinder. Thus, they are able to follow the changing contours of the cylinder wall and thereby provide adequate sealing (preventing blow-by) and oil control. Figure 6–36 shows a set of replacement rings for tapered cylinder walls. Figure 14–60 is a disassembled view of these same rings.

It may or may not be necessary to hone the cylinder walls lightly (§ 356) before ring installation to "break the glaze." Cylinder walls take on a hard, smooth glaze after the engine has been in use for a while. It is the practice of some engine servicemen to knock off this glaze by running a hone up and down the cylinder a few times before putting in new rings. However, at least one ring manufacturer says this does not need to be done on cast-iron cylinder walls, *provided the walls are not wavy or scuffed.* The glaze is a good antiscuff material and will not unduly retard the wear-in of new rings if the walls are reasonably concentric and in relatively good condition.

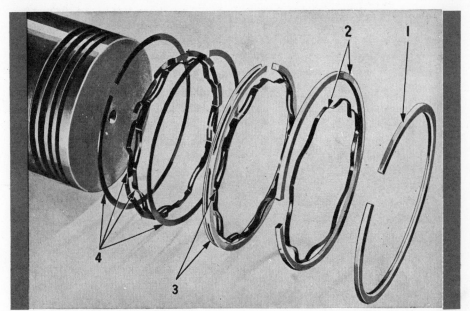

Fig. 14–60. Disassembled view of one type of replacement piston rings: 1, top compression ring; 2, second compression ring, which includes an expander ring; 3, upper oil-control ring; 4, lower oil-control ring. The last is of a three-part construction; it consists of an upper and lower rail with an expanding spring. (*Plymouth Division of Chrysler Corporation*)

Fig. 14–61. Ring gap being measured with ring in cylinder. 1, feeler gauge; 2, piston ring. (*Plymouth Division of Chrysler Corporation*)

§ 341. Fitting piston rings Piston rings must be fitted to the cylinder and to the ring groove in the piston. As a first step, the ring should be pushed down into the cylinder with a piston and the ring gap (space between ends of the ring) checked with a feeler gauge (Fig. 14–61). If the ring gap is too small, the ends of the ring should be filed with a fine-cut file. The file should be clamped into a vise and the ring worked back and forth on the file (with the ring ends on the two sides of the file). Use care to avoid distorting the ring.

▶ CAUTION: If the cylinder is worn tapered, the diameter at the lower limit of ring travel (in the assembled engine) will be smaller than the diameter

335

Fig. 14–62. Checking fit of ring in ring groove. (*Chevrolet Motor Division of General Motors Corporation*)

at the top (Fig. 14–77). In this type of cylinder, *the ring must be fitted to the diameter at the lower limit of ring travel.* If fitted to the upper part of the cylinder, the ring gap will not be great enough as the ring is moved down to its lower limit of travel. This means that the ring ends will come together and the ring will be broken or the cylinder walls scuffed. In tapered cylinders, file the ring gap so that the ring fits the cylinder at the point of minimum diameter, or the lower limit of ring travel.

After the ring gap has been corrected, the outside surface of the ring should be inserted into the proper ring groove in the piston and the ring rolled around in the groove to make sure that the ring has a free fit around the entire piston circumference (Fig. 14–62). An excessively tight fit probably means that the ring groove is dirty, and it

should be cleaned (Fig. 14–54). After the rings are installed in the ring groove (by using the ring tool as shown in Fig. 14–53), fit should again be tested. This test is made by inserting a feeler gauge between the ring and the side of the groove (Fig. 14–63).

§ 342. Installing piston in cylinder
To install the piston in the cylinder after the piston, rings, and rod are reassembled, it is necessary to compress the rings in their grooves so that they will enter the cylinder. A piston-ring compressor (Fig. 14–64) may be used for this operation. The compressor clamps around the rings, compressing them into their grooves so that the piston-and-ring assembly can be pushed into the cylinder. (See § 330, 3, for replacement procedure on rod-and-piston assemblies.)

CRANKSHAFT AND MAIN BEARINGS
§ 343. Crankshaft and bearing service Main bearings of the precision-insert type can be replaced without

Fig. 14–63. Piston-ring clearance being tested with gauge. (*Chevrolet Motor Division of General Motors Corporation*)

removing the crankshaft. Bearings that require finishing after installation cannot be replaced without removing the crankshaft. Replacing precision-insert main bearings without removing the crankshaft requires about 5 hours. To remove the crankshaft and install, fit, and adjust semifinished bearings requires about 19 to 22 hours. Some idea of the condition of the bearings can be gained by using the bearing oil-leak detector (§ 326). An accurate analysis of the bearing fit and the condition of bearings and crankshaft journals requires removal of the bearing caps as noted below.

§ 344. Checking crankshaft journals

Both the crankpins and the crankshaft

Fig. 14–64. Using a piston-ring compressor tool to install a piston with rings. (*Plymouth Division of Chrysler Corporation*)

journals should be checked whenever the bearings are removed. Checking crankpins has already been discussed (§ 336, 1). Journals can be checked on the engine with a special crankshaft gauge or with a special micrometer. Measurements should be taken in several places along the journal to check for taper. Also, the crankshaft should be rotated by quarter or eighth turns to check for out-of-round wear. (See § 334 for discussions of what a tapered, ridged, or out-of-round journal will do to a bearing.) If journals are tapered or out of round by more than 0.003 inch, they should be reground (§ 351). As a matter of fact, some authorities consider 0.0015 inch the outside tolerable limit; they point out that *any* appreciable eccentricity or taper will shorten bearing life.

To check journals, remove the oil pan (§ 329) and bearing caps. It is not necessary to detach the connecting rods from the crankshaft, but the spark plugs should be removed so that the engine can be turned over easily.

1. Removing bearing caps. Remove only one bearing cap at a time if journals and bearings are being checked. Remove all caps if the crankshaft is to come out of the engine. Caps should be marked so that they can be replaced on the same journals from which they were removed. To remove a cap, loosen the nuts or bolts. Cut lock wire (if used), or bend back lock-washer tangs (if used). Also, disconnect oil lines where necessary.

NOTE: Use new lock washers or lock wires on reassembly.

If the cap sticks, work it loose carefully to avoid distorting it. In some en-

337

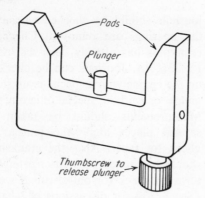

Fig. 14–65. Special gauge for checking journal diameter. *(Federal-Mogul Corporation)*

gines, a bearing-cap puller can be used; the puller bolt is screwed into the oil-coupling hole. In other engines, a screw driver or pry bar can be used to work the cap loose. Sometimes tapping the cap lightly on one side and then on the other with a brass hammer will loosen it.

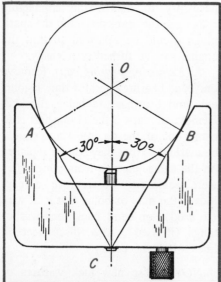

Fig. 14–66. Using gauge to check journal diameter. *(Federal-Mogul Corporation)*

▶ *CAUTION:* Heavy hammering or prying will distort the cap, bend the dowel pins, or damage the dowel holes. In such a case, the bearing may not fit when the cap is replaced, and early bearing failure will occur.

2. *Measuring journal with special crankshaft gauge.* The special gauge (Fig. 14–65) is used as shown in Fig. 14–66. The journal and the gauge pads and plunger must be clean. Then, the plunger is retracted, the gauge held tightly against the journal (Fig. 14–66), and the plunger released so that it contacts the journal. The plunger is then locked in this position by tightening the thumbscrew. Finally, a micrometer is used to measure the distance between *D,* or the end of the plunger and *C,* or the button on the bottom of the gauge. This measurement, multiplied by 2, is the diameter of the journal.

3. *Measuring journal with micrometer.* To use the micrometer, the upper bearing half must be removed. If it is the precision-insert type, this can be done with a special "roll-out" tool as explained in § 347. Then, the micrometer can be used as shown in Fig. 14–67.

§ 345. Checking main bearings Main, or crankshaft, bearings are of two types, precision-insert and semi-finished. They should be replaced if they are worn, burned, scored, pitted, rough, flaked, cracked, or otherwise damaged. (See § 334 on bearing failures.) It is very important to check the crankshaft journals (§ 344) before installing new bearings; if the journals are not in good condition, the new bearings may soon fail. A compromise

repair using taper shim bearing adjusters.(§ 336) can be made where journals and bearings are in good condition but have too much clearance. Following articles describe checking of bearing fit, replacement of bearings, and servicing of crankshaft journals.

§ **346. Checking main-bearing fit**
Bearing fit (or oil clearance) should always be checked after new bearings are installed. The fit should also be checked at other times when the condition of the bearings is being determined. Crankshaft-journal condition should also be checked at the same time.

1. Precision-insert type. Bearing clearance can be checked with feeler stock or Plastigage.

a. With feeler stock. Put a piece of feeler stock of the right size and thickness in the bearing cap after the cap has been removed (Fig. 14–68). Coat feeler stock lightly with oil. Replace cap, and tighten cap nuts or bolts to the specified tension. Note the ease with which the crankshaft can be turned. If it drags noticeably, bearing clearance is less than the thickness of the feeler stock. If it does not, an additional thickness of feeler stock should be placed on top of the first and the ease of crankshaft movement again checked. Clearance normally should be about 0.002 inch (see engine manufacturer's specifications for exact clearance).

b. With Plastigage. Wipe journal and bearing clean of oil. Put a strip of Plastigage lengthwise in the center of the bearing cap (Fig. 14–48); replace and tighten the cap. Then remove the cap, and measure the amount the

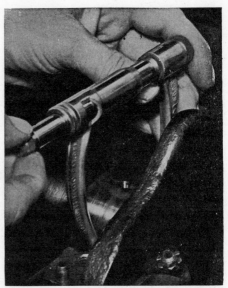

Fig. 14–67. Crankshaft-journal diameter being measured with special micrometer. (*Kaiser Motors Corporation*)

Plastigage has been flattened. Do not turn the crankshaft with the Plastigage in place. (See § 335 for more information on Plastigage.)

2. Semifitted (shim-adjusted) main bearings. Loosen all bearing caps just enough to permit the crankshaft to turn freely. Take off the rear main-bearing cap, and remove one shim from each side of the cap. Replace and tighten the cap bolts or nuts to the specified tension. Rotate crankshaft to see whether it now drags. If it does not drag, remove additional shims (in pairs) and check for drag after each pair is removed. When a drag is felt, replace one shim on each side of the cap. If the crankshaft now turns freely when the cap is tightened, clearance is correct. Loosen cap bolts or nuts. Go to the next bearing, and adjust its clearance in the same way. Finally, when all bearings are adjusted, tighten

Fig. 14–68. Main-bearing clearance being checked with feeler stock: 1, feeler stock; 2, bearing cap. (*Dodge Division of Chrysler Corporation*)

Fig. 14–69. Crankshaft end play being checked with feeler gauge. 1, pry bar; 2, feeler gauge. (*Plymouth Division of Chrysler Corporation*)

Fig. 14–70. Installing a new main upper bearing with a special "roll-out" tool inserted into the crankshaft oilhole. 1, special tool; 2, main bearing. (*Plymouth Division of Chrysler Corporation*)

all cap bolts or nuts to the proper tension, and recheck for crankshaft drag as it is turned. If it drags, then recheck and readjust the bearings.

3. Checking crankshaft end play. Crankshaft end play will become excessive if the end-thrust bearings are worn. This produces a noticeable sharp, irregular knock. If the wear is considerable, the knock will occur every time the clutch is released and applied; this action causes sudden endwise movements of the crankshaft. Check end play by forcing the crankshaft endwise as far as it will go with a pry bar, and then measure the clearance at the end-thrust bearing with a feeler gauge (Fig. 14–69). Consult the engine manufacturer's shop manual for allowable end play.

§ 347. Replacing precision main bearings Before replacing bearings, crankshaft journals should be checked (§ 344). Also, after bearings are installed, bearing fit should be checked (§ 346). Precision-insert main bearings can be replaced without removing the crankshaft. However, some authorities do not advocate this. They say that you are working blind. You cannot be sure that the counterbore in the cylinder block is perfectly clean and that the shell is seating tightly.

To install a precision-insert main bearing without removing the crankshaft, use a special roll-out tool as shown in Fig. 14–70. The tool is inserted into the oilhole in the crankshaft journal, as shown. Then, the crankshaft is rotated. The tool forces the bearing shell to rotate with the crankshaft so that it is turned out of the bore. The crankshaft must be rotated in the proper direction so that the lock, or tang, in the bearing is raised

Fig. 14–71. Crankshaft rear-main-bearing oil seal: 1, oil seal; 2, left cap gasket; 3, right cap gasket; 4, oil seal. (*Plymouth Division of Chrysler Corporation*)

up out of the notch in the cylinder block.

To install a new bearing half, coat it with engine oil. Make sure the bore, or bearing seat, in the block is clean. Do not file the edges of the shell (this would remove crush). Use the tool as shown in Fig. 14–70 to slide the bearing shell into place. Then place a new bearing shell in the cap. Install the cap, and tighten the cap bolts or nuts to the specified tension. Tap the crown of the cap lightly with a brass hammer while tightening it. This helps to align the bearings properly. After all bearings are in place, check bearing fit.

While removing and replacing the upper bearing shell of a rear main bearing, hold the oil seal in position in the cylinder block so that it does not come out of position (see § 348 on oil-seal replacement).

On all but a very few engines, pre-

cision-insert bearings are installed without shims. Never use shims on these bearings unless the engine manufacturer specifies them. Similarly, bearing caps must not be filed in an attempt to improve bearing fit.

§ 348. Replacing main-bearing oil seal   An oil seal is required at the rear main bearing to prevent oil leakage at that point (Fig. 14–71). When main-bearing service is being performed, or whenever leakage is noted at the rear main bearing, the oil seal must be replaced.

The procedure of replacement varies with different constructions. On some engines using a split-type oil seal, the crankshaft must be removed and a special oil-seal compressor or installer used to insert the new seal in the cylinder-block bearing. The seal should then be trimmed flush with the block as shown in Fig. 14–72. The oil seal in the cap can be replaced by removing the cap, installing the oil seal, and trimming it flush. On other engines (the type shown in Fig. 14–71, for example), it is not necessary to remove the crankshaft since removal of the flywheel will permit access to the upper oil-seal retainer. Retainer cap screws can then be removed along with the retainer for oil-seal replacement. Some engines use a one-piece rubber-type oil seal which can be pulled from around the crankshaft with a pair of pliers and a new oil seal then worked into place. It should be coated with cup grease (except on the ends, since this would prevent the ends from meeting tightly). Then, one end of the seal should be forced up into the slot on one side until it is at the top of the

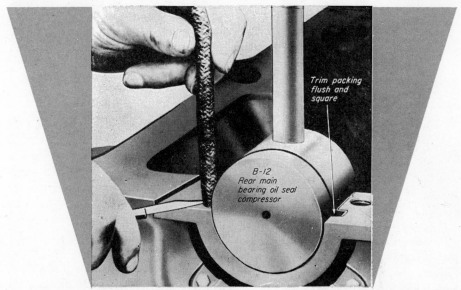

Fig. 14–72. Installation of rear-main-bearing oil seal in cylinder block with special tool. Same tool is used to install seal in cap. (*Oldsmobile Division of General Motors Corporation*)

bearing. Next, the other end can be forced up into the slot on the opposite side, so that the ends meet at the top of the bearing.

§ 349. Replacing semifitted bearings To replace these bearings, the crankshaft must be removed. Then, after the bearings are installed, they must be machined to size with a special boring machine (Fig. 14–73). Also, the end-thrust-bearing faces must be machined, or "faced," so as to provide the correct amount of crankshaft end play (Fig. 14–74).

§ 350. Removing the crankshaft Such parts as the oil pan, timing-gear, or timing-chain, cover, crankshaft timing gear, or sprocket, interfering oil lines, and oil pump must be removed before the crankshaft can be taken off.

Also, on some engines, the flywheel must be detached from the crankshaft. With other parts off, the bearing caps are removed to release the crankshaft.

§ 351. Servicing crankshaft Check crankshaft for alignment and for journal and crankpin wear. Alignment can be checked with the setup shown in Fig. 14–75. As the crankshaft is rotated in the V blocks, the dial indicator will show any misalignment. A bent crankshaft can sometimes be straightened in a heavy press.

▶ *CAUTION:* Do not leave a crankshaft supported only at the ends as shown in Fig. 14–75. This could cause the crankshaft to ultimately sag and go out of alignment. Support the crankshaft on wood blocks of equal thickness placed under each journal. Or set the crankshaft on end.

Fig. 14–73. Main-bearing boring machine installed on engine: 1, 2, 3, 4, 5, supporting clamps, bolts, and bearings; 6, boring bar; 7, 8, 9, feed-screw arrangement; 10, turning handle, 11, boring-bar cutters. (*Chevrolet Motor Division of General Motors Corporation*)

Fig. 14–74. Facing end-thrust bearing with facing cutters. (*Chevrolet Motor Division of General Motors Corporation*)

Checking of the journals and crankpins for taper or eccentricity has already been discussed (§§ 336 and 344). If journal or crankpin taper or eccentricity exceeds safe limits, or if they are rough, scratched, pitted, or otherwise damaged, they must be ground undersized. Then new undersized bearings must be installed. Journals and crankpins must be ground down to fit the next undersize bearing available.

NOTE: It is possible to "metalize" journals and crankpins and then regrind them to their original sizes. This is done by first rough-turning the journals and crankpins in a lathe. Then, a high-temperature flame is used to spray liquid metal onto the prepared surfaces. This metal adheres and can be ground to form a new journal surface.

1. Finishing journals and crankpins. A special grinder or lathe is required to service journals and crankpins. The bearing surfaces must be finished to extreme smoothness. The grinding wheel may leave a certain amount of "fuzz" on the reground surfaces; this may be removed with fine crocus cloth, as follows: Cover journals and crankpins with oil, and wrap a long strip of crocus cloth halfway around a journal. Take the ends of the strip in your two hands and pull the strip back and forth, working uniformly all around each journal and crankpin. This removes any roughness. As a final test, wipe off oil, and rub a copper penny across the surface. If it leaves any trace of copper on the steel, there is still roughness that should be removed.

▶*CAUTION:* Be sure to relieve (grind back) the journal and crankpin radii (where they curve up to the crank cheeks). This will guard against bearing failure from radii ride (§ 334, 5).

2. Cleaning crankshaft. After grinding journals or crankpins, or at any time that the crankshaft has been removed from the engine, the crankshaft should be thoroughly cleaned in a suitable solvent. A rifle-type brush should be used to clean out oil passages (Fig. 14–76). Remember, any trace of abrasive left in an oil passage could work out onto bearing surfaces and cause early bearing failure. Reoil the bearing surfaces immediately after they

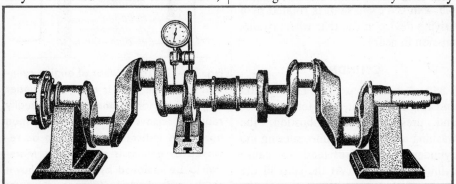

Fig. 14–75. Checking crankshaft for alignment with V blocks and dial indicator.

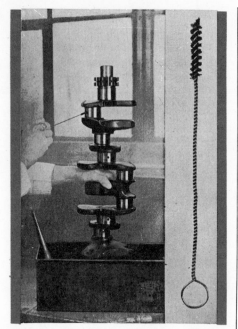

Fig. 14-76. Using a small brush to clean out oil passages in the crankshaft. (Federal-Mogul Corporation)

have been cleaned to keep them from rusting.

3. Grinding crankpins on engine. With the use of a special grinder, crankpins may be ground with the crankshaft still in the engine. To do this, the grinder is attached to a crankpin, and the crankshaft is rotated by a driving device at the rear wheel (transmission in gear).

CYLINDERS

§ 352. **Cylinder wear** The piston and ring movement, high temperatures and pressures of combustion, the washing action of gasoline entering the cylinder — all these tend to cause cylinder-wall wear. At the start of the power stroke, when pressures are the greatest, the compression rings are

forced with the greatest pressure against the cylinder wall. Also, at the same time, the temperatures are highest, and the oil film is therefore least effective in protecting the cylinder walls. Thus, it is obvious that most wear will take place at the top of the cylinder. As the piston moves down on the power stroke, the combustion pressure and temperature decrease so that less wear takes place. The cylinder thus wears irregularly, as shown in Fig. 14–77.

The cylinder also tends to wear somewhat oval-shaped. This is due to the side thrust of the piston as it moves down in the cylinder on the power stroke. The side thrust results from

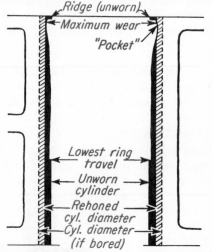

Fig. 14–77. Taper wear of engine cylinder. Maximum wear is at top, just under ring ridge. Honing the cylinder usually requires removal of less material than boring, as indicated. Material to be removed by honing is shown solid. Material to be removed by boring is shown solid and shaded. (Sunnen Products Company)

the swing, from vertical, of the connecting rod. Another factor is the washing action of the gasoline. At times the air-fuel mixture is not perfectly blended, and small droplets of gasoline, still unvaporized, enter the cylinder. They strike the cylinder wall (at a point opposite the intake valve) and wash away the oil film. Therefore, this area wears somewhat more rapidly.

§ 353. Cylinder service There are certain limits to which cylinders may wear tapered or out of round before they will require refinishing. As mentioned in § 340, special drastic replacement rings will control compression and oil in cylinders with some taper and out-of-round wear. But when wear goes beyond a certain point, even the severest rings cannot hold compression and control oil; loss of compression, high oil consumption, poor performance, and heavy carbon accumulations in the cylinders will result. In such a case, the only way to get the engine back into good operating condition is to refinish the cylinders and fit new pistons (or resized pistons) and new rings to them.

Refinishing cylinders requires 12 to 20 hours (according to the type of engine). This includes fitting and installing new pistons, rings, piston pins, and connecting rods. When new bearings are fitted, about 10 additional hours is required. Grinding valves would require several more hours. These various times are mentioned since an engine that requires cylinder refinishing is usually in need of a general overhaul and these other services would also be required.

§ 354. Checking cylinder walls Wipe walls, and examine them for scores and spotty wear (which shows up as dark, unpolished spots). Hold a light at the opposite end of the cylinder so that you can see the walls better. Scores or spots mean the walls must be refinished. Even drastic rings cannot give satisfactory performance on such walls.

Next, measure the cylinders for taper and oval wear. This can be done with an inside micrometer, with a telescope gauge and an outside micrometer, or with a special dial indicator. The dial indicator is shown in use in Fig. 14–78. It should be moved up and down in the cylinder and rotated in various positions to detect

Fig. 14–78. Using a cylinder-bore indicator (1) to detect variations in cylinder diameter. (*Plymouth Division of Chrysler Corporation*)

irregularities. Any irregularities will be indicated by movement of the needle.

If irregularities are too great, the cylinders must be rebored or honed.

§ 355. Refinishing cylinders As a first step, the block should be cleaned (§ 360). A decision must be made on whether the cylinders are to be honed or bored. The boring machine uses a revolving cutting tool. The hone has a set of abrasive stones which are turned in the cylinder. Where cylinder wear is not too great, only honing is necessary. But if wear has gone so far that a considerable amount of metal must be

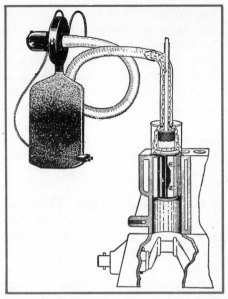

Fig. 14–80. Vacuum device for use with cylinder hone. The arrows indicate the direction of air flow to the vacuum device. This device draws out dust produced by the honing operation. (Kent-Moore Organization, Inc.)

removed, then honing will not do the job; a reboring job is required.

§ 356. Honing cylinders If wear, taper, or eccentricity is not excessive, only honing will be required. Figure 14–79 shows a cylinder hone in place, ready for the honing operation.

For dry honing, a vacuum device is desirable (Fig. 14–80). This device removes dust raised by the honing operation.

Clean up cylinders after honing (§ 358).

§ 357. Boring cylinders If wear is too great to be taken care of by honing, cylinders must be bored. The size to which the cylinders must be rebored is determined by the amount of

Fig. 14–79. Cylinder hone in place in cylinder. In operation, the hone revolves in the cylinder, and the abrasive stones in the hone remove material from the cylinder wall. (Hall Manufacturing Company)

material that needs to be removed from the walls. In addition, the type of piston to be installed must be considered. With a semifinished piston, only enough material need be removed to clean up the bores. Then, the pistons are finished to fit the cylinders.

Fig. 14–82. Centering fingers extended to center the cutting head of boring bar in cylinder.

But when new, finished pistons are to be installed, the bores will have to be finished to the proper size to take the correct oversize piston (and matching new rings).

Figure 14–81 shows one type of boring bar. Figure 14–82 shows the centering fingers of the cutting head extended so that the head is centrally located in the cylinder. Figure 14–83 shows the cutting tool in place and cutting as the head revolves. This is one of several types of boring bar.

§ 358. Cleaning cylinders Cylinders must be cleaned thoroughly after the honing or boring operation. Even slight traces of grit or dust left on the cylinder walls may cause rapid ring and wall wear and early engine failure. As a first step, some engine manufacturers recommend wiping down the cylinder walls with very fine crocus cloth. This loosens embedded grit and also knocks off "fuzz" left by the honing stones or cutting tool. Then use a swab and light engine oil or hot, soapy water to wash down the walls. A small cotton-

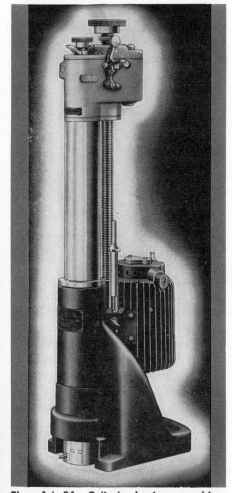

Fig. 14–81. Cylinder-boring machine. The cutting tool is carried in a rotating bar that feeds down into the cylinder as it rotates. This causes the cutting tool to remove material from the cylinder wall. (*Rottler Boring Bar Company*)

Fig. 14–83. Revolving head of cylinder-boring machine, showing cutting tool.

string mop makes a good swab. Make sure the cleanup job is done thoroughly. For instance, when swabbing down with oil, scrub the walls with the oily swab, and then use a clean cloth to wipe off the oil. Do this several times or until the cloth will remain absolutely clean when rubbed on the walls.

Clean out all oil passages in the block, as well as stud- and boltholes, after the walls are cleaned.

NOTE: Gasoline or kerosene will

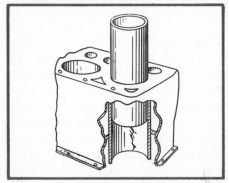

Fig. 14–84. Cracked blocks and badly scored or worn cylinder bores can often be repaired by installing cylinder sleeves. (*Sealed Power Corporation*)

not remove all the grit from the cylinder walls; their use to clean up the cylinder walls is not recommended.

§ 359. **Replacing cylinder sleeves** On engines equipped with cylinder sleeves, the sleeves usually can be removed and replaced at room temperature. A special sleeve puller is required.

Cracked blocks, scored cylinders, cylinders worn so badly that they must be bored to an excessively large oversize — all these can often be repaired by the installation of cylinder sleeves (Fig. 14–84). As a first step, the cylinder must be bored out with a boring machine to take the cylinder sleeve. Then the sleeve should be installed and bored to the proper size.

§ 360. **Cylinder-block cleaning** Before a honing or boring operation, or at any time that the engine is torn down, the block should be cleaned. This means that the oiled sections should be cleaned of sludge and the water-jacket sections cleaned of lime, rust, and other deposits. To remove sludge, the various engine parts should be washed with a good solvent and a brush. Steam-cleaning the block and other parts will help dispose of the sludge. The cooling system can be flushed out without tearing down the engine. A cleaning compound should be used (directions on the cleaner container should be followed). Then water under pressure should be forced through the engine water jackets to wash out loosened scale and rust. The cooling-system thermostat must be removed when the engine block is flushed out.

§ 361. Replacing expansion plugs

If an expansion plug must be removed from the block (because of water leakage past the plug, for example), it can be drilled in the center and then pried out with a punch or small pry bar. To install a new plug, scrape out all rust from the recess, coat the base and sides of the recess with red lead, and place the new plug in the recess, curved (convex) side out. Tap the center of the plug with a hammer to make sure that the plug is seated. Then use a flat-ended drift or punch to drive against the plug. This flattens and expands the plug so that it fits the recess tightly.

REVIEW QUESTIONS

1. What is the first step to be taken before any engine service is performed?
2. Describe the operating characteristics of valves in good condition.
3. Describe various valve troubles, the possible causes, and cures.
4. Mention seven or eight valve-servicing jobs.
5. Explain how to check and adjust valve-tappet clearance in an L-head engine.
6. Describe a self-locking tappet-adjusting screw.
7. Describe the procedure of checking and adjusting valve-tappet clearance on an overhead-valve engine (two types).
8. Why is it desirable to use a valve rack when valves are removed from the engine?
9. Describe the procedure of removing the valves from an L-head engine. From a Ford engine. From an overhead-valve engine.
10. How are valve springs tested?
11. Explain how to remove, inspect, and replace cylinder heads.
12. Explain how to clean carbon from the head and block.
13. Describe the procedure of refacing valves.
14. When are new valve-seat inserts required?
15. Describe the procedure of concentric valve-seat grinding.
16. Describe the procedure of eccentric valve-seat grinding.
17. What is one of the greatest hazards in valve-seat grinding where pistons are not removed from the engine?
18. What is meant by valve-seat width, and how is the proper width secured?
19. How are valves and seats tested?
20. What services are required on valve guides?
21. How is a valve guide tested for wear?
22. In what two ways should a camshaft be tested after its removal from the engine?
23. What is meant by valve timing?
24. Explain how to use the bearing oil-leak detector.
25. What is the first step in piston and rod removal when removal is to be made from the top of the engine?
26. What is a ring ridge, and how is it caused? What would be likely to happen if the piston were taken out from the top of the engine before the ring ridge was removed?
27. Explain how to remove and replace piston-and-rod assemblies.
28. How is connecting-rod alignment checked?

29. Explain how to check, replace, and ream or hone a set of piston-pin bushings.
30. Describe different types of bearing failure and their causes.
31. Describe checking of rod-bearing clearance on precision-insert-type bearings.
32. Describe the adjustment of direct-babbitted rod bearings.
33. Explain how to install new rod bearings.
34. What is a taper shim bearing adjuster?
35. When are oversized pistons required in an engine?
36. Why is it desirable to use a piston vise for piston work?
37. What is a ring-groove cleanout tool?
38. How is the fit of the piston in the cylinder checked?
39. What is piston resizing? How is it done?
40. Describe the procedure of fitting piston rings.
41. Describe the procedure of installing a piston in a cylinder.
42. On what does the selection of new piston rings depend?
43. Explain how to check crankshaft journals and crankpins.
44. Explain how to check main-bearing fit. Crankshaft end play.
45. Explain how to replace precision-insert main bearings. The main-bearing oil seal.
46. Explain how to service the crankshaft.
47. Discuss types and causes of cylinder wear.
48. Explain how to check cylinder walls.
49. What is a cylinder-boring machine? How does it operate?
50. What is a cylinder hone? How does it operate?
51. Discuss in detail how to hone cylinder walls. How to bore a cylinder.
52. Explain how to replace cylinder sleeves.

STUDY QUESTIONS

1. If low compression is obtained when engine cylinders are checked with the compression tester, what should you do to determine where leakage is occurring?
2. List various valve troubles, their causes, and cures.
3. Make a list of the steps required in adjusting valve-tappet clearance on an L-head engine. An overhead-valve engine.
4. Write a sequence story on the procedure of removing valves in an L-head engine. A Ford engine. An overhead-valve engine.
5. Refer to the shop manual on a car using semifitted main bearings, and write a sequence story on installing, machining, and fitting the main bearings.
6. Make a list of the steps required in the removal of piston and connecting-rod assemblies from the top of the cylinder block.
7. Refer to a car shop manual to find the procedure for selecting piston rings.
8. Write a sequence story on removing, servicing, and replacing piston-and-rod assemblies.
9. Write a sequence story on honing cylinder walls. On boring cylinder walls.

THIS CHAPTER DESCRIBES THE servicing of the various components of the electric system on the automobile, including the battery, cranking motor, regulator, generator, and ignition system.

STORAGE BATTERY

§ 362. Battery-testing methods Batteries are tested to determine two conditions, (1) the chemical condition of the electrolyte, and (2) the capacity of the battery or its ability to deliver current. The chemical condition is tested by a hydrometer that measures the specific gravity of the electrolyte.

The ability of the battery to deliver current is determined by means of a high-discharge test. This test measures the battery voltage while the battery is being discharged at a high rate.

1. Hydrometer test. We have already seen that, as the battery is discharged, the electrolyte loses sulfuric acid and gains water (§ 164). The sulfuric acid is nearly twice as heavy as water. Thus, measuring the weight per unit volume, or the specific gravity, of the electrolyte will disclose the state of charge of the battery. The hydrometer (Fig. 15–1), a device for measuring specific gravity, contains

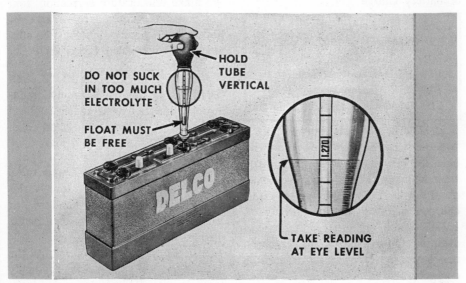

DO NOT SUCK IN TOO MUCH ELECTROLYTE

HOLD TUBE VERTICAL

FLOAT MUST BE FREE

.270

TAKE READING AT EYE LEVEL

Fig. 15–1. Hydrometer being used to measure specific gravity of battery electrolyte. (*Delco-Remy Division of General Motors Corporation*)

a float that floats in the electrolyte which is drawn into the hydrometer tube from the battery. The float stem protrudes varying amounts from the electrolyte, according to the amount of sulfuric acid in the electrolyte. The stem of the float is so calibrated that the amount the stem protrudes above the electrolyte indicates the specific gravity of the electrolyte.

2. *Variations of specific gravity.* The specific gravity of battery electrolyte varies as a result of several conditions: state of charge, temperature, age of battery, and self-discharge.

a. *Variation of specific gravity with state of charge.* As the state of charge of the battery changes, more or less sulfuric acid will be present in the electrolyte, causing a higher or lower specific-gravity reading when the battery is tested with a hydrometer. The following specific-gravity readings are an approximate guide to the condition of battery charge:

1.265–1.299	Fully charged battery
1.235–1.265	Three-fourths charged
1.205–1.235	One-half charged
1.170–1.205	One-fourth charged
1.140–1.170	Barely operative
1.110–1.140	Completely discharged

NOTE: Some of the late-model 12-volt batteries for passenger-car service have a somewhat lower specific gravity when charged. For instance, one type of 12-volt Delco battery is fully charged with a specific gravity of 1.270. There are other batteries, for example those used in hot climates, that have a specific gravity, when fully charged, of 1.225.

The decimal point is not normally referred to in a discussion of specific gravity. For example, "twelve twenty-five" means 1.225, and "eleven fifty" means 1.150. Also, the word "specific" is dropped, so that the term becomes just "gravity."

b. *Variation of gravity with temperature.* In addition to the effect of varying states of charge on gravity, temperature also changes the gravity. This effect is due to the fact that as a liquid cools it becomes thicker and gains gravity, while as a liquid warms it becomes thinner and loses gravity. Thus temperature must be considered when a gravity reading is taken. A correction must be made if the temperature varies from standard. This correction involves the adding or subtracting of gravity points, according to whether the electrolyte temperature is above or below the 80°F standard. The gravity of electrolyte changes about four points, or thousandths (0.004), for every 10° temperature. To make temperature correction, four points must be added for every 10° above 80°F. Four points must be subtracted for every 10° below 80°F.

EXAMPLES: 1.250 at 120°F. Add 0.016 (4 × 0.004). Corrected reading is 1.266. 1.230 at 20°F. Subtract 0.024 (6 × 0.004). Corrected reading is 1.206.

It is not necessary to make these corrections if the temperature varies only slightly from the standard, or when only an approximate idea of the gravity is desired.

c. *Loss of gravity from age.* As the battery ages, the electrolyte gradually loses gravity. This is because of the loss of active material from the plates (as it sheds and drops into the bottom

of the cells) and because of the loss of acid due to gassing. Over a period of 2 years, for example, battery electrolyte may drop to a top gravity, when fully charged, of not more than 1.250 from an original top gravity, when new, of possibly 1.290. Little can be done to restore gravity in such circumstances, since the loss is an indication of an aging battery.

d. *Loss of gravity from self-discharge.* If a battery is allowed to stand idle for a long period of time, it will slowly self-discharge. This condition is brought about by internal chemical reactions between the battery materials, which, although not productive of a flow of current at the time, are chemically active. The higher the battery temperature, the more rapidly will self-discharge take place. The lead sulfate that forms on the battery plates as a result of self-discharge is difficult to reconvert into active material; thus a battery that has badly self-discharged may be ruined.

e. *Battery gravities for hot climates.* In hot climates, where the chemical activities can take place more readily in the battery, it is often desirable to adjust the gravity reading to as low as 1.210 (28.5 percent acid) for a fully charged battery. This reduces the amount of self-discharge and prolongs the life of the battery. On discharge, the battery electrolyte may be reduced to a gravity as low as 1.075 before the battery stops delivering current. Where there is no danger of freezing, these low gravities may be used with safety.

f. *Freezing point of electrolyte.* The higher the gravity of the electrolyte, the lower its temperature must be before it will freeze. The battery must be kept in a sufficiently charged condition to prevent its freezing. Freezing usually ruins the battery (see Table 15–1).

3. *High-discharge test.* The gravity reading establishes only the chemical condition of the battery and is not necessarily an indication of the actual battery condition. To gain more information on this matter, the battery may be subjected to a high-discharge test. Essentially, the high-discharge test consists in placing a heavy load across the battery, so that 150 to 250 amperes is withdrawn. At the same time, the battery voltage is measured to determine how well the battery voltage stands up under this high rate of discharge. The battery gravity should be at least 1.225 before a high-discharge test is made, and the battery temperature should be 60 to 90°F. A high-discharge test of the battery may be made on the car by operating the

Table 15–1. SPECIFIC GRAVITY AND FREEZING TEMPERATURES

Specific gravity	Freezing temperature, degrees F	Specific gravity	Freezing temperature, degrees F
1.100	18	1.220	−31
1.160	1	1.260	−75
1.200	−17	1.300	−95

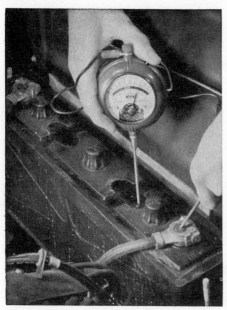

Fig. 15–2a. Making high-discharge test with low-reading voltmeter of battery on car. (Delco-Remy Division of General Motors Corporation)

cranking motor with the ignition switch off and checking each cell with a low-reading voltmeter (Fig. 15–2a).

The cranking motor draws 150 to 250 amperes from the battery, and during this interval each battery cell should be quickly checked — all three cells within 15 seconds (all six cells on 12-volt batteries).

▶CAUTION: Never operate the cranking motor for more than 30 seconds at a time without pausing for several minutes to allow the cranking motor to cool off. Otherwise, the cranking motor may overheat and be damaged.

If the cell voltages fall below about 1.5 volts, or if there is a difference of more than 0.2 volt between cells, bat-

tery trouble should be suspected (see § 363).

An individual-cell tester, consisting of a low-reading voltmeter and a heavy fixed resistance, can be used for making the high-discharge test. The two prods of this instrument are placed across the terminal posts of each battery cell in turn, causing each cell to discharge a heavy current through the resistance. At the same time, the voltage of the cell under this load is indicated on the voltmeter.

▶CAUTION: The gases that form in the battery during charge are very explosive. Tops of cells should be blown out before the individual-cell tester is used, since sparks are often caused as the tester prods are removed from the terminal posts. Such sparks could set off an explosion if gas were present in the battery cells. Such an explosion might be violent enough to blow the battery apart. Not only sparks, but any open flame, could produce such an explosion. Thus, sparks and open flames should be kept away from a battery.

Various other types of high-discharge tester are available for testing the battery either on or off the car. They all function on the principles discussed above. That is, they test the battery-cell voltage while the battery is being subjected to a heavy discharge.

4. Open-circuit voltage test. The voltage of the battery cells, when on open circuit (without anything connected to the terminals), is related to the strength of the electrolyte. For instance, a battery cell in good condition, with a specific gravity of 1.290,

might have an open-circuit voltage reading of 2.15 volts. This same cell, if discharged down to 1.250, would then have an open-circuit voltage of 2.11 volts. Thus, it can be seen that an accurate voltmeter could be used as a sort of "electrical hydrometer."

However, the voltmeter must be accurate. Note that each 0.01 volt is equal to about 0.010 difference in specific gravity. The difference between a fully charged and a discharged battery cell would be only about 0.15 volt.

The voltmeter should not be used to test batteries that have just been under charge. The gas on the plate surfaces, which collects during charging, will give a falsely high reading. These gases will be dissipated if the battery is allowed to stand for several hours. Or they will pass off the plates if the battery is given a high discharge for a few moments.

§ 363. Battery service Battery service can be divided into four parts: testing, repair, charging, and care of batteries in stock.

1. Battery testing. Battery testing should include not only an analysis of the condition of the battery but an analysis of any abnormality found. In addition, the cause of any abnormal battery condition should be determined, so that correction can be made. This will prevent a repetition of the trouble.

a. Adding water. The first step in testing a battery is to check the electrolyte level in the battery cells. This is done at the time that the hydrometer check is made. Add water, if necessary, after the hydrometer check is made. Distilled water is preferred, but any water that is fit to drink can be used. If the electrolyte level is too low for a hydrometer check, add water and charge the battery for an hour before taking the hydrometer reading. This mixes the water with the electrolyte so that an accurate test can be made.

▶*CAUTION:* Avoid overfilling the battery.

b. Overcharging. If the battery requires a considerable amount of water, the indication is that it is being overcharged, that is, too much current is being supplied to the battery. This is a damaging condition, since the active materials in the battery are overworked, causing battery life to be shortened. In addition, overcharging causes a more rapid loss of water from the battery electrolyte. Unless this water is replaced at frequent intervals, the electrolyte level is likely to fall below the tops of the plates, exposing the plates and separators to the air. This may ruin the plates and the separators. A badly overcharged battery is fairly easy to detect since the overcharging causes the positive-plate grids to swell and push up the positive sides of the cell covers. Thus, when a battery is found with the positive sides of the cell covers raised above the edge of the battery case, it is probable that the battery has been badly overcharged. In addition to this action, the swelling of the grids causes them to crumble and the plates to buckle. Thus, a battery subjected to severe overcharging will soon be ruined. Where overcharging is experienced or suspected, the generator-regulator system should be checked and adjusted if necessary, so that the current input to

the battery is brought within reasonable limits (§ 366).

c. Undercharging. If the battery is discharged, the battery should be recharged as outlined in a following paragraph. In addition, an attempt should be made to determine the cause of the discharged battery. It could be caused by generator-regulator-system malfunctioning (§ 366); by defective connections in the charging circuit between the generator and the battery (§ 366); by excessive load demands on the battery; by a defective battery; or by permitting the battery to stand idle for long periods, so that it self-discharges excessively. In addition, an old battery may have a low specific-gravity reading because it is approaching failure.

d. Sulfation. The active materials in the plates are converted into lead sulfate during discharge, as has already been noted. This lead sulfate is reconverted into active material during recharge. However, if the battery is allowed to stand for long periods in a discharged condition, the lead sulfate becomes converted into a hard, crystalline substance that is difficult to reconvert into active materials by normal charging processes. Such a battery should be charged at half the normal rate for 60 to 100 hours. Even though this long charging period may reconvert the sulfate to active material, the battery may still remain in a damaged condition, because the crystalline sulfate, as it forms, tends to break the plate grids.

e. Cell readings more than 25 gravity points apart. This condition may be caused by a partial short in the low cell or loss of acid from the low cell. The battery should be further tested by being brought up to charge and then given a high-discharge test. If the cell voltages are within 0.2 volt with the gravity readings still more than 25 points apart, the probability is that the low cell has lost acid and the electrolyte may be readjusted as explained below. Older batteries usually have a greater unbalance between cells than new batteries, as to both gravity and high-discharge voltage readings.

f. Cracked case. A cracked case may result from excessively loose or tight hold-down clamps, from battery freezing, or from flying stones.

g. Bulged cases. Bulged cases result from tight hold-down clamps or from high temperatures.

h. Corroded terminals and cable clamps. This condition occurs naturally on batteries, and the serviceman should be prepared to remove excessive corrosion periodically from terminals and clamps. Cable clamps should be disconnected from the terminals and both be cleaned with steel wool or cleaning tools. After the clamps are replaced, they may be coated with petroleum jelly to retard the formation of corrosion.

i. Corroded battery holder. Since some spraying of battery electrolyte is natural as the battery is being charged, the battery holder may become corroded from the effects of the electrolyte. Such corrosion may be cleaned off, when the battery is removed, by use of a wire brush and common baking-soda solution.

j. Dirty battery top. The top of the battery may become covered with dirt and grime, mixed with electrolyte that has been sprayed from the battery. This should be cleaned off periodically

by tightening the battery vent plugs, sprinkling the battery top with soda solution, waiting until the foaming stops, and then flushing off with clean water. Care should be used so that the solution will not get into the battery.

2. Battery removal and repair. Several minor repairs may be made to the battery without completely rebuilding it.

a. Removing and replacing a battery. To remove a battery from a car, first take off the grounded-battery-terminal cable clamp, to prevent accidental grounding of the insulated terminal when it is disconnected. Use a wrench to loosen the cable-clamp nut. Do not use pliers, since this might break the cell cover. Also, use a clamp puller, if the clamp sticks. Prying on the clamp with a screw driver or similar tool may damage the battery internally. After the grounded cable is disconnected, disconnect the insulated terminal cable, loosen the battery hold-downs, and take out the battery. When installing a battery, temporarily put cable clamps on the terminals and turn on the lights to check polarity. If the ammeter reads on the "charge" side with the lights on, the battery is in backward. If the battery is in correctly, remove the grounded clamp temporarily, connect the insulated cable, and then connect the grounded cable. Apply corrosion inhibitor to clamps and terminals, install, and tighten the hold-downs. Avoid overtightening.

b. Readjusting battery-electrolyte gravity. When the gravity of the electrolyte requires readjustment, either of two methods may be used. The battery may be charged, the electrolyte dumped out, and new electrolyte of the correct gravity added; or part of the electrolyte may be removed and some new electrolyte of a higher gravity added. (Where the original electrolyte gravity was too high, remove some electrolyte and add water only.) After further recharging, the battery should be checked and further readjustment made if necessary. Never adjust the gravity of any cell that does not gas freely on charge, since this indicates a cell defect.

c. Replacing elements. Occasionally one cell may be found defective on a fairly new battery, and, if so, additional battery life will be obtained by repairing the defective cell. This is done by cutting, drilling out, or melting off connectors; digging or melting out the sealing compound around the cell cover; and lifting the element from the case. The element can then be separated into plate groups, and plates or separators can be replaced as necessary. New plates can be welded onto the plate strap with a torch, provided that only one or two new plates are needed.

▶*CAUTION:* Sulfuric acid is very corrosive and will destroy most things with which it comes in contact. It will cause painful and serious burns if it gets on the skin. In case of accident, the acid should be quickly flushed away with a large quantity of water, which dilutes while washing away the acid. Also, baking soda may be used to neutralize the acid. A quantity of baking soda may be kept at hand to sprinkle on anything on which the acid is spilled. Water should then be used to flush off the acid and soda.

▶ *CAUTION:* The gases that form in the tops of the cells during battery charging are very explosive. An open flame should never be brought near batteries that have been recently charged, without first blowing out the gas from the tops of the cells.

d. Preparing electrolyte. Electrolyte must be prepared with extreme care to avoid accidents. Only glass, china, lead, rubber, or earthenware containers should be used as receptacles for sulfuric acid. The acid must always be slowly poured into the water. *Never pour water into concentrated acid.* Heat is produced as the two mix. Pouring water into the acid will cause the water to turn into steam with such violence that an explosion may occur, causing acid to be thrown a considerable distance. Table 15–2 indicates the approximate proportions of water and full-strength sulfuric acid required to obtain solutions of different gravities.

e. Battery "dopes." "Dopes" is a term given to certain chemical compounds that are supposed to restore a battery to a charged condition when they are placed in the cells. Such chemicals should never be added to the battery. Their use can void the battery guarantee and could cause battery failure.

3. Battery charging. Two methods of charging batteries are in use, the constant-current and the constant-voltage (constant-potential) methods. In the constant-current method, the current input to the battery is adjusted to 1 ampere per positive plate per cell. A 17-plate battery, for example, would be charged at an 8-ampere rate. The charging is continued until the battery is gassing freely and there is no further rise in gravity for 2 hours. In the constant-voltage method, the voltage is held at a constant value. The battery, as it approaches a charged condition, increases in resistance to the charging current. At the same time, the current input gradually tapers off until, when the battery is fully charged, the current input has been reduced to a few amperes. This action is based on the assumption that the battery-electrolyte temperature will remain within bounds. If the battery-electrolyte temperature increases excessively, the resistance of the battery to the charging rate will remain low. Consequently the battery will be subject to damaging overcharge unless it is removed from the charging line in time.

A number of so-called "quick chargers" have recently come into use. These devices operate by charging the

Table 15–2

Parts of water by volume	Parts of water by weight	Specific gravity corrected to 60°F
4.4	2.5	1.200
3.2	1.8	1.250
2.5	1.4	1.300
2.0	1.1	1.350
1.6	0.88	1.400

battery at a high rate (as much as 100 amperes) for a short time — 30 to 45 minutes — so that the battery· is brought up to a fair state of charge before the battery temperature increases to excessive values. If the battery is not subject to excessive temperatures, the quick-charger method of battery charging does not seem to be damaging to the battery. It should be remembered, however, that high charging rates combined with battery-electrolyte temperatures of above 125°F are very damaging to the battery. It is also true that quick chargers cannot, as a rule, bring a battery up to *full* charge in a short time. If the battery is quick-charged for a short time, and then the charging operation is finished by a slow-charging method, the battery will come up to full charge.

▶*CAUTION:* A battery with discolored electrolyte (from cycling) or with gravity readings more than 25 points apart should not be quick-charged. Likewise, a badly sulfated battery should not be quick-charged. Such batteries may be on the verge of failure but may give additional life if slow-charged. However, quick-charging them might further damage them. During quick-charging, check color of electrolyte and stop charging if it becomes discolored as a result of the stirring up of washed-out active material. Likewise, cell voltages should be checked every few minutes and charging stopped if cell voltages vary more than 0.2 volt.

4. Care of batteries in stock. Batteries are perishable. They are subject to self-discharge, which, if allowed to proceed for too long a time, will com-

Fig. 15–2b. Adding electrolyte from special container to dry charged battery. (*Delco-Remy Division of General Motors Corporation*)

pletely ruin them. To prevent this, batteries in stock should be recharged at 30-day intervals. They should not be stacked on top of each other without some means of individual support. The weight of a battery resting on the posts of another battery will cause the plate assemblies on the lower one to collapse so that short circuits will occur.

5. Dry charged batteries. Dry charged batteries contain fully charged positive and negative plates but no electrolyte. The batteries are sealed with rubber or plastic seals placed in the vent plugs. Since the batteries contain no moisture, practically no chemical action can take place in them. This means they will remain in good condition for many months—as long as 36 months, the manufacturers say, provided they are properly stored.

The dry charged battery manufacturers also supply ready-mixed electro-

lyte in special cartons. The carton contains an acid-proof plastic bag which holds the electrolyte. To get a battery ready for service, all that is necessary is the following:

a. Remove vent plugs and take out the plastic seals.

b. Remove lid from electrolyte container. Unfold top of plastic bag and cut a small opening in one corner of the bag.

c. Use a glass or acid-proof plastic funnel and fill each battery cell as shown in Fig. 15–2*b. Wear goggles and observe all cautions already noted regarding sulfuric acid.* Wait a few minutes and then add more electrolyte if necessary. Some electrolyte will probably be left; do not attempt to use it all. Do not overfill the battery.

d. Before discarding the container, empty it and rinse out the bag thoroughly with water. Otherwise, someone who handles the carton might be severely burned by the remaining electrolyte.

CRANKING MOTOR

§ 364. Cranking-motor testing The testing of cranking motors may be divided into two parts: the tests made on the car when trouble occurs, to determine whether the cranking motor or some other component is at fault, and the tests to be made on the cranking motor when it has been removed from the engine.

1. Car testing of cranking motor. The procedure of using the lights and operating the cranking-motor switch to locate the source of trouble if the engine does not turn over has already been outlined (§ 291). If the lights stay bright without cranking action when an attempt is made to operate the cranking motor, some further analysis may be made to determine whether the trouble lies in the cranking motor, switch, or control circuit (on automatically or remotely controlled cranking-motor systems).

a. Remotely or automatically controlled cranking motor. To determine whether the trouble lies in the control circuit or the cranking motor, turn on the ignition switch and close the remote-control switch or depress the accelerator pedal, according to the type of control. The magnetic switch or the solenoid on the cranking motor will or will not work. When it does not, the indication is that current is not getting to or through the magnetic switch of the solenoid. Most magnetic switches and solenoids may be operated by hand to see whether or not the cranking motor is capable of operation. If the cranking motor does operate as the magnetic switch or the solenoid is operated by hand, then the trouble is in the control circuit. A jumper lead may be connected around the control devices and switches, so that the unit not operating can be located. Where the solenoid has a relay, the relay cover may be removed and the relay points closed by hand. If the solenoid and the cranking motor now operate, the relay is defective.

If the magnetic switch or the solenoid operates when the attempt to start is made, without operation of the cranking motor, there is an open circuit inside the cranking motor or switch. Usually, under this condition the trouble will be found in the motor. Remove the cover band, and check the

brushes and the commutator. A dirty or burned commutator, worn or jammed brushes, or weak brush-spring tension will prevent the brushes from making good contact with the commutator, so that the cranking motor will not function. Defects or failure to locate the trouble require removal of the cranking motor for further analysis and correction (see following paragraphs):

b. Manually operated cranking motor. When depressing the cranking-motor pedal fails to cause the cranking motor to operate with the lights remaining bright, the linkage should first be inspected to make sure that the cranking-motor switch is closing. The cover band should then be removed so that the brushes and the commutator can be inspected as detailed in the previous paragraph.

NOTE: When failure to start is due to a dirty commutator, starting may sometimes be accomplished by rotating the armature slightly by hand to form better contact. (Do not use a screw driver, for this might damage the commutator.) Number 00 sandpaper may then be held against the revolving commutator by means of a piece of wood, with the ignition off so that the engine does not start. This will clean off the commutator. Do not operate the cranking motor more than 30 seconds. The commutator should be turned down in a lathe and the mica undercut at the first opportunity (§ 365).

2. Testing detached cranking motor. No-load and torque tests may be made on a detached cranking motor to determine whether or not it is up to specifications. These, plus the use of a

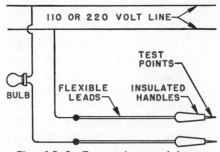

Fig. 15–3. Test points and lamp.

set of test points and a test lamp (Fig. 15–3), should provide full information as to the condition of the unit.

a. No-load test. When the no-load test is made, the cranking motor is connected to a battery of the correct voltage, in series with a high-reading ammeter, and the rpm (revolutions per minute) and current draw measured. These should be compared with the manufacturer's specifications for the motor.

b. Torque test. As was explained in § 77, torque is turning effort and is measured in pound-feet. A torque tester for measuring the stall torque of cranking motors is illustrated in Fig. 15–4. Stall torque is the torque developed with the armature stalled, or not rotating. If the brake arm is 1 foot long, the scale will read pound-feet directly.

c. Interpreting no-load and torque test results. The following tabulation lists the six most common combinations of conditions found in testing cranking motors, along with further tests to be made to determine the cause of trouble.

1. Rated torque, current draw, and no-load speed indicate normal condition of the cranking motor.
2. Low free speed and high current

draw with a low-developed torque may result from:

a. Tight, dirty, or worn bearings; bent armature shaft; or loose field-pole screws, which allow the armature to drag on the pole shoes.

b. Grounded armature or fields. Raise the grounded brushes from the commutator and insulate them with cardboard. Then check with the test lamp between the insulated terminal of the cranking motor and the frame. If the test lamp lights, indicating a ground, raise the other brushes from the commutator and check fields and commutator separately, to determine which is grounded. On some units, one end of the field circuit is normally grounded, and the ground screw or screws must be re-

moved before the field can be tested for ground.

c. Shorted armature. Check the armature further on a growler (§ 365).

3. Failure to operate at all with a high current draw indicates:

a. Direct ground in the switch, terminal, or fields. This may be found with a test lamp, by raising the grounded brushes as in b under item 2 above.

b. Frozen shaft bearings, which prevent the armature from turning.

c. Grounded armature windings, due, for instance, to thrown windings.

4. Failure to operate with no current draw indicates:

a. Open field circuit. Inspect internal connections, and trace circuit with a test lamp, check-

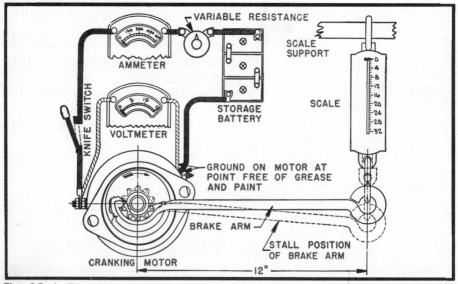

Fig. 15—4. Test setup to measure cranking-motor torque. (Delco-Remy Division of General Motors Corporation)

ing the brushes, armature, and fields.

b. Open armature coils. This condition causes badly burned commutator bars (§ 365).

c. Broken or weak brush springs, worn brushes, high mica on the commutator, glazed or dirty commutator, or any other condition that would prevent good contact between the commutator and the brushes and thus prevent operation of the cranking motor. Most of these can be found by visual inspection.

5. Low no-load speed with low torque and low current draw indicates:

a. An open field winding. Raise and insulate the ungrounded brushes from the commutator, and check the fields with a test lamp. Lamp should light as points are connected across each field.

b. High internal resistance due to poor connections, defective leads, dirty commutator, or any other condition listed in c under item 4 above.

6. High free speed with low-developed torque and a high current draw indicate shorted fields. Since the fields already have a low resistance, there is no practical way to test for this condition. If shorted fields are suspected, replace the fields and check for improvement in performance. But, first check the other components of the cranking motor before going to this trouble.

§ 365. Cranking-motor service At periodic intervals of about 5,000 miles, the cranking motor should be lubricated and the cover band removed (on units so equipped) to check brushes and commutator. At 25,000-mile intervals, it is recommended that the cranking motor be removed and disassembled so that all parts can be cleaned and worn parts replaced. About 2 hours is required to overhaul a cranking motor, including turning the commutator, undercutting the mica, and testing the reassembled unit. Damaged parts that may be found in the cranking motor, as well as the disassembly, repair, and assembly of the motor, are discussed in following paragraphs. In addition to these services on the cranking motor itself, it is desirable to check the cranking-motor-to-battery circuit, as explained below under item 4, for excessive resistance, since this would prevent proper cranking action even though the cranking motor is in good condition.

1. Damaged parts, their cause and correction. When a cranking motor is disassembled for repair or for periodic service, several types of defect may be found.

a. Thrown armature windings. Thrown armature windings are normally found only in the overrunning-clutch type of cranking motor. This condition results from excessive armature speed that has thrown the windings from the armature. Improper adjustment of the throttle-opening linkage, leaving the foot on the starter pedal too long after starting, and opening the throttle too wide all put an excessive burden on the overrunning clutch so that it tends to overheat, seize, and cause the armature to be

spun at high speed. A defective over-running clutch produces the same condition. Usually, the armature is so damaged that it cannot be repaired.

b. Burned commutator bars. Burned commutator bars usually indicate an open-circuited armature. The open normally will be found at one or more commutator riser bars and is most often caused by excessively long cranking periods. Such long cranking periods overheat the cranking motor so that the solder at the riser-bar connection is melted. This not only throws solder (thrown solder may be found on the cover band) but also causes the connection to loosen. Arcing then takes place each time the bar with the bad connection passes under the brushes, and the bar soon burns. If the bars are not too badly burned, the armature may be repaired by re-soldering the connections at the riser bars (using rosin, not acid flux) and then turning the commutator and undercutting the mica.

c. Broken or distorted Bendix spring. A broken or distorted Bendix spring or a broken drive housing is usually caused by an attempted meshing while the engine is on a rockback or by an engine backfire during cranking. On Bendix-drive cranking motors, several seconds should elapse between attempts to start, so that the drive pinion will not go into mesh with the flywheel when the engine is rocking backward. If the ignition is out of time, it may cause the engine to backfire during cranking and this could cause a damaged drive or housing.

d. Dirty or gummy commutator. The commutator over a period of time sometimes becomes covered with a film of dirt or gum. Although this may be cleaned off with No. 00 sandpaper held against the commutator while the cranking motor is being operated (not more than 30 seconds), it is usually best to correct this condition by turning the commutator and undercutting the mica.

2. Cranking-motor disassembly, repair, and assembly. The disassembly of the cranking motor is usually simple. The solenoid or switch, where present, is removed first. Next, the cover band is removed, and the brush leads are disconnected. Or, where leads are soldered, the brushes are removed from the holders. Then, after taking out the through bolts, the commutator end frame, field frame, and drive end can be separated. The Bendix drive can be removed from the armature shaft by taking out the drivehead attaching screw. The Folo-Thru drive is removed from the armature shaft by compressing the spring so that the end anchor plate clears the drive pin. The drive pin can then be pushed out of the shaft and the drive slid off the shaft. On overrunning-clutch cranking motors, the overrunning clutch can be slid off the shaft. Some models have a retainer and snap ring; these must be removed first before the overrunning clutch can be slid off. Figure 7–30 illustrates a disassembled view of a typical passenger-car cranking motor.

a. Cleaning cranking-motor parts. The armature and fields should never be cleaned in any solvent or cleaning solution that dissolves or damages the insulation. Instead, they should be wiped off with a clean cloth.

b. Field-winding service. Test for a grounded field with test-lamp points

366

Fig. 15–5. Pole-shoe screw driver being used on field frame. Note that there is a pole-shoe spreader in place.

on terminal stud and frame. If the lamp lights, the field is grounded. Test for open with points at two ends of the field circuit. The lamp should light. If field windings require replacement, use a pole-shoe screw driver (Fig. 15–5) and pole-shoe spreader (Fig. 15–6) The pole-shoe screw driver prevents damage to the pole-shoe screws and assures tight reassembly of the shoes. The spreader prevents distortion of the field frame and holds the shoes firmly in place during reassembly. Rapping the frame with a plastic hammer while the screws are being tightened helps align the shoes properly. When re-soldering connections, use rosin flux. Where moist conditions will be encountered, manufacturers recommend applications of special insulating varnish to field windings after reassembly, to reduce the effects of moisture.

    c. Armature service. Causes and correction of thrown armature windings and burned commutator bars have already been discussed in previous paragraphs. In addition to these conditions, inspect the armature lamination for rub marks, which would mean a worn bearing or a bent shaft that has allowed the insulation to rub on the pole shoes. A check for a bent shaft can be made by putting the arma-

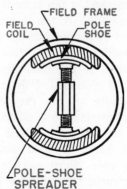

Fig. 15–6. Pole-shoe spreader.

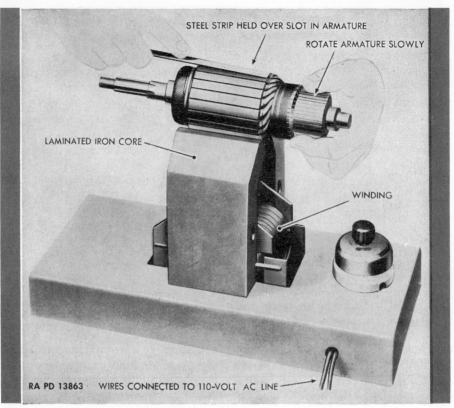

STEEL STRIP HELD OVER SLOT IN ARMATURE

ROTATE ARMATURE SLOWLY

LAMINATED IRON CORE

WINDING

RA PD 13863   WIRES CONNECTED TO 110-VOLT AC LINE

Fig. 15–7. Using growler to test armature for short circuits.

ture in V blocks and rotating it while a dial indicator is placed in position to measure run-out. The run-out, or out-of-roundness, of the commutator can be checked at the same time.

The armature is tested electrically for ground by placing one test point on the lamination and the other on the commutator. If the lamp lights, the armature is grounded. It is tested for short circuits on the growler (Fig. 15–7). The armature is placed on the growler and slowly revolved while a hack-saw blade is held above the armature core. Short circuits in the armature cause the hack-saw blade to vibrate against the core when it is held above the slot containing the shorted winding.

If the commutator is out of round, or worn, or if it has high mica, it should be turned in a lathe (Fig. 15–8). The cut should be as smooth and as light as possible. Then, the mica should be undercut 1/32 inch deep. This operation may be done with a ground-down hack-saw blade (Fig. 15–9) or with a motor-driven undercutter. In either case, the undercutting should be 0.002 inch wider than the mica, to assure removal of all mica. Sand off all burrs with No. 00 sandpaper. Be sure that no burrs or copper dust between bars remain.

Fig. 15–8. Lathe for turning armature commutator with undercutting attachment for undercutting mica. (*St. Joe Lathe Company*)

Where moist conditions are encountered, manufacturers recommend application of special insulating varnish to the armature, to reduce the effects of moisture. Varnish should be kept off shaft and commutator.

d. Brush service. Brushes that are worn to one-half their original length should be replaced. When the brush lead is soldered, unsolder it and unclinch the lead from the connector. Where the lead terminal clip is riveted to the frame, unsolder and unclamp the lead from the clip, so that the lead

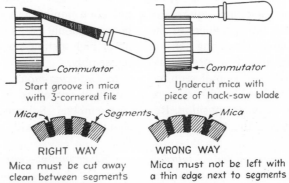

Fig. 15–9. Undercutting mica on armature commutator with hack-saw blade. (*Delco-Remy Division of General Motors Corporation*)

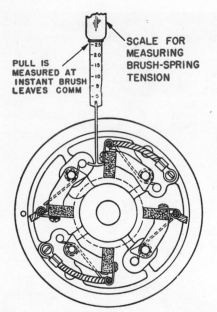

PULL IS
MEASURED AT
INSTANT BRUSH
LEAVES COMM

SCALE FOR
MEASURING
BRUSH-SPRING
TENSION

Fig. 15–10. Testing brush-spring tension with a spring scale. Refer to manufacturer's specifications for actual tension of unit under check. (Delco-Remy Division of General Motors Corporation)

of a new brush can be clamped and soldered to the clip. With new brushes in place, put the armature into position so that the brushes rest on the commutator. If the brushes do not align with the commutator bars, the brush holders are bent and this requires replacement of the brush holders or the end frame. The brush-spring tension should be checked with a spring scale (Fig. 15–10). Note the pull required to raise the brushes, brush arms, or holders from the contact position. Replace the springs if the tension is not correct.

e. Cranking-motor-drive lubrication. The Bendix-type drive should be cleaned by washing in solvent and then lubricated with a small amount of light

engine oil. The Folo-Thru drive should not be oiled; it should work normally after it has been cleaned in kerosene. The overrunning-clutch type of drive must never be cleaned by a high-temperature or grease-dissolving method, since this would remove the grease originally packed in the clutch. With the grease thus removed, the clutch would soon fail.

f. Testing the overrunning clutch. The overrunning-clutch pinion should turn freely and smoothly in the overrunning direction and should not slip in the cranking position with normal cranking torque imposed on it. If the pinion turns roughly in the overrunning direction, the rollers are chipped or worn and the clutch should be replaced. If the pinion slips in the cranking direction, the clutch should be replaced.

g. Cranking-motor lubrication. After reassembly of the cranking motor, all bearings should be lubricated with a few drops of light engine oil. Many cranking motors have oilless bearings that have no provision for oiling. They should be lubricated, however, before cranking-motor reassembly, with a few drops of light engine oil. On gear-reduction motors, the gear-reduction housing should be packed with graphite or high-melting-point grease before reassembly.

h. Cranking-motor assembly. The assembly procedure is the reverse of disassembly. Soldered connections should be made with rosin, not acid, flux.

i. Overrunning-clutch-pinion clearance. On the overrunning-clutch type of cranking motor, the clearance be-tween the pinion and the thrust

washer, retainer, or housing should be measured with the pinion in the cranking position after assembly is completed. It should be 5/64 inch on Auto-Lite cranking motors, measured between the thrust washer and the pinion. On Delco-Remy units not using a retainer and snap ring on the armature shaft, the clearance between pinion and housing should be 3/16 inch. On Delco-Remy units with the retainer and snap ring, clearance between the pinion and retainer should be 0.010 to 0.140 inch. Adjustment on some manual types is made by turning the starting-switch button in or out and on many solenoid types by turning the solenoid-plunger stud in or out. Some solenoids do not have an adjustable stud; on these, adjustment is made by loosening the four mounting screws and then moving the solenoid back or forth as necessary to obtain the proper clearance.

j. Folo-Thru drive. On the Folo-Thru drive, do not turn pinion out to the extended, or cranking, position. In this position, a lockpin drops into a detent in the sleeve thread to lock the pinion in the cranking position (see Fig. 7–31*b*). The only way the pinion can be unlocked is to mount the cranking motor on the engine and start the engine. When engine speed increases to around 400 rpm, the lockpin will be retracted by centrifugal force. The pinion will then de-mesh and move back to the retracted position.

k. Testing assembled cranking motor. The cranking motor should be submitted to no-load and torque tests, as outlined above, to make sure it can operate according to specifications.

3. Installing cranking motor. When-ever a cranking motor is being installed or removed, the battery ground cable should be disconnected from the battery terminal, in order to avoid shorting the battery by an accidental grounding of the insulated cable. When installing the cranking motor, connect leads after the motor is bolted into place in the flywheel housing. Then check the throttle-cracker linkage on cars so equipped, and adjust as necessary, in order to obtain proper throttle opening during cranking. This is particularly important on overrunning-clutch cranking motors since excessive throttle opening might spin the overrunning clutch at high speed during initial engine operation, thus causing the clutch to be overloaded.

4. Meter testing the cranking-motor circuit. After the cranking motor has been reinstalled on the engine, or whenever the circuit requires checking, the cables and connections may be tested with a low-reading voltmeter. This procedure will locate any excessive resistance due to poor connections or bad cables, which would prevent the delivery of a normal amount of current to the cranking motor.

With the cranking motor in operation, drawing high amperage from the battery, any excessive resistance in the circuit will show up, because it will cause an excessive voltage drop. Too much voltage drop will reduce the voltage at the cranking motor to such an extent that normal operation will not be achieved. A low-reading voltmeter will quickly find excessive resistance (Fig. 15–11).

Remove the lead from the high-tension terminal of the coil, or leave the ignition switch off, so that the en-

gine will not start. Operate the crank-ing motor, and *very quickly* check (1) from the grounded battery termi-nal to the car frame, (2) from the cranking-motor housing to the car frame, and (3) from the ungrounded battery terminal to the cranking-motor terminal stud. (Do not use the crank-ing motor more than 30 seconds.) More than 0.1 volt reading (0.2 volt on 12-volt system) on any of these in-dicates excessive resistance, which may be due to a bad connection, frayed cable, or broken cable strands.

NOTE: Some authorities claim that the voltage drop can be 0.2 volt with-out causing any trouble.

The remedy for excessive resistance is to disconnect the cables and clean the terminals and cable clamps with steel wool. Use new cables if the old ones seem in bad condition. Be sure

that all connections are tight when the cables are refastened to the terminals. Always use cables of adequate size, since undersized cables will have ex-cessive resistance and may prevent normal cranking motor performance.

REGULATORS

§ 366. Testing generator-regulator system When abnormal operation is noted in the generator-regulator system in a car, it is often necessary to make preliminary checks to determine whether the regulator or the generator is causing the trouble. The first step is to check the condition of charge of the battery and the charging rate to the battery with the generator operating at medium speed. A hydrometer should be used to determine the state of charge of the battery. In checking the charg-ing rate, the car ammeter should *not* be· used, since it is not an accurate

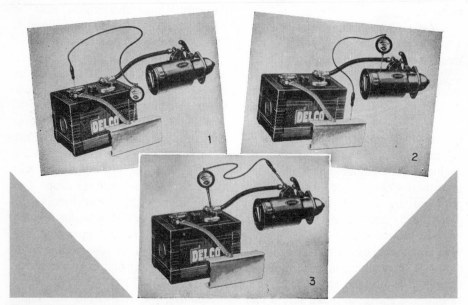

Fig. 15–11. Checking cranking-motor-to-battery circuit with voltmeter. (*Delco-Remy Division of General Motors Corporation*)

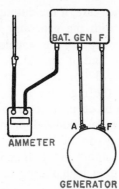

Fig. 15–12. Ammeter connections to check generator output.

indicator of the amperes of charging rate. A test ammeter should be connected into the charging circuit at the regulator BAT. or AMM terminal as shown in Fig. 15–12.

Any one of four conditions may be found in checking the battery and the charging rate: (1) charged battery and a low charging rate, (2) charged battery and a high charging rate, (3) discharged battery and a high charging rate, and (4) a discharged battery and a low charging rate. Let us investigate further the meaning of these conditions and the defects implied when any of them is found.

1. Charged battery and a low charging rate. This is a normal condition, since the voltage regulator reduces generator output as the battery comes up to charge. The settings of the voltage regulator and the current regulator (where present) may be checked as outlined in following paragraphs, which discuss the various makes of regulators and their checks and adjustments.

2. Charged battery and a high charging rate. With the ammeter connected as shown in Fig. 15–13, operate

the generator at medium speed, and disconnect the lead from the regulator F (field) terminal. This opens the generator field circuit, and if the generator is in normal condition, the output will drop off. If it does not, the generator is at fault and it should be checked further as outlined in § 370. If the output does drop off when the F-terminal lead is disconnected, the trouble is in the regulator and it should be checked for a high voltage setting or a shorted condition. (See the following paragraphs, which discuss various makes of regulators.)

3. Discharged battery and a high charging rate. This is a normal condition, since the regulator permits the generator output to increase when the battery is in a low state of charge.

4. Discharged battery and a low charging rate. Defective leads and bad connections in the circuit between the generator and the battery will cause the regulator to operate as though the battery were fully charged, so that the

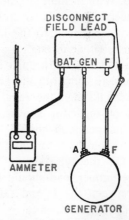

Fig. 15–13. Field lead is disconnected from regulator F (field) terminal to locate trouble if high output is obtained with charged battery.

charging rate is reduced to a low value even though the battery is in a discharged condition. Thus, where a low charging rate is found with a discharged battery, the wiring and connections should be inspected as a first step in an analysis of the trouble. If the circuit appears to be in good condition, the second step is to short out the generator field circuit in the regulator. This will determine whether or not the generator or the regulator is responsible for the faulty operation of the system. The manner in which the generator field circuit is shorted out depends upon the type of regulator under consideration. As was illustrated in Fig. 7–46, Auto-Lite and Delco-Remy standard-duty or passenger-car regulators normally ground the generator field circuit through the regulator contact points or regulator resistance. As shown in Fig. 7–47, heavy-duty Auto-Lite and Delco-Remy and all Ford regulators operate with a generator that has the field circuit internally grounded. With this circuit, the regulator connects the insulated end of the generator field circuit to the insulated main brush, either through the regulator contact points or through a resistance. Thus, to short out the generator field circuit through the regulator on the type of regulator shown in Fig. 7–46, a jumper lead should be connected between the F terminal and the ground. On the type shown in Fig. 7–47, the jumper lead should be connected between the F and GEN (or ARM. or A) terminals.

NOTE: Correct connections must be made, according to the type of regulator, to avoid damage to the equipment.

In either case, if the output does not increase with the generator operating at medium speed, the trouble is in the generator and it should be checked further (§ 370). If the output does increase, the regulator is at fault and it should be checked for a low voltage setting or for oxidized or dirty contact points. In addition, it might be that the cutout relay is not closing because of a high setting or an open winding.

▶ CAUTION: After any regulator or generator tests, or after installation of either unit on the car, the generator must be polarized to make sure it has the correct polarity with respect to the battery. This prevents arcing and burning of the cutout-relay points that might otherwise occur. The procedure varies according to whether the generator field is externally grounded (Fig. 7–46) or internally grounded (Fig. 7–47). When the field is externally grounded, polarize the generator by momentarily connecting a jumper lead between the ammeter (or battery) and generator terminals of the regulator or the relay. When the field is internally grounded, polarize the generator by disconnecting the field lead from the F (field) terminal of the regulator and momentarily touching this lead to the regulator battery terminal. In either case, this should be done after all leads are connected and before the engine is started. The action allows a momentary flash of current to flow through the generator field so that the generator is correctly polarized.

▶ CAUTION: Never operate the generator on open circuit, that is, with the charging circuit disconnected. This

would allow a damagingly high voltage to build up in the generator.

5. Checking circuit for resistance. The charging circuit can be checked for excessive voltage drop by connecting an ammeter into the circuit (Fig. 15–12) and grounding the regulator field terminal (on externally grounded field type, Fig. 7–46) or connecting field terminal to generator terminal (on internally grounded field type, Fig. 7–47). Then, with only the ignition turned on, the engine should be operated fast enough to give 20 amperes generator output. Voltage should be checked at the battery terminals and at the generator. If the difference is more than 3/4 volt, there is excessive resistance and the leads and connections should be checked, so that it can be located and eliminated.

§ 367. Auto-Lite regulators

To service the Auto-Lite regulators, the following steps are taken:

1. Cleaning contact points. Using a No. 3 American Swiss file, file the points parallel with the length of the armature. Clean after filing with carbon tetrachloride, and then pull clean linen tape between the points.

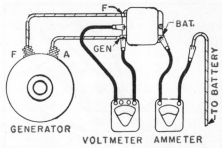

Fig. 15–14. Meter connections to check circuit breaker, or cutout relay. Always make meter connections according to terminal markings and not according to positions shown in this illustration. Terminal markings vary for different units. A, ARM., or GEN is used on the terminal connected to the generator A (armature) terminal. B, BAT., or AMM is used on the terminal connected to the car ammeter and battery.

Never use sandpaper or emery cloth to clean points.

2. Circuit-breaker adjustment (separately mounted or TC type).

a. Closing voltage and reverse amperage. Connect a test voltmeter between the A terminal and base of unit, and connect an ammeter into the circuit at the B terminal (Fig. 15–14). Slowly increase the generator speed,

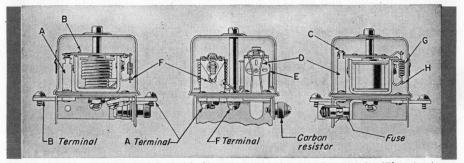

Fig. 15–15. Adjustments of circuit breaker and TC regulator unit. (*Electric Auto-Lite Company*)

375

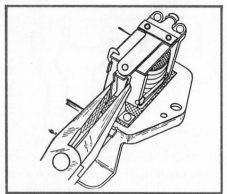

Fig. 15–16. Adjusting bridge supporting stationary contact to raise or lower contact. (*Electric Auto-Lite Company*)

and note the closing voltage. Decrease the speed, and note the reverse amperage at which points open.

Adjust the closing voltage by bending down on the lower spring hanger *F* in Fig. 15–15 to increase the closing voltage or up to lower it.

Adjust reverse amperage by increasing the air gap (raising contact) to lower the reverse amperage or reducing the air gap (lowering contact) to increase it (Fig. 15–16). Additional adjustments, if required, should be made with the unit removed from the car.

b. Air gap. Measure the air gap between the armature and the core with the contact points held closed. Adjust by raising or lowering the stationary contact on bridge *A* in Fig. 15–15. This is done by expanding or contracting the bridge on which the contact is supported (Fig. 15–16).

c. Contact-point opening. Adjust by bending the upper armature stop *B* in Fig. 15–15.

3. Circuit-breaker adjustment (type mounted on voltage regulator).

a. Closing voltage. Connect the

voltmeter and ammeter as shown in Fig. 15–14. Slowly increase the generator speed, and note the relay closing voltage.

First procedure. For circuit breakers with contact point mounted on a spring, increase the voltage until the contacts just close, and immediately decrease the voltage until the contacts open.

Second procedure. For circuit breakers with contact point mounted directly on the armature, increase the voltage, and note the closing voltage. Then further increase the generator speed to obtain 15 amperes output. Slow the generator, and note the reverse current at which contacts open.

Adjust the closing voltage by bending the spring hanger down, to increase the closing voltage, or up, to lower it. If adjustment cannot be satisfactorily made, remove from the car and make further adjustments as follows:

b. Air gap. Check between armature and core with points open. Adjust by bending the upper armature stop.

c. Point opening. Adjust by bending contact support bridge (Fig. 15–16).

d. Opening voltage or amperage. Adjust by raising the lower point to increase the opening voltage or reduce the opening amperage. Lower the point to reduce the opening voltage or increase the opening amperage.

4. Voltage-regulator adjustment [type with either cutout relay (circuit breaker) alone or with both cutout relay and current regulator].

a. Operating voltage. Make meter connections as shown in Fig. 15–17. Slowly increase the generator speed

until 10 amperes output is being obtained, and note the voltage setting. If less than 10 amperes is obtained, turn on the lights and adjust the speed for 10 amperes. The regulator must be at operating temperature. Adjust by bending down on the lower spring hanger, to increase the setting, or up, to lower it. Retest by slowing the generator until relay points open, replacing the regulator cover, and bringing the generator back to speed.

b. Air gap. Check with the armature pushed down so that points barely touch (do not touch flat contact spring), and adjust by loosening the upper contact bracket screw and raising or lowering the bracket as required.

5. Current-regulator adjustment.

a. Operating amperage. Use meter connections shown in Fig. 15–17, and place across the battery an electric load roughly equal to the current-regulator setting. For example, if the regulator setting should be 30 amperes, connect a 30-ampere load across the battery during the test. This prevents the voltage regulator from operating. A similar result may be obtained by using the cranking motor for a few seconds and then turning on car lights and accessories during the test. Adjust the setting by bending the lower spring hanger down, to increase the setting, or up, to lower it.

b. Air gap. The air gap is checked and adjusted as for the voltage regulator.

§ 368. Delco-Remy regulators To service the Delco-Remy regulators, the following steps are taken.

1. Cleaning contact points. Use a clean, fine-cut contact file to clean

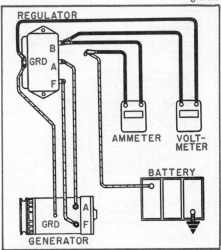

Fig. 15–17. Meter connections to check Auto-Lite voltage-regulator setting.

the points. Clean each point separately, and do not use file on rounded point excessively. The rounded point is of a softer material and can be filed away more easily than the flat point. Cavities in the flat point can be removed with a spoon or riffler file. Never use emery cloth or sandpaper to clean points.

2. Cutout-relay adjustment (type mounted separately or with step-voltage control or regulator).

a. Closing voltage. Connect a voltmeter from the GEN terminal to the relay base. Increase the generator speed, and note the closing voltage. Adjust by bending spring post or turning the adjusting screw. Increasing the flat or spiral spring tension (according to the type of spring on the unit) increases the closing voltage, or decreasing the tension lowers voltage. Other adjustments, if necessary, require removal of the unit from the car.

b. Air gap. Measure the air gap between the armature and the core

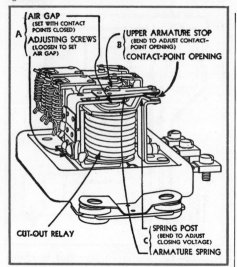

Fig. 15–18. Cutout-relay adjustments. (Delco-Remy Division of General Motors Corporation)

with points held closed. Adjust by loosening the two armature mounting screws and raising or lowering the armature as required (Fig. 15–18).

c. *Point opening*. Adjust by bend-

ing the upper armature stop (Fig. 15–18).

3. *Voltage-regulator adjustment (type with either cutout relay or both cutout relay and current regulator).*

a. *Operating voltage.* The setting must be checked by one of the three methods given below. The regulator must be at operating temperature, and the cover must be in place.

Fixed-resistance method. Substitute a 3/4-ohm fixed resistance (1 1/2 ohms on 12-volt circuit) for the remainder of the circuit as shown in Fig. 15–19. The resistance is connected between the BAT. terminal and the regulator base, with a voltmeter connected to the same places.

Variable-resistance method. Insert a 1/4-ohm variable resistance into the charging circuit in series with an ammeter at the BAT. terminal, and connect a voltmeter from the BAT. terminal to the base (Fig. 15–20). With the generator operating at

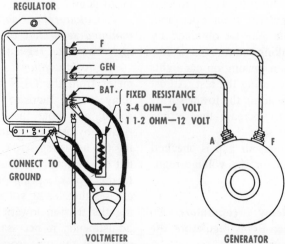

Fig. 15–19. Meter and resistance connections to check voltage regulator by the fixed-resistance method. (Delco-Remy Division of General Motors Corporation)

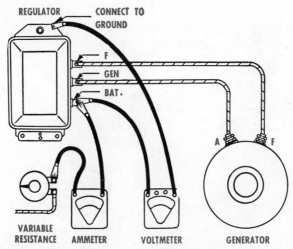

Fig. 15–20. Meter and variable-resistance connections to check voltage regulator by the variable-resistance method. (*Delco-Remy Division of General Motors Corporation*)

medium speed, vary the resistance to obtain 10 amperes. It may be necessary to turn on the lights and then vary the resistance.

Fixed-resistance-plus-battery meth- od. This is for late-type 12-volt passenger-car units. Disconnect lead from BAT. terminal, and connect resistances and voltmeter as shown in Fig. 15–21. Increase generator speed to specified

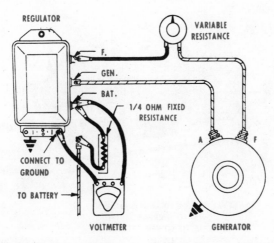

Fig: 15–21. Fixed-resistance connections to check voltage-regulator setting. Variable resistance is used to control and cycle the generator. (*Delco-Remy Division of General Motors Corporation*)

379

Fig. 15–22. Voltage adjustment on type of regulator with adjusting screw. (*Delco-Remy Division of General Motors Corporation*)

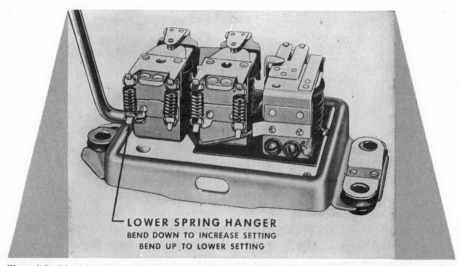

Fig. 15–23. Voltage adjustment on type of regulator with adjustable spring hangers. (*Delco-Remy Division of General Motors Corporation*)

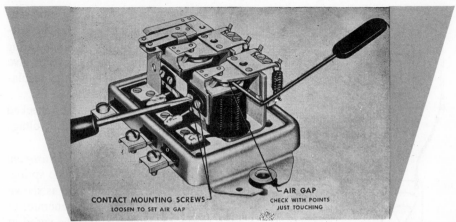

CONTACT MOUNTING SCREWS
LOOSEN TO SET AIR GAP

AIR GAP
CHECK WITH POINTS
JUST TOUCHING

Fig. 15–24. Checking and adjusting regulator air gap. (Delco-Remy Division of General Motors Corporation)

value, and note voltage setting (of lower contacts on double-contact unit). On double-contact unit, cut in resistance to check upper contact voltage.

Adjust the voltage setting according to type by turning the adjustment screw (Fig. 15–22) or by bending the lower spring hanger of one spiral spring down, to raise the voltage, or up, to lower it (Fig. 15–23). On double-contact unit, adjust lower set as above; then turn screw in center of the armature to adjust upper set. Replace the cover, slow the generator until the relay points open, and then bring back to speed. With the variable-resistance method, readjust the current output to 10 amperes before taking the reading. The regulator must be hot.

b. Air gap. Push the armature down by hand, release it until the points just touch, and measure the air gap between the armature and the core. Adjust by loosening the two contact mounting screws (Fig. 15–24) and raising or lowering the upper contact. mounting bracket as required. On dou-

ble-contact unit, bend upper contact support to adjust air gap.

c. Two-spring voltage-regulator adjustment. If adjusting one spring does not give correct setting, remove one spring; connect a test voltmeter from the GEN terminal of the regulator to the regulator base. Connect the regulator to a suitable generator in a normal manner. Slowly increase generator speed until it is operating at a speed 25 percent above the speed at which full output would be obtained. Adjust the spring tension to get 4.0 to 4.5 volts (8 to 9 volts on 12-volt regulator or 18 to 20 volts on 24-volt unit). Then install the second spring, and complete the adjustment on it alone to specified setting as detailed in a previous paragraph.

4. Current-regulator adjustment.

a. Operating amperage. Connect an ammeter into the circuit at the regulator BAT. terminal, and connect a jumper lead across the voltage-regulator points to prevent voltage-regulator action as shown in Fig. 15–25. The

381

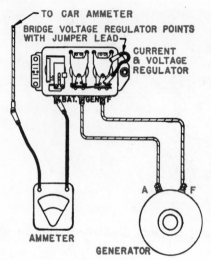

Fig. 15–25. Meter- and jumper-lead connections to check current-regulator setting. (Delco-Remy Division of General Motors Corporation)

voltage regulator may also be prevented from operating by placing a load on the battery as explained at end of § 367. Operate the generator at medium speed, and note the current setting. Adjust by turning the adjusting screw (Fig. 15–22) or by bending the

spring hanger of one spring only. Increasing the tension increases the current setting. If adjustment of one spring (on a two-spring unit) does not give the proper setting, remove the regulator for further adjustment.

b. *Air gap.* The air gap is checked in the same manner as for the voltage regulator.

c. *Complete amperage adjustment (two-spring type).* Remove one spring, and, with the unit connected as shown in Fig. 15–25, operate the generator at a speed 25 percent above the speed at which full output would be obtained. Then adjust the spring tension to get approximately two-thirds of the specified setting. Install the second spring, and complete adjustment on it alone to obtain the specified setting.

5. *Regulator repair.*

a. *Replacing upper contact points.* If the upper contact points require replacement, follow the diagram in Fig. 15–26. Use the new insulators furnished with the service contact points.

b. *Replacing armatures.* The arma-

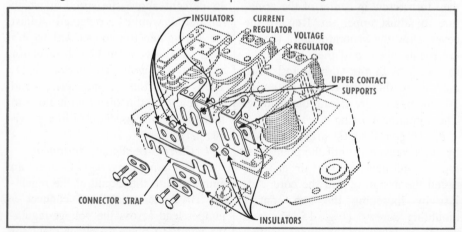

Fig. 15–26. Contact-support assembly, showing relationship of insulators. (Delco-Remy Division of General Motors Corporation)

tures may be replaced by drilling out the two rivets that hold them to the regulator frame. Replacement regulator armatures are supplied with screws, nuts, and lock washers. Assemble the screws down, so that they will not ground on the regulator cover.

§ **369. Servicing Ford regulators** Two types of Ford current and voltage regulators are described below. One has adjusting screws to adjust air gaps; the other is a riveted construction.

1. Type with adjusting screws (Fig. 15–27).

a. Cutout-relay checks and adjustments

1) Closing voltage is checked with a voltmeter connected between the regulator ARM. terminal and the regulator ground terminal. Increase generator speed, and note the relay closing voltage.

2) Reverse current to open the contacts is checked at the same time that the closing voltage is checked with an ammeter connected into the circuit at the regulator BAT. terminal. After the relay has closed, reduce generator speed and note the reverse current at the instant points open.

3) If readings are not correct, remove the regulator cover by taking out the two rivets at the two ends. A special rivet remover and replacer is available from the Ford factory. Then, adjust the closing voltage by bending the spring support (Fig. 15–28). Bend inward to increase the spring tension and closing voltage. Temporarily replace the cover and cycle generator to test new setting.

4) Air-gap adjustment is required if the reverse current is not correct. The regulator should be off the vehicle for this. Place a 0.014-inch round gauge between the armature and the core (Fig. 15–29), and, with the armature pushed down on the gauge, insert a flat 0.010-inch gauge between

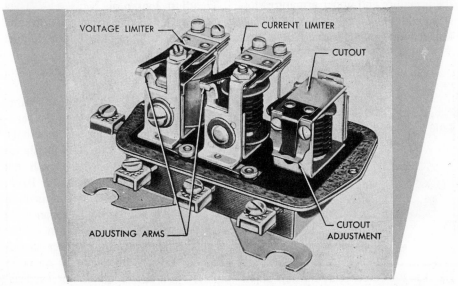

Fig. 15–27. Ford regulator with cover removed. (Ford Motor Company)

VOLTAGE LIMITER

CURRENT LIMITER

CUTOUT

ADJUSTING ARMS

CUTOUT ADJUSTMENT

Fig. 15–28. Adjusting cutout-relay closing voltage. (*Ford Motor Company*)

the armature and upper armature stop. It should fit snugly, and at the same time contact points should be closed.

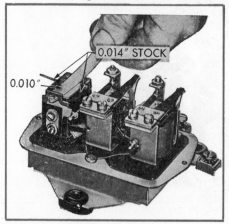

Fig. 15–29. Cutout-relay air-gap adjustment. (*Ford Motor Company*)

To adjust, loosen the two screws. Then raise or lower the armature stop, and also raise or lower the lower contact support as necessary.

b. Voltage regulator checks and adjustments

1) To check the voltage setting, connect a voltmeter between the regulator ARM. and the ground terminals. Connect a 1/4-ohm variable resistance and an ammeter in series with the charging circuit at the regulator BAT. terminal. Run the generator at medium speed, and adjust the resistance to obtain 8 to 12 amperes. Turn on the lights if less than 8 amperes is obtained. Then, with regulator cover in place, with the regulator hot (at least 20 minutes' operation), cycle genera-

Fig. 15–30. Voltage-regulator air-gap adjustment. (*Ford Motor Company*)

tor, and note the voltage reading. Adjust, if necessary, by removing the cover with a rivet remover and then bending the adjusting arm (Fig. 15–27). Bending the arm up increases the spring tension and voltage setting. Bending down lowers the setting. After each adjustment, replace the cover and cycle generator.

2) Air gap is checked and adjusted with the regulator off the vehicle. To check the air gap, place a gauge between the armature and the core (not the rivet in the core) as shown in Fig. 15–30. Then loosen the contact lock nut, and turn the adjustable contact screw in or out until the contact points just touch. Tighten the lock nut, and recheck the setting. Points should just touch, with the armature held down against the gauge.

c. Current regulator checks and adjustments

1) Current setting is checked with an ammeter connected into the charging circuit at the regulator BAT. terminal and with a load connected across the battery (see end of § 367) that

approximates the current-limiter setting. With the generator operating at medium speed, note the current setting. Adjust, as with the voltage regulator, by bending the adjusting arm (Fig. 15–27).

NOTE: If the reading is low, a quick check as to whether it is the fault of the regulator or of the generator can be made by momentarily connecting the ARM. and F (field) terminals of the regulator together. If the output increases, the trouble is in the regulator. If it does not, the generator or the generator circuit is at fault.

2) Air gap is checked and adjusted as for the voltage regulator.

2. Riveted standard type (Figs. 15–31 and 15–32). There are two separate constructions of the riveted standard-type Ford current and voltage regulator. In one, the contacts are mounted on an armature spring. In the other, the contacts mount directly on the armatures. Both operate and are

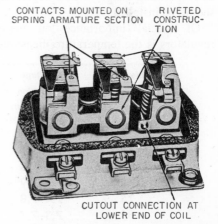

Fig. 15–31. Late-type standard Ford regulator with contacts mounted on armature springs. (*Ford Motor Company*)

385

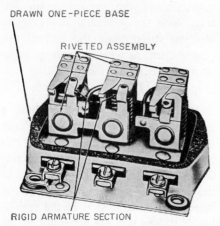

DRAWN ONE-PIECE BASE

RIVETED ASSEMBLY

RIGID ARMATURE SECTION

Fig. 15-32. Late-type standard Ford regulator with contacts mounted on the armature. (Ford Motor Company)

checked and adjusted in the same manner. Checking and adjusting procedures are similar to those for the Ford regulator already described. However, in this unit, there is no provision for air-gap adjustments in the field. If adjusting the electrical settings does not bring the regulator into specified operating range, a new regulator should be installed.

Of special importance on these regulators is the temperature measure-ments. As will be noted from the table of regulator readings (Fig. 15-33), the voltage setting varies considerably as the temperature of the air surrounding the regulator changes (dropping about a volt, for example, as temperature goes up from 35 to 145°). Thus, in checking the voltage-regulator setting on this unit, it is necessary to use a thermometer to measure the air temperature. Figure 15-34 shows the recommended thermometer. The magnet will hold the thermometer close to the regulator (should be within one-half inch). Do not attach the magnet to the regulator cover, however, as this would change the regulator reading.

Be sure that the regulator is at normal operating temperature. This temperature is considered to have been reached after the regulator has been in operation for 30 minutes on the vehicle. Ford has made available, in the special test apparatus used to check the regulator off the vehicle, a radiant-heating unit to heat the regulator to operating temperature in a few minutes. Then, using the special equipment and connections shown in Fig. 15-35, and making the equipment

Ambient* air temperature, °F	Voltage regulation setting, volts	Ambient* air temperature, °F	Voltage regulation setting, volts
35	7.8–8.2	95	7.2–7.6
45	7.7–8.1	105	7.1–7.5
55	7.6–8.0	115	7.0–7.4
65	7.5–7.9	125	6.9–7.3
75	7.4–7.8	135	6.8–7.2
85	7.3–7.7	145	6.7–7.1

*Temperature of air in contact with regulators   Ford Motor Company

Fig. 15-33. Voltage-regulator settings as related to the temperature of the air surrounding the regulator. (Ford Motor Company)

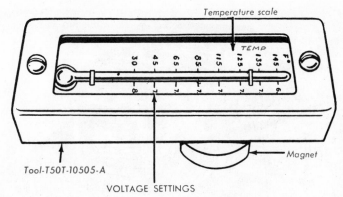

Fig. 15–34. Special thermometer to measure temperature of air surrounding the regulator. Magnet holds the thermometer in place during the test. (*Ford Motor Company*)

adjustments indicated, check the electrical settings as follows:

a. Cutout-relay closing voltage. Start the engine and run it at 1,500 rpm. Decrease field resistance, and watch the voltmeter needle move around to indicate increased voltage. When the cutout-relay closing voltage is reached, the cutout relay should close. This is indicated by a rise in the ammeter needle and a dip of the voltmeter needle. Repeat the check to make sure you read the voltage correctly.

b. Voltage-regulator setting. Reduce field resistance to zero. The ammeter should now read about 10 amperes (engine running at 1,500 rpm). The voltmeter will indicate the voltage-regulator setting.

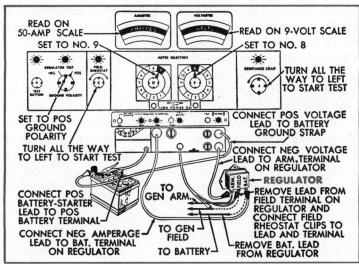

Fig. 15–35. Meter connections and equipment adjustments to check electrical settings of standard Ford regulators. (*Ford Motor Company*)

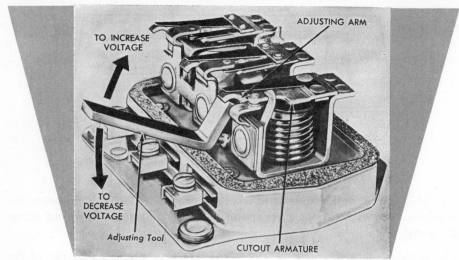

TO INCREASE
VOLTAGE

ADJUSTING ARM

TO
DECREASE
VOLTAGE

Adjusting Tool

CUTOUT ARMATURE

Fig. 15–36. Adjusting cutout-relay closing voltage. (Ford Motor Company)

c. Current-regulator setting. With engine running at 1,500 rpm, press the push button to connect the carbon-pile rheostat, and slowly decrease the resistance until the voltmeter reading drops to 6.5 volts (13 volts on 12-volt system). The ammeter will indicate the current-regulator setting.

d. Adjusting electrical settings. The cover can be removed for electrical adjustments by removing two attaching screws. There is an adjusting arm on each of the three units. When the arm is bent up, the armature-spring tension and the electrical setting are increased. When the arm is bent down, the armature-spring tension and the electrical setting are reduced. Figure 15–36 shows the use of a special adjusting tool to bend the adjusting arm up or down to increase or reduce the cutout-relay closing voltage. The current-regulator and voltage-regulator settings are adjusted in a similar manner. Replace cover and cycle generator when checking adjustments.

388

e. Other adjustments. There are no other adjustments prescribed in the Ford shop manual. If the above adjustments do not bring the regulator within proper operating range, replace it with a new unit.

GENERATORS

§ 370. **Testing generators** If the generator is found to be malfunctioning (as determined by the generator-regulator tests outlined in § 366), it should be analyzed further as follows:

1. Generator produces no output. Remove the generator cover band, and check for sticking brushes, gummed or burned commutator, or poor connections. If trouble is not readily apparent, remove the generator from the car and test further with a test light and points (Fig. 15–3). The procedure to be used depends upon the type of generator being checked. One type (Fig. 7–46) grounds the generator field in the regulator, while the second type (Fig. 7–47) grounds the generator field within

the generator. Tracing the field leads in the generator will determine which type the generator is. If one of the leads is connected to an insulated brush, it is of the *first* type. If one field lead is connected to a grounded brush or screw, the generator is of the *second* type.

a. *First type (Fig. 7–46)*

1) Test for ground by raising the grounded generator brush from the commutator and checking with a test lamp from the generator armature terminal to the frame. If the lamp lights, the generator is grounded. Raise the other brush or brushes, and check the field circuit (field terminal to frame) and the armature (commutator to frame) separately for ground.

2) Check for an open field by placing test points from the armature to field terminals of the generator. If the light does not burn, the field circuit is open.

3) Check for a shorted field by connecting an ammeter and a battery of the specified voltage in series with the field windings. Proceed with care, since a shorted field will draw a high current that might damage the ammeter. If a shorted field is found, the regulator contact points should be checked. They are probably burned from the high field current resulting from the shorted field.

4) Open circuits in the armature are usually readily apparent, since this condition causes burned commutator bars. Another sign of open circuits is thrown solder on the cover band. This usually develops from the overloading and overheating of the generator so that the solder at the commutator-bar connections is melted and thrown out,

with a consequent development of bad connections. Where this is found, the regulator should be checked for a high setting. The bad connections cause heavy arcing to take place when the bars pass under the generator brushes, so that the bars are quickly burned. If the burning is not too serious, repair may be made by resoldering the connections at the commutator bars (using rosin, not acid, flux) and then turning the commutator and undercutting the mica ($\S$ 365).

5) The armature may be tested for short circuits on a growler ($\S$ 371).

b. *Second type (Fig. 7–47)*

1) Test for grounded armature by raising the grounded brush from the commutator and checking with a test lamp from the armature terminal to the generator frame. If the lamp lights, the armature, or insulated brush-to-terminal circuit, is grounded.

2) Test for grounded fields by disconnecting the field lead from the grounded brush or frame and checking from the field terminal to the frame with a test lamp. If the lamp lights, the field is grounded.

3) Check for an open field circuit by connecting test points between the field terminal and lead disconnected in previous test. The lamp should light. If it does not, the circuit is open.

4) Check for a shorted field by connecting a battery of the specified voltage and an ammeter in series with the field windings. Proceed with care, since a shorted field will draw a high current. Check the regulator points if a shorted field is found.

5) Open circuits in the armature are, as a rule, easy to detect, since they

389

cause burned commutator bars, and thrown solder may be found on the cover band [see item 4) above, under *First type*].

6) Short circuits in the armature may be detected on a growler (§ 371).

2. *Generator produces excessive output.* Excessive output from the type of generator that normally has the field grounded in the regulator (Fig. 7–46) will result from a grounded field circuit in the generator. This can be quickly detected by raising the grounded brush and checking from the field terminal to the generator frame with a test lamp.

Excessive output from the type of generator that has the field circuit internally grounded (Fig. 7–47) may result from a shorted field or from a short between the field and the insulated brush.

3. *Generator produces unsteady or low output.* Low or unsteady output from a generator may be caused by:

a. Loose or worn drive belt, which causes belt slippage.

b. Sticking or worn brushes, low brush-spring tension, glazed or burned commutator, or other conditions that might prevent good contact between brushes and commutator.

c. Out-of-round, dirty, rough, or worn commutator. Dirt in the commutator slots or high mica also causes low or unsteady output.

4. *Noisy generator.* There is some noise inherent in generator operation, but it may become excessive if the mounting, drive pulley, or gear is loose. Worn or dirty bearings or improperly seated brushes also may produce noise.

§ 371. **Generator service** Generator manufacturers recommend that generators be lubricated every 1,000 miles. At 5,000-mile intervals, the generator should be checked on the car. At 25,000-mile intervals, the generator should be checked on the car. At so that all parts can be cleaned and worn parts be replaced. Generator overhaul, including turning the commutator, undercutting the mica, and testing the reassembled unit, requires about 2 hours. The correction of troubles, as well as the disassembly and assembly procedures, is discussed below.

1. *The 5,000-mile check.* At intervals of 5,000 miles, on the average, the cover band (on units so equipped) should be removed from the generator and the brushes and commutator inspected. Look through the windows in the end frame to inspect brushes and commutator on units without a cover band. If the brushes are worn, they should be replaced. A dirty commutator can be cleaned by holding a strip of No. 00 sandpaper against it with a piece of soft wood while the generator is operating. Emery cloth must never be used, since particles of emery will embed and cause rapid brush wear. If the commutator is rough or out of round, has high mica, or is very dirty or gummy, it should be turned down in a lathe and the mica undercut (§ 365). If particles of solder are found on the inside of the cover band, it means the generator has been overloaded and overheated so that the solder at the commutator bars has melted and been thrown out. The armature may be repaired, if the bars have not become too badly burned, by

resoldering the connections with rosin flux. Then, the commutator should be turned down and the mica undercut. Be sure that all leads, nuts, screws, and terminals are tight. The generator mounting, drive-belt tension, and pulley nut should be checked. As a final step, the generator output should be tested.

2. *Generator disassembly, repair, and assembly.* The disassembly of the generator is usually simple. The cover band (on units so equipped) should be removed and the leads from the fields and the terminal disconnected from the brush holders. The through bolts or commutator end-frame attaching screws should be removed, followed by the field frame. The armature may then be placed in the soft jaws of a vise so that the pulley nut, pulley, and drive end frame can be removed. Figure 7–42 illustrates a disassembled view of a typical passenger-car generator.

a. *Cleaning generator parts.* The armature and fields should never be cleaned in any solvent or cleaning solution that dissolves or damages the insulation. Instead, they should be wiped off with a clean cloth.

b. *Ball bearings.* If not of the sealed type, ball bearings should be carefully cleaned by being washed in clean gasoline, kerosene, or carbon tetrachloride. Swish the bearings in the cleaner, and revolve them while submerged. After cleaning, spin the bearings in clean, light oil, and immediately relubricate them with ball-bearing grease.

c. *Field-winding service.* Test fields for open by putting test points on the two ends of the field-winding circuit. If the lamp does not light, the field circuit is open. Test fields for ground by disconnecting the lead from the brush or the ground and putting test points on the field terminal and frame. If the lamp lights, the field circuit is grounded. Test fields for shorts by connecting them in series with an ammeter and a battery of the specified voltage. Proceed with care, because a shorted field may draw a current that is too high for the ammeter.

NOTE: If a shorted field is found, check the regulator contact points, since the high current draw may have burned the points of the regulator that was used with the generator.

Defective field windings should be replaced by use of a pole-shoe screw driver and a pole-shoe spreader (§ 365). As a rule, it is not economical to attempt to repair shorted or open field windings. In some cases, grounded field windings can be repaired with additional insulation. However, excessive bulkiness must be avoided, since the pole shoes might cut through the extra insulation and produce another ground. Make soldered connections with rosin flux. Where excessively moist operating conditions prevail, field windings may be treated with insulating varnish, after installation, as specified by generator manufacturer.

d. *Armature service.* As with cranking-motor armatures, generator armatures may be checked for run-out with V blocks and a dial indicator. Also, they may be checked for grounds with test points and for opens on a growler (§ 365).

EXCEPTION: Some few armatures have internal connections that cause

391

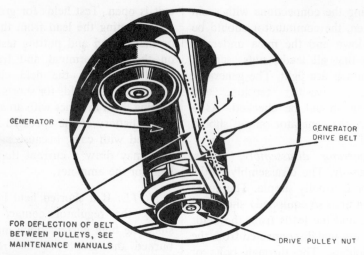

GENERATOR

GENERATOR
DRIVE BELT

FOR DEFLECTION OF BELT
BETWEEN PULLEYS, SEE
MAINTENANCE MANUALS

DRIVE PULLEY NUT

Fig. 15–37. Checking generator drive-belt tension. The tension on the belt deter-mines how much it will deflect when pressed in with thumb pressure, as shown. Adjustment is made by loosening generator clamp bolts and swinging generator toward or away from engine as required. Then, clamp bolts should be tightened.

them to check shorted on the growler. On these, a special 3-volt alternating-current voltmeter must be used to check voltage between bars while the armature is held on the growler.

Burned commutator bars indicate open windings in the armature. Usu-ally, the opens occur at the bar, and repair can be made (if the bars are not too badly burned) by resoldering the connections (using rosin flux) and then turning the commutator and under-cutting the mica (§ 365). Likewise, a commutator that is out of round or worn, or one with high mica, should be repaired by turning. Mica should then be undercut.

Where moist conditions are en-countered, manufacturers recommend application of special insulating var-nish to the armature. Varnish should be kept off the shaft and the com-mutator.

e. Brush service. Brushes worn to one-half their original length should be replaced. Seat new brushes with No. 00 sandpaper or brush-seating stone. Then, with the armature in place in the commutator end frame, check brush-spring tension as well as brush align-ment. If the brushes do not align with the commutator bars, the brush holders are bent and should be replaced. Tension is checked by measuring with a spring scale the pull required to raise brushes, brush arms, or holders from contact position. Replace the springs if the tension is not correct.

f. Reassembly. Reassembly is the reverse of disassembly. Make sure that the pulley nut is drawn up to proper tension and that brush leads are tight. Test the generator after reassembly is complete, and if it has an adjustable third brush, adjust it to obtain the proper generator output.

g. Polarizing generator. After any regulator or generator tests, or after the removal and installation of either unit, the generator must be polarized so that it will have the proper polarity with respect to the battery (see Caution at end of § 366).

h. Belt adjustment. After reinstallation of the generator, the belt must be adjusted to the correct tension by moving the generator out from or up from the engine block, according to the type of generator mounting. The amount of belt tension varies according to application. Figure 15–37 illustrates the adjusting procedure on one application.

IGNITION SYSTEM

§ 372. Testing the ignition system   A number of ignition-system tests are required. There are several types of testing equipment available to make these tests.

1. Ignition testing equipment. A variety of testing equipment is required to test the various components in the ignition system. They include the following:

a. Ignition-coil tester. Two types of ignition-coil tester are in general use, the spark-gap type and the high-frequency type. The latter type is preferred.

b. Condenser tester. A good condenser tester should be able to test the condenser for grounds or shorts and to measure the insulation resistance, series tions all affect the performance of the ignition.

c. Distributor tester. Distributor testers are variable-speed devices that drive the distributor at various speeds so that the operation of the centrifugal

advance can be checked. They also may include a cam-angle meter to measure cam angle (Fig. 15–40). In addition, they usually have a vacuum device to test the operation of vacuum-advance mechanisms.

d. Contact-point-opening   testers. Since the opening of the distributor contact points must be correct to assure good ignition performance, their adjustment is of great importance. Three methods of testing the amount of contact-point opening are in use. One makes use of a feeler gauge placed between the points with the breaker cam turned so that the lever-arm rubbing block rests on the high point of one cam lobe. This method, while satisfactory for new points, should not be used for worn points (Fig. 15–38). Points that have been used are likely to be rough, even though they are still good for many more miles of service. To test such points, a dial indicator (Fig. 15–39) or a cam-angle meter should be used. The cam angle (contact, or dwell, an-

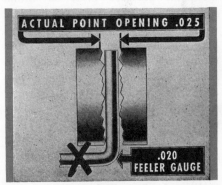

Fig. 15–38. A feeler gauge may not accurately measure the point opening of used and roughened points. Roughness of points is exaggerated. (*Delco-Remy Division of General Motors Corporation*)

Fig. 15–39. Two types of dial indicators used to measure contact-point opening. (Delco-Remy Division of General Motors Corporation)

gle) is the number of degrees of cam rotation from the instant the contact points close until they open again (Fig. 15–40). Increasing the cam angle decreases the contact-point opening, and vice versa. Adjustment is made by loosening a locking screw and turning an eccentric, or by loosening a locking nut and turning the contact screw. On the unit shown to the right in Fig. 7–55, the contacts are adjusted without removing the cap. The window can be raised to expose the adjusting screw.

e. Contact-pressure gauge. The contact-point pressure must be within specifications, since low point pressure will allow the points to bounce and burn, while high pressure will cause rapid wear of the points, cam, and rubbing block. A spring gauge may be used to measure the spring pressure. Adjustment is made by bending the breaker-lever spring.

f. Ignition timing devices. The contact points must be timed to close and open in proper relation to the piston positions in the cylinders. Several timing methods are in use. On many engines, the flywheel or dynamic balancer has a mark that aligns with a pointer on the housing when cylinder 1 is

ready to fire (Fig. 12–7). At this instant, the contact points should separate, so that a spark is produced. A test lamp connected across the points will indicate whether the points are opened or closed at this instant. The distributor can be loosened in its mounting and rotated so that the points will just open with the flywheel marking and pointer aligned. A second method makes use of a stroboscopic light as shown in Fig. 12–7 and described in § 285. The third method makes use of a piston-position gauge that is inserted into the cylinder through the spark-plug hole (or a special timing hole). This permits the

Fig. 15–40. Cam angle. (Delco-Remy Division of General Motors Corporation)

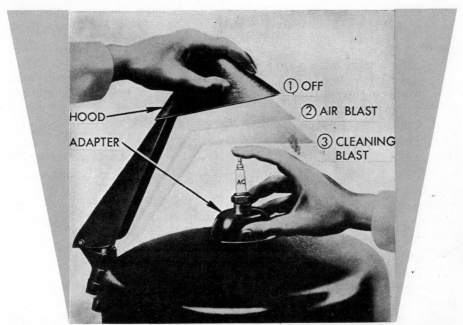

HOOD

ADAPTER

① OFF

② AIR BLAST

③ CLEANING BLAST

Fig. 15–41. Using spark-plug cleaner. Moving the hood down to position 2 directs an air blast against the plug, while position 3 provides the cleaning blast. (*Buick Motor Division of General Motors Corporation*)

location of top dead center in cylinder 1, so that the distributor can be timed to open its points at this instant.

g. *Spark-plug cleaner.* A number of spark-plug cleaning devices are in use. They operate on the sandblast principle and send a blast of gritty ceramic material against the cylinder end of the spark plug placed in the cleaner (Fig. 15–41). After cleaning, the gap should be adjusted by bending the outside electrode. The center electrode should never be bent, since this will break the porcelain shell.

2. *Causes of ignition failure.* Ignition failure can be classified under three main headings, as follows:

1. Loss of energy in the primary circuit. This, in turn, may be caused by several conditions.

a. Resistance in the primary circuit due to defective leads, bad connections, burned distributor contact points or switch, or open coil primary.

b. Points not properly set.

c. Discharged battery, defective generator.

d. Defective condenser (shorted, low insulation resistance, high series resistance).

e. Grounded primary circuit in coil, wiring, or distributor.

2. Loss of energy in secondary circuit.

a. Plugs fouled, broken, or out of adjustment.

b. Defective high-tension wiring, which allows high-tension leaks.

c. High-tension leakage across coil head, distributor cap, or rotor.

395

    d. Defective connections in high-tension circuits.

3. Out of time.

    a. Timing not set properly.

    b. Distributor bearing or shaft worn, or shaft bent.

    c. Vacuum advance defective.

    d. Centrifugal advance defective.

    e. Preignition, due to plugs of wrong heat range, fouled plugs, etc.

3. Quick checks. A number of quick checks can be made to determine whether or not the ignition is at fault if the engine does not operate normally.

a. Engine does not run. Article 293 outlines a procedure of testing the ignition system to see whether the ignition-coil secondary is producing sparks when the engine is being cranked. If a good spark occurs, the ignition primary and secondary can be considered in satisfactory condition. If no spark occurs, the dash ammeter (or a test ammeter installed in the primary circuit) should be watched during cranking.

If there is a small, steady reading that fluctuates somewhat, the primary circuit is probably all right. The trouble is probably due to a defective coil secondary, to secondary leads, a defective condenser, or high-tension leakage across the cap, rotor, or coil head.

If the ammeter shows a fairly high and steady reading, the contact points are out of adjustment, the condenser is shorted, or the coil primary circuit is grounded.

If there is no ammeter reading, the primary circuit is open because of a loose connection, defective wiring or switch, out-of-adjustment distributor contact points, or open coil primary.

b. Engine misses. Missing will be caused by such defects in the ignition system as bad or out-of-adjustment contact points; defective condenser; improper operation of centrifugal or vacuum advance; defective secondary wiring; defective coil; poor connections; high-tension leakage across coil head, rotor, or cap; or defective spark plugs.

c. Overheating and spark rap. These conditions may be caused by improper ignition timing.

§ 373. Ignition service Any check of the ignition system should start at the battery and cables and should take in the coil, distributor, condenser, low- and high-tension wiring, and spark plugs. The high-tension wiring insulation must be in good condition, since poor insulation will allow the high-voltage surges to leak to ground instead of entering the spark plugs. The distributor cap and rotor and the coil head should be examined for carbonized paths that allow high-tension leakage. The distributor contact points should be examined, checked, and adjusted as necessary. Points that are burned or oxidized may be cleaned with a thin, fine-cut contact file or stone. Emery cloth must never be used, since particles of emery may become embedded and cause rapid burning away of the points. On the full-vacuum-control distributor (§ 192, 4), the spark advance should be checked and adjusted, as necessary. The distributor should be lubricated periodically.

1. Summary of ignition troubles. Various troubles that may occur in the components of the ignition system are discussed below.

a. Burned or oxidized contact points. It is normal for ignition-distributor contact points gradually to burn away over a long period of time. Rapid burning or oxidizing of the points may be due to several conditions.

1) Excessive resistance in the condenser circuit caused by high series resistance in the condenser or by a loose mounting or connection.

2) High voltage produced by a high-voltage-regulator or -generator third-brush setting.

3) Contact angle too large (point opening too small). The points, remaining closed too much of the total operating time, burn away rapidly.

4) Weak spring tension that causes the contact points to bounce and arc.

5) Oil or crankcase vapors entering the distributor housing are deposited on the point surfaces, causing them to burn rapidly. A glance at the breaker plate usually discloses this condition, since it causes a black smudge on the breaker plate under the points. Clogged engine breather pipes and worn distributor bearings may produce this trouble.

b. Sooty, burned, or cracked spark-plug insulator. Spark plugs may fail from a variety of reasons. Spark-plug manufacturers usually recommend replacement of spark plugs at 10,000-mile intervals, in order to forestall failure and maintain the engine at good operating efficiency. One cause of spark-plug trouble is the installation of plugs of the wrong heat range. Heat range is a means of designating how hot a plug will run in operation (Fig.

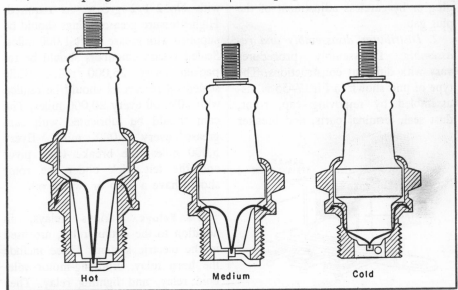

Fig. 15–42. Heat range of spark plugs. The longer the heat path (indicated by arrows), the hotter the plug runs.

15–42). The temperature that a plug will attain depends on the length the heat must travel from the center electrode to reach the outer shell of the plug and enter the cylinder head. If the path of heat travel is long, the plug will run hotter than if the path is short. When a plug runs too cold, there will be a sooty carbon deposit on the insulator around the center electrode. A hotter-running plug will burn this carbon away or prevent its formation. Carbon deposit may also be caused by excessive choking or by excessive oil in the cylinder.

If the plug runs too hot, the insulator may take on a white or grayish cast and may appear blistered. A plug that runs hot will wear more rapidly, since the higher temperatures cause the electrodes to burn away more quickly.

Cracked insulators are usually caused by careless installation of the plug or by careless adjustment of the plug gap.

2. *Distributor disassembly and reassembly.* Disassembly procedures vary with different constructions. The type of unit shown in Fig. 7–55 is disassembled by removing cap, rotor, dust seal, terminal parts, and breaker

plate. Then the coupling or gear is taken off after the head of the pin has been filed off and the pin driven out. This permits removal of the shaft from the housing.

Reassembly is the reverse of disassembly. Replace the bearing in housing if it is worn and allows excessive side play or wobble of the shaft. The old bearing can be pressed out and the new one pressed in with an arbor press. Some bearings. will require reaming to size after installation. When installing the coupling or the gear, add or remove shims (between coupling or gear and housing) before pin end is peened over to get correct shaft end play.

3. *Distributor lubrication.* Hinge-cap oilers should have 8 to 10 drops of light engine oil every 1,000 miles. Grease cups should be turned down one turn every 1,000 miles and filled with No. 2 1/2 grease, as required. High-pressure grease fittings should be supplied with grease every 1,000 miles. Sealed grease chambers should be repacked every 25,000 miles, while sealed oil reservoirs should be refilled with 20W oil every 20,000 miles. The cam should be lubricated with cam grease every 1,000 miles. Every 5,000 miles, the breaker-lever pivot and the felt wick under the rotor should have a drop or two of oil.

§ **374. Relays** Various relays, in addition to the cutout relay, are used in the electric system. These include the horn relay, cranking-motor solenoid relay, and lighting relay. They operate to close their contact points when their winding is energized, and this directly connects the battery to the

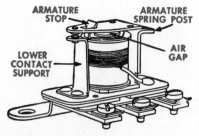

Fig. 15–43. Horn-relay checks and adjustments. (*Delco-Remy Division of General Motors Corporation*)

horns, cranking-motor solenoid, or lights. Adjustment is similar to that used on the cutout relay (Fig. 15–43).

The air gap is checked with the points closed and is adjusted by bending the lower contact support. The contact-point opening is adjusted by bending the armature stop, while the closing voltage is adjusted by bending the armature spring post.

§ 375. **Headlights** Sealed-beam headlights, now in use on all passenger cars, require only one adjustment — aiming. Two general aiming devices are used. One consists of a screen on which the head-lamp illuminating pattern can be studied at a distance of 25 feet. A second device, which does not require so much space, consists of a series of prisms and reflectors that throw a miniature pattern of the illuminating pattern on a screen only a foot or so from the lens. Adjustment is made by loosening screws or nuts to permit swinging of the lamps up or down or to the right or left, as required.

Earlier-model cars require, in addition, polishing and cleaning of reflectors and lenses, since their headlights are not sealed and dirt and moisture can enter and cause loss of lighting efficiency.

REVIEW QUESTIONS

1. Name several testing instruments for electric-system service, and describe the manner in which they are used.
2. In what two ways are batteries tested?
3. Describe the hydrometer test of battery electrolyte.
4. Explain how the specific gravity of the electrolyte varies with the state of charge of the battery.
5. How does gravity vary with temperature? How is correction made for temperature?
6. What effect does age have on battery gravity?
7. What is battery self-discharge?
8. How is battery gravity adjusted for hot climates?
9. Does a discharged or a charged battery freeze more easily?
10. What is the purpose of the high-discharge test? How is this test made on the car?
11. How is the open-circuit-voltage battery test made, and what do the readings mean?
12. What cautions must be observed with regard to the gases that form in the battery during battery charge?
13. What are the four divisions of battery service?
14. Why is overcharging harmful to the battery?
15. What does a variation in gravity readings between battery cells indicate?
16. What causes cracked battery cases? Bulged cases?
17. How are corroded battery terminals and cable clamps serviced? A corroded battery holder? A dirty battery top?
18. How may the battery-electrolyte gravity be readjusted?
19. Explain the process of replacing a battery element.
20. How is battery electrolyte prepared? What cautions should be observed?
21. What are the two methods of charging batteries?

22. What is a quick charger?

23. What are battery dopes?

24. Name two cautions to be observed in caring for batteries in storage.

25. Describe the process of testing a cranking motor on a car.

26. Describe the testing of a detached cranking motor.

27. What is the most common cause of thrown cranking-motor armature windings?

28. What causes burned commutator bars on a cranking-motor armature?

29. What produces broken Bendix springs?

30. What is a pole-shoe screw driver? How is it used?

31. How is an armature tested on a growler?

32. What cautions must be observed in cleaning cranking-motor parts?

33. How is an overrunning clutch tested?

34. What is the overrunning-clutch-pinion clearance?

35. What are the four conditions that may be found when the battery and generator charging rate are checked?

36. What is the procedure to follow if a discharged battery and a low charging rate are found?

37. What is the procedure to follow if a charged battery and a high charging rate are found?

38. Why must the generator be correctly polarized? How is this done?

39. Should the generator be operated on open circuit? What might happen?

40. What are some of the things to look for if a generator produces no output?

41. What should you look for if the generator produces excessive output?

42. What should you look for if the generator output is unsteady or low?

43. Describe briefly the 5,000-mile generator check.

44. What is the polarizing caution? How should the generator be re-polarized after reinstallation on the engine?

45. Name several pieces of testing equipment for testing the components of the ignition system.

46. What is the cam angle?

47. What is meant by ignition timing? How is this timing checked?

48. How do you check the ignition system if the engine is cranked normally but will not run?

49. What conditions in the ignition system will cause the engine to miss?

50. Name a few causes of burned or oxidized distributor contact points.

51. Name several causes of spark-plug failure.

52. What does heat range mean in reference to spark plugs?

53. What is meant by headlight aiming?

STUDY QUESTIONS

1. Why does the specific gravity of the battery electrolyte change with the state of charge of the battery? With temperature?

2. List the six most common combinations of conditions found in testing cranking motors, and either explain what they mean or describe the process to be followed to track down the trouble.

3. Describe the process of repairing burned commutator bars.
4. Describe the procedure of disassembling a cranking motor.
5. How is an armature commutator turned?
6. How is the armature-commutator mica undercut?
7. How would you apply torque on a cranking-motor overrunning-clutch pinion to check it?
8. Describe the procedure for checking and adjusting an Auto-Lite voltage regulator; current regulator.
9. Describe the procedure for checking and adjusting a Delco-Remy voltage regulator. A current regulator.

10. Describe the procedure for checking a generator that produces no output if the generator is of the *first* type (Fig. 7–46). If the generator is of the *second* type (Fig. 7–47).
11. Describe the procedure of disassembling a generator.
12. Explain how to measure distributor contact-point opening. How to measure cam angle.
13. Explain the procedure of adjusting the ignition timing.
14. Make a list of the causes of burned or oxidized distributor contact points.
15. Explain what is meant by heat range in spark plugs.

THIS CHAPTER DESCRIBES various types of trouble that the fuel system has and discusses the services required on the different fuel-system components.

§ 376. Analyzing fuel-system troubles Fuel-system troubles usually show up in engine operation, causing such troubles as poor acceleration, missing, loss of power, failure to start, back-firing, stalling, and so on. These various conditions have already been discussed in detail (§§ 290–303). Fuel-pump testers (§ 284) can be used to determine the condition of the fuel pump. Fuel-mileage testers (§ 283) will measure the miles per gallon that the engine is delivering. These, and other checking devices will help track down trouble causes. An engine tune-up (§ 288) will disclose malfunctioning fuel-system components since the carburetor and fuel pump are checked during the tune-up job. Quick checks of carburetor circuits plus servicing of the fuel-system components are discussed below.

§ 377. Quick carburetor checks A number of quick checks can be made that will give a rough idea of whether the various carburetor circuits are functioning satisfactorily. The results of these checks should not be considered final. Accurate analysis of carburetor operation requires the use of an exhaust-gas analyzer and an intake manifold vacuum gauge. (See the footnote in § 302 for the spark-plug test for an excessively rich mixture.)

1. *Float-level adjustment.* With the engine running at idling speed, remove the air cleaner, and note the condition of the high-speed nozzle. If the nozzle tip is wet or is discharging gasoline, the probability is that the float level is high, causing a continuous discharge of gasoline from the nozzle.

2. *Low-speed and idle circuits.* If the engine does not idle smoothly, the idle circuit is malfunctioning. Slowly open the throttle to give about 25 mph (miles per hour) engine speed. If the speed does not increase evenly and the engine runs roughly through this speed range, the low-speed circuit is out of order.

3. *Accelerator-pump circuit.* Open the throttle suddenly, and note whether the accelerator-pump circuit discharges a flow of gasoline into the air horn. The flow should continue a few moments after throttle reaches "open" position. On some carburetors, this may be better observed with the engine not running.

4. *High-speed circuit.* With the engine running at approximately 25 mph, slowly cover part of the air horn with the hand. The engine should speed up slightly, since this should cause a

normally operating high-speed circuit to discharge more gasoline. The high-speed circuit is probably working improperly if the engine does not speed up somewhat.

§ 378. Cautions in fuel-system work
The following cautions should be carefully observed in fuel-system work:

1. Remember that only a trace of dirt in a carburetor or fuel pump can cause fuel-system, and engine, trouble. Be very careful about dirt when repairing these units. Your hands, the workbench, the tools, should be clean.

2. Gasoline vapor is very explosive. Wipe up spilled gasoline at once, and put cloths outside to dry. Never bring an open flame near gasoline!

3. When air-drying parts with the air hose, handle the hose with care (see § 28).

§ 379. Air-cleaner service Periodically, air cleaners should be removed (Fig. 16–1) so that the filter element can be washed. The element should be

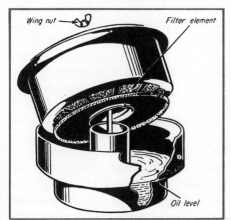

Fig. 16–1. Air cleaner with wing nut and filter element removed and the side partly cut away to show oil level.

washed in clean gasoline or cleaning fluid. It should then be dipped in clean engine oil and allowed to drain. On oil-bath cleaners, the old oil should be drained and the cleaner case washed. The oil reservoir should be filled with· clean oil up to the oil-level mark. Then, the filter element should be replaced and the cleaner reinstalled on the carburetor.

§ 380. Automatic chokes As a rule, automatic chokes require no service once they are adjusted for the operating conditions and engine. To adjust an automatic choke (type shown in Fig. 16–2), loosen the cover clamp screws, and turn the cover one way or the other to enrich or lean out the mixture. Where the heat tube is attached to the cover, it also will have to be loosened before the cover can be turned. The choke is normally disassembled only at the time that the carburetor is removed and disassembled for service.

§ 381. Fuel gauges There is very little in the way of service that fuel gauges require. Defects in either the dash unit or the tank unit usually require replacement of the defective unit. However, on the type of gauge that makes use of vibrating thermostatic blades, dirty contact points, which may cause fluctuations of the needle, can be cleaned by pulling a strip of clean bond paper between them.

§ 382. Fuel-pump service Checking the fuel pump and vacuum pump have already been discussed (§ 284). Periodically, the sediment bowl should be

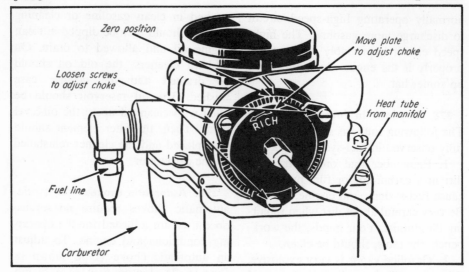

Fig. 16–2. Adjustment of automatic choke.

removed and washed out to remove accumulated water and dirt.

§ **383. Fuel-pump troubles** Fuel-system troubles that might be caused by the fuel pump are discussed below.

1. Insufficient fuel delivery. This could result from low pump pressure, which in turn could be due to any of the following:

a. Broken, worn-out, or cracked diaphragm

b. Improperly operating fuel-pump valves

c. Broken or damaged rocker arm

d. Clogged pump-filter screen

e. Leakage of air into sediment bowl because of loose bowl or worn gasket

In addition to these causes of insufficient fuel delivery due to conditions within the pump, many other conditions outside the pump could prevent delivery of normal amounts of fuel. These include such things as a clogged fuel-tank-cap vent, clogged fuel line or filter, air leaks into the fuel line, and vapor lock. Of course, in the carburetor, an incorrect float level, clogged inlet screen, or malfunctioning inlet needle valve would prevent delivery of adequate amounts of fuel to the carburetor.

2. Excessive pump pressure. High pump pressure will cause delivery of too much fuel to the carburetor. The excessive pressure will tend to lift the needle valve off its seat so that the fuel level in the float bowl will be too high. This results in an overrich mixture and excessive fuel consumption. Usually, high pump pressure would result only after a fuel pump has been removed, repaired, and replaced. If a fuel pump has been operating satisfactorily, it is hardly likely that its pressure would increase enough to cause trouble. High pressure could come from installation of an excessively strong diaphragm spring or from incorrect reinstallation of the diaphragm. If the diaphragm is not flexed

properly when the cover and housing are reattached, it will have too much tension and will produce too much pressure.

3. Fuel-pump leaks. The fuel pump will leak fuel from any point where screws have not been properly tightened and also where the gasket is damaged or incorrectly installed. If tightening screws does not stop the leak, then the gasket or diaphragm will require replacement. Note, also, that leaks may occur at fuel-line connections which are loose or improperly coupled.

4. Fuel-pump noises. A noisy pump is usually the result of worn or broken parts within the pump. These include a weak or broken rocker-arm spring, worn or broken rocker-arm pin or rocker arm, or a broken diaphragm spring. In addition, a loose fuel pump or a scored rocker arm or cam on the camshaft may cause noise. Fuel-pump noise may sound something like engine-valve tappet noise since its frequency is the same as camshaft speed. If the noise is bad enough, it can actually be "felt" by gripping the fuel pump firmly in the hand. Also, careful listening will usually disclose that the noise is originating in the vicinity of the fuel pump. Tappet noise is usually distributed along the engine or is located more distinctly in the valve compartment of the engine.

§ **384. Fuel-pump removal** As a first step in removing the fuel pump, wipe off any dirt or accumulated grease so that dirt will not get into the engine. Then take off the heat shield (where present), and disconnect the fuel lines and vacuum-pump lines (on combination pump). Remove attaching nuts or bolts, and lift off the pump. If it sticks, work it gently from side to side or pry lightly under the mounting flange or attaching studs. On engine using a push rod to operate the fuel pump, remove the rod so that it can be examined for wear or sticking.

§ **385. Fuel-pump disassembly and assembly** Many automotive service departments do not attempt to disassemble and repair fuel pumps because pump manufacturers have arranged a special pump-exchange program. The old pumps can be traded in on new or factory rebuilt units. For those who prefer to repair fuel pumps, special repair kits are supplied. These repair kits contain diaphragms, valves, springs, and gaskets. Figure 16–3 shows an overhaul kit for a combination pump. Refer to the manufacturer's shop manual for overhaul procedures on specific models.

§ **386. Fuel-pump installation** Make sure that the fuel-line connections are clean and in good condition. Connect the fuel and vacuum lines to the pump before attaching the pump to the engine. Then place a new gasket on the studs of the fuel-pump mounting or over the opening in the crankcase. The mounting surface of the engine should be clean. Insert the rocker arm of the fuel pump into the opening, making sure that the arm goes on the proper side of the camshaft (or that it is centered over the push rod). If it is hard to get the holes in the fuel-pump flange to align with the holes in the crankcase, turn the engine over until the low side of the camshaft eccentric

is under the fuel-pump rocker arm. Now the pump can be installed without forcing or prying it into place. Attach with bolts or nuts. Check pump operation as explained in § 284.

§ 387. **Carburetor troubles** The trouble-shooting chart and trouble explanations in § § 290 to 303 related many engine troubles to fuel system and carbureter troubles. Let us now list these various troubles that can be caused by the carburetor. Remember, many other conditions outside the carburetor can also cause these troubles, as previously noted.

1. Excessive fuel consumption can result from a high float level or a leaky float, sticking or dirty float needle valve, worn jets or nozzles, stuck metering rod or full-power piston, idle too rich or too fast, stuck accelerator-pump check valve, or a leaky carburetor.

2. Lack of engine power, acceleration, or high-speed performance can result from a malfunctioning accelerator pump, from the power step-up on the metering rod not clearing the jet, from dirt or gum clogging fuel nozzle or jets, from a stuck power piston or valve, a low float level, dirty air filter,

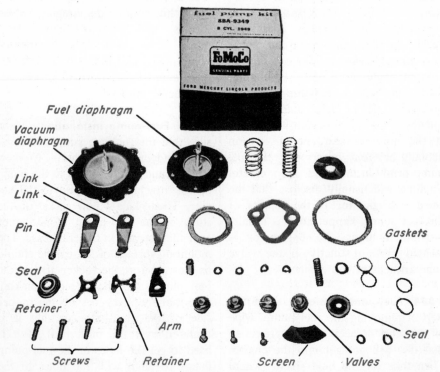

Fig. 16–3. Repair kit for a combination fuel and vacuum pump. (Ford Motor Company)

choke stuck or not operating, air leaks into manifold, antipercolator valve stuck, throttle valve not fully opening, or a rich mixture due to causes listed in the previous paragraph.

3. Poor idle can result from an incorrectly adjusted idle mixture or speed, a clogged idle circuit, or any of the causes listed in the previous paragraph.

4. Failure of the engine to start unless primed could be due to carburetor jets or lines being clogged, a defective choke, a clogged fuel filter, or air leaks into the manifold.

5. Hard starting with the engine warm could be due to a defective choke, closed choke valve, or improperly adjusted throttle-cracker linkage.

6. Slow engine warm-up could be due to a defectively operating choke.

7. A smoky, black exhaust is due to a very rich mixture. Carburetor conditions that could cause this are listed in item 1 above.

8. If the engine stalls as it warms up, this could be due to a defective choke or closed choke valve.

9. If the engine stalls after a period of high-speed driving, this could be due to a malfunctioning antipercolator.

10. If the engine backfires, this could be due to an excessively rich or lean mixture.

11. If the engine runs but misses, it could be that the proper amount and ratio of air-fuel mixture are not reaching the engine and this might be due to clogged or worn carburetor jets or to an incorrect fuel level in the float bowl.

Several of the conditions noted above can be corrected by carburetor adjustment. Other conditions require removal of the carburetor from the engine so that it can be disassembled, repaired, and reassembled. Following sections discuss carburetor adjustments and servicing procedures.

§ 388. Carburetor adjustments An estimated 500 different models of carburetor have been used in automotive vehicles during the past 10 years. Thus, it is obviously beyond the scope of this book to provide detailed adjustment and servicing procedures for all. However, we do discuss certain adjusting and servicing fundamentals. For servicing procedures on specific carburetor models, refer to the manufacturer's shop manuals.

1. Idle-speed and idle-mixture adjustments (Fig. 16–4). These are made together and determine the engine idling speed and mixture richness. Idling speed is adjusted by turning the adjusting screw in or out until the

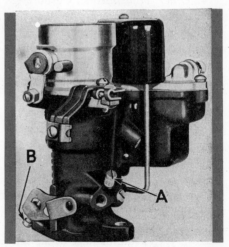

Fig. 16–4. Idle-mixture screw (A) and idle-speed adjusting screw (B) on one type of carburetor. (Chevrolet Motor Division of General Motors Corporation)

specified engine rpm (revolutions per minute) is attained. Then, the idle mixture is adjusted by turning the idle-mixture screw in or out. Correct setting gives smoothest idle. On most carburetors, the proper setting is one or two turns of the screw back from the "fully seated" position. On dual or quadrijet carburetors, there are two idle-mixture screws to adjust.

2. Throttle linkage. The throttle linkage on the car must be adjusted so that the throttle opens wide when the foot pedal is fully depressed. In addition, the throttle must be fully closed when the foot pedal is released.

3. Accelerator pump. Some carburetors have an adjustable accelerator pump. A linkage rod can be shifted into various holes provided in the throttle or pump lever. Thus, a longer stroke, and richer mixture, can be obtained for winter operation and a shorter stroke for summer operation.

4. Other adjustments. Carburetors also require adjustments to the float or floats, metering rod or rods, antipercolator, and so on. These adjustments are covered in the applicable manufacturer's shop manual.

§ 389. Carburetor removal To remove a carburetor, first take off the air cleaner, and then disconnect the throttle and choke linkages. Disconnect the hot-air tube to the choke (if present). Disconnect the fuel line and distributor vacuum-advance line from the carburetor, using two wrenches, as necessary, to avoid damage to the lines or couplings. Disconnect wires from switches and other electric controls (where present). Take off the carburetor attaching nuts or bolts, and lift off

the carburetor. Try to avoid jarring the carburetor, since it might have accumulations of dirt in the float bowl and rough treatment might stir this dirt up and cause it to get into carburetor jets or circuits.

After the carburetor is off, it should be put in a clean place where dirt or dust cannot get into the fuel inlet or other openings.

§ 390. Carburetor overhaul procedures Disassembly and reassembly procedures on carburetors vary according to their design; the manufacturer's recommendations should be carefully followed. The time required to overhaul a carburetor varies from approximately 3/4 to 2 hours, according to type. Special carburetor tools are required. Gauges particularly are needed to gauge float clearance, float centering, float height, choke clearance, and so on.

Special carburetor overhaul kits are supplied for many carburetors. These kits contain all necessary parts (jets, gaskets, washers, and so forth) required to overhaul the carburetor and restore it to its original performing condition.

1. General overhaul instructions. Jets or nozzles should never be cleaned with drills or wires since this would probably enlarge the openings and cause an excessively rich mixture. Instead, the openings should be cleaned out with denatured alcohol or similar recommended solvent. This solvent will remove any gum that is clogging the opening. Similarly, all circuits or passages in the carburetor body should be washed out with solvent and then blown out with compressed air.

Double-check passages with a flashlight to be sure they are cleaned out.

Power pistons that are scored or burred should be replaced; the piston must slide freely in the bore in the carburetor body. Worn or scored needle valves or seats must be replaced. Filter screens must be clean. Accelerator-pump plungers must fit snugly in their wells. If the leather is damaged, a new plunger must be used.

If the air horn is coated with dirt or carbon, it should be scraped lightly or sanded with sandpaper and then washed in solvent. Never use emery cloth, since particles of emery may embed and later loosen to clog jets or circuits in the carburetor.

Be sure that all residue is washed from the carburetor and that the carburetor body is clean inside and out.

New carburetor gaskets should be used when the carburetor is reassembled. The old gaskets are usually damaged when the carburetor is torn down, and there is no use taking a chance on a leak developing later that would require disassembling the carburetor again.

2. *Cautions.* Several important cautions should be observed in carburetor work.

a. Be sure your hands, the workbench, and tools are really clean.

b. Gasoline, as well as denatured alcohol or other solvent used to dissolve the gum from carburetor jets and other parts, is highly flammable. Extreme care must be used in handling these liquids, particularly some of the solvents, since they will ignite easily.

c. Handle the air hose with care. Remember, high-pressure air can drive dirt particles at high speed. If one of these particles should be blown into the eye, it might damage the eye irreparably. Wear goggles when using the air hose to be safe.

d. Never clean carburetor jets or orifices with wire or drills. This would probably enlarge the openings and result in excessive fuel consumption.

e. Always use new gaskets on reassembling the carburetor.

f. The correct carburetor parts must be used on reassembly. Substitute parts that may be somewhat different should not be installed unless the carburetor manual specifically states that this may be done. Otherwise, performance and economy may be lost.

g. Carburetor adjustments should not be made until other components affecting engine operation are in good order. Adjusting the carburetor to compensate for faulty conditions elsewhere will probably result in poorer engine performance and higher fuel consumption.

h. Do not oil the automatic-choke linkage or the automatic choke.

§ **391. Carburetor installation** Examine the carburetor gasket, and make sure it is in perfect condition. Replace it if you have any doubt as to its condition. Put carburetor into position on intake manifold, and attach with nuts or bolts. Connect fuel line and distributor vacuum-advance line to carburetor, using two wrenches as necessary to avoid damage to the lines or couplings. Connect wires to switches and other electric controls (where present). Make idle-speed, idle-mixture, and other adjustments as already noted. Install air cleaner.

REVIEW QUESTIONS

1. Explain how to quickly check the carburetor float-level adjustment.
2. Explain how to quickly check the low-speed circuit.
3. Explain how to quickly check the accelerator-pump action.
4. Explain how you can get an idea of the operating condition of the high-speed circuit.
5. What cautions should be observed in any fuel-system work?
6. Describe air-cleaner service.
7. Explain how to determine whether it is the tank unit or the dash unit that is at fault when the fuel gauge is not operating correctly.
8. Describe various fuel-pump troubles and their causes.
9. Explain how to remove and install a fuel pump.
10. Mention various engine-operating conditions that could result from faulty fuel-system actions.
11. Describe typical carburetor adjustments.
12. Explain how to remove and install a carburetor.
13. What are the important points to watch during carburetor overhaul?

STUDY QUESTIONS

1. List and describe the quick carburetor checks.
2. Write down the cautions you must observe when doing fuel-system work.
3. List and describe the various fuel-system troubles.
4. List the various engine conditions that could result from faulty fuel-system operation.
5. List various carburetor adjustments.
6. Describe in detail the various general overhaul instructions on carburetors.
7. Select a carburetor for which the servicing instructions are available, and overhaul the carburetor. Write down the important steps of overhaul as you do them.

THIS CHAPTER DISCUSSES VARIOUS types of trouble that might occur in the engine lubricating system and explains the services required on the lubricating-system components.

§ 392. **Trouble tracing in lubricating system** Few troubles occur in the lubricating system that are not intimately related to engine troubles. We have already discussed causes of excessive oil consumption (§§ 260 and 300), oil dilution and water-sludge formation (§ 257), and why it is necessary to change oil periodically (§ 259). Figure 17–1 shows places in the engine where oil may be lost, to cause high oil consumption. Using the bearing oil-leak detector to check for excessive bearing wear has also been

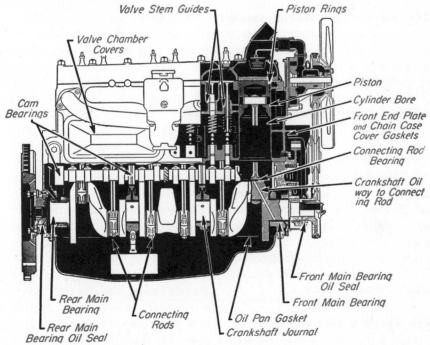

Valve Stem Guides — Piston Rings

Valve Chamber Covers

Cam Bearings

Piston

Cylinder Bore

Front End Plate and Chain Case Cover Gaskets

Connecting Rod Bearing

Crankshaft Oil way to Connecting Rod

Front Main Bearing Oil Seal

Front Main Bearing

Oil Pan Gasket

Crankshaft Journal

Rear Main Bearing

Connecting Rods

Rear Main Bearing Oil Seal

Fig. 17–1. Partial sectional view of engine, showing points where oil may be lost. (Federal-Mogul Corporation)

described (§ 326). Other lubricating-system troubles that might require checking into include low oil pressure and high oil pressure.

1. Low oil pressure. Low oil pressure can result from a weak relief-valve spring, a worn oil pump, a broken or cracked oil line, obstructions in the oil lines, insufficient or excessively thin oil, or bearings so badly worn that they can pass more oil than the oil pump is capable of delivering. A defective oil-pressure indicator may be recording low.

2. Excessive oil pressure. This may result from a stuck relief valve, an excessively strong valve spring, a clogged oil line, or excessively heavy oil. A defective oil-pressure indicator may read high.

§ **393. Lubricating - system service** There are certain lubricating-system jobs that are done more or less automatically when an engine is repaired. For example, the oil pan is removed and cleaned during such engine-overhaul jobs as replacing bearings or rings (§ 329). When the crankshaft is removed, it is the usual procedure to clean out the oil passages in the crankshaft. Chapter 14 describes the various engine-servicing jobs. Following sections describe such lubricating-system service jobs as changing oil, cleaning the oil pan, servicing the relief valve, changing or cleaning the oil filter, and servicing the oil pump and the oil-pressure indicator.

§ **394. Checking oil level** Most engines use a bayonet type of oil-level gauge (the dip stick) that can be withdrawn from the crankcase to determine the oil level in the crankcase. The gauge should be withdrawn, wiped clean, reinserted, and again withdrawn so that the oil level on the gauge can be seen. The gauge is usually marked to indicate the proper oil level. The appearance of the oil should be noted to see whether it is dirty, thin, or thick. A few drops of oil can be placed between the thumb and fingers and rubbed, to detect dirt or to find out whether the oil has sufficient body, that is, whether it is sticky. If the oil level is low, oil should be added to the crankcase. If the oil is thin or dirty, it should be drained and the crankcase refilled with clean oil.

§ **395. Changing oil** Standard practice is to change the engine oil at 500-, 1,000-, or 2,000-mile intervals, according to the type of operation (§ 259). Oil filters installed in the system tend to reduce the frequency with which oil will require changing. But they do not eliminate the need for oil changes. Oil should be changed more frequently during cold weather, particularly when short-trip operation predominates. With short-trip operation, the engine operates cold a greater part of the time, and this increases the chances for water sludge to form. More frequent oil changes will remove this sludge before dangerous amounts can accumulate. When the car is operated on very dusty roads, the oil should be changed more frequently. Despite the air filters in the carburetor air cleaner and crankcase ventilator, dust does work its way into the engines, and this is particularly true when the car operates in dusty areas. Changing oil flushes this dust out so

that it cannot harm the engine. Car manufacturers recommend that a car that has been driven through a dust storm, for example, should have the oil changed immediately, regardless of how recently the last oil change was made. At the same time, the air filter should be cleaned and the oil filter (if used) changed. In addition to the changing of engine oil, the lubrication of various points in the engine accessories and chassis is periodically necessary, as shown in the typical lubrication chart in Fig. 17–2.

§ 396. Oil-pan service
Removing and cleaning the oil pan has already been discussed (§ 329).

§ 397. Relief valve
Relief valves are not usually adjustable although springs of different tension may be installed to change the regulating pressure. This is not usually recommended, however, since a spring of the proper tension was originally installed on the engine. Any change of pressure is usually brought about by some defect that requires correction. For example, badly worn bearings may pass so much oil that the oil pump cannot deliver sufficient oil to maintain normal pressure in the lines. Installing a stronger spring in the relief valve would not increase oil pressure; the relief valve is not operating under the circumstances.

§ 398. Oil filters
Oil filters are serviced by replacing the oil-filter element or the complete filter, according to the type. Oil screens are serviced by flushing out accumulated sludge and dirt. Where the application is equipped with a floating type of oil in-take, the float and screen should also be cleaned.

As the oil filter becomes clogged, it passes less and less oil. Some indication of the condition of the oil filter can be had by feeling it after the engine has been operated for a short time. If the filter is hot to the touch, this indicates that oil is flowing through the filter. If it is cold, the probability is that the filter is clogged and is not passing oil. An additional check can be made by disconnecting the filter outlet with the engine running at low speed to see whether oil is flowing through the filter. However, rather than depend on some such check as this to determine filter efficiency, the best procedure is to replace the filter or filter element at periodic intervals. The usual recommendation is to replace the filter element every 5,000 miles. More frequent replacement should be made if the car is operated in unusually dusty conditions.

§ 399. Filter - element replacement
To replace the filter element, remove drain plug (if present) from bottom of housing. Take cover off by loosening center bolt or clamp. Lift out element. If filter housing has no drain plug, remove old oil or sediment with a siphon gun. Wipe out inside of housing with clean cloth. Be sure no traces of lint or dirt remain. Install new filter element. Replace plug and cover, using a new gasket. Start engine, and check for leaks around the cover. Note whether oil pressure has changed (with a new element, which passes oil more easily, it may be lower). Check level of oil in crankcase, and add oil if necessary. Installing a new filter ele-

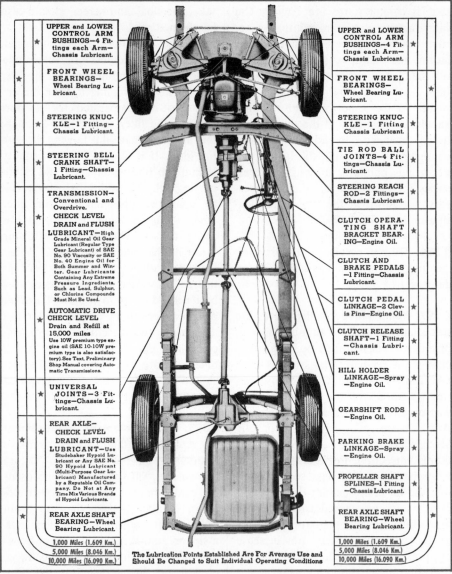

	UPPER and LOWER CONTROL ARM BUSHINGS—4 Fittings each Arm—Chassis Lubricant.	UPPER and LOWER CONTROL ARM BUSHINGS—4 Fittings each Arm—Chassis Lubricant.
	FRONT WHEEL BEARINGS—Wheel Bearing Lubricant.	FRONT WHEEL BEARINGS—Wheel Bearing Lubricant.
	STEERING KNUCKLE—1 Fitting—Chassis Lubricant.	STEERING KNUCKLE—1 Fitting Chassis Lubricant.
	STEERING BELL CRANK SHAFT—1 Fitting—Chassis Lubricant.	TIE ROD BALL JOINTS—4 Fittings—Chassis Lubricant.
		STEERING REACH ROD—2 Fittings—Chassis Lubricant.
	TRANSMISSION—Conventional and Overdrive. CHECK LEVEL DRAIN and FLUSH LUBRICANT—High Grade Mineral Oil Gear Lubricant (Regular Type Gear Lubricant) of SAE No. 90 Viscosity or SAE No. 40 Engine Oil for Both Summer and Winter. Gear Lubricants Containing Any Extreme Pressure Ingredients, Such as Lead, Sulphur, or Chlorine Compounds Must Not Be Used.	CLUTCH OPERATING SHAFT BRACKET BEARING—Engine Oil.
		CLUTCH AND BRAKE PEDALS—1 Fitting—Chassis Lubricant.
	AUTOMATIC DRIVE CHECK LEVEL Drain and Refill at 15,000 miles Use 10W premium type engine oil (SAE 10-10W premium type is also satisfactory). See Text, Preliminary Shop Manual covering Automatic Transmissions.	CLUTCH PEDAL LINKAGE—2 Clevis Pins—Engine Oil.
		CLUTCH RELEASE SHAFT—1 Fitting—Chassis Lubricant.
		HILL HOLDER LINKAGE—Spray—Engine Oil.
	UNIVERSAL JOINTS—3 Fittings—Chassis Lubricant.	GEARSHIFT RODS—Engine Oil.
	REAR AXLE—CHECK LEVEL DRAIN and FLUSH LUBRICANT—Use Studebaker Hypoid Lubricant or Any SAE No. 90 Hypoid Lubricant (Multi-Purpose Gear Lubricant) Manufactured by a Reputable Oil Company. Do Not at Any Time Mix Various Brands of Hypoid Lubricants.	PARKING BRAKE LINKAGE—Spray—Engine Oil.
		PROPELLER SHAFT SPLINES—1 Fitting—Chassis Lubricant.
	REAR AXLE SHAFT BEARING—Wheel Bearing Lubricant.	REAR AXLE SHAFT BEARING—Wheel Bearing Lubricant.
1,000 Miles (1.609 Km.) 5,000 Miles (8.046 Km.) 10,000 Miles (16.090 Km.)	The Lubrication Points Established Are For Average Use and Should Be Changed to Suit Individual Operating Conditions	1,000 Miles (1.609 Km.) 5,000 Miles (8.046 Km.) 10,000 Miles (16.090 Km.)

Fig. 17–2. Chassis of one model automobile from bottom, showing items requiring lubrication, type of lubricant to use, and frequency with which service is required. (*Studebaker-Packard Corporation*)

ment usually requires the addition of a quart of oil to bring oil level up to proper height in crankcase.

NOTE: It is always the best policy to change the oil whenever the oil filter is changed. The new oil filter should start out with clean oil.

On the type of filter that does not have a replaceable element, the complete filter is replaced. This is done by

disconnecting the oil lines to the old filter, dismounting the filter, and then installing the new filter and connecting the oil lines to it.

After a filter element or filter is replaced, the mileage should be marked on the doorjamb sticker and the filter housing. Then, after 5,000 miles (or the specified replacement mileage) the driver and serviceman will know that it is time to replace the filter element again.

§ 400. Oil pumps   Oil pumps are relatively simple mechanisms and require little service in normal operation. If a pump is badly worn, it will not maintain oil pressure and should be removed for repair or replacement. In such case, refer to the applicable manufacturer's shop manual for details of servicing.

§ 401. Oil-pressure indicators   Oil-pressure indicators are discussed in detail in § 265. These units require very little in the way of service. Defects in either the dash unit or the engine unit usually require replacement of the defective unit. On the type of unit that makes use of vibrating thermostatic blades, dirty contact points, which may cause incorrect readings, may usually be cleaned by pulling a strip of bond paper between them. Be sure that no particles of paper are left between the points. Never use emery cloth to clean the points since particles of emery might embed and prevent normal indicator action. If the indicator is not functioning in a normal manner, a new engine indicating unit may be temporarily substituted for the old one in order to determine whether the fault is in the engine unit or the dash unit.

REVIEW QUESTIONS

1. What could cause low oil pressure? High oil pressure?
2. Explain how to check the oil level in the oil pan.
3. Explain why the engine oil must be changed periodically.
4. Explain how to replace an oil-filter element.

STUDY QUESTIONS

1. Write down the procedure of servicing an oil pump as explained in a manufacturer's shop manual.
2. If an engine has badly worn bearings, would you recommend using a stronger spring in the relief valve in order to maintain pressure? What is the reason for your answer?

THIS CHAPTER DESCRIBES THE testing, care, servicing, and repair of automotive-engine cooling-system components.

§ **402. Cooling-system tests** Over a period of time, rust and scale accumulate in the radiator and engine water jackets; the rust and scale restrict the circulation of water, and the engine tends to overheat (Fig. 18–1). In addition, the hose and connections between the radiator and the engine may de-

teriorate, causing leakage or inadequate passage of water. The thermostat, if stuck or distorted, may not close and open properly and will thus reduce the effectiveness of the cooling system. A number of tests of the cooling system and its components can be made to determine the condition of these parts. In addition, the strength of the antifreeze solution can be tested.

1. Testing thermostat. The action of the thermostat can be observed by placing it in a pan of water and heating

Fig. 18–1. Accumulation of rust and scale in engine water jackets. (*Chevrolet Motor Division of General Motors Corporation*)

the pan. A thermometer should be suspended in the water, so that the temperature at which the thermostat starts to open, as well as the full-open temperature, can be determined. The thermostat should not be placed on the bottom of the pan but suspended by a wire or placed on a screen an inch or so above the bottom (see Fig. 18–2). Thermostats are calibrated to operate at various temperatures. If a thermostat does not function according to specifications, it should be replaced.

2. Testing system for rust and scale. The appearance of the water is some indication of whether rust and scale have accumulated in the cooling system. If the water is rusty or muddy in appearance, rust is present. A fairly accurate measurement of the amount of rust and scale present can be made if the capacity of the cooling system is known. All water should be drained and fresh water measured and added until the system is filled. Comparison of the amount of added water with the specified capacity of the system provides an indication of the amount of rust and scale present.

3. Testing radiator for restriction. If the radiator-hose connections are removed, the radiator drained, and a stream of water from an ordinary garden hose introduced into the top of the radiator, the water should run through the radiator and out without filling up the radiator. If the water runs out slowly, the radiator is clogged. Another test for restrictions in the radiator is to start the engine, allow it to warm up, and then turn the engine off and feel the radiator with the hand. It should be hot at the top and warm at the bottom, with an even tempera-

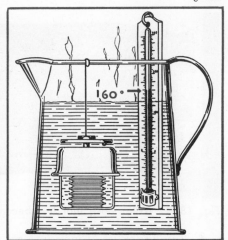

Fig. 18–2. Testing cooling-system thermostat.

ture increase from bottom to top. Cold spots indicate clogged sections.

▶ *CAUTION:* Be sure the engine is turned off. More than one person has injured his hand seriously by placing it too near an engine fan when the engine was running.

4. Examining hose and hose connections. The appearance of the hose and connections will usually indicate their condition. If the hose is rotted and soft and collapses easily when squeezed, it should be replaced. Figure 18–3 illustrates a badly deteriorated section of hose that has been split open to show the internal appearance.

5. Testing water pump. There is no accurate way to test the action of the water pump on the car. However, some idea as to its operating condition may be obtained by squeezing the upper-hose connection in the hand, with the engine warm and running. If pressure can be felt as the engine is speeded up, this is an indication that the water pump is operating in a normal manner.

417

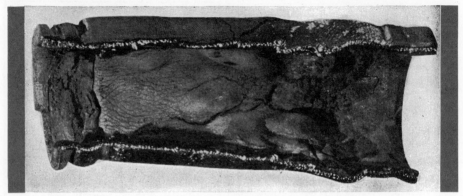

Fig. 18–3. Water hose that has become defective. (*Federal-Mogul Corporation*)

6. Testing for air suction into system. If leaks exist at any point between the radiator and the water pump, air will be drawn into the system as shown in Fig. 18–4. Air bubbles will cause foaming and loss of the cooling water.

The water could, of course, be replaced, but if antifreeze is also lost, then replacement is an expense. There is also the danger of losing antifreeze protection in this way. Air in the system speeds up corrosion and rust. To

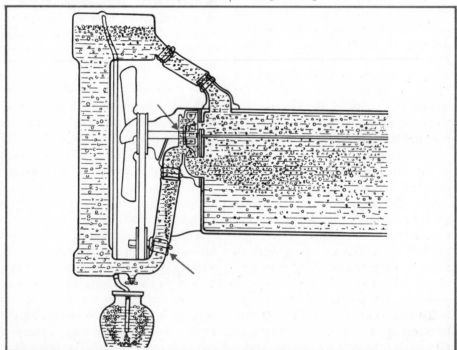

Fig. 18–4. Testing for air suction into cooling system. Arrows indicate points at which air might enter.

418

check for air suction, fill the radiator, attach a hose from the overflow pipe, and put the lower end of the hose into a container of water, as shown (Fig. 18–4). Start the engine, and run it until it is warmed up. If bubbles appear in the container of water, then air is being sucked into the cooling system. (It might be exhaust-gas leakage, as noted in the following paragraph.) Repair by tightening or replacing hose and hose clamps. If this does not cure the trouble, then either there is exhaust-gas leakage or the water pump is leaking. Check the system as noted in the following paragraph. If no exhaust-gas leakage is found, then the trouble is probably in the pump, and it should be repaired (§ 406).

7. *Testing for exhaust-gas leakage.* A defective cylinder-head gasket may allow exhaust gas to leak into the cooling system. This is very damaging, since strong acids will form as the gas unites with the water in the cooling system. These acids corrode the radiator and other parts in the cooling system. A test for exhaust-gas leakage may be made by disconnecting the upper hose, removing the thermostat and the fan belt, and draining the system until the water level stands just above the top of the cylinder head (Fig. 18–5). The engine should be started and accelerated quickly several times. If the water level rises appreciably, or if bubbles appear, exhaust gas is leaking into the cooling system. A new gasket should be installed and the cylinder-head bolts properly tightened.

8. *Testing fan belt.* Fan-belt adjustment should be checked as shown in

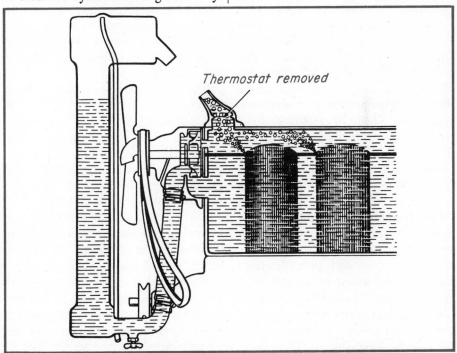

Fig. 18–5. Testing for exhaust-gas leakage into system.

Fig. 15–37. The fan belt should be checked every few thousand miles to make sure that it is still in good condition. A belt that has become worn or frayed or that has separated plies should be discarded and a new belt installed. A defective or loose belt will not only cause overheating of the engine, but may also result in a run-down battery, since it cannot drive the generator fast enough to keep the battery charged.

9. *Testing antifreeze - solution strength.* The strength of the antifreeze solution must not be below that required to furnish adequate protection in the lowest temperatures expected. The strength of the solution is tested by use of a special antifreeze-solution hydrometer, which measures its specific gravity, or heaviness. The so-called "permanent" antifreeze compounds (ethylene glycol) are heavier than water, while alcohol-base antifreeze compounds are lighter than water. The specific-gravity reading will determine what percentage of the solution is water and what percentage is antifreeze compound. Then, by reference to a chart, the lowest temperature at which the solution will remain a liquid can be determined. Additional antifreeze compound can be added if required.

§ 403. Cooling-system-trouble diagnosis

Complaints that may lead the mechanic to check the cooling system include slow warm-up and overheating. Slow warm-up could be caused by a thermostat that fails and remains open. This causes the water to circulate between the radiator and the engine block, even when the engine is cold, and makes it necessary for the engine to run for a longer period of time before reaching operating temperature.

Overheating, when due to trouble in the cooling system, is most often caused by accumulations of rust and scale, defective hose or connections, malfunctioning of the water pump or thermostat, or a loose or defective fan belt. If the engine overheats without the radiator's becoming normally warm, and if the fan belt is tight and in good condition, the thermostat is probably not opening and will therefore require replacement. If the radiator is hot, test the water pump by pinching closed the upper hose by hand as described in § 402. If the thermostat and water pump seem to be operating normally and the hose appears to be in good condition, the overheating, if actually caused by troubles in the cooling system, is probably due to accumulations of rust or scale in the cooling system. Such rust or scale should be cleaned and flushed out (§ 404).

The water may start to boil after the engine has been turned off; this is called *afterboil*. This could happen, for example, after a long, hard drive. The engine has so much heat in it (though it has not actually overheated) that, after the engine is turned off, the water in the cooling system boils (Fig. 18–6), owing to the fact that it is still absorbing heat from the engine, which it cannot get rid of because the cooling system is no longer working

Boiling can also occur if the radiator has frozen up. This hinders or stops the circulation of the cooling water. Consequently, the water in the water jackets becomes so hot that it boils.

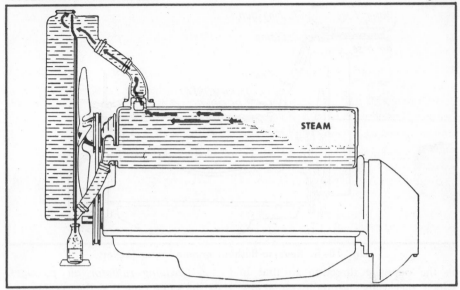

Fig. 18–6. Afterboil of water after engine is stopped.

It must be remembered that there are other causes of engine overheating, which have nothing to do with conditions in the cooling system. High-altitude operation, insufficient oil, overloading of the engine, hot-climate operation, improperly timed ignition, long periods of low-speed or idling operation — any of these may cause overheating of the engine (see § 296).

§ 404. Cleaning the cooling system
The cooling system should be cleaned at periodic intervals to prevent the accumulation of excessive rust and scale. Accumulated rust and scale can be loosened by a good cleaning compound. There are various types of cleaning compounds; all must be used carefully in accordance with the manufacturer's instructions. A general cleaning procedure is outlined below. If considerable scale and rust have accumulated, it may be that cleaning alone will not remove it all. In this case, the radiator and engine water jackets must be flushed out with special air-pressure guns as shown in Figs. 18–7 and 18–8. The hot-water heater can be flushed out at the same time. Some car manufacturers recommend reverse flushing, that is, flushing in which the water is forced through the radiator and water jackets

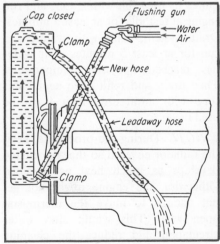

Fig. 18–7. Reverse-flushing radiator

421

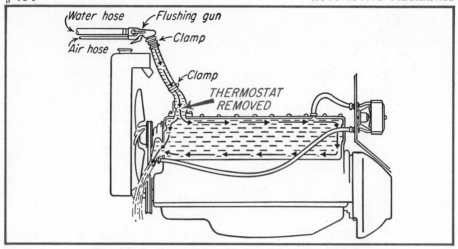

Water hose ⎯Flushing gun
Air hose ⎯Clamp
⎯Clamp
THERMOSTAT REMOVED

Fig. 18–8. Reverse-flushing engine water jackets.

in the opposite direction to that in which the water normally circulates. This gets behind the scale and loosens it so that it will be flushed out.

1. Cooling-system cleaning procedure. Completely drain the system by opening drain cocks. Add cleaning compound, and fill system with water. Run engine on fast idle for at least 30 minutes after engine reaches operating temperature. Completely drain system again, add neutralizer (if cleaner requires its use), fill with water, and run engine at fast idle for at least 5 minutes. Drain system, refill with water, and run for at least 5 minutes after water has reached operating temperature. Then drain and refill once again, this time with antifreeze (if it is to be used).

NOTE: During the procedure, keep the radiator covered so that the engine develops as much heat as possible. Otherwise, the engine might not get hot enough to make the thermostat open wide. This would slow water circulation and reduce the cleaning effect.

2. Cleaning radiator air passages. At the same time that the cooling system is cleaned, the radiator air passages should be cleaned out. This can be done by blowing them out, from back to front, with compressed air. This removes insects, leaves, and dirt that could clog the air passages and reduce the cooling efficiency of the radiator.

3. Flushing radiator. If cleaning alone does not remove all the accumulated rust and scale, the radiator and water jackets should be flushed. This job is done with a flushing gun that uses air pressure to force the water through. The radiator can be straight-flushed or reverse-flushed. For reverse flushing, a new hose is attached to the lower tank of the radiator, and a lead-away hose is attached to the upper tank (Fig. 18–7). The water will, of course, drain out as this is done. Clamp flushing gun in hose to lower tank, as shown, and turn on water to fill radiator. When water runs out the leadaway hose, apply air pressure to force water out. Apply the pressure

gradually, to avoid damaging the radiator. Sudden full-pressure application might rupture the radiator core. Refill radiator, and again apply air pressure. Repeat until water running from leadaway hose is clean.

To straight-flush the radiator, follow the above procedure, but attach leadaway hose to the lower tank of the radiator and the flushing-gun hose to the upper tank. This will circulate the water through the radiator in the normal direction.

4. Flushing engine water jackets. Engine water jackets also may be straight-flushed or reverse-flushed. Some engine manufacturers warn that seals and other engine parts may be damaged if their engines are reverse-flushed. Make sure the specifications permit reverse flushing before doing the job. To reverse-flush, remove the thermostat and attach the flushing gun to the thermostat housing with a short length of hose (Fig. 18–8). The illus-

tration does not show a leadaway hose from the water-pump inlet, but to avoid getting water all over the engine, it is best to use a leadaway hose. Fill the water jackets with water, and then apply air. Repeat as for the radiator until the water runs clear from the leadaway hose.

To straight-flush the water jackets, follow the above procedure, but attach the leadaway hose to the thermostat housing and the flushing-gun hose to the pump-inlet connection.

▶*CAUTION:* Do not apply too much air pressure or sudden bursts of pressure. This might damage engine seals, gaskets, or other parts.

5. Refilling system. When the cooling system has been cleaned, the thermostat replaced, and all hoses and clamps reconnected, the system should be refilled. Since the water that is put in will probably be cold, the thermostat may close and prevent quick fill-

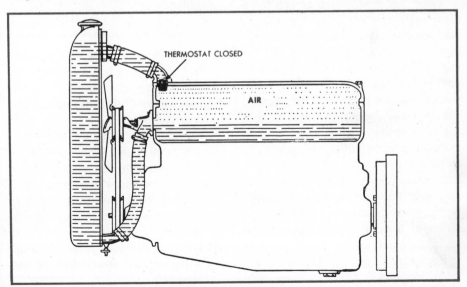

Fig. 18–9. Air trapped back of closed thermostat as engine cooling system is filled.

ing. With the thermostat closed, air is trapped below the thermostat in the engine water jackets (Fig. 18–9). The thermostat usually has a small hole or two that permits this air to leak out. But it takes a little time for the air to escape. This means that you may have to fill and refill the radiator several times, waiting each time for some of the trapped air to get out. Then, as a final step, the engine should be started and run long enough for the thermostat to heat up and open. After this happens, more water can be added to make sure the system is filled.

§ 405. Locating and repairing radiator leaks

Leaks in the radiator core are usually obvious, since telltale scale marks or watermarks will form on the outside of the core below the leaks. An accurate way to locate radiator leaks is to remove the core from the car, drain out all the water, close the openings at top and bottom, and immerse the core in water. Air bubbles will escape from the core through any leaks. Small leaks may sometimes be repaired without removing the radiator from the car, by use of certain liquid compounds poured into the radiator. These compounds, seeping through the leaks, harden upon coming in contact with the air, sealing off the openings. A more effective way of repairing leaks is to solder them. If there are several leaks at various places in the core, it may not be worthwhile to attempt repair, since the core is probably corroded to a point where other leaks would soon develop.

Removing a radiator core is a relatively simple job although there is a considerable amount of work involved. The procedure varies somewhat from car to car but, in general, is as follows: first, drain the engine and radiator by opening the drain cocks in the radiator and engine block. Then detach the upper and lower radiator hoses. Remove any support bolts, horns, wiring harness, and so forth, that might interfere with core removal. With these parts out of the way and the core loose, lift it straight up and off the car.

§ 406. Water-pump service

The water pump is a relatively simple mechanism that requires little service in normal operation. Some pumps require periodic lubrication. Others, with sealed ball bearings, require no lubrication. If the pump develops noise or leaks or becomes otherwise defective, it must be removed for repair. Refer to the applicable manufacturer's shop manual for details of the servicing procedure.

REVIEW QUESTIONS

1. Describe how to test a thermostat.
2. Explain how to test a cooling system for rust or scale.
3. Explain how to test a radiator for restrictions.
4. Explain how to test a cooling system for air being sucked into it.
5. Explain how to test a cooling system for exhaust-gas leakage.
6. Explain how a fan belt is adjusted.
7. Explain how to test the strength of antifreeze solutions.
8. What could cause slow warm-up of the engine? Overheating of the engine?

9. What is afterboil?
10. Explain how to clean the cooling system.

STUDY QUESTIONS

1. Make a list of various cooling-system tests. How is each made?

2. Write an essay describing in detail how to clean a cooling system by reverse-flushing it.
3. Refer to a manufacturer's shop manual, and write a step-by-step story on overhauling a water pump.

GETTING ALONG IN THE SHOP

Whether you are going to school or working in an automotive repair shop or garage, you should always conduct yourself properly. Remember, the teacher, shop foreman, or manager is watching you, grading you, evaluating your ability, judging you as a person and as a fellow worker. There are many things you can do to get a high rating. It is also true that thoughtless or careless actions can reduce your rating severely.

For instance, there is nothing so annoying to other workers or students, or to the instructor or boss, as the fellow who is given to horseplay or is always creating some disturbance. This fellow is not only wasting everyone's time, but is also a menace. He is dangerous. Practical jokes and foolish actions can distract another person's attention and cause him to get seriously hurt. He might be distracted from his job at a critical moment and get his hand caught in a running machine. He might trip and fall.

Thoughtlessness or carelessness are also menaces in the shop. Here are some "don'ts" to remember:

Don't scatter tools and equipment on the floor or in aisles where someone could trip on them.

Don't let jack handles or creepers stick out in aisles.

Don't put sharp objects or tools in your pockets. For example, a screw driver, bit end out, in a back pocket can snag your wrist or forearm severely.

Don't wear the wrong clothes. For example, a dangling tie or loose sleeves can get tangled with rotating machinery with terrible results.

Don't let your hands or tools become too dirty or covered with grease. This makes the tools hard to handle and hang on to.

Don't point the compressed air hose at yourself or others. It can blow dust particles at such high speed that they might penetrate the skin, or worse, might get into your eyes.

Don't attempt to do a grinding or machining job without wearing the goggles provided.

Paying attention to such details marks the good student and worker. Failure to heed these details marks the poor student and worker—the person who is apt to fail the course or get fired from the job.

THIS CHAPTER DISCUSSES THE purpose, construction, and operation of automotive clutches. The clutch is located in the power train (§ 45) between the engine and the transmission as shown in Fig. 2–17.

§ 407. Purpose of clutch   The clutch shown in Fig. 19–1 is of the type used with standard transmissions (not automatic). Its purpose is to permit the driver to couple or uncouple the engine and transmission. When the clutch is in the coupling (or normal running) position, power flows through it from the engine to the transmission. If the transmission is in gear (see § 425), then power flows on through to the car wheels so that the car moves. Essentially, then, the clutch has the job of permitting the driver to uncouple the engine temporarily so that the gears can be shifted from one to another forward gear position (or into reverse or neutral). It is necessary to interrupt the flow of power (by uncoupling) before gears are shifted. Otherwise, gear shifting would be extremely difficult if not impossible.

The clutch (Fig. 19–1) contains a friction disk (or driven plate) about a foot in diameter. It also contains a spring arrangement and a pressure plate for pressing this disk tightly against the smooth rear face of the flywheel. The friction disk is splined to

the clutch shaft. The splines consist of two sets of teeth, an internal set on the hub of the friction disk, and a matching external set on the clutch shaft. They permit the friction disk to slide back and forth along the shaft but force the disk and the shaft to rotate together. External splines can be seen on the shaft in Fig. 19–1. Figure 27–10 shows both external splines (No. 8) and internal splines (No. 17).

The flywheel, which is attached to the end of the engine crankshaft, rotates when the engine is running. When the clutch is engaged (that is, in the coupling position), the friction disk is held tightly against the flywheel (by the clutch springs) so that it must rotate with the flywheel. This rotary motion is carried through the friction disk and clutch shaft to the transmission.

To disengage (or uncouple) the clutch, the clutch pedal is pushed down by the foot. This causes the clutch fork to pivot so that the clutch throwout bearing is forced inward. As the throwout bearing moves inward, it operates release levers. The release levers take up the spring pressure and lift the pressure plate away from the friction disk. The friction disk is no longer pressed against the flywheel face, and the engine can run independently of the power train. Releasing the clutch pedal permits the clutch fork to release the

throwout bearing so that the springs once again cause the pressure plate to force the friction disk against the flywheel face. The two again revolve together.

§ 408. Types of clutch All automotive clutches used with standard transmissions are very similar in construction and operation. There are some differences in the details of the linkages as well as in the pressure-plate assembly. Figures 19–2 and 19–3 are cutaway and disassembled views of a clutch and linkage. Three types of clutch are described in following sections. These are the coil pressure-spring type, the diaphragm-spring type, and the crown pressure-spring type.

§ 409. Coil pressure-spring clutch The clutches of this type may contain three to nine coil springs. The purpose of the coil springs is to spring-load the friction disk between the pressure plate and the engine flywheel in the coupling (or clutch-engaged) position. In this position, the friction between the flywheel and the friction disk, and between the pressure plate and the friction disk, causes the friction disk to rotate with the flywheel and pressure plate. The hub of the friction disk is splined to the clutch shaft. The

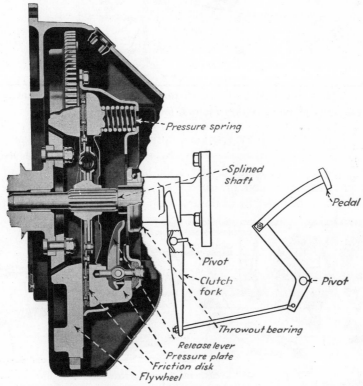

Fig. 19–1. Sectional view of a clutch, with linkage to clutch pedal shown schematically. (*Plymouth Division of Chrysler Corporation*)

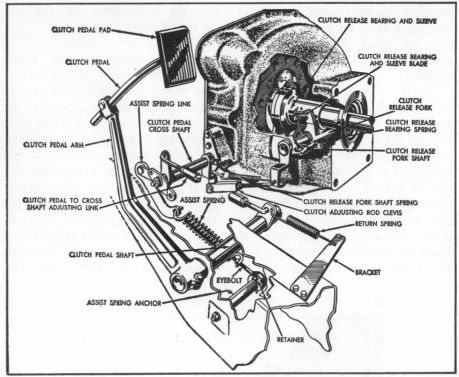

Fig. 19–2. Clutch and linkage to clutch pedal. Housing partly cut away so that clutch parts may be seen. (*Willys Motors, Inc.*)

shaft must thus rotate with the friction disk.

Figure 19–4 is a disassembled view of a clutch using nine coil pressure springs. You can see how one of these springs is positioned in the assembly by referring to Fig. 19–1. Note that the housing cover is bolted to the flywheel. The cover, pressure plate, springs, and other clutch parts rotate

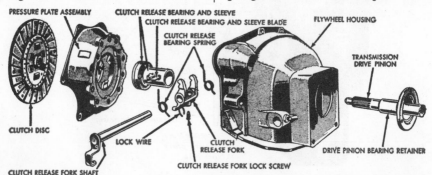

Fig. 19–3. Exploded view of clutch, showing relationship of clutch parts. (*Willys Motors, Inc.*)

with the flywheel. In the coupling position, as shown, the spring is forcing the pressure plate to clamp the friction disk between the plate and the flywheel.

To uncouple the transmission from the engine, the clutch pressure plate must be moved away from the friction disk. When this happens, the pressure on the friction disk is relieved and it no longer has to revolve with the flywheel and pressure plate.

The driver pushes down on the clutch pedal to produce this effect. As he does so, the linkage from the pedal to the clutch causes movement of a clutch fork, or yoke. A simple linkage to a clutch fork is shown schematically in Fig. 19–1. The fork is pivoted so that, as the outer end is pulled back by the linkage, the inner end moves forward, toward the clutch. This action causes a throwout bearing to move inward. Figure 19–5 shows a clutch-fork assembly with its throwout bearing. As the bearing is forced inward, it moves against the inner ends of three release levers which are evenly spaced around the clutch. You can see one of the release levers in the clutch shown in Fig. 19–1. As the throwout bearing moves in against the release levers, it causes the release levers to pivot on their supporting pins. This, in turn, causes the outer ends of the release levers to move away from the friction disk. This movement forces the pressure plate away from the friction disk so that the clutch is uncoupled. Figure 19–6 shows the engaged and released positions of the clutch. Note that the outer end of the release lever exerts its actuating force on the pressure plate through a strut.

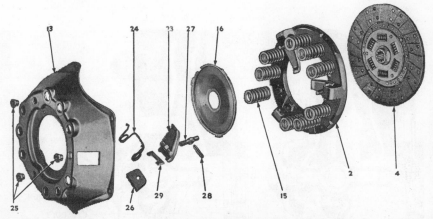

Fig. 19–4. Exploded view of clutch illustrated in Fig. 19–1. The flywheel is not shown. (*Plymouth Division of Chrysler Corporation*)

2. Pressure plate
4. Disk assembly
13. Cover
15. Pressure spring
16. Pressure-plate baffle
23. Release lever
24. Release-lever spring
25. Release-lever eyebolt nuts
26. Pressure-plate driving-lug grease pad
27. Release-lever eyebolt
28. Release-lever pin
29. Release-lever strut

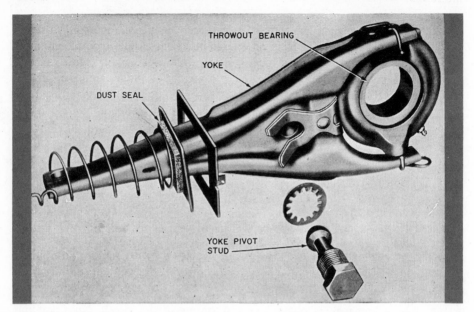

Fig. 19–5. Clutch-fork assembly with throwout bearing. (*Oldsmobile Division ot General Motors Corporation*)

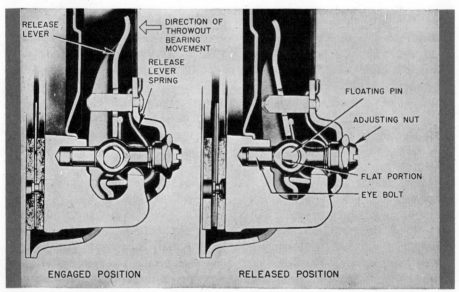

Fig. 19–6. The two limiting positions of the pressure plate and release lever. (*Oldsmobile Division of General Motors Corporation*)

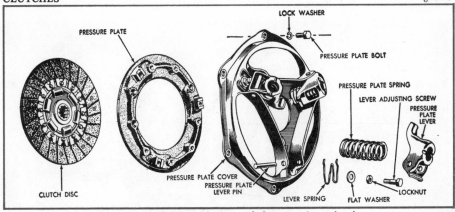

Fig. 19–7. Exploded view of three-spring clutch.

Figure 19–7 is a disassembled view of a three-spring clutch. This clutch operates in the same way as the nine-spring clutch described in the previous paragraphs.

§ **410. Friction disk**   The friction disk (Fig. 19–8) consists of a hub and plate assembly to which is attached a series of facings. The disk usually includes a cushioning device as well as a dampen-

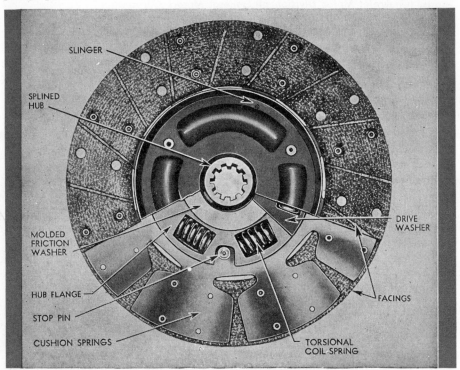

Fig. 19–8. Typical friction disk, or driven plate. (*Buick Motor Division of General Motors Corporation*)

431

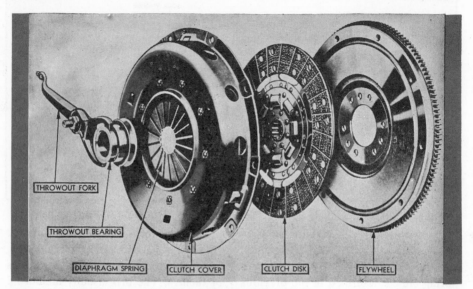

Fig. 19–9. Diaphragm-spring clutch in disassembled view showing relationship of parts. (*Chevrolet Motor Division of General Motors Corporation*)

ing device. The cushioning device provides a cushioning effect as the clutch is engaged so that smoother engagement results. In Fig. 19–8, the cushioning device consists of waved cushion springs to which the friction facings are attached. The waves compress slightly as the clutch engages to provide the cushioning effect. The dampening device uses a series of heavy coil springs placed between the drive washers, riveted to the cushion

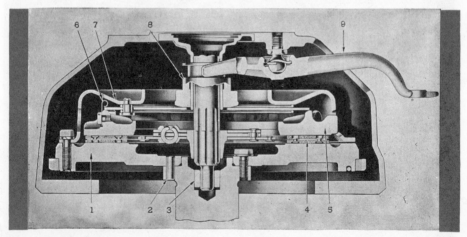

Fig. 19–10. Diaphragm-spring clutch in sectional view (from top): 1, flywheel; 2, dowel; 3, bushing; 4, driven disk; 5, pressure plate; 6, spring; 7, cover; 8, throwout bearing; 9, fork. (*Chevrolet Motor Division of General Motors Corporation*)

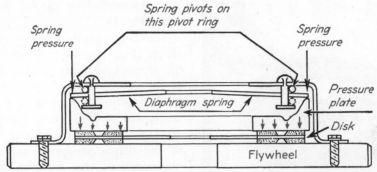

Fig. 19–11. Diaphragm-spring clutch in engaged position. (*Chevrolet Motor Division of General Motors Corporation*)

springs, and the hub flange. The disk hub is thus driven through the springs, and they absorb a certain amount of torsional vibration. Stop pins limit the relative motion between the hub flange and the drive washers. A molded friction ring, compressed between the hub flange and the drive washers, provides frictional dampening that prevents oscillation between the hub flange and the drive washers.

§ 411. Diaphragm-spring clutch One type of clutch incorporates a diaphragm spring that not only provides the spring pressure required to hold the friction disk against the flywheel but also acts as the release levers that take up the spring pressure when the clutch is disengaged. Two variations of this design are in general use, the tapering-finger type (Figs. 19–9 and 19–10) and the crown-pressure-spring type (Fig. 19–13). Although somewhat different in construction, both are alike in action.

The tapering-finger-type unit has a one-piece diaphragm that is a solid ring on the outer diameter, with a series of tapering fingers pointing inward toward the clutch. The action of the clutch diaphragm is somewhat like the flexing action that takes place when the bottom of an oilcan is depressed. When the throwout bearing moves in against the ends of the fingers, the

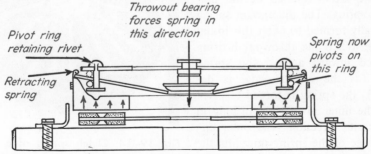

Fig. 19–12. Diaphragm-spring clutch in disengaged position. (*Chevrolet Motor Division of General Motors Corporation*)

433

Fig. 19–13. Pressure-plate assembly of a crown pressure-spring clutch. The operator is shown removing a retaining spring so that the diaphragm and cover can be separated (see Fig. 19–14). (*Buick Motor Division of General Motors Corporation*)

entire diaphragm is forced against a pivot ring, causing the diaphragm to dish inward. This raises the pressure plate from the friction disk.

Figures 19–11 and 19–12 illustrate the two positions of the diaphragm spring and clutch parts. In the engaged position (Fig. 19–11), the diaphragm spring is slightly dished, with the tapering fingers pointing slightly away from the flywheel. This places spring pressure against the pressure plate around the entire circumference of the diaphragm spring. The diaphragm spring is naturally formed to exert this initial pressure. When the throwout bearing is moved inward against the spring fingers (as the clutch pedal is depressed), the spring is forced to pivot round the inner pivot ring, dishing in the opposite direction. The outer circumference of the spring now lifts the pressure plate away, through a series of retracting springs placed about the

outer circumference of the pressure plate (Fig. 19–12).

The crown-pressure-spring type of clutch (Fig. 19–13) is a variation of the diaphragm-spring clutch. In the crown-pressure-spring type, the diaphragm spring is formed of a single corrugated plate of spring metal (Fig. 19–14). The action is similar to that of the diaphragm-spring clutch; the movement of the throwout bearing against the central section of the diaphragm causes it to flex so that the outer circumference lifts the pressure plate away from the friction disk and the flywheel, thus relieving the pressure and disengaging the clutch.

§ 412. Semicentrifugal clutch   In construction, the semicentrifugal clutch is much like the type of clutch shown in Fig. 19–1. The semicentrifugal-clutch release levers, however, have weights placed at their outer ends. The weights are so related to the release levers that, as speed increases, centrifugal force on the weights causes the release levers to exert added pressure

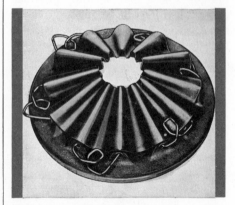

Fig. 19–14. Clutch spring of a crown-pressure-spring clutch. (*Buick Motor Division of General Motors Corporation*)

Fig. 19–15. Semicentrifugal clutch partly disassembled. (*Cadillac Motor Car Division of General Motors Corporation*)

on the pressure plate. Figure 19–15 illustrates a clutch of this type partly disassembled. Figure 19–16 shows in disassembled view one of the release levers from this type of clutch. When the clutch is not rotating and is engaged, the only pressure on the pressure plate is produced by the springs. However, as soon as the clutch begins to revolve, centrifugal action on the release-lever weights causes the release levers to increase the pressure on the pressure plate. The higher the speed, the greater the pressure.

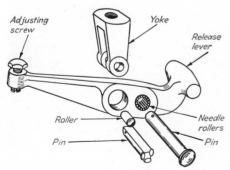

Fig. 19–16. Assembly details of semicentrifugal-clutch release lever. (*Monmouth Products Company*)

REVIEW QUESTIONS

1. What is the purpose of the clutch?
2. Is the clutch placed between the transmission and the engine, or is the transmission between the clutch and the engine?
3. On what factors does the type of clutch used depend?
4. What is the purpose of the pressure plate in the clutch?
5. What is the purpose of the friction disk in the clutch?
6. In what way is the friction disk connected to the clutch shaft?
7. What is the purpose of the clutch release levers?
8. What causes the clutch throwout bearing to move along the clutch shaft?

435

9. Describe the cushioning device used on some friction disks. The dampening device.
10. Describe the operation of the diaphragm spring in the clutch using this type of spring.
11. How does the semicentrifugal clutch differ from other clutches?
12. What holds pressure plate, friction disk, and flywheel facing together when clutch is engaged?

STUDY QUESTIONS

1. Make a sketch of a clutch, and name essential parts.
2. Write a sequence story of the actions that take place when the clutch pedal is depressed.
3. What do you suppose would be damaged in the clutch if a driver habitually "rode the clutch," or kept his foot continually on the clutch pedal?

THIS CHAPTER DESCRIBES THE trouble-shooting, removal, overhaul, adjustment, reassembly, and installation of various types of clutches used on passenger cars.

§ 413. Clutch trouble-shooting Several types of clutch trouble may be experienced. Usually, the trouble itself is fairly obvious and falls into one of the following categories: slipping, chattering or grabbing when engaging, spinning or dragging when disengaged, clutch noises, clutch-pedal pulsations, and rapid friction-disk-facing wear. Following sections discuss each of these troubles in detail and explain how to find their causes.

§ 414. Clutch slips while engaged Slipping of the clutch while it is engaged is extremely hard on the clutch facings. The facings wear and burn badly so that a slipping clutch may soon become completely inoperative.

Clutch slippage is particularly noticeable during acceleration, especially from a standing start or in low gear. A rough test for clutch slippage can be made by starting the engine, setting the hand brake, shifting into high gear, and then slowly releasing the clutch pedal while accelerating the engine slowly. If the clutch is in good condition, it should hold so that the engine stalls immediately as clutch engagement is completed.

Several conditions can cause clutch slippage. The clutch linkage may not be properly adjusted. With an incorrect adjustment that reduces pedal lash too much, the throwout bearing will still press against the release levers even with a fully released clutch pedal. This takes up part of the spring pressure; the pressure plate will not exert sufficient pressure to hold the friction disk tightly enough against the flywheel. As a result, there is slippage between the surfaces. The correction here is to readjust the linkage (§ 421).

If the clutch-release linkage binds, it may not return to the fully engaged position when the clutch pedal is released. This, of course, causes clutch slippage. Binding can be eliminated by lubricating all points of friction in the linkage and realigning and readjusting the linkage if necessary (§ 421). If readjustment, lubricating, and freeing of the linkage does not eliminate the slippage, then the trouble is probably inside the clutch itself and this requires removal of the clutch from the car so that it can be disassembled for service. Conditions in the clutch itself that could cause slippage include the following:

Weak or broken pressure springs (or diaphragm spring) will not exert suffi-

437

cient pressure; new springs should be installed. Worn friction-disk facings or grease or oil on the disk facings will permit slippage; the facings or the complete disk should be replaced if this is the case (§ 424).

Incorrectly adjusted release levers (adjustable type) may act in the same manner as an incorrectly adjusted clutch linkage or a binding clutch-release linkage. That is, they may prevent full spring pressure on the pressure plate with a resulting clutch slippage. Release levers must be adjusted as explained in the applicable manufacturer's shop manual.

§ **415. Clutch chatters or grabs when engaging** As a rule, this trouble is inside the clutch itself, and the clutch will have to be taken off the car for servicing. Before this is done, however, the clutch linkage should be carefully checked to make sure it is not binding; if it binds, it may release suddenly to throw the clutch into quick engagement, with a resulting heavy jerk.

In the clutch, the trouble could be due to oil or grease on the disk facings or to glazed or loose facings. Also, binding of the friction-disk hub on the clutch shaft could prevent smooth engagement of the clutch; this condition requires cleaning up of the splines in the hub and on the shaft and lubrication of the splines. Broken parts in the clutch, such as broken disk facings, broken cushion or coil springs in the friction disk, or a broken pressure plate could cause poor clutching action and grabbing.

§ **416. Clutch spins or drags when disengaged** The clutch friction disk

spins briefly after disengagement when the transmission is in neutral. It takes a moment for the friction disk to come to rest. This normal spinning should not be confused with a dragging clutch. When the clutch drags, the friction disk is not being fully released from the flywheel or pressure plate as the clutch pedal is depressed; the friction disk continues to rotate with or to rub against the flywheel or pressure plate.

The first thing to check with this condition is the pedal-linkage adjustment. If there is excessive pedal lash or "free" travel, even full movement of the pedal to the floor board will not force the throwout bearing in against the release levers (or diaphragm spring) far enough to release the clutch fully. If adjustment of the linkage to reduce pedal lash or free travel does not correct the trouble (see § 421), the trouble is in the clutch and the clutch must be removed for disassembly and service.

In the clutch, the trouble could be due to a warped friction disk or pressure plate or a loose friction-disk facing. On the type of clutch with adjustable release levers, improper adjustment would prevent full disengagement so that the clutch would drag. The friction-disk hub may bind on the clutch shaft so that it does not move back and forth freely. The result is that the friction disk rubs against the flywheel when the clutch is released. Binding may be relieved by cleaning up the splines on the shaft and in the hub and lubricating the splines.

§ **417. Clutch noises** Clutch noises are usually most noticeable when the engine is idling. To diagnose clutch

noise, first note whether it is heard when the clutch is engaged or when the clutch is disengaged.

Noises that come from the clutch when the clutch is engaged could be due to a friction-disk hub that is loose on the clutch shaft. This would require replacement of the disk or clutch shaft, or perhaps both if both are excessively worn. Friction-disk dampener springs that are broken or weak will cause noise, and this requires replacement of the complete disk. Misalignment of the engine and transmission will cause a backward-and-forward movement of the friction disk on the clutch shaft; alignment must be corrected.

Noises that come from the clutch when the clutch is disengaged could be due to a defective clutch throwout bearing that is worn, is binding, or has lost its lubricant. Such a bearing squeals when the clutch pedal is depressed and the bearing comes into operation. The bearing should be re-lubricated or replaced. If the release levers are not properly adjusted, they will rub against the friction-disk hub when the clutch pedal is depressed. The release levers should be readjust-ed. If the pilot bearing in the crank-shaft is worn or lacks lubricant, it will produce a high-pitched whine when the transmission is in gear, the clutch is disengaged, and the car is station-ary. Under these conditions, the clutch shaft, which is piloted in the bearing in the crankshaft, is stationary, but the crankshaft and bearing are turning. The bearing should be lubricated or replaced.

In the diaphragm-spring clutch, worn or weak retracting springs will cause a rattling noise when the clutch is dis-engaged and the engine is idling. This noise can be eliminated by replacing the springs, a job that can be done without removing the clutch from the engine.

§ 418. **Clutch-pedal pulsation** Clutch-pedal pulsation, sometimes called a nervous pedal, is noticeable when a slight pressure is applied to the clutch pedal with the engine running. The pulsations can be felt by the foot as a series of slight pedal movements. As the pedal pressure is increased, the pulsations cease. This condition is often an indication of trouble that must be corrected before serious damage to the clutch results. One possible cause of the condition is misalignment of the engine and transmission. If the two are not in line, the friction disk or other clutch parts will move back and forth with every revolution. The result is rapid wear of clutch parts. Correction is to detach the transmis-sion, remove the clutch, and then check the housing alignment with the engine and crankshaft. At the same time, the flywheel can be checked for wobble since a bent crankshaft flange, or a flywheel that is not seated on the crankshaft flange, will also produce clutch-pedal pulsations. A flywheel that is not seated on the crankshaft flange should be removed and re-mounted to make sure it does seat evenly. If the flange itself is bent, then a new flange, or crankshaft, is re-quired.

If the clutch housing is distorted or shifted so that alignment between the engine and transmission has been lost, it is sometimes possible to restore alignment by installing shims between

439

the housing and engine block and between the housing and transmission case. Otherwise, a new clutch housing will be required.

Other causes of clutch-pedal pulsations include uneven release-lever adjustments (so that release levers do not meet the throwout bearing and pressure plate together) and a warped friction disk or pressure plate. Release levers (adjustable type) should be readjusted. A warped friction disk usually must be replaced. If the pressure plate is out of line because of a distorted clutch cover, then the cover sometimes can be straightened to restore alignment.

§ 419. Rapid friction-disk-facing wear

Rapid wear of the friction-disk facings will be caused by any condition that permits slippage between the facings and the flywheel or pressure plate. Thus, if the driver has the habit of "riding" the clutch (that is, if he keeps his foot resting on the clutch) part of the pressure-plate spring pressure will be taken up so that slipping may take place. Likewise, frequent use of the clutch or excessively slow releasing of the clutch after declutching will increase clutch-facing wear. The remedy here is for the driver to use the clutch properly and only when necessary.

Several conditions in the clutch itself may cause this trouble. For example, weak or broken pressure springs will cause slippage and facing wear. In this case, the springs must be replaced. If the pressure plate or friction disk are warped or out of line, they must be replaced or realignment must be reestablished. In addition to these conditions in the clutch, improper pedal-linkage adjustment or binding of the linkage may prevent full spring pressure from being applied to the friction disk. With less than full spring pressure, slippage and wear are apt to take place. The linkage must be readjusted and lubricated at all points of friction.

§ 420. Clutch pedal stiff

A stiff clutch pedal, or a pedal that is hard to depress, is likely to result from lack of lubricant in the clutch linkage, from binding of the clutch-pedal shaft in the floor-board seal, or from misaligned linkage parts that are binding. In addition, the overcenter spring (on cars so equipped) may be out of adjustment. Also, if the clutch pedal has been bent so that it rubs on the floor board, it may not operate easily. The remedy in each of these cases is obvious: parts must be realigned, lubricated, or readjusted as necessary.

§ 421. Clutch-pedal adjustment

Clutch-pedal-linkage adjustment may be required from time to time to compensate for friction-disk-facing wear. Also, the linkage requires periodic lubrication. The adjustment must provide the proper amount of free clutch pedal travel (also called pedal *lash*). The free travel is the pedal movement before the throwout bearing comes up against the clutch release levers. After this occurs, there is a definite increase in the amount of pressure required to actuate the release levers and disengage the clutch. If the pedal lash is too great, the clutch may not release fully and this could cause clutch spinning during disengagement (§ 416). If the pedal lash is too small, the clutch may

not be able to engage fully (§ 414) and this could cause rapid friction-disk-facing wear. Methods of making the adjustment vary in different cars. Refer to the manufacturer's shop manual for details and specifications.

§ 422. Clutch removal and replacement

Variations in construction and design require that different removal and replacement procedures be used on different cars. First, the transmission must be removed (§ 439). Then, the clutch-housing pan or flywheel lower cover must be removed and the clutch linkage detached. Finally, the clutch can be detached from the flywheel and removed. Refer to the manufacturer's shop manual for details.

§ 423. Clutch overhaul

No general instructions that would apply to all types of clutches can be given. Whenever a clutch is to be disassembled, serviced, reassembled, and adjusted, refer to the shop manual describing these procedures.

§ 424. Inspecting and servicing clutch parts

The various clutch parts can be checked as follows when they are removed from the clutch:

1. Clutch pressure springs. If the pressure springs have overheated, the paint will burn off or the springs will turn blue. Overheated springs should be replaced since they may have lost tension and will not operate satisfactorily. Spring pressure can be tested with a spring-tension tester.

2. Pressure plate. A warped or badly scored pressure plate should be replaced. Slight scores or scratches can be cleaned off with fine emery cloth. All traces of emery should be removed.

3. Friction disk. The friction disk should be carefully inspected to make sure it is in good condition. Several points should be considered.

▶*CAUTION:* Do not get any trace of oil or grease on the friction-disk facings. Even small traces may cause clutch grabbing or slipping.

a. Facings. If the facings are worn down nearly to the heads of the rivets, then the facings or friction disk should be replaced. Many manufacturers recommend replacement of the complete disk; some supply facing-replacement data along with strong cautions to be extremely careful if installation of new facings on the disk is attempted.

b. Cushion springs. If the cushion springs under the facings appear to be cracked or weak, the friction disk should be replaced.

c. Torsional springs. Torsional springs that are loose and seem to have lost tension require replacement of the complete friction disk.

d. Hub splines. The fit of the hub to the clutch shaft should be tested. It should slide on without difficulty and should not have any noticeable rotary play. Excessive play means worn splines, and either (or both) the shaft and disk should be replaced.

4. Throwout bearing. The throwout, or release, bearing should never be cleaned in any cleaning solvent or degreasing compound since this would remove the lubricant that is placed in the bearing on original assembly and thereby ruin the bearing. If the bearing

Fig. 20–1. Using a special alignment arbor and dial indicator to check the alignment of the clutch housing to the engine. (*Plymouth Division of Chrysler Corporation*)

runs roughly or seems loose or noisy, it should be replaced.

5. *Housing alignment.* Normally, there need be no concern about the clutch-housing alignment since it was correct on original assembly and alignment should not be lost even if the transmission has been removed and re-

Fig. 20–2. View from under the car, showing the use of a special tool to remove and replace the pilot bushing in the crankshaft. (*Chevrolet Motor Division of General Motors Corporation*)

placed. However, if clutch-pedal pulsations are noticed or if gear shifting is hard and gears jump out of mesh, then alignment should be checked. This requires a special alignment arbor and dial indicator as shown in Fig. 20–1.

6. *Pilot bearing in crankshaft.* The pilot bearing in the crankshaft is usually either a bushing or a ball bearing. The old bushing can be removed and a new one installed with a special tool (Fig. 20–2). A small amount of short-fiber grease should then be placed in the bushing. Do not put grease on the end of the clutch shaft.

REVIEW QUESTIONS

1. Name several causes of clutch slippage.
2. What could cause the clutch to grab or chatter while it was being engaged?
3. What could cause the clutch to spin or drag while disengaged?
4. Into what two groupings can clutch noises be divided?
5. When clutch noise is heard with the clutch engaged, what could be the possible causes of the noise?
6. If the clutch noise is heard with the clutch disengaged, what could be the possible causes?
7. What causes a "nervous" clutch pedal?
8. What could cause abnormally rapid friction-disk wear?
9. Give some general instructions for making the clutch-pedal adjustment.
10. Give some general instructions on inspecting and servicing clutch parts.

STUDY QUESTIONS

1. Make a list of clutch troubles with their causes.
2. Refer to a car shop manual, and make a list of the steps in removing a clutch from a car.
3. Write a sequence story of the disassembly procedure on a coil-pressure-spring type of clutch. On a diaphragm-spring type. On a crown-pressure-spring type.
4. Write a sequence story on the procedure for adjusting the release levers on one type of clutch.

THIS CHAPTER DISCUSSES THE purpose, construction, and operation of standard, manually shifted transmissions. Following chapters describe overdrives and the various types of automatic transmissions in use on late-model automobiles.

§ 425. **Purpose of transmissions** The transmission, or change gears, provides a means of varying the gear ratio between the engine and rear wheels. Thus the engine crankshaft may be made to turn four, eight, or twelve times for each wheel revolution (approximately). In addition, a reverse gear is provided that permits backing the car.

In automatic transmissions, the varying ratios between the engine crankshaft and the wheels are achieved by automatic means. That is, the driver does not need to shift gears, because the automatic controls in the automatic transmission supply the proper ratio to suit the driving conditions. Such trans-

missions make use of a fluid coupling or a torque converter, as well as mechanical, hydraulic, or electrical controls. All these are discussed in detail in later chapters.

§ 426. **Gears and torque** Before we consider the transmission further, we might take a closer look at gear action. The relative speed of rotation between two meshing gears (the gear ratio) is determined by the number of teeth in the gears. For instance, when two meshing gears have the same number of teeth, they will both turn at the same speed (Fig. 21–1). However, when one gear has more teeth than the other, the smaller gear will turn more rapidly than the larger one. Thus, a gear with 12 teeth will turn 2 times as fast as a gear with 24 teeth (Fig. 21–2). The gear ratio between the two gears is 2:1. If the 12-tooth gear were meshed with a 36-tooth gear, the 12-tooth gear would turn 3 times for every revolution of the larger gear. The gear ratio between these gears would be 3:1.

1. Torque. Not only does the gear ratio change with the relative number of teeth in the meshing gears, but the *torque* also changes. As you will recall from § 77, torque is twisting, or turning effort. When you loosen the lid on a jar, you apply a twisting force, or torque, to it (Fig. 4–4). Torque is measured in pound-feet (lb-ft).

Fig. 21–1. Two meshing gears with same number of teeth.

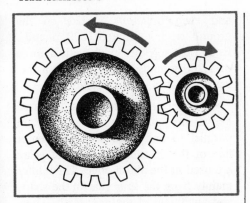

Fig. 21–2. Two meshing gears of different sizes. The smaller gear will turn more rapidly than the larger one.

Any shaft or gear that is being turned has torque applied to it. The engine pistons and connecting rods push on the cranks on the crankshaft, thereby applying torque to the crankshaft and causing it to turn. The crankshaft applies torque to the gears in the transmission so that the gears turn. This turning effort, or torque, is carried through the power train to the rear wheels so that they turn.

2. Torque in gears. Torque on shafts or gears is measured as a straight-line force at a distance from the center of the shaft or gear. For instance, suppose we want to measure the torque in the gears shown in Fig. 21–2. If we could hook a spring scale to the gear teeth and get a measurement of the pull, we could determine the torque. (Actually, a spring scale could not be used, although there are devices to measure torque of rotating parts.) Suppose, for example, we found that the tooth of the driving gear is pushing against the tooth of the driven gear with a 25-pound force (Fig. 21–3). This force, at a distance

of one foot (the radius, or distance from the center of the driving gear), means a torque of 25 lb-ft. That is, the smaller, driving gear is delivering a torque of 25 lb-ft.

The 25-pound push from the gear teeth of the smaller gear is applied to the gear teeth of the larger gear. But it is applied at a distance of 2 feet from the center. Therefore, the torque on the larger gear is 50 lb-ft (25 × 2). The same force is acting on the teeth of the larger gear, but it is acting at twice the distance from the shaft center.

3. Torque and gear ratio. Now, the important point of all this is that, if the smaller gear is driving the larger gear, the gear ratio will be 2:1. But the torque ratio will be 1:2. The larger gear will turn only half as fast as the smaller gear. But the larger gear will have *twice* the torque of the smaller gear. In gear systems, *speed reduction means torque increase.* For example, in the previous article we mentioned that, when the transmission

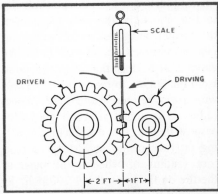

Fig. 21–3. The torque on a gear is the force on the gear teeth times the distance from the center of the shaft to the point on the tooth where the force is applied.

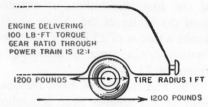

ENGINE DELIVERING
100 LB-FT TORQUE
GEAR RATIO THROUGH
POWER TRAIN IS 12:1

1200 POUNDS ←   TIRE RADIUS 1 FT

→ 1200 POUNDS

Fig. 21–4. How torque at the rear wheels is translated into a forward push on the car. The tire is turned with a torque of 1,200 lb-ft. Since, in the example shown, the tire radius is 1 foot, then the push of the tire on the ground will be 1,200 pounds. That is, a 1,200-pound force pushes the car forward.

is in low gear, there is a speed reduction (or gear reduction) of 12:1 from engine to wheels. That is, the crankshaft turns 12 times to turn the rear wheels once. This means that the torque *increases* 12 times (ignoring losses due to friction). In other words, if the engine produced a torque of 100 lb-ft, then 1,200 lb-ft torque would be applied to the rear wheels.

To see how this torque produces the forward thrust or push on the car, refer to Fig. 21–4. In the example shown, the torque being delivered by the engine is assumed to be 100 lb-ft. We assume also that the gear reduction from the engine to rear wheels is 12:1, with a torque increase of 1:12. Wheel radius is assumed to be 1 foot (for ease of figuring). With the torque acting on the ground at a distance of 1 foot (radius of wheel), the push of the tire on the ground is 1,200 pounds. Consequently, the push on the wheel axle, and thus the car, is 1,200 pounds.

NOTE: Actually, the torque is split between the two rear wheels. Thus, the torque on each rear wheel is 600 lb-ft,

and each tire thus pushes on the ground with a force of 600 pounds. Both tires together push with a force of 1,200 pounds, giving the car a forward thrust of 1,200 pounds.

4. Other gears. The gears discussed above are spur gears. The teeth are parallel to and align with the center line of the gear. Many types of gears are used in the automobile. They differ mainly from the spur gear in the shape and alignment of the gear teeth. Thus, helical gears are like spur gears except that the teeth have, in effect, been twisted at an angle to the gear center line. Bevel gears are shaped like cones with the tops cut off; the teeth point inward toward the apex of the cone. Bevel gears are used to transmit motion through angles. Some gears have their teeth pointing inward; these are internal gears. Several typical gears are shown in Fig. 21–5.

§ 427. Operation of transmission We shall use a simplified version of a standard transmission to discuss transmission operation (Fig. 21–6). In the drawing, it is represented by three shafts and eight gears of various sizes. Only the moving parts are shown. The transmission housing and bearings are not shown.

Four of the gears are rigidly connected to the countershaft (Fig. 21–6). These are the drive gear, second gear, low gear, and reverse gear. When the clutch is engaged and the engine is running, the clutch-shaft gear drives the countershaft drive gear. This turns the countershaft and the other gears on the countershaft. The countershaft rotates in a direction opposite, or counter, to the rotation of the clutch-

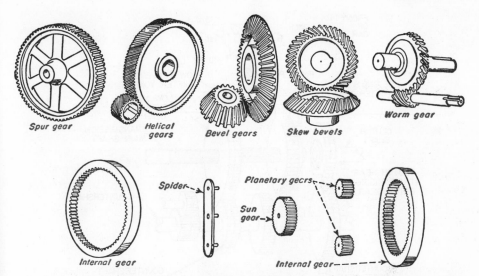

Spur gear

Helical gears

Bevel gears

Skew bevels

Worm gear

Internal gear

Spider

Sun gear

Planetary gears

Internal gear

Fig. 21–5. Various types of gears. The disassembled view of a planetary-gear system above shows the relationship of the spider, sun, two planetary, and internal gears. Planetary gears are used in overdrives and automatic transmissions. The "spider" is also called a planet-pinion cage.

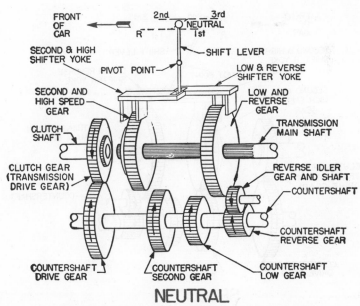

FRONT OF CAR

2nd   3rd   NEUTRAL

R   1st

SHIFT LEVER

SECOND & HIGH SHIFTER YOKE

PIVOT POINT

LOW & REVERSE SHIFTER YOKE

SECOND AND HIGH SPEED GEAR

LOW AND REVERSE GEAR

CLUTCH SHAFT

TRANSMISSION MAIN SHAFT

CLUTCH GEAR (TRANSMISSION DRIVE GEAR)

REVERSE IDLER GEAR AND SHAFT

COUNTERSHAFT

COUNTERSHAFT REVERSE GEAR

COUNTERSHAFT DRIVE GEAR

COUNTERSHAFT SECOND GEAR

COUNTERSHAFT LOW GEAR

NEUTRAL

Fig. 21–6. Transmission with gears in neutral.

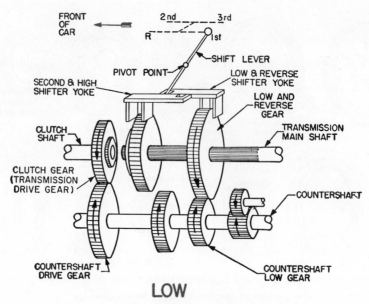

Fig. 21–7. Transmission with gears in low.

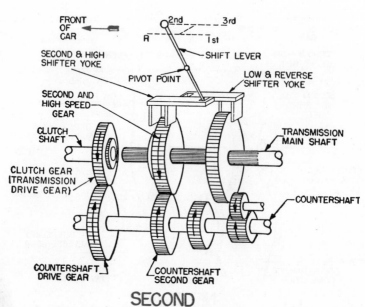

Fig. 21–8. Transmission with gears in second.

shaft gear. With the gears in neutral as shown in Fig. 21–6, and the car stationary, the transmission main shaft is not turning.

The transmission main shaft is mechanically connected by shafts and gears in the final drive to the car wheels. The two gears on the transmission main shaft may be shifted back and forth along the splines on the shaft by operation of the gearshift lever in the driving compartment. The splines are matching internal and external teeth that permit endwise (axial) movement of the gears but cause the gears and shaft to rotate together. Note, in the illustrations that follow, that a floor-board shift lever is shown. This type of lever is shown since it illustrates more clearly the lever action in shifting gears. The transmission action is the same, regardless of whether a floor-board type of shift lever or a steering-column lever is used.

1. Low gear. When the gearshift lever is operated to place the gears in low (Fig. 21–7), the large gear on the transmission main shaft is moved along the shaft until it meshes with the small gear on the countershaft. The clutch is disengaged for this operation, so that the clutch shaft and the countershaft stop rotating. When the clutch is again engaged, the transmission main shaft is caused to rotate as the driving gear on the clutch shaft drives it through the countershaft. Since the countershaft is turning more slowly than the clutch shaft, and since the small countershaft gear is engaged with the large transmission main-shaft gear, a gear reduction of approximately 3:1 is achieved. That is, the clutch shaft turns

3 times for each revolution of the transmission main shaft. Further gear reduction in the differential at the rear wheels produces a still higher gear ratio (approximately 12:1) between the engine crankshaft and the wheels.

2. Second gear. When the clutch is operated and the gearshift lever moved to *second* (Fig. 21–8), the large gear on the transmission main shaft de-meshes from the small countershaft gear. The smaller transmission main-shaft gear is slid into mesh with the large countershaft gear. This provides a somewhat reduced gear ratio, so that the engine crankshaft turns only about twice to the transmission main shaft's once. The differential gear reduction increases this gear ratio to approximately 8:1.

3. High gear. When the gears are shifted into *high* (Fig. 21–9), the two gears on the transmission main shaft are de-meshed from the countershaft gears and the smaller transmission-shaft gear is forced axially against the driving gear. Teeth on the ends of the two gears mesh so that the transmission main shaft turns with the clutch shaft, and a ratio of 1:1 is obtained. The differential reduction produces a gear ratio of about 4:1 between engine crankshaft and wheels.

4. Reverse gear. When the gears are placed in reverse (Fig. 21–10), the larger of the transmission-main-shaft gears is meshed with the reverse idler gear. This reverse idler gear is always in mesh with the small gear on the end of the countershaft. Interposing the idler gear between the countershaft gear and the transmission-main-shaft gear causes the transmission shaft to be rotated in the opposite direction or

449

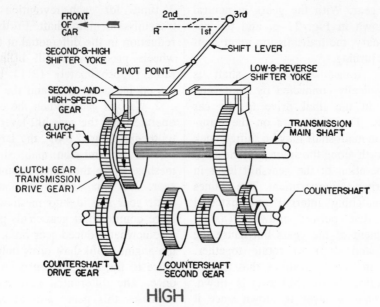

FRONT OF CAR

2nd — 3rd

R — 1st

SHIFT LEVER

SECOND-&-HIGH SHIFTER YOKE

PIVOT POINT

LOW-&-REVERSE SHIFTER YOKE

SECOND-AND-HIGH-SPEED GEAR

CLUTCH SHAFT

TRANSMISSION MAIN SHAFT

CLUTCH GEAR TRANSMISSION DRIVE GEAR)

COUNTERSHAFT

COUNTERSHAFT DRIVE GEAR

COUNTERSHAFT SECOND GEAR

HIGH

Fig. 21–9. Transmission with gears in high.

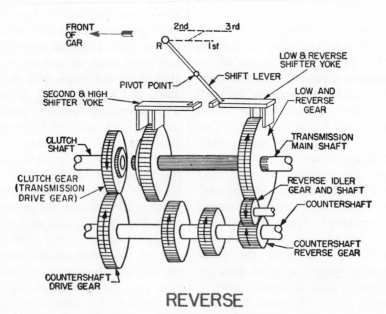

FRONT OF CAR

2nd — 3rd

R — 1st

SHIFT LEVER

LOW & REVERSE SHIFTER YOKE

PIVOT POINT

LOW AND REVERSE GEAR

SECOND & HIGH SHIFTER YOKE

CLUTCH SHAFT

TRANSMISSION MAIN SHAFT

CLUTCH GEAR (TRANSMISSION DRIVE GEAR)

REVERSE IDLER GEAR AND SHAFT

COUNTERSHAFT

COUNTERSHAFT REVERSE GEAR

COUNTERSHAFT DRIVE GEAR

REVERSE

Fig. 21–10. Transmission with gears in reverse.

in the same direction as the countershaft. This reverses the rotation of the wheels, so that the car backs.

While the above description outlines the basic principles of all transmissions, somewhat more complex transmissions are used on modern cars. These include helical or herringbone gears and gear shifting in conjunction with synchromesh devices that synchronize the rotation of gears that are about to be meshed. This eliminates clashing of gears and facilitates gear shifting.

§ **428. Operation of a typical transmission** Let us now discuss the operation of a typical automotive transmission (Figs. 21–11 and 21–12). Shifting is accomplished when either of the shifter levers (No. 28 or No. 29 in Fig. 21–11) is operated by movement of the gearshift lever on the steering column. Figure 21–12 shows how the shifter forks mount in the side cover of the transmission. When the levers are moved, they move the shifter forks. This, in turn, moves the gears. The four gear positions of a somewhat similar transmission are shown in Fig. 21–13, while Fig. 21–14 is a disassembled view of this transmission.

1. Gearshift-lever action. In any transmission, operation of the gearshift lever does two things: (1) it selects the gear assembly to be moved and (2) it moves the gear assembly in the proper direction so that the correct gears mesh. Linkages between the gearshift lever and the transmission are described in § 430.

2. Transmission in neutral. When the clutch is engaged and the engine is running, the clutch gear (No. 3 in Fig. 21–11) is turning and driving the countergear assembly (or cluster as it is also called). The countergear assembly is not visible in Fig. 21–11 although it can be seen in the similar transmission shown disassembled in Fig. 21–14. The second-speed gear on the countergear assembly is always in mesh with the second-speed gear on the main shaft (No. 10 in Fig. 21–11). The second-speed gear can turn freely on the main shaft since it is supported by a bearing. In neutral, when the clutch is engaged and the engine is running, the countergear assembly and the main-shaft second-speed gear are turning.

3. Shifting into first. When the shift to first is made, the operation of the gearshift lever produces two actions. First, the linkage to the first-and-reverse shifter lever (No. 29 in Fig. 21–11) is selected. Then, this lever is actuated to cause the first-and-reverse shifter fork (No. 31 in Fig. 21–11) to move to the left (Fig. 21–11), so that the first-and-reverse gear (No. 8) is also moved to the left (toward front of car). As it moves to the left, it is meshed with the counter low-speed drive gear. When the engine clutch is engaged, the clutch gear, driving through the counterdriven and low-speed drive gears, causes the first-and-reverse gear to rotate. This rotary motion passes through the synchronizing drum, or clutch sleeve (No. 7), to the main shaft. The clutch sleeve is held in position by the second-and-third-speed shifter fork (No. 23) so that it cannot move endwise on the main shaft. The first-and-reverse gear, sleeve, and main shaft rotate as a unit without relative motion between the three.

4. Shifting into reverse. Reverse is

451

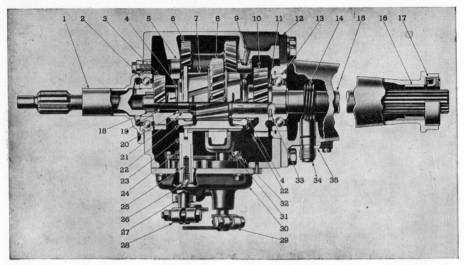

Fig. 21—11. Sectional view (*from top*) of transmission incorporating synchromesh, three forward, and one reverse speeds. (*Chevrolet Motor Division of General Motors Corporation*)

1. Clutch-gear-bearing retainer
2. Clutch gear bearing
3. Clutch gear
4. Energizing spring
5. Reverse idler shaft
6. Reverse idler gear
7. Second- and third-speed clutch sleeve
8. First-and-reverse sliding gear
9. Reverse idler shaft pin
10. Second-speed gear
11. Thrust washer
12. Case extension
13. Main-shaft rear bearing
14. Speedometer drive gear
15. Mainshaft
16. Bushing
17. Oil seal

18. Front pilot bearing rollers
19. Thrust washer
20. Thrust washer
21. Rear pilot bearing rollers
22. Synchronizer ring
23. Second-and-third shifter fork
24. Second-and-third shifter shaft
25. Detent spring
26. Detent ball
27. Oil seal
28. Second-and-third shifter lever
29. First-and-reverse shifter lever
30. Side cover
31. First-and-reverse shifter fork
32. Interlock retainer
33. Thrust-washer drive pin
34. Speedometer shaft fitting
35. Lock plate

attained by moving the first-and-re-verse gear to the right (Fig. 21–11) and into mesh with the reverse idler gear, causing the drive to be through this gear from the countershaft. This imposes an extra gear in the gear train, so that the main shaft is rotated in the. reverse direction.

5. The synchronizing device. A synchronizing device comes into operation when a shift is made to second and to high gear. This device syn-

Fig. 21–12. Side cover of transmission with shifter-lever forks in place. (*Chevrolet Motor Division of General Motors Corporation*)

chronizes gears that are approaching mesh so that the teeth which are about to mesh are moving at the same speed. Thus, the teeth mesh without clashing. The synchronizing device on the transmission under discussion is a simple cone clutch. Let us consider the second-gear synchronizer, which is practically identical to the high-gear synchronizer. The synchronizer drum, or clutch sleeve (No. 7 in Fig. 21–11), has a cone braking surface at its end. A synchronizing ring (No. 22) fits loosely into this section of the sleeve, held in position by a ring retainer. The outer face of the ring matches the inner cone face of the clutch sleeve, and the braking effect, which produces synchronization, takes

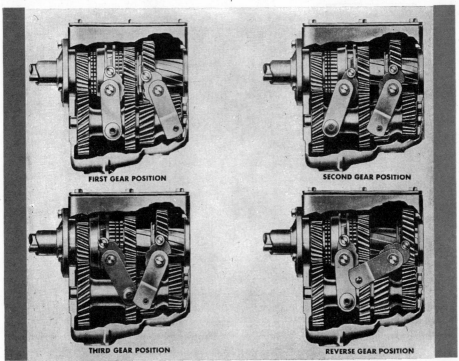

Fig. 21–13. Positions of the gears and yokes in the four gear positions. (*Willys Motors, Inc.*)

453

place between these two surfaces. Two cams on the inner face of the synchronizing ring fit into two grooves on the small gear section of the second-speed gear. This causes the synchronizing ring to turn with the second-speed gear.

6. *Shifting into second.* Let us shift into second and note the actions that take place. The selector selects the second-and-third shifter lever and fork (Nos. 28 and 23 in Fig. 12–11). The two fingers of the fork extend on both sides of the collar around the outside of the left end of the clutch sleeve (No. 7). Movement of the second-and-

third shifter fork to the right thus causes the complete clutch sleeve to move to the right. Meanwhile, the first-and-reverse gear on the outside of the sleeve is prevented from moving endwise by the first-and-reverse shifter fork. As the clutch sleeve moves to the right, it presses against the synchronizing ring so that the ring is also moved to the right. At this stage, the clutch sleeve and the second-speed gear may be turning at different speeds; synchronization has not yet taken place.

As the synchronizing ring is pushed to the right by the sleeve, the two cams on the inner face of the ring strike a

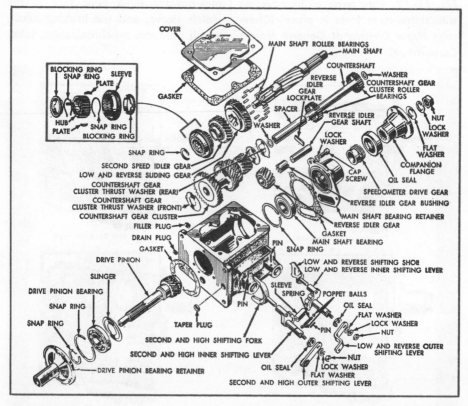

Fig. 21–14. Exploded view of the transmission shown in Fig. 21–13. (*Willys Motors, Inc.*)

small ring spring placed in an undercut back of the small gear section of the second-speed gear. This momentarily halts the endwise movement of the synchronizing ring, causing the outer face of the ring to press hard against the inner cone face of the clutch sleeve. During this interval, the car is in motion, and the main shaft and clutch sleeve are revolving, being driven, for the moment, by the car. Since the engine clutch has been released, the second-speed gear, countergear assembly, and clutch gear are revolving freely without being driven by the engine. However, as soon as pressure is exerted between the inner cone face of the sleeve and the outer face of the synchronizing ring, the friction between the two surfaces imposes a drag on the second-speed gear. The synchronizing ring, it will be remembered, is rotating with the second-speed gear. This frictional drag brings the sleeve and the second-speed gear into synchronism, so that both are turning at the same speed.

As the sleeve moves to the right, the two cams on the inner face of the synchronizing ring compress the small ring spring in the second-gear undercut. The cams ride over the spring, allowing the ring to move farther to the right and clear the small gear section of the second-speed gear. As this is happening, the clutch sleeve is also moving to the right and the teeth on its inner surface mesh with the small gear section of the second-speed gear. Meshing is thus completed without clash. When the engine clutch is engaged, the engine drives the main shaft through the clutch gear, countergear

assembly, and second-speed gear. The main shaft rotates at the same speed as the second-speed gear, being driven through the clutch sleeve.

7. *Shifting into high.* Essentially the same action takes place when the gears are shifted into high, or direct, gear. When this action takes place, the clutch sleeve is moved toward the front of the car (left in figure). Frictional drag between the inner cone face at the left end of the clutch sleeve and the left synchronizing ring brings the clutch gear into synchronism with the clutch sleeve. Further movement of the sleeve to the left causes the teeth on the inner face of the sleeve to mesh with the small gear section on the end of the clutch-gear shaft. The main shaft and the clutch-gear shaft must then turn together, so that there is a direct drive through the transmission.

8. *Other standard transmissions.* Figures 21–13 and 21–14 illustrate a transmission that is similar in many respects to the one covered in the preceding paragraphs. There are a number of differences, however, as will become evident if the various illustrations are compared. Note particularly that the countershaft-gear cluster (also called the *countergear assembly*) contains four gears instead of three as on the transmission previously described. The additional gear meshes with the reverse idler gear to drive it. On the other transmission (Fig. 21–11), the reverse-idler-gear assembly has two gears, one of which meshes with the counter low-speed drive gear. The other gear is the reverse idler gear, with which the first-and-reverse gear moves into mesh when the shift into

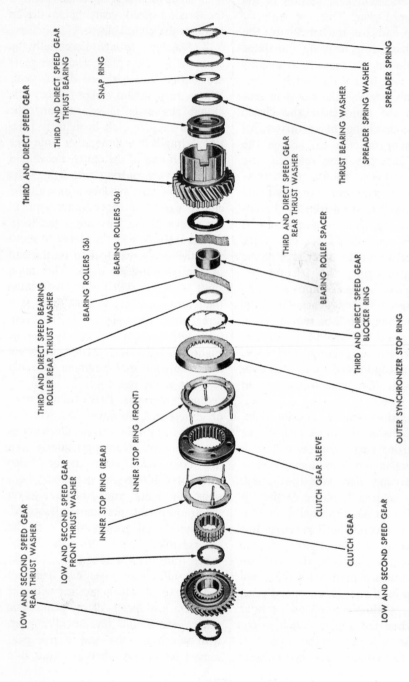

LOW AND SECOND SPEED GEAR REAR THRUST WASHER

LOW AND SECOND SPEED GEAR FRONT THRUST WASHER

INNER STOP RING (REAR)

INNER STOP RING (FRONT)

THIRD AND DIRECT SPEED BEARING ROLLER REAR THRUST WASHER

BEARING ROLLERS (36)

BEARING ROLLERS (36)

THIRD AND DIRECT SPEED GEAR

THIRD AND DIRECT SPEED GEAR THRUST BEARING

SNAP RING

SPREADER SPRING

SPREADER SPRING WASHER

THRUST BEARING WASHER

THIRD AND DIRECT SPEED GEAR REAR THRUST WASHER

BEARING ROLLER SPACER

THIRD AND DIRECT SPEED GEAR BLOCKER RING

OUTER SYNCHRONIZER STOP RING

CLUTCH GEAR SLEEVE

CLUTCH GEAR

LOW AND SECOND SPEED GEAR

Fig. 21–15. Disassembled view of a pin-type synchronizing device used to assure gear synchronization in shifting into second and third gears. (Dodge Division of Chrysler Corporation)

456

reverse is made. Also, note that the first-and-reverse gear on the transmission shown in Fig. 21–13 is mounted directly on the main shaft and not on the clutch sleeve. Other differences in construction can be noted.

9. *Other synchronizing devices.* The synchronizing device described above consists of a pair of cone clutches. Other synchronizing devices are also used. For example, the one shown in Fig. 21–15 makes use of a pair of stop rings, each having three pins which pin them to the clutch-gear sleeve. The clutch gear is splined to the main shaft; external teeth on the clutch gear mesh with internal teeth in the clutch-gear sleeve. Thus, the clutch gear, clutch-gear sleeve, and two stop rings are always rotating with the main shaft. When the shift is made into second, the main shaft and associated parts may be rotating at a different speed from the second-speed gear. However, as the clutch-gear sleeve is moved toward the second-speed gear, the rear inner stop ring moves against the face of the second-speed gear, bringing it into synchronous rotation with the clutch-gear sleeve. This permits alignment of the external teeth on the clutch gear and the teeth on the small diameter of the second-speed gear. Now, the clutch-gear sleeve can slip over the teeth of the second-speed gear to couple the second-speed gear and the clutch gear. Then, when the clutch is engaged and the engine again delivers power through it, the second-speed gear drives the main shaft through the clutch gear and the clutch-gear sleeve.

The action in shifting to high is very similar. The third-and-direct-speed gear is supported on roller bearings.

§ **429. Constant-mesh transmission** Some transmissions are of the constant-mesh type. On these, the mainshaft and countershaft gears are in constant mesh (Fig. 21–16). The mainshaft gears are mounted on bearings so that they may rotate independently of the main shaft. When the gears are shifted, external and internal teeth are meshed. Synchromesh devices come into use when gears are shifted into second and high.

When the gears are shifted into first, the first-and-reverse sliding gear to the right on the main shaft (Fig. 21–16) is moved to the left, so that its inner teeth mesh with the small gear section on the mainshaft first gear next to it. Shifting into second brings the synchromesh device into action. The second-and-high shifter fork moves the synchronizing drum to the right, causing the drum and the synchronizing ring surfaces to throw a frictional drag on the engine clutch shaft and countershaft so that synchronism takes place and the small gear section of the second-speed gear is meshed with the gear teeth on the inner face of the synchronizing drum. Shifting into high is accomplished by moving the synchronizing drum to the left.

§ **430. Selector and shifter** Two separate motions of the gearshift lever are required in shifting gears. The first motion selects the gear assembly to be shifted; the second motion moves the gear assembly in the proper direction. A number of different types of selec-

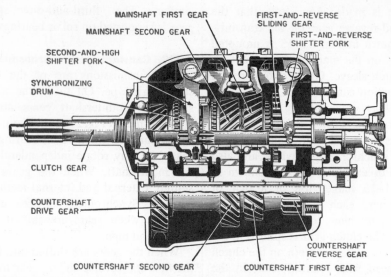

Fig. 21–16. Constant-meshing transmission with synchromesh on second- and high-speed gears. (*Studebaker-Packard Corporation*)

tor and shifter devices are in use. Practically all modern passenger cars have the gearshift lever mounted on the steering column. One type is shown in Figs. 21–17 and 21–18. Figure 21–17 is a top view of the steering column, with the shift lever and linkages shown. Figure 21–18 is a close-up view of the gear selector and shifter rods, with the transmission in neutral. The tongue is

Fig. 21–17. Steering-column gearshift mechanism and linkages. (*Studebaker-Packard Corporation*)

458

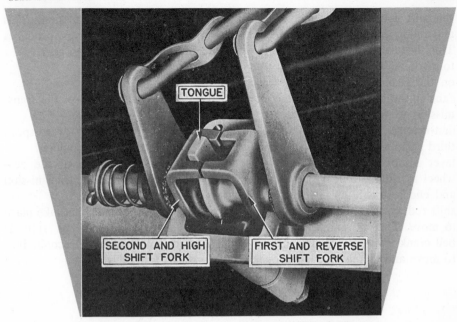

Fig. 21–18. Close-up of the actuating mechanism that is at the lower end of the steering column of the gearshift mechanism shown in Fig. 21–17. (*Studebaker-Packard Corporation*)

attached to the lower end of the shift-control shaft and is raised or lowered as the gearshift lever is lifted or released. This action places the tongue in either the first-and-reverse shift fork or in the second-and-high shift fork. After the fork has been selected, the gearshift lever is moved parallel to the steering wheel to complete the shift. This causes the tongue to rotate, producing a rotary motion of the fork that has been selected. The fork is linked to the transmission (Fig. 21–17), and the direction of rotation determines the direction in which the gear assembly is moved.

A similar type of linkage between the gearshift lever and the transmission is shown in Fig. 21–19. The shifter forks with which this linkage is con-

nected are shown in place in the side cover of the transmission in Fig. 21–12. When the gearshift lever is moved up or down to select either the first-reverse position or the second-third position, the tongue, or control-shaft lever, moves into either the upper or the lower shifter gate. If the gearshift lever is lifted, then the control lever moves into the upper gate. When the gearshift lever is moved parallel to the steering wheel to shift into either first or reverse, the outer lever on the upper side is rotated, causing the first-reverse control rod to move and thereby move the first-reverse shifter lever in the transmission side cover.

Another linkage system is shown in Fig. 21–20 in disassembled view. In this system, raising or lowering the

gearshift lever causes the rod lever and end assembly to move up or down. This, in turn, causes the selector lever to pivot. As it pivots, it pushes or pulls on the gearshift selector rod, thereby causing the selector lever in the transmission to turn and select either the first-reverse position or the second-third position. Now, when the gearshift lever is moved parallel to the steering wheel to shift into gear, the rod lever and end assembly turn with the gearshift rod, causing the front control rod to move. This movement, through the bell crank, causes the rear control rod to move and thereby move the operat-ing lever in the transmission. This operating lever, as it moves, produces the shifting of the selected gear.

REVIEW QUESTIONS

1. What is the purpose of the transmission?
2. What are the three forward-speed gear ratios usually provided?
3. What characteristics of the gasoline engine make the transmission necessary?
4. Explain the actions that take place in the transmission as shift is made into first. Into second. Into third. Into reverse.

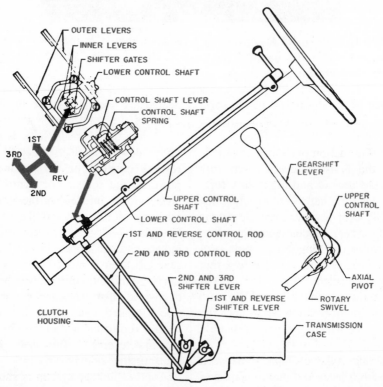

Fig. 21–19. Linkage arrangement between the gearshift lever and the shifter lever on the transmission. (Chevrolet Motor Division of General Motors Corporation)

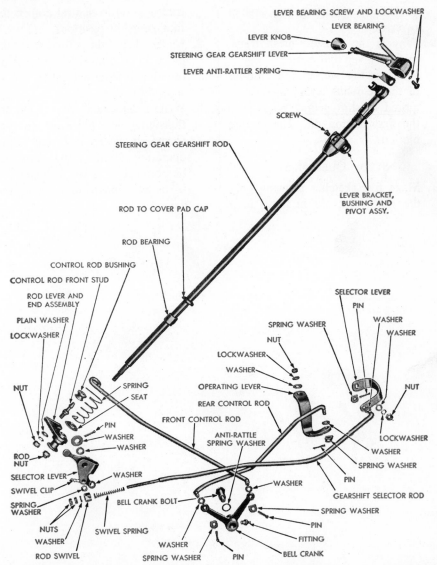

LEVER BEARING SCREW AND LOCKWASHER

LEVER BEARING

LEVER KNOB

STEERING GEAR GEARSHIFT LEVER

LEVER ANTI-RATTLER SPRING

SCREW

STEERING GEAR GEARSHIFT ROD

LEVER BRACKET, BUSHING AND PIVOT ASSY.

ROD TO COVER PAD CAP

ROD BEARING

CONTROL ROD BUSHING

CONTROL ROD FRONT STUD

ROD LEVER AND END ASSEMBLY

PLAIN WASHER

LOCKWASHER

SELECTOR LEVER

PIN

WASHER

WASHER

SPRING WASHER

NUT

LOCKWASHER

WASHER

OPERATING LEVER

REAR CONTROL ROD

FRONT CONTROL ROD

ANTI-RATTLE SPRING WASHER

NUT

SPRING

SEAT

PIN

WASHER

WASHER

NUT

LOCKWASHER

WASHER

SPRING WASHER

PIN

GEARSHIFT SELECTOR ROD

ROD NUT

SELECTOR LEVER

SWIVEL CLIP

WASHER

WASHER

SPRING WASHER

NUTS

SWIVEL SPRING

WASHER

ROD SWIVEL

BELL CRANK BOLT

WASHER

SPRING WASHER

PIN

SPRING WASHER

PIN

FITTING

BELL CRANK

Fig. 21–20. Disassembled view of a linkage arrangement between the gearshift lever and the selector and operating levers on the transmission. (*Dodge Division of Chrysler Corporation*)

5. In a gear system, does speed reduction mean torque reduction or torque increase?

6. What is the purpose of synchromesh devices?

7. Explain how the synchromesh functions as the shift is made from first to second. From second to third.

8. Why is no synchromesh device

provided for shifting into first or reverse?

9. Why is the constant-mesh transmission given that name?

10. What are the two separate motions of the gearshift lever that are required to shift gears? What does the first motion do? The second motion?

STUDY QUESTIONS

1. Make five sketches showing only the gears that are in mesh in a transmission in neutral and in the four gearshift positions.

2. Make a list of the actions that take place in a transmission as gears are shifted from neutral to first to second to third.

3. Write a sequence story of the actions that take place as the synchromesh device is brought into operation. If the actual unit can be obtained, this will help toward a better understanding of the device.

THIS CHAPTER DISCUSSES THE purpose and function of the overdrive and describes the manner in which it operates. The description of the planetary-gear system in the pages that follow is especially important since planetary-gear systems are used in many automatic transmissions. In order to understand the automatic transmissions, you must understand planetary-gear systems. Thus, be sure you spend enough time studying planetary gears so that you understand how they operate.

§ 431. Purpose of overdrive In standard transmissions, the high-gear position imposes a direct, or 1:1, ratio between the clutch shaft and the transmission main shaft. It is desirable at intermediate and high car speeds, however, to establish a still more favorable ratio between the two shafts, so that the transmission main shaft will turn more rapidly than the clutch shaft. This will reduce engine speed at high car speeds and provide more economical operation and less engine and accessory wear per car-mile.

For these reasons, several car manufacturers supply *overdrive* mechanisms as special equipment. Overdrives cause the main shaft to overdrive, or turn more rapidly than, the clutch shaft. While the ratio varies somewhat on different cars, the overdrive, when brought into operation, drops the engine speed about 30 percent without any change of car speed. Thus, on a car where direct or high gear provides a 40-mph (miles per hour) car speed at 2,000 engine rpm (revolutions per minute), the overdrive would drop the engine speed to 1,400 rpm while still maintaining a car speed of 40 mph.

Overdrives as used on modern cars are automatic, coming into operation when the car speed reaches a predetermined value, usually somewhere around 30 mph. They contain a selective feature that permits the car driver to remain in direct drive or, if he prefers, to shift into overdrive by merely raising his foot from the accelerator momentarily. When the car driver wishes to come out of overdrive, he merely depresses the throttle past "wide-open" position. This actuates a throttle switch that causes electric circuits to function and bring the car out of overdrive. There are thus two separate controls: a centrifugal device, or governor, that places the car into overdrive when the "cut-in" speed is reached, and an electric control that brings the car out of overdrive when the driver wishes it.

§ 432. Overdrive components The overdrive is located just back of the transmission, between the transmission and the propeller shaft (Fig. 22–1).

463

Fig. 22–1. The overdrive is located between the transmission and propeller shaft.

Essentially, it is made up of two parts, a planetary-gear system and a free-wheeling mechanism, together with the necessary controls and supports. It is important to understand the operation of these devices since this will lead to a more ready understanding of the automatic transmissions described in following chapters. Automatic transmissions commonly use planetary-gear systems. Let us examine the freewheel-

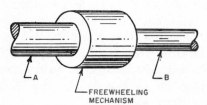

Fig. 22–2. The freewheeling mechanism provides solid drive when shaft A is turning shaft B. But if shaft A slows or stops, shaft B can still "freewheel" or turn faster than (overrun) shaft A.

ing mechanism and the planetary-gear system in greater detail.

§ 433. Freewheeling mechanism

Essentially, the freewheeling mechanism is a coupling between two shafts that are in line with each other (Fig. 22–2). This coupling contains an inner and an outer shell (race) with rollers between. The coupling is often called an overrunning clutch. The name comes from the action of the mechanism. When shaft A (Fig. 22–2) is applying driving torque through the coupling, or overrunning clutch, the clutch acts as a solid drive and causes shaft B to turn at the same speed as shaft A. However, if shaft A should slow down or stop, shaft B could still turn faster than, or *overrun*, shaft A. In this case, the clutch "uncouples" the two shafts and thereby permits shaft B to overrun.

464

Fig. 22–3. The inner parts of an overrunning clutch, or freewheeling mechanism, used in an overdrive. The rubber band is not part of the assembly but is shown since it is temporarily holding the rollers in place. In the actual assembly, an outer race holds the rollers in place. (*Studebaker-Packard Corporation*)

In the car, shaft A would be attached to the transmission output shaft, while shaft B would be attached to the propeller shaft. With the engine driving the car, the overrunning clutch would "clutch" and act as a solid drive so that shafts A and B would turn at the same speed. But with the accelerator pedal released so that the engine slows down, shaft B could then overrun shaft A and the car would therefore coast, or freewheel. This is the actual operation of freewheeling devices used on cars a number of years ago. In the overdrive, however, the action is somewhat different.

Figure 22–3 shows the inner parts of an overrunning clutch used in an overdrive. The only additional item needed to complete the overrunning clutch shown is an outer shell, or race, that encloses the rollers. Figure 22–4 shows, in end view, the action of the overrunning clutch. The clutch contains an inner shell, or race, which has a series of high spots, or cams, evenly spaced around its entire circumference. There is one cam for each roller. This inner race, with cams, is usually called the clutch cam. A number of hardened-steel rollers lie in the low areas between the high spots on the clutch cam. These rollers, in turn, are held in place by an outer shell, or race. There is also a roller retainer, or roller cage, as shown in Fig. 22–3, which simply retains the rollers in the proper relative positions. The inner race drives, the outer race is driven. Also, the outer race can overrun, or turn faster than, the inner race.

When the inner race is driving, and turning the outer race at the same speed, then the condition is as shown

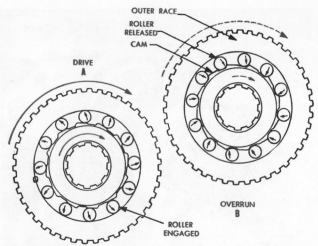

Fig. 22–4. Action in the overrunning clutch during driving (A) and during overrunning (B). (*American Motors Corporation*)

at *A,* in Fig. 22–4. The rollers have been turned up onto the high spots, or cams, of the inner race, thus jamming between the two races. The outer race therefore is forced to turn with the inner race. The overrunning clutch acts as a solid drive.

However, if the inner race should slow down or stop, the outer race can continue to turn faster than, or overrun, the inner race. As this happens, the rollers are rolled forward into the low spots on the clutch cam. There, they no longer jam between the two races, and the outer race can overrun freely (*B* in Fig. 22–4). But when the inner race speeds up again and catches up with the outer race, the rollers

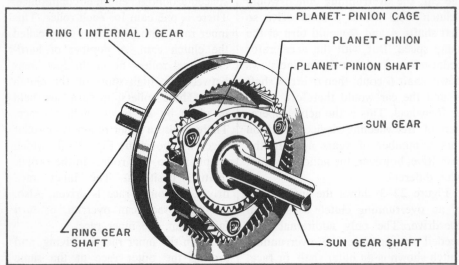

Fig. 22–5. Parts in a planetary-gear system. (*American Motors Corporation*)

Conditions	1	2	3	4	5	6
Ring Gear	D	T	H	H	T	D
Cage	T	D	D	T	H	H
Sun Gear	H	H	T	D	D	T
Speed	I	L	L	I	IR	LR

D—Driven   L—Reduction of Speed
H—Hold   R—Reverse
I—Increasing of Speed   T—Turn or Drive

Fig. 22–6. Chart showing the various conditions that are possible in the planetary-gear system if one member is held and another is turned.

once more jam so that the inner race drives the outer race; both again turn at the same speed.

§ **434. Planetary-gear system** The planetary-gear system, as used in the overdrive and in automatic transmissions, consists of an outer ring gear (sometimes called the internal gear because its teeth are inside), three planet pinions held on pinion shafts in a cage, and a sun gear (Fig. 22–5). The planetary-gear system gets its name from the fact that the pinions revolve around the sun gear and rotate at the same time, just as the planets in our solar system rotate and revolve around the sun.

Before we discuss the manner in which the planetary-gear system is used in the overdrive, let us see how the system functions when we hold one of the three members (ring gear, planet-pinion cage, or sun gear) stationary and turn another member. The chart (Fig. 22–6), shows what will happen with different combinations, and following paragraphs explain these various combinations.

1. Speed increase. If we turn the planet-pinion cage and hold the sun gear stationary, the planet-pinion shafts will be carried around with the cage. As this happens, the planet pinions must rotate on their shafts since the pinions are meshed with the sun gear. In a sense, they "walk around" the stationary sun gear, rotating on their shafts as they, and the cage, revolve around the sun gear. And since the planet pinions are meshed with the ring gear, they also cause the ring gear to rotate. Actually, the ring gear, in this case, will rotate faster than the planet-pinion cage.

Figure 22–7 illustrates how the stationary sun gear causes the ring gear to turn faster than the planet-pinion cage. At any given instant, the pinion tooth meshed with the sun gear is stationary since the sun gear itself is stationary. The pinion, therefore, can be said to be pivoting around this stationary tooth. If the pinion shaft is moving 1 foot per second, as shown in the illustration, then the outside tooth must be moving faster than 1 foot per second. That is, the outside tooth, and

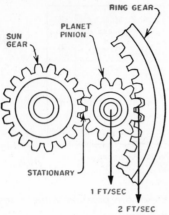

Fig. 22–7. If the sun gear is stationary and the planet-pinion cage is turned, the ring gear will turn faster than the cage. The planet pinion pivots about the stationary teeth. If the center of the pinion shaft is moving at 1 foot per second, the tooth opposite the stationary tooth must move at 2 feet per second (it is twice as far away from the stationary tooth as the center of the shaft).

also the ring gear with which it is meshed, moves faster than the shaft. Thus the ring gear rotates faster than the planet-pinion cage.

The ratio between the planet-pinion cage and the ring gear can be altered by changing the sizes of the different gears. In the example shown in Fig. 22–8, the ring gear makes 1 complete revolution while the planet-pinion cage turns only 0.7 revolution. In other words, the ring gear is running faster than the cage, and the gear ratio between the two is 1:0.7. The system functions as a speed-increasing mechanism since the driven member (ring gear) turns faster than the driving member (planet-pinion cage).

2. Speed reduction. If we turn the *ring gear* while holding the sun gear

stationary (Fig. 22–6), the planet-pinion cage will turn more slowly than the ring gear. In this case, the system functions as a speed-reducing mechanism since the driven member (planet-pinion cage) turns more slowly than the driving member (ring gear).

3. Speed reduction. Let us try still another combination and see what happens if we hold the ring gear stationary and turn the sun gear. We shall find that the planet pinions will turn on their shafts. They must also "walk around" the ring gear since they are in mesh with it. As they do this, the planet-pinion cage is carried around. The cage therefore rotates, but at a speed less than the sun-gear speed. In this case, the system functions as a speed-reducing mechanism. The driven member (planet-pinion cage) turns more slowly than the driving member (sun gear).

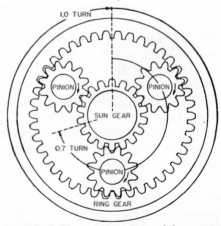

Fig. 22–8. The relative sizes of the gears, as shown, cause the ring gear to turn once while the planet-pinion cage is turned 0.7 time with the sun gear held stationary.

4. Speed increase. Another combination would be to hold the ring gear and turn the planet-pinion cage. In this case, the sun gear would be forced to rotate faster than the cage, and the system would function as a speed-increasing mechanism. The driven member (sun gear) turns faster than the driving member (planet-pinion cage).

5. Reverse. Still another combination would be to hold the planet-carrier cage stationary and turn the ring gear. In this case, the planet pinions act as idlers, similar to the reverse-idler gear in a standard transmission, and thereby cause the sun gear to turn in the reverse direction to ring-gear rotation. Thus, the system functions as a reverse-rotation system, with the sun gear turning faster than the ring gear.

6. Reverse. There is still one more combination. If the cage is held and the sun gear is turned, then the ring gear will turn in a reverse direction, but slower than the sun gear.

7. Direct drive. If any two of the three members (sun gear, cage, ring gear) are locked together, then the entire planetary-gear system is locked out and the input shaft and output shaft must turn at the same speeds. That is, there is no change of speed through the system, and the drive ratio is 1:1. On the other hand, if no member is held stationary and no two members are locked together, then the system will not transmit power at all. The input shaft may turn, but the output shaft does not.

8. Planetary-gear system applied to overdrive. In the overdrive, the ring gear is attached to the output shaft while the three planet pinions are assembled into a cage that is splined to the transmission main shaft. The sun gear has an arrangement whereby it may be permitted to turn, or it may be locked in a stationary position. When it is locked, the ring gear (and thus the output shaft) is forced to turn faster than the transmission main shaft. In other words, the output shaft *overdrives* the transmission main shaft. Various views of the overdrive parts show the planetary-gear members (Figs. 22–9 to 22–14).

§ 435. Overdrive operation Figure 22–9 shows the component parts of one type of overdrive in exploded view, with all major parts disassembled but lined up in their approximate relationship in the actual assembly. Figure 22–10 shows the operating components in partial cutaway view. Figures 22–9 to 22–14 show various operating aspects of the overdrive assembly. Figure 22–11 illustrates the relationship of the overdrive parts and the power path through the overdrive when it is in direct drive. The transmission main shaft and the output shaft turn at the same speed, and the driving action is through the overrunning clutch, or freewheeling mechanism. The power path is shown by lines and arrows. Note that the power path is directly to the clutch cam, which is splined to the transmission main shaft. From the clutch cam, it passes through the rollers to the outer shell, or race, which is attached to the output shaft.

1. Going into overdrive. In Fig. 22–11, although the overdrive is in direct drive, it is ready to go into overdrive just as soon as the car speed is great enough and the driver momen-

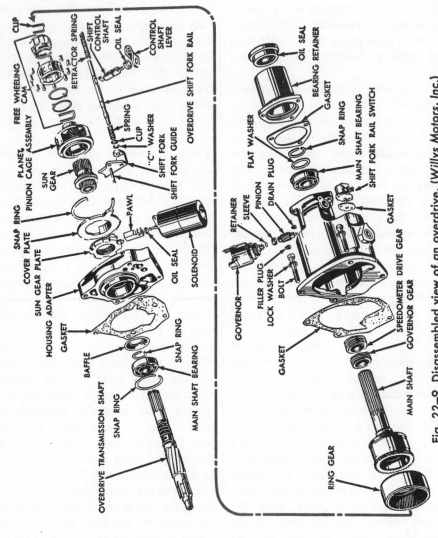

RETRACTOR SPRING

SHIFT CONTROL SHAFT

OIL SEAL

CONTROL SHAFT LEVER

OVERDRIVE SHIFT FORK RAIL

CLIP

FREE WHEELING CAM

PLANET PINION CAGE ASSEMBLY

SUN GEAR

SNAP RING

COVER PLATE

SUN GEAR PLATE

HOUSING ADAPTER

GASKET

BAFFLE

SNAP RING

SNAP RING

MAIN SHAFT BEARING

OVERDRIVE TRANSMISSION SHAFT

SPRING

CUP

"C" WASHER

SHIFT FORK

SHIFT FORK GUIDE

PAWL

OIL SEAL

SOLENOID

OIL SEAL

BEARING RETAINER

GASKET

SNAP RING

FLAT WASHER

MAIN SHAFT BEARING

SHIFT FORK RAIL SWITCH

RETAINER

SLEEVE

PINION

DRAIN PLUG

GOVERNOR

FILLER PLUG

LOCK WASHER

BOLT

GASKET

GASKET

SPEEDOMETER DRIVE GEAR

GOVERNOR GEAR

MAIN SHAFT

RING GEAR

Fig. 22–9. Disassembled view of an overdrive. (Willys Motors, Inc.)

470

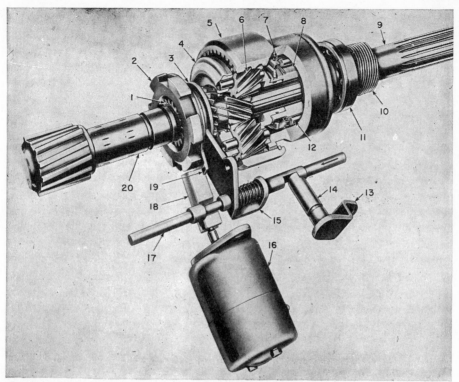

Fig. 22–10. Overdrive operating components, partly cut away. (*Chevrolet Motor Division of General Motors Corporation*)

1. Sun gear
2. Sun-gear conrrol plate
3. Sun-gear shift collar
4. Pinion-cage assembly
5. Output-shaft ring gear
6. Pinion
7. Clutch-cam-roller retainer
8. Cam
9. Output shaft
10. Speedometer drive gear
11. Output-shaft bearing
12. Clutch cam roller
13. Control lever
14. Control shaft and lever
15. Shift fork
16. Solenoid assembly
17. Control rod
18. Sun-gear pawl
19. Blocker ring
20. Transmission main shaft

tarily releases the accelerator. Note that, in the figure, the pawl is out of the way of the sun-gear control plate. It is held in this position by the blocker ring as shown at *A* in Fig. 22–12. The blocker ring is loosely assembled onto the sun-gear control plate so that it can turn a few degrees one way or the other.

When the car reaches overdrive cut-in speed (roughly between 18 and 21 mph), a governor driven from the overdrive output shaft closes electrical contacts. This connects the solenoid to

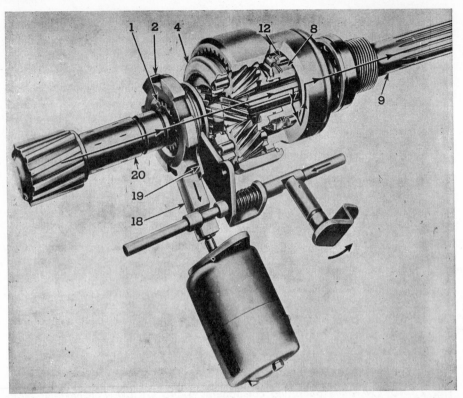

Fig. 22–11. Direct drive through the clutch: 1, sun gear; 2, sun-gear control plate; 4, pinion-cage assembly; 8, cam; 9, output shaft; 12, clutch cam roller; 18, sun-gear pawl; 19, blocker ring; 20, transmission main shaft. (*Chevrolet Motor Division of General Motors Corporation*)

the battery and the solenoid is therefore energized. This spring-loads the solenoid pawl so that it attempts to move upward and into a notch in the sun-gear control plate. However, the pawl is held away by the blocker ring as shown in Fig. 22–12A.

When the driver momentarily releases the accelerator pedal, the engine speed drops. As it drops, the free-wheeling mechanism goes into action to permit the output shaft to overrun the transmission main shaft. When this happens, the sun gear slows and then reverses directions. It does this because

the ring gear (which rotates with the output shaft) begins to drive it through the planet pinions.

At the moment that the sun gear reverses directions, it moves the blocker ring around a few degrees to the position shown at B in Fig. 22–12. When this happens, the pawl can move inward and into the next notch on the sun-gear control plate that comes around. This locks the control plate in a stationary position.

Since the control plate is splined to the sun gear, this action also locks the sun gear in a stationary position. Now,

472

when the driver again steps on the accelerator and engine speed increases, the car goes into overdrive. With the sun gear locked, the power flow is as shown in Fig. 22–13. The transmission main shaft drives through the planet-pinion cage (splined to the transmission main shaft) and causes the pinions to rotate around the sun gear as shown in Fig. 22–7. The ring gear is attached to the output shaft through the outer race of the freewheeling mechanism. Thus the ring gear and output shaft overdrive (turn faster than) the transmission main shaft. Note that under this condition the freewheeling mechanism is freewheeling. That is, the outer race is overrunning the clutch cam and thus the transmission main shaft.

2. *Coming out of overdrive.* To come out of overdrive, the driver merely pushes the accelerator all the way down. This would be the action the driver would take when he wants an extra burst of power, as, for example, to pass another car. Pushing

the accelerator all the way down causes the accelerator pedal to operate a kick-down switch. Operation of this switch produces two actions. First, it opens the solenoid circuit so that the solenoid attempts to withdraw the pawl from the sun-gear control plate. However, there is considerable pressure on the pawl since it is holding the sun gear stationary and the planet pinions are thrusting hard against the sun gear as they drive the ring gear.

The second action of the kick-down switch momentarily relieves this drive, however, since the kick-down switch also grounds out the ignition circuit and thereby prevents the engine from delivering power. Since the engine will slow down if it is not delivering power, the driving thrust of the planet pinions on the sun gear is almost instantly relieved. This frees the sun gear and sun-gear control plate, and the drive pawl is pulled back by the spring in the solenoid. As the drive-pawl plunger in the solenoid bottoms, it opens the ground-out contacts and the engine

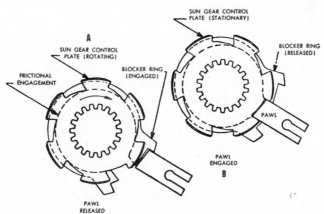

Fig. 22–12. Positions of the sun-gear control plate, blocker ring, and pawl with the pawl released (A) and with the pawl engaged (B). With the pawl engaged, the sun gear is held stationary.

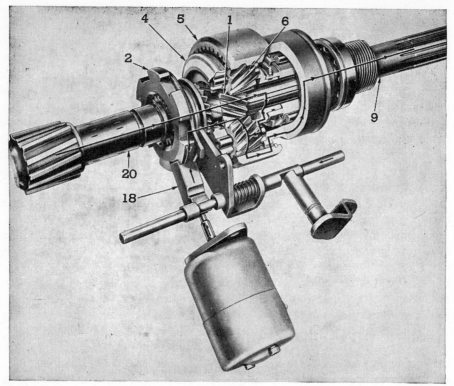

Fig. 22–13. Overdrive mechanism in overdrive: 1, sun-gear; 2, sun-gear control plate; 4, pinion-cage assembly; 5, output-shaft ring gear; 6, pinion; 9, output shaft; 18, sun-gear pawl; 20, transmission main shaft. (*Chevrolet Motor Division of General Motors Corporation*)

once again begins to deliver power. Now, with the sun gear unlocked, drive is again direct as shown in Fig. 22–11.

The ignition system is disconnected for such a short time that the interruption of the flow of power is not noticeable. The entire sequence of events that takes place when the kick-down switch is closed may be completed in less than a second; the car goes from overdrive into direct drive very quickly.

When the driver again wants to go into overdrive, he has merely to lift his foot momentarily from the ac-

celerator pedal as already explained.

The electric controls involved in the overdrive action are described in the following section. Figure 22–15 illustrates the wiring circuit of the controls.

3. Locking out the overdrive. If the driver wants to lock out the overdrive, he pulls out a control knob on the car dash. This forces the control rod in the direction shown in Fig. 22–14. As the control rod moves in this direction, it forces the sun-gear control plate and sun gear to move toward the planet-pinion cage. The sun-gear teeth enter into mesh with internal teeth in the

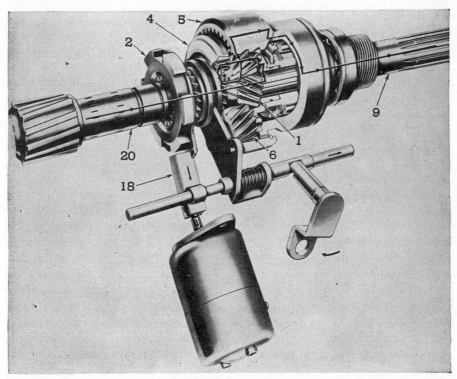

Fig. 22–14. Overdrive locked out: 1, sun-gear; 2, sun-gear control plate; 4, pinion-cage assembly; 5, output-shaft ring gear; 6, pinion; 9, output shaft; 18, sun-gear pawl; 20, transmission main shaft. (*Chevrolet Motor Division of General Motors Corporation*)

planet-pinion cage so that the two lock up. Under this condition, the sun gear and pinion cage must turn together, and thus the entire assembly turns as a unit so that there can be no overrunning effect. The movement of the control rod also locks out the sun-gear pawl, as shown. On some systems, movement of the control rod operates an electric switch that opens the solenoid circuits so that the overdrive electric system is inoperative.

4. Reverse. For reverse, the overdrive must be locked out. This is taken care of by the transmission reverse-shaft mechanism, which moves the overdrive control rod to the "lockout" position when a shift to reverse is made.

NOTE: The overdrive explained above is but one of several types that have been used on automobiles. It is typical of them all, however, since all are essentially similar in construction and action.

§ 436. Overdrive electric controls Various types of electric controls for overdrives have been used, but, essentially, all have the same purpose. They must energize the solenoid as the car reaches cut-in speed. They must

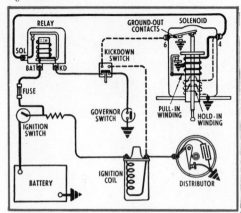

Fig. 22–15. Electric circuit of the overdrive control. Kick-down switch is shown upside down in the illustration. Actually, the contacts connected by dashed lines are the lower, or ground-out, contacts. (Chevrolet Motor Division of General Motors Corporation)

also disconnect the ignition circuit momentarily and at the same time open the solenoid circuit when the kickdown switch is closed as the driver wants to come out of overdrive.

Figure 22–15 shows a wiring circuit of the electric control system used with the overdrive described on previous pages. Some systems also have an overdrive lockout switch which is connected into the circuit between the governor switch and the solenoid. When the overdrive is locked out, this switch is open so that the electric control circuit is inoperative.

When the driver wants to go into overdrive, he pushes in the control knob on the dash. This places the system in the condition shown in Fig. 22–11. When the car reaches cut-in speed, the governor closes its contacts to connect the overdrive-relay winding to the battery. The overdrive relay, in turn, closes its contacts to connect the

solenoid to the battery. Now, the overdrive is ready to go into action. When the driver momentarily releases the accelerator pedal, the solenoid can send the pawl into a notch in the sun-gear control plate. This puts the transmission into overdrive.

To come out of overdrive, the driver pushes all the way down on the accelerator pedal, thus causing the upper contacts of the kick-down switch to open and the lower contacts to close. Opening the upper contacts opens the overdrive-relay circuit. The overdrive relay therefore opens its contacts to open the solenoid circuit. Also, closing the lower contacts in the kick-down switch directly grounds the ignition coil and thereby prevents any ignition. With this interruption of ignition-system action, the engine stops delivering power and begins to slow down. As it does this, the thrust on the solenoid pawl is relieved, and the spring pressure pulls the pawl out of the notch in the sun-gear control plate. When the solenoid pawl snaps into the "out" position, the ground-out contacts in the solenoid are opened to "unground" the ignition coil and thereby permit the ignition system to function again. The engine again begins to deliver power. This series of actions takes place so quickly that no appreciable lag in power delivery is noticeable.

REVIEW QUESTIONS

1. What is the purpose of the overdrive?

2. When the overdrive is in operation, does the propeller shaft turn faster or slower than the engine crankshaft?

3. How does the driver shift into

overdrive? How does he come out of overdrive?

4. Describe a freewheeling mechanism used in an overdrive.

5. Describe the actions in the overdrive as the driver lifts his foot from the accelerator momentarily in order to go into overdrive. Describe the actions as the driver pushes the accelerator past wide-open throttle in order to come out of overdrive.

6. Describe the actions that take place in the electric control circuit as the driver closes the throttle switch.

1. Refer to the chart showing different possible combinations in the planetary-gear system, and write down descriptions of the actions taking place during each combination.

2. Write a sequence story of the actions that take place as the overdrive comes into operation. The actions that take place when the car is brought out of overdrive.

3. Write an essay explaining how the overdrive electric control system operates.

THIS CHAPTER DISCUSSES trouble-shooting, removal, overhaul, and re-assembly of standard transmissions and overdrives. Following chapters describe different semiautomatic and automatic transmissions in use on passenger cars.

§ **437. Transmission and overdrive troubles** As a first step in any transmission or overdrive service, diagnosis of the trouble should be made in an attempt to pin-point the trouble in the malfunctioning unit. Sometimes it is not possible to determine the exact location of a trouble, and the unit must be removed from the car so that it can be torn down and examined. At other times, diagnosis will lead to the point of trouble so that it can be eliminated without major disassembly.

The chart that follows lists the various complaints that might be blamed on the transmission or overdrive, together with their possible causes, the checks to be made, and corrections needed.

§ **438. Transmission and overdrive trouble-shooting chart** This chart is divided into two parts, "Transmission Troubles" and "Overdrive Troubles." Most transmission troubles can be grouped under a few headings such as "Hard shifting," "Transmission slips out of gear," "Transmission noisy . . . ," and so on, as listed in the chart.

NOTE: The complaints and possible causes are not listed in the chart in the order of frequency of occurrence. That is, item 1 (or item *a* under "Possible Cause") does not necessarily occur more frequently than item 2 (or item *b*).

TRANSMISSION AND OVERDRIVE TROUBLE-SHOOTING CHART

Transmission Troubles

Complaint	*Possible Cause*	*Check or Correction*
1. Hard shifting into gear	*a.* Clutch not releasing	Adjust (see § 421)
	b. Gearshift linkage out of adjustment	Adjust
	c. Improper lubrication of linkage	Lubricate

478

Complaint	*Possible Cause*	*Check or Correction*
	d. Shifter fork bent	Replace or straighten
	e. Sliding gear tight on shaft splines	Clean splines or replace shaft or gear
	f. Sliding-gear teeth battered	Replace
	g. Synchronizing unit damaged	Replace defective parts
2. Transmission sticks in gear	a. Clutch not releasing	Adjust (see § 421)
	b. Gearshift linkage out of adjustment	Adjust
	c. Improper lubrication of linkage	Lubricate
	d. Detent balls (lockout) stuck	Free
	e. Gears tight on shaft splines	Clean splines or replace shaft or gears
3. Transmission slips out of first or reverse	a. Gearshift linkage out of adjustment	Adjust
	b. Gear loose on main shaft	Replace shaft or gear
	c. Gear teeth worn	Replace gear
	d. Excessive end play of gears	Replace worn or loose parts
	e. Insufficient shift-lever spring (lockout) tension	Install new spring
	f. Bearings worn	Replace
4. Transmission slips out of second	a. Gearshift linkage out of adjustment	Adjust
	b. Gear or drum loose on main shaft	Replace worn parts
	c. Excessive main-shaft end play	Replace worn or defective parts
	d. Gear teeth worn	Replace gears
	e. Insufficient shift-lever spring (lockout) tension	Install new spring
5. Transmission slips out of high	a. Gearshift linkage out of adjustment	Adjust
	b. Misalignment between engine and transmission	Realign
	c. Excessive main-shaft end play	Replace worn or defective parts

Complaint	*Possible Cause*	*Check or Correction*
	d. Gear teeth worn	Replace gears
	e. Insufficient shift-lever spring (lockout) tension	Replace spring
	f. Bearings worn	Replace
	g. Synchronizing unit worn or defective	Replace worn parts
6. No power through transmission	*a.* Clutch slipping	Adjust (see § 421)
	b. Gear teeth stripped	Replace gear
	c. Shifter fork or other linkage part broken	Replace
	d. Gear or shaft broken	Replace
	e. Drive key sheared	Replace
7. Transmission noisy in neutral	*a.* Transmission misaligned with engine	Realign
	b. Bearings worn or dry	Replace, lubricate
	c. Gears worn	Replace
	d. Countershaft worn or bent	Replace
	e. Excessive end play of countershaft	Replace worn parts
8. Transmission noisy in gear	*a.* Clutch friction disk defective	Replace
	b. Engine torsional-vibration dampener defective	Replace or adjust
	c. Main rear bearing of transmission worn or dry	Replace or lubricate
	d. Gears loose on main shaft	Replace worn parts
	e. Gear teeth worn	Replace gears
	f. Speedometer gears worn	Replace
	g. Conditions noted in item 7. Transmission noisy in neutral. Refer to item 7 above for other causes	
9. Gears clash in shifting	*a.* Clutch not releasing	Adjust
	b. Synchronizer defective	Replace defective parts
	c. Gears sticky on main shaft	Free. Replace defective parts
10. Oil leaks	*a.* Foaming due to improper lubricant	Use recommended lubricant

Complaint	*Possible Cause*	*Check or Correction*
	b. Lubricant level too high	Use proper amount, no more
	c. Gaskets broken or missing	Install new gaskets
	d. Oil seals damaged or missing	Install new oil seals
	e. Oil slingers damaged, improperly installed, or missing	Install oil slingers properly
	f. Drain plug loose	Tighten
	g. Transmission - bearing retainer bolts loose	Tighten
	h. Transmission case cracked	Use new case

Overdrive Troubles

(The overdrive may have any of the troubles listed below. Be careful, in analyzing trouble on a car equipped with overdrive, not to blame the overdrive for troubles in the transmission, or vice versa. For example, a certain overdrive trouble may prevent shifting the transmission into reverse. It would be easy to blame this on the transmission, whereas the fault would actually lie in the overdrive.)

Complaint	*Possible Cause*	*Check or Correction*
11. Will not go into overdrive	a. Wiring defective	Tighten connections, install new wiring
	b. Governor defective	Install new governor
	c. Kick-down switch defective	Install new switch
	d. Relay defective	Install new relay
	e. Solenoid defective	Install new solenoid
	f. Linkage to control knob on dash out of adjustment	Adjust
	g. Defect in overdrive including gear jammed or broken, over-running clutch defective, excessive shaft end play	Disassemble overdrive to eliminate defective part, tighten flange nut
12. Will not come out of overdrive	a. Wiring defective	Tighten connections, install new wiring
	b. Kick-down switch defective	Install new switch

Complaint	Possible Cause	Check or Correction
	c. Solenoid defective	Install new solenoid
	d. Pawl jammed	Free pawl
	e. Sun gear jammed	Disassemble overdrive to eliminate jam, and replace defective parts
13. Cannot shift into reverse, and overdrive dash knob jammed in OD ("overdrive") position	a. Pawl jammed in sun-gear control plate	Replace solenoid
	b. Solenoid defective	Replace solenoid
	c. Relay defective	Replace relay
	d. Governor grounded	Replace governor
	e. Reverse lockout switch grounded	Replace switch
	f. Kick-down switch defective	Replace switch
	g. Wiring defective	Tighten connections, replace wiring
	h. Sun gear jammed	Disassemble overdrive to eliminate jam
	i. Linkage to dash knob out of adjustment	Adjust
14. No power through overdrive	a. Overrunning clutch slipping	Replace defective parts in overdrive
	b. Planetary parts broken	Replace defective parts
15. Noises in overdrive	a. Gears worn, chipped, broken	Replace defective gears
	b. Main-shaft bearing worn or scored	Replace
	c. Overrunning-clutch parts worn or scored	Replace
16. Oil leaks	a. Defective or broken gaskets or oil seals	Replace
	b. Loose mounting	Tighten mounting bolts
	c. Excessive lubricant	Put in only specified amount, no more

§ 439. Transmission removal and installation Because of the variations in construction of transmissions on different automobiles, different procedures must be followed in the removal, disassembly, repair, assembly, and installation of their transmissions. These operations require about 5 to 7 hours, the difference in time being due to variations in the procedures. Basically, the procedures are similar. However, refer to the manufacturer's shop manual before attempting such work. In general, the following steps are required:

1. Drain lubricant. Some manufac-

Fig. 23–1. Installing engine support prior to removal of transmission.

turers recommend flushing the transmission before removal. This is done by filling the transmission with gasoline or kerosene, after the lubricant is drained, and then operating the engine with the transmission in neutral for 15 seconds. Then the cleaner should be drained.

2. Disconnect rear axle or front end of propeller shaft or universal joint, according to type. Where needle bearings are used, tape the bearing retainers to the shaft to avoid losing needles.

3. Disconnect shifting linkages from transmission, hand-brake linkage or spring, and speedometer cable.

4. Install engine support, where specified (see Fig. 23–1).

5. Remove attaching bolts or stud nuts. Where recommended, two pilot, or guide, pins should be used (Fig. 23–2). These pins are substituted for transmission bolts and prevent damage to the clutch friction disk as the transmission is moved back. The transmission is then moved toward the rear until the main gear shaft clears the clutch disk. It can then be lowered

to the floor or raised up through the body, as specified.

6. In general, installation is the reverse of removal. Be sure the matching faces of the transmission and flywheel housing are clean. Place a small amount of lubricant on the splines of the main gear shaft. Carefully support transmission (using guide pins if specified), and move it forward into position. Turn shaft, if necessary, to secure alignment of shaft and clutch-disk hub splines. Put bolts in place, and tighten them to the correct tension.

▶*CAUTION:* If the transmission does not fit snugly against the flywheel housing, do not force it. Roughness or dirt, or possibly a loose snap ring or other parts, may be blocking the transmission. If the bolts are tightened under such circumstances, the transmission case may be broken.

§ **440. Transmission and overdrive overhaul** The overhaul procedures differ for each model of transmission and overdrive. Thus, before disassembling, servicing, and reassembling a

483

GUIDE PINS J 851

Fig. 23–2. Use of guide, or pilot, pins in transmission removal or replacement. The pins maintain transmission alignment with the clutch as the transmission is moved back or forward so that the clutch will not be damaged. (*Buick Motor Division of General Motors Corporation*)

transmission or overdrive, always refer to the shop manual that covers the specific model being repaired Follow the instructions step by step.

§ 441. Gearshift-linkage adjustments The linkage between the gearshift lever and the shifter levers on the transmission must be properly adjusted; this permits proper selection of gears and completion of gearshifts. Typically, the adjustment is made in two steps. First, an adustment is made which positions the gearshift lever so far as up-and-down movement is concerned. This determines the distance between the lever and the steering wheel. Second, the radial position of the lever must be established with

reference to the steering wheel. Since these adjustments are different on different cars, refer to the applicable shop manual before attempting to make any adjustment on a car.

REVIEW QUESTIONS

1. What could cause hard shifting into gear?
2. What could cause the transmission to stick in gear?
3. What might cause the transmission to slip out of first or reverse?
4. What could cause the transmission to slip out of second?
5. What could cause the transmission to slip out of high?
6. What would prevent delivery of power through the transmission?

7. Describe the various conditions that could cause the transmission to be noisy.
8. What would cause the gears to clash while shifts were made?
9. What could cause oil to be lost from the transmission?
10. What could prevent an overdrive from going into overdrive?
11. What would prevent the overdrive from coming out of overdrive?
12. What in the overdrive might prevent shifting into reverse?
13. What would prevent power transmission through the overdrive?
14. What might cause noise in the overdrive?
15. Describe in a general way the procedure for removing and installing a transmission.

STUDY QUESTIONS

1. Make a list of all types of transmission troubles, together with their possible causes and corrections.
2. Write a detailed transmission removal, overhaul, reinstallation, and adjustment story, basing it on a manufacturer's shop manual or an actual job in the shop.

THE PURPOSE OF THIS CHAPTER is to explain hydraulic theory as it applies to automatic transmissions, to describe the operation of fluid couplings, and to discuss the construction and operation of transmissions using fluid couplings. The following chapter discusses the construction and operation of transmissions using *torque converters;* these devices are a special form of fluid coupling.

§ **442. Hydraulics** Before we discuss fluid couplings and the various transmissions with which they are used, we should first understand something about hydraulics. Hydraulics is the science of liquids such as water or oil. Our special interest, so far as automatic transmissions are concerned, is in the pressures that can be exerted by liquids.

1. Incompressibility of liquids. If a

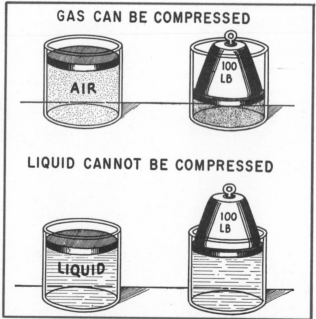

GAS CAN BE COMPRESSED

AIR

100 LB

LIQUID CANNOT BE COMPRESSED

LIQUID

100 LB

Fig. 24–1. Gas can be compressed when pressure is applied. Liquid, however, cannot be compressed by application of pressure. (*Pontiac Motor Division of General Motors Corporation*)

gas, such as air, is put under pressure, it can be compressed into a smaller volume (Fig. 24–1). However, applying pressure to a liquid will not cause it to compress; it stays the same volume.

2. Transmitting motion by liquid. Since liquid is not compressible, motion may be transmitted by liquid. For example, Fig. 24–2 shows two pistons in a cylinder with a liquid between them. When the applying piston is moved into the cylinder 8 inches, as shown, then the output piston will be pushed along the cylinder the same distance. In the figure, you could substitute a solid connecting rod between piston *A* and piston *B* and get the same result. But the advantage of such a system is that you can transmit motion between cylinders by a tube (Fig. 24–3). In Fig. 24–3, as the applying piston is moved, liquid is forced out of cylinder *A,* through the tube, and into cylinder *B.* This causes the output piston to move in its cylinder.

3. Transmitting pressure by liquid. The pressure applied to a liquid is transmitted by the liquid, in all directions and to every part of the liquid. For example (Fig. 24–4), when a piston with 1 square inch of area applies a force of 100 pounds on a liquid, the pressure on the liquid is 100 psi (pounds per square inch). This pressure will be registered throughout the entire hydraulic system. If the area of the piston is 2 square inches and the piston applies a force of 100 pounds, then the pressure is only 50 psi (Fig. 24–5).

With an input-output system (Fig. 24–6), we can determine the force applied to any output piston by multiplying the pressure in psi by the area of the output piston in square inches. For example, the pressure shown in Fig. 24–6 is 100 psi. The output piston to the left has an area of 0.5 square

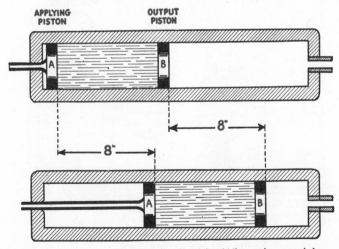

Fig. 24–2. Motion can be transmitted by liquids. When the applying piston A is moved 8 inches, then the output piston is also moved 8 inches. (*Pontiac Motor Division of General Motors Corporation*)

487

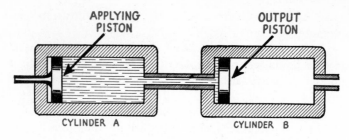

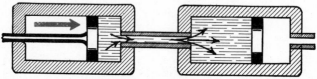

Fig. 24–3. Motion may be transmitted through a tube from one cylinder to another by hydraulic pressure. *(Pontiac Motor Division of General Motors Corporation)*

inch. Thus, the output force on this piston is 100 times 0.5, or 50 pounds. The center piston has an area of 1 square inch, and its output force is therefore 100 pounds. The right-hand piston has an area of 2 square inches, and its output force is therefore 200 pounds (100 × 2). The bigger the output piston, the greater the output force. If the area of the piston were 100 square inches, for example, then the output force would be 10,000

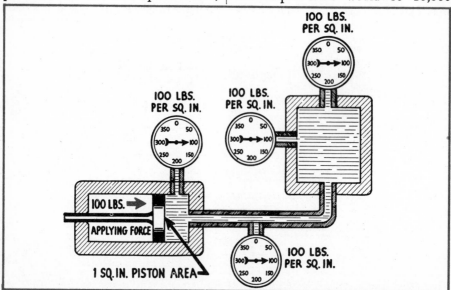

Fig. 24–4. The pressure applied to a liquid is transmitted equally in all directions. *(Pontiac Motor Division of General Motors Corporation)*

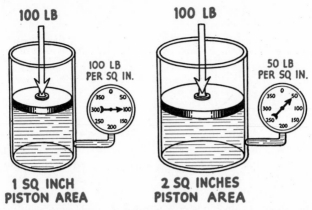

Fig. 24—5. The hydraulic pressure (in psi) in the system is determined by dividing the applying force (pounds) by the area (square inches) of the applying piston. (*Pontiac Motor Division of General Motors Corporation*)

pounds. Likewise, the higher the hydraulic pressure, the greater the output force. If the hydraulic pressure on the 2-square-inch piston went up to 1,000 psi, then the output force on the piston would be 2,000 pounds.

In all the illustrations above, a piston-cylinder arrangement has been shown as the means of producing the pressure. However, any sort of pump can be used. We shall learn, in studying the various automatic transmissions, that several types of pump have been used (gear, rotor, vane).

4. Hydraulic valves. A simple application of the above principles is

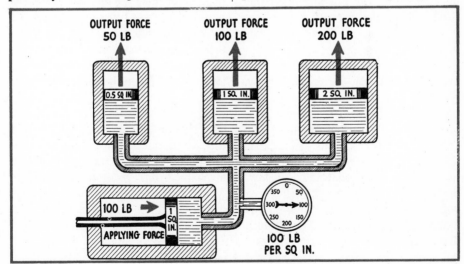

Fig. 24—6. The force (pounds) applied to the output piston is the pressure in the system in psi times the area (square inches) of the output piston. (*Pontiac Motor Division of General Motors Corporation*)

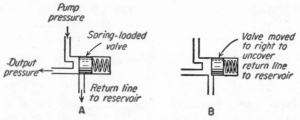

Fig. 24–7. A pressure-regulating valve (A). As pump pressure increases, the spring-loaded valve moves back against spring pressure (as at B), dumping more of the oil from the pump into the return line. This maintains a constant output pressure.

found in a pressure-regulating valve (Fig. 24–7). The valve is spring-loaded and is essentially a small piston that can move back and forth in a cylinder. The valve acts to produce a constant pressure from a variable-pressure source. For example, suppose the pressure source is an oil pump being driven by an automobile engine. When the engine is operating at high speed, the oil pump is also being operated at high speed and will produce a high pressure. The pressure-regulating valve reduces this pressure to a preset value, however, in the following manner:

As the pressure goes up, there is an increasing force on the valve. Finally, when the preset value is reached, the oil pressure is great enough (in psi), to overcome the spring pressure. The valve is moved back in its cylinder. As it moves back, it uncovers an opening, or port, which is connected to a low-pressure return line to the oil reservoir. Now, part of the oil from the pump can flow through this return line. This reduces the pressure so that the valve starts forward again (moved by the spring pressure). However, as it moves forward, it partly shuts off the port to the return line. Since less

490

oil can now escape, the oil pressure goes up and the valve is again moved back. Actually, the valve does not normally move back and forth, as described above. Instead, it seeks, and finds, the position at which the oil pressure just balances the spring pressure. Then, if the oil pressure changes (owing to a change in pump speed), the valve position will change. In action, the valve maintains a constant output pressure by dumping a smaller or greater part of the oil from the pump. As pump pressure goes up, for example (which means that the pump delivers more oil), the valve moves back to open the port wider and permit more of the oil to flow into the return line.

5. *Balanced valve.* In automatic transmissions, balanced valves are used to produce pressure changes that are proportional to the movement of mechanical linkage or to variations in spring pressure. A balanced valve is shown in Fig. 24–8. It contains a valve spool which is essentially a solid cylinder with an undercut section. The valve spool moves back and forth in a cylinder. Oil pressure works against it on one end and spring pressure against it on the other end. In the centered

position shown in Fig. 24–8, input oil, under constant pressure, passes into the cylinder, around the undercut section of the valve spool, through the by-pass line, and then out through the return line and the output-pressure line. Input pressure is held constant by a pressure-regulating valve as explained in the previous paragraph. Let us see how variations in spring pressure can cause variations in output pressure.

In Fig. 24–9A, the mechanical linkage has been moved so as to increase the spring pressure against the end of the valve spool. The valve spool therefore moves (to the left in the figure). This movement tends to close the return line. As the return line is closed, pressure begins to build up on the output end of the valve (just as in the pressure-regulator valve discussed above). The increasing pressure acts against the output end of the valve, and this pressure works against spring pressure. When a balanced condition is reached (output pressure balances spring pressure), the valve stops moving.

If the spring pressure is reduced by movement of the linkage (B in Fig. 24–9), then the pressure on the output end of the valve can move the valve (to the right in the figure). As the valve moves, it tends to close off the input-pressure line. Consequently, less oil can enter, and a lowered pressure results. The pressure falls off until a balanced condition results (output pressure balances spring pressure) Then the valve stops moving.

To show you exactly how the valve might work, let us look at a couple of examples. Suppose the output end of the valve has an area of 1 square inch and that the input pressure is 100 psi. Now, let us apply a spring pressure of 10 pounds on the valve spool (see Fig. 24–10). For the valve to balance, there must be only 10 pounds force

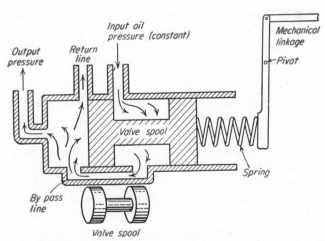

Fig. 24–8. Schematic layout of a balanced valve. The small drawing at the bottom is a perspective view of the valve spool; this gives you a better idea of what the valve spool looks like.

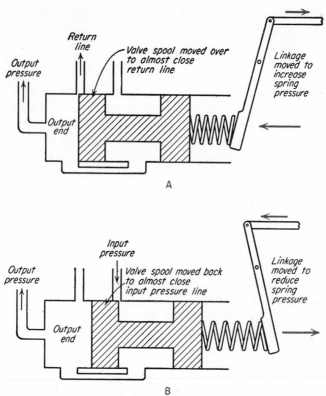

Fig. 24–9. If the linkage is moved to increase the spring pressure (A), then the valve spool will be moved toward the output end to partly close off the return line and permit a hydraulic-pressure increase to balance the spring-pressure increase. However, if the linkage is moved to reduce the spring pressure (B), then the hydraulic pressure forces the valve spool away from the output end to partly close off the input-pressure line so that hydraulic pressure is reduced to balance the spring-pressure reduction.

on the output end. The oil pressure, as it enters and goes through the bypass to the output end, forces the valve to the right (in the figure). This movement tends to shut off the input pressure. The pressure is therefore reduced until a balance is attained. At this point, the output oil pressure would be 10 psi. If the pressure on the spring reaches 100 pounds, then the full input pressure (of 100 psi) can pass unhampered through the valve; this then

becomes the output pressure. A spring pressure of above 100 pounds cannot, however, raise the pressure above 100 psi since that is all the pressure (the input pressure) that is available.

6. *Servos.* Let us take a look at a different sort of hydraulic device used in automatic transmissions (and countless other mechanisms). This device is the servo (Fig. 24–11). Essentially, the servo is a cylinder and piston. Hydraulic pressure can be admitted to

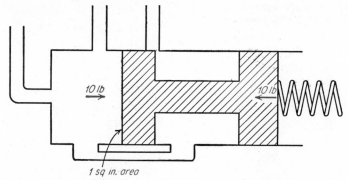

Fig. 24–10. If a spring pressure of 10 pounds is applied, the valve will be moved to the right just enough to admit an input pressure of 10 pounds (output end having an area of 1 square inch).

one or the other end of the cylinder. This causes the piston to move; mechanical linkage from the piston then causes movement of some mechanism. Thus, hydraulic pressure is used to produce a mechanical action. In Fig. 24–11, if hydraulic pressure is applied to the piston, the piston will move (to the right in the figure). This action causes the piston rod to apply the brake band. Thus, the brake drum can be made to stop turning by increasing the hydraulic pressure. As a matter of fact, the hydraulic brakes used in automobiles work on exactly this principle. Operation of a foot pedal increases the hydraulic pressure in the master-brake cylinder, and this increasing hydraulic pressure causes pistons in the wheel cylinders to move. As the wheel-cylinder pistons move, they force the brake shoes against the brake drums so that the car is braked.

In automatic transmissions, we shall find several different types of servos as well as several varieties of control,

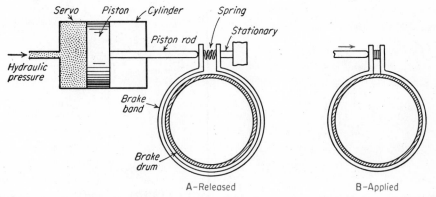

Fig. 24–11. The servo consists of a piston that moves in a cylinder in accordance with changing hydraulic pressure. This movement may be used to perform some job, applying a brake, for example.

**AIR IS THE "FLUID" USED AS THE
MEDIUM OF POWER TRANSFER**

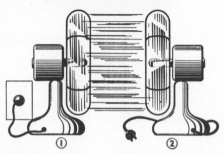

① ②

Fig. 24–12. Rotation of fan 1 causes fan 2 to rotate. This is a simple fluid coupling with air serving as the fluid.

regulating, and balanced valves. All operate on the principles described above.

§ 443. Operation of fluid coupling
Fluid couplings in one form or another are used in automatic transmissions. The power flows through the fluid coupling from the engine to the transmission gears. Since the power flows through a fluid (instead of through a mechanical device like a clutch) torsional vibration from the engine, as

well as roughness resulting from changing the gear ratio, is smoothed out. Let us discuss fluid couplings, their construction and operation.

1. Fluid coupling. A simple fluid coupling could be made with two electric fans. If the fans were placed a few inches apart and facing each other, and if one fan were plugged in so that it ran, the current of air from it would cause the blades of the other fan to turn (Fig. 24–12). In this case, the air is the fluid, but since the two fans are not enclosed or closely coupled, this sort of fluid coupling is not very efficient. To make a more efficient fluid coupling, oil is used as the fluid and the two halves, or "members," of the coupling are mounted very close together and enclosed in a housing. Figure 24–13 shows the two members of a fluid coupling. Note that they

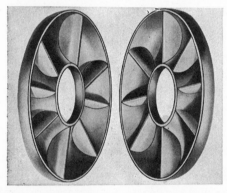

Fig. 24–13. Simplified version of two members of a fluid coupling. (*Chevrolet Motor Division of General Motors Corporation*)

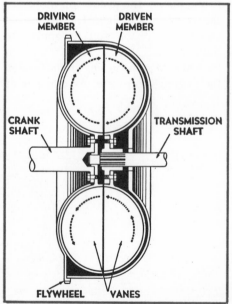

Fig. 24–14. Cross-sectional view of a fluid coupling. (*Studebaker-Packard Corporation*)

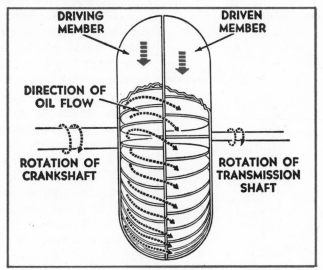

Fig. 24–15. Fluid coupling in action. Oil is thrown from driving into driven member. Outer casings have been cut away so that vanes can be seen. (*Studebaker-Packard Corporation*)

resemble a hollowed-out doughnut sliced in half, with blades, or vanes, set radially into the hollow halves. Figure 24–14 is a cross section of a fluid coupling. The driving member is attached to the engine crankshaft, while the driven member is attached to the transmission shaft. This shaft, in turn, is connected through gearing and the propeller shaft, to the differential and the rear wheels.

The hollow space in the two members is filled with oil. When the driving member begins to rotate (as the engine is started and runs), the oil is set into motion. The vanes in the driving member start to carry the oil around with them. As the oil is thus spun round, it is thrown outward, or away from the shaft, by centrifugal force. This means that the oil moves outward in the driving member in a circular path, as shown by the dotted arrows in Fig. 24–14. Also, since the oil is being car-

ried round with the rotating driving member, it is thrown into the driven member at an angle, as shown in Fig. 24–15. The oil thus strikes the vanes of the driven member at an angle, as shown, thereby imparting torque, or turning effort, to the driven member. The faster the driving member turns, the driven member being stationary, the harder the oil strikes the vanes of the driven member. The harder the oil strikes the vanes, the greater the turning effort imparted to the driven member (within limits).

This turning effort, carried to the wheels, sets the car into motion. As the driven member approaches the speed of the driving member, the effective force of the oil on the driven-member vanes is reduced. If the two members turn at the same speed, then the oil will not pass from one to the other member. With no oil passing from one to the other member, no

495

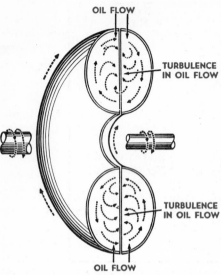

Fig. 24–16. Turbulence in oil flow in center sections of fluid-coupling members. (*Studebaker-Packard Corporation*)

power is being transmitted through the coupling. Thus, this "same-speed" condition will not exist when the engine is driving the car. The driving member always has to be turning a little faster than the driven member for engine power to flow through the fluid coupling to the car wheels.

However, if the engine speed is reduced so that the car begins to drive the engine, there will be a point at which both members turn at the same speed. Then, as the engine slows further, the driven member will temporarily become the driving member (since the car will be driving it). As this happens, the normally driven member will begin to pass oil into the normally driving member. Now, the engine will exert a braking effect on the car (the same condition that results in a clutch-equipped car when you release the accelerator and coast).

2. Guide ring. The simple fluid coupling described in previous paragraphs would not be very efficient under many conditions because of the turbulence that would be set up in the oil. Turbulence is a state of violent random motion or agitation. Thus, under certain conditions (when there is considerable difference in speed between the driving and driven members), the oil would be striking the vanes of the driven member with great force. This would cause the oil to swirl about in all directions, particularly in the center sections of the members (Fig. 24–16). To reduce this turbulence, and thereby make the coupling more efficient, some fluid couplings use a split guide ring centered in the members (Fig. 24–17). The guide ring looks much like a hollowed-out doughnut, sliced in half. Each half is attach-

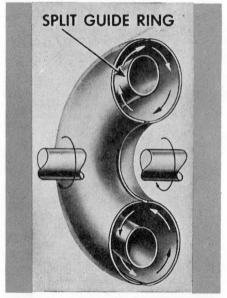

Fig. 24–17. Split guide ring designed to reduce oil turbulence. (*Chevrolet Motor Division of General Motors Corporation*)

ed to the vanes of one of the coupling members. With this arrangement, the oil does not have a chance to set up the turbulences as shown in Fig. 24–16.

3. *Operating characteristics of fluid coupling.* The fluid coupling operates at maximum efficiency when the driven member approaches the speed of the driving member. If there is a big difference in the speeds of the two members, power is lost and efficiency is low. In the following chapter, on torque converters, we will examine more closely the reason for this loss of efficiency. The fluid coupling is used with a gear-shifting mechanism and a form of transmission which provides the varying gear ratios between the engine and rear wheels. Following sections describe various transmissions using fluid couplings.

§ 444. Fluid coupling and clutch Figure 24–18 is a sectional view of a fluid coupling and conventional-type clutch. This assembly is used with an automatic transmission on cars manufactured by the Chrysler Corporation. The fluid coupling is called, by the manufacturer, a *Fluid Drive*. On late-model cars, the fluid coupling, or Fluid Drive, has been replaced with a torque converter (Chap. 25), or *Fluid-Torque Drive,* as it is called by the manufacturer. The transmission itself is a four-forward and one-reverse-speed unit (§ 445). An automatic control system (§ 446) provides control of the transmission so that the driver is not required to do more than a minimum of gear shifting. The transmission has two manually selected "forward-operating" positions (low and high) as well as reverse. In the

"low" position, the transmission will automatically shift from first to second or from second to first, according to car speed and throttle movement. In the "high" position, the transmission will automatically shift from third to fourth, or from fourth to third, according to car speed and throttle movement. These actions are described in following articles.

The fluid coupling is used with the transmission to provide a flexible coupling that will cushion and absorb the shock of de-meshing from one gear position and meshing in another gear position. The clutch is used when a shift is manually made into or out of the "high," "low," or "reverse-operating" positions.

§ 445. Transmission used with fluid coupling The transmission used with the fluid coupling described in the previous article is shown partly disassembled in Fig. 24–19. The direct-speed clutch sleeve and the third-speed gear are assembled onto the shaft on bearings so that they can turn independently of the shaft. The first-speed gear can likewise turn independently of the main shaft. The countershaft has a freewheeling gear assembled on it, and this freewheeling gear has, under it, a form of overrunning clutch much like the one used in the overdrive (§ 433). This permits the freewheeling gear to drive the main shaft through the countershaft gears under certain conditions and to idle without transmitting power under other conditions. Refer to Figs. 24–20 to 24–24 to see how the power travels through the transmission in the four forward- and one reverse-gear positions. Remember

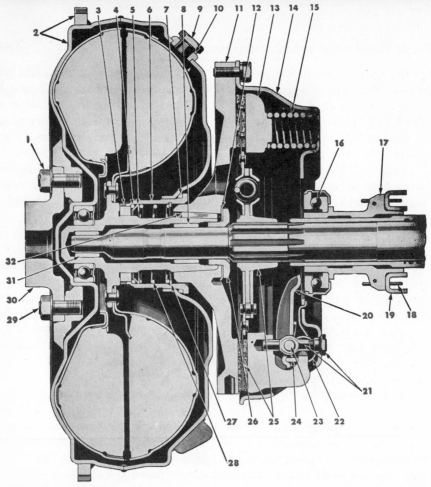

Fig. 24–18. Sectional view of a fluid coupling and conventional clutch. (*Dodge Division of Chrysler Corporation*)

1. Flange stud nut
2. Fluid Drive assembly
3. Floating seal ring
4. Seal-ring gasket
5. Seal-ring-gasket retainer
6. Seal housing
7. Seal-housing gasket
8. Runner bushing— rear
9. Filler plug
10. Filler-plug gasket
11. Clutch driving plate
12. Driving-plate lock washer
13. Clutch pressure plate
14. Clutch cover
15. Clutch pressure spring
16. Clutch-release bearing
17. Clutch-release-bearing sleeve
18. Clutch-release bearing-sleeve pullback spring
19. Clutch-release fork
20. Clutch-release lever
21. Clutch-release-lever eyebolt and nut
22. Clutch-release-lever spring
23. Clutch-release-lever pin
24. Clutch-release-lever strut
25. Clutch-disk assembly
26. Driving-plate nut
27. Seal-spring-retainer snap ring
28. Seal spring
29. Driving-flange stud
30. Crankshaft
31. Runner bushing— front
32. Driving-plate key

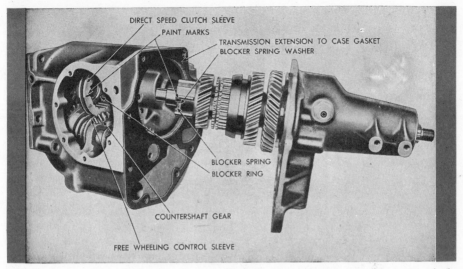

Fig. 24–19. Transmission partly disassembled, showing the gears on the main shaft. (*Dodge Division of Chrysler Corporation*)

that the transmission automatically shifts between first and second in low, and between third and fourth in high.

§ **446. Transmission controls** The transmission described in the previous section has a control system utilizing the controls shown in Fig. 24–25. In addition, the carburetor contains a kick-down switch and an antistall control. The wiring circuit of the system is shown in Fig. 24–26. Control of the transmission depends on car speed and throttle movement. The governor, which is mounted on the transmission case as shown in Fig. 24–25 and is driven from the countershaft, turns faster or slower as car speed is increased or decreased. When the proper speed is attained, the governor opens a set of contacts, causing the transmission to upshift into a higher gear (from first to second, or from third to fourth). This deenergizes the solenoid

and allows the ball valve to seat. Now, oil pressure moves the direct-speed piston to the left so that the shift is made as soon as the accelerator is momentarily released.

If the driver wishes to downshift so as to have more power for passing, for example, he pushes the accelerator pedal all the way down. This closes the kick-down switch in the carburetor, producing the downshift action.

§ **447. Hydra-Matic**
There are two versions of the Hydra-Matic transmission that have been used on a number of different cars. The type shown in Fig. 24–28 is the later version. It has two fluid couplings as compared with the one fluid coupling the earlier version has (Fig. 24–27). This section describes the transmission with the single fluid coupling; the following section (§ 448) describes the transmission with two fluid couplings.

499

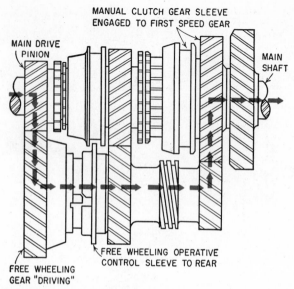

Fig. 24–20. Transmission gears in first, or low, gear. (*Dodge Division of Chrysler Corporation*)

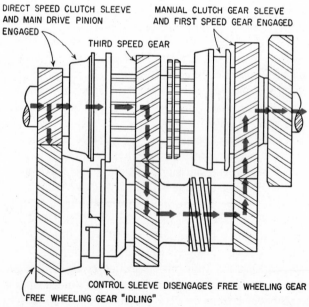

Fig. 24–21. Transmission gears in second. (*Dodge Division of Chrysler Corporation*)

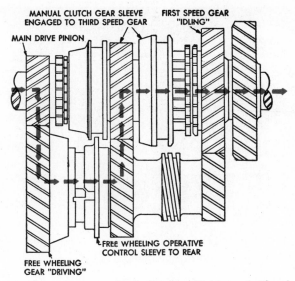

Fig. 24–22. Transmission gears in third. (*Dodge Division of Chrysler Corporation*)

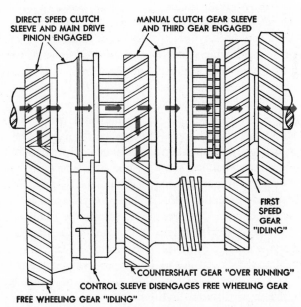

Fig. 24–23. Transmission gears in fourth. (*Dodge Division of Chrysler Corporation*)

REVERSE IDLER GEAR—DISENGAGED   REVERSE IDLER GEAR—ENGAGED

Fig. 24–24. Reverse-idler gear in the "disengaged" and in the "engaged" positions. (*Dodge Division of Chrysler Corporation*)

The transmission consists of a fluid coupling, described in § 443 (called a *torus* by the manufacturer), plus three planetary-gear systems (§ 434) and the controls needed to produce proper action in the planetary-gear systems. In addition, there is a hydraulic system consisting of two oil pumps, a governor and control valves, and cylinders with pistons (or *servos*) which function on oil pressure from the oil pumps. The pistons move in response to changing oil pressure to exercise control of the planetary-gear systems.

The Hydra-Matic may appear somewhat complex at first glance, but when we sort out the parts, we shall see that it operates on the simple principles we have already discussed. Essentially the Hydra-Matic is a mechanism that provides four forward speeds and one reverse speed. When the selector lever on the steering column is placed in the DR ("drive") position, the transmission will automatically shift from first to second to third to fourth speed in

accordance with engine and car speeds and throttle opening. (On some models the shift is from second to third to fourth in DR, the first speed position being absent in DR.) In the LO (low) range, only the first- and second-gear positions are attained. N is neutral and R is reverse on the selector-lever indicator plate. Some later models are known as dual-range transmissions and have an additional lever position. This additional lever position is indicated on some cars by an S on the indicator plate; the "S" stands for super performance. On other cars, the additional position is indicated by DR 3 and DR 4 or by two arrows side by side under DR on the indicator plate. One of the arrows is for the standard DR range, the other for the performance or super-performance range. Regardless of the way it is indicated, the purpose of the additional lever position is to provide another DR range. This performance or super-performance range still provides the

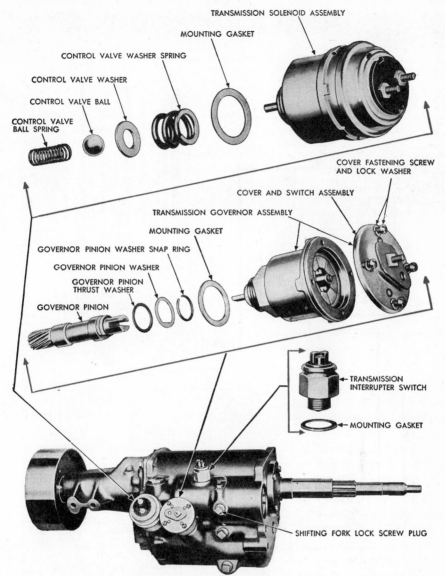

TRANSMISSION SOLENOID ASSEMBLY

MOUNTING GASKET

CONTROL VALVE WASHER SPRING

CONTROL VALVE WASHER

CONTROL VALVE BALL

CONTROL VALVE BALL SPRING

COVER FASTENING SCREW AND LOCK WASHER

COVER AND SWITCH ASSEMBLY

TRANSMISSION GOVERNOR ASSEMBLY

MOUNTING GASKET

GOVERNOR PINION WASHER SNAP RING

GOVERNOR PINION WASHER

GOVERNOR PINION THRUST WASHER

GOVERNOR PINION

TRANSMISSION INTERRUPTER SWITCH

MOUNTING GASKET

SHIFTING FORK LOCK SCREW PLUG

Fig. 24–25. Transmission controls. (*Dodge Division of Chrysler Corporation*)

first to second to third to fourth shifts. However, the shift to fourth does not take place until a relatively high car speed is attained (as much as 75 mph at full throttle). The performance range is said to provide better control of the car in heavy traffic and hilly roads; automatic shifting is reduced, and better acceleration is achieved. In addition, there is an increase in engine braking effort when the car descends hills.

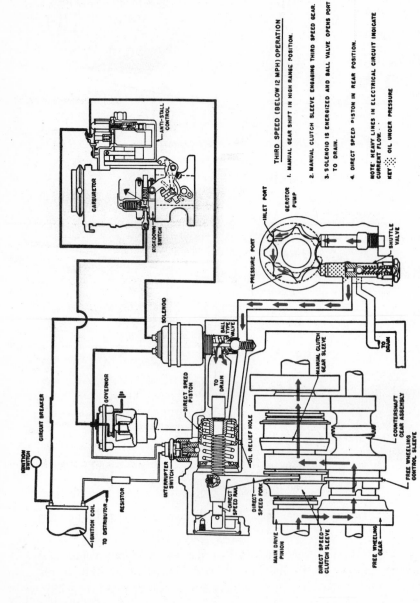

THIRD SPEED (BELOW 12 MPH) OPERATION

1. MANUAL GEAR SHIFT IN HIGH RANGE POSITION.

2. MANUAL CLUTCH SLEEVE ENGAGING THIRD SPEED GEAR.

3. SOLENOID IS ENERGIZED AND BALL VALVE OPENS PORT TO DRAIN.

4. DIRECT SPEED PISTON IN REAR POSITION.

NOTE: HEAVY LINES IN ELECTRICAL CIRCUIT INDICATE CURRENT FLOW.

KEY: OIL UNDER PRESSURE

Fig. 24–27. Control circuit for transmission, showing conditions when transmission is in third speed below 12 mph. (*Dodge Division of Chrysler Corporation*)

§ 448. Hydra-Matic with two fluid couplings

The Hydra-Matic transmission with two fluid couplings is shown in Figs. 24–28 and 24–29. The larger fluid coupling is similar to that used in the earlier models. The second coupling is smaller and is of the controlled type. That is, it can be filled with oil to provide a coupling effect, or it can be emptied to take it out of action entirely. When the second coupling is filled, it locks the front planetary-gear system (located in the first coupling housing). This provides direct drive through the front planetary-gear system. When the second coupling is emptied, it has no coupling action, and this permits the front planetary-gear system to go into reduction. The use of the second coupling provides a smooth transition as the front planetary system upshifts.

§ 449. Planetary gears in Hydra-Matic

We have already described planetary gears in some detail, and you should review § 434 if you are not sure you understand their construction and operation. Figure 24–30 shows a planetary-gear set used in the Hydra-Matic transmission. It contains the usual three members; sun gear, planet pinions in a cage, and ring gear (or internal gear, as it is often called). As already explained (§ 434), holding one member and turning another causes the assembly to become a speed-reducing or a speed-increasing unit, while locking two members together produces a direct drive (1:1) through the gear set. Also, if the cage is held stationary and the ring gear is turned, the sun gear will turn in the reverse direction. In the Hydra-Matic, the planetary-gear systems function either as direct drives or as speed-reducing units. In addition, the systems function together when the selector lever is in reverse to produce reverse rotation of the tail shaft (output shaft) and backing of the car.

§ 450. Planetary-gear-system control

Figure 24–31 illustrates the mechanisms used with a planetary system to achieve the various conditions. There are two of these mechanisms: a multiple-plate clutch, and a brake band and brake drum. Note that the input shaft has the internal gear (ring gear) on it, while the planet-pinion cage (carrier) is attached to the output shaft. The sun gear is separately mounted, and it has a brake drum as part of the sun-gear assembly. The sun gear and brake drum turn together as a unit.

NOTE: This is the arrangement used on the front planetary-gear system in the Hydra-Matic. In the rear (not reverse) planetary-gear system, the brake drum and internal, or ring, gear are integral, while the planet-pinion cage is directly attached to the output shaft. Also, the sun gear is integral with the intermediate shaft, which is splined to the driven member of the fluid coupling. The reverse planetary-gear system has still another arrangement as explained in following paragraphs.

The brake band is operated by a servo as shown in Fig. 24–32. The servo consists of two pistons on a single stem (rod), all mounted in a

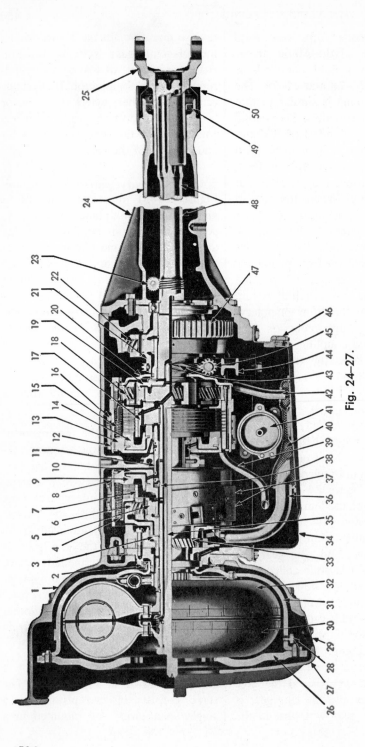

Fig. 24–27.

Fig. 24–27. Partial cutaway view of the Hydra-Matic. (Cadillac Motor Car Division of General Motors Corporation)

1. Flywheel-housing rear cover
2. Front-cover oil seal
3. Front-unit drive gear
4. Front-unit clutch-release springs
5. Front-unit center gear
6. Front-unit planetary gears
7. Front-unit clutch hub
8. Front-unit brake drum
9. Front-unit clutch piston
10. Front-unit clutch cover
11. Oil-delivery sleeve
12. Rear-unit brake drum
13. Rear-unit clutch cover
14. Rear-unit clutch piston
15. Rear-unit clutch-release springs
16. Rear-unit band
17. Rear-unit clutch hub
18. Rear-unit planetary gears
19. Rear-unit planet carrier
20. Reverse-unit drive flange
21. Reverse-unit planet carrier
22. Reverse-unit planetary gears
23. Speedometer pinion
24. Main-shaft extension housing
25. Universal-joint yoke
26. Flywheel
27. Lower flywheel housing
28. Cover drain plug
29. Inspection-hole cover
30. Driven member
31. Cover
32. Driving member
33. Front oil-pump drive gear
34. Oil pan
35. Main shaft
36. Front oil-pump inlet pipe
37. Front-unit band
38. Intermediate shaft
39. Oil-transfer pipe
40. Oil screen
41. Rear servo
42. Rear oil-pump inlet pipe
43. Rear pump and governor drive gear
44. Rear oil pump
45. Rear oil pump and governor driven gear
46. Oil-pan drain plug
47. Reverse-unit internal
48. Driven shaft
49. Rear oil seal
50. Rear-bearing dust shield

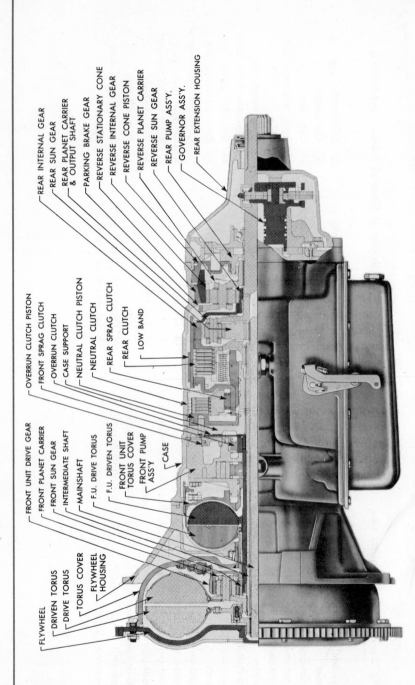

FLYWHEEL
DRIVEN TORUS
DRIVE TORUS
TORUS COVER
FLYWHEEL HOUSING

FRONT UNIT DRIVE GEAR
FRONT PLANET CARRIER
FRONT SUN GEAR
INTERMEDIATE SHAFT
MAINSHAFT
F.U. DRIVE TORUS
F.U. DRIVEN TORUS
FRONT UNIT TORUS COVER
FRONT PUMP ASS'Y
CASE

OVERRUN CLUTCH PISTON
FRONT SPRAG CLUTCH
OVERRUN CLUTCH
CASE SUPPORT
NEUTRAL CLUTCH PISTON
NEUTRAL CLUTCH
REAR SPRAG CLUTCH
REAR CLUTCH
LOW BAND

REAR INTERNAL GEAR
REAR SUN GEAR
REAR PLANET CARRIER & OUTPUT SHAFT
PARKING BRAKE GEAR
REVERSE STATIONARY CONE
REVERSE INTERNAL GEAR
REVERSE CONE PISTON
REVERSE PLANET CARRIER
REVERSE SUN GEAR
REAR PUMP ASS'Y.
GOVERNOR ASS'Y.
REAR EXTENSION HOUSING

Fig. 24–28. Partial sectional view of Hydra-Matic transmission using two fluid couplings. (Oldsmobile Division of General Motors Corporation)

508

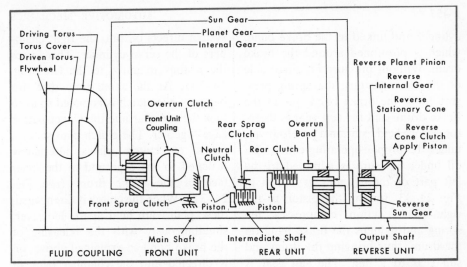

Fig. 24–29. Schematic drawing showing the relationship of the various mechanisms in the Hydra-Matic with two fluid couplings. (*Cadillac Motor Car Division of General Motors Corporation*)

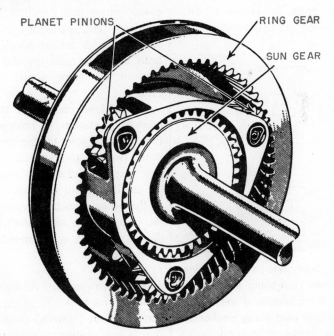

Fig. 24–30. Planetary-gear set as used in the Hydra-Matic. (*American Motors Corporation*)

509

cylinder and linked to the brake band, which is positioned around the brake drum. Without pressure on either side of the servo pistons, the spring pressure holds the brake band free of the brake drum, and the sun gear is therefore not held stationary. However, under the proper operating conditions, oil under pressure is admitted to the left part of the cylinder as shown in Fig. 24–33, forcing the piston to the right. This action compresses the spring and tightens the brake band on the drum, thus bringing the drum and sun gear to a halt. The sun gear is therefore held stationary. With the ring gear being turned and the sun gear held, condition 2 (Fig. 22–6) is obtained, and there is speed reduction, or gear reduction, through the system.

Under certain other conditions, the brake band must be released. This takes place when the hydraulic control

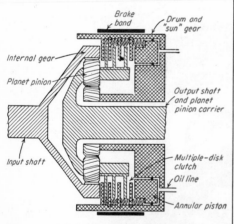

Fig. 24–31. Schematic sectional view showing the two controlling mechanisms used in the front planetary set in the Hydra-Matic. One controlling mechanism consists of a brake drum and brake band; the other is a multiple-disk clutch. (*American Motors Corporation*)

system directs oil into the right chambers of the servo cylinder. This forces the pistons to move to the left (Fig. 24–34). At the same time that this happens, the clutch is actuated so as to lock the sun gear and the planet-pinion cage together. The clutch consists of a series of clutch plates alternately fastened to the cage and to the inner face of the brake drum (see Fig. 24–31). When the clutch is disengaged, these plates are held apart. However, simultaneously with the releasing of the brake band as explained above, oil is directed into the chamber back of the annular (ring-shaped) piston in the brake-drum-sun-gear assembly. This forces the piston to the left (Fig. 24–35) so that the clutch plates are forced together. Then, friction between the plates locks the sun gear and the planet-pinion cage together. When this happens, the planetary-gear system acts like a direct-drive coupling and both the input and the output shafts turn at the same speed (1:1 gear ratio).

To achieve reverse, a third planetary-gear system is incorporated in the transmission, to the rear of the other two. In this special system, the ring gear is locked for reverse. This action, in combination with the action of the other planetary systems, causes the transmission main shaft to reverse directions. This is explained in a following section.

§ 451. Shift control As we have seen, applying the brake band on the planetary-gear set (system) so that the sun gear is held stationary produces a gear reduction through the system. On the other hand, if the brake band is re-

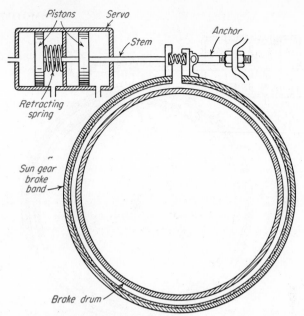

Fig. 24–32. Arrangement of the servo, brake band, and brake drum. (*American Motors Corporation*)

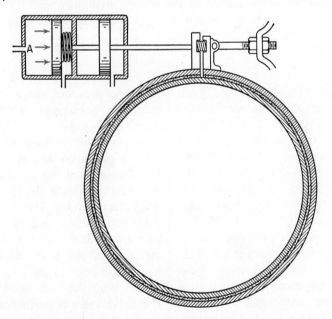

Fig. 24–33. When hydraulic pressure is applied back of the piston at A, the piston and rod move (to the right in the illustration) to cause the brake band to tighten on the brake drum. The brake drum (and sun gear) is thus held stationary. (*American Motors Corporation*)

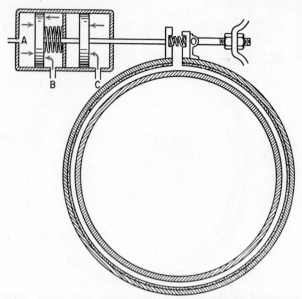

Fig. 24–34. When the hydraulic control system admits oil under pressure at B and C, the pressure forces the pistons to the left (in illustration) and thereby causes the brake to release the brake drum and sun gear so that the sun gear can rotate. (*American Motors Corporation*)

leased and at the same time the clutch is applied, the planetary set upshifts or goes into direct drive. This shifting must be controlled so as to take place only under certain operating conditions. Figure 24–36 illustrates the shifting control circuit schematically.

Let us see what produces an upshift, that is, what causes the brake band to release and the clutch to apply. There are two controlling factors in the shift: car speed and throttle opening. These two factors produce two varying oil pressures that work against opposite ends of the shift valve. One pressure is from the governor and is based on car speed. The other pressure is from the throttle valve and is based on throttle opening. The two pressures are called governor pressure and throttle pressure [or sometimes TV (throttle-valve) pressure].

1. Governor pressure. The governor consists essentially of a rotor, or housing, driven from the tail shaft of the transmission. Inside the housing there is a governor valve. The valve has two opposing forces acting on it: centrifugal force due to rotation of the housing, and oil pressure (from the oil pump) admitted to the housing by the valve. With low car and governor speed, the valve is positioned near the center of the housing and passes only a small oil pressure. However, as car speed increases, the governor housing rotates more rapidly and centrifugal force causes the valve to move out-

ward. The valve thus passes a larger percentage of the pump pressure. This increasing pressure (governor pressure) is applied to one end of the shift valve.

2. Throttle pressure. Opposing governor pressure on the shift valve are spring pressure and also throttle pressure (from the throttle valve). The throttle valve, as you will note, is our old friend, the balanced valve (§ 442, 5). In this valve, output pressure equals spring pressure. With only a small throttle opening, only a small spring pressure will be applied, and thus there will be only a small output pressure (throttle pressure). But as the throttle is opened wider, the spring pressure is increased and thus the throttle pressure is also increased. The throttle pressure is applied to the spring end of the shift valve (end opposite governor-pressure end).

3. Effects of governor and throttle pressures on shift valve. We have seen how the two varying oil pressures are applied to the two ends of the shift valve. Now, let us see how these two oil pressures (throttle and governor) control the shift valve and thus the band and clutch in the planetary-gear set. As car speed increases, governor pressure also increases. This pressure, applied to one end of the shift valve, tries to move the shift valve. However, the other end of the shift valve has spring pressure and throttle pressure against it. With a small throttle opening, throttle pressure is low. This means that car speed, and governor pressure, do not have to go very high to overcome the spring pressure (and low throttle pressure). Thus, when governor pressure goes up enough, it

forces the shift valve to move. As the shift valve moves, it uncovers the inlet port, which admits pump pressure to the valve body. This pump pressure now travels through the valve body and connecting tubes to the clutch and servo. Pump pressure thus releases the brake and applies the clutch. With the clutch applied, the planetary set goes into direct drive.

If the throttle is opened wider, the throttle pressure is increased. This means that higher governor pressure (and higher car speed) is required for upshifting. Thus, upshifting is controlled by both throttle opening and car speed. With a light throttle (small throttle opening), upshifting will occur at a relatively low car speed. But with

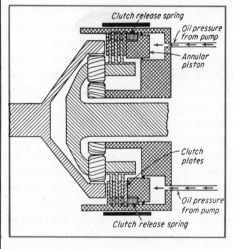

Fig. 24-35. One set of clutch plates is splined to the sun-gear drum. The other set is splined to the planet-pinion carrier. When the hydraulic control system directs oil back of the annular piston, the clutch plates are forced together so that the sun gear and planet-pinion carrier are locked together. (*American Motors Corporation*)

513

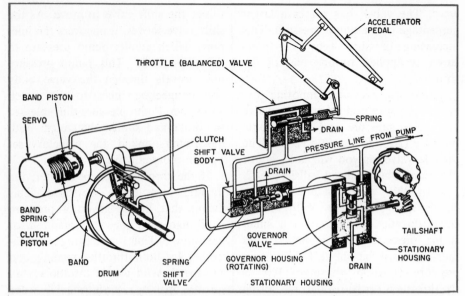

Fig. 24–36. Schematic diagram showing the hydraulic control system for the brake-band servo and the clutch. In the system shown, the band is normally on and the clutch off; this produces gear reduction. But when the shift valve is moved, pressure from the oil pump is admitted to the front of the brake-band piston and to the clutch piston. This causes the brake to release and the clutch to apply. Now, with the clutch locking two planetary members together, the planetary system goes into direct drive. (*Oldsmobile Division of General Motors Corporation*)

a heavy throttle, upshifting will not occur until a much higher car speed is reached. This improves performance since the transmission remains in the lower gear during heavy acceleration. When the driver wants to accelerate quickly, as when passing another car, he holds the throttle down. This keeps the transmission in the lower gear, where acceleration is better. On the other hand, in cruising along the highway at intermediate speed and with a light throttle, it is desirable to upshift as early as possible in order to take advantage of the higher, and more economical, gear ratio.

To sum up: The shift valve is an "on-off" valve. Either it admits oil pressure to the servo and clutch, or it shuts off the pressure. When it admits pressure, the planetary-gear set is in direct drive. When it shuts off the pressure, the planetary-gear set drops into gear reduction.

The governor pressure varies with car speed. The throttle pressure varies with throttle opening. These two pressures oppose each other on the two ends of the shift valve. Governor pressure must go high enough to overcome throttle pressure (and the spring pressure) to produce shift-valve movement and an upshift.

4. Other valves in the hydraulic system. There are other valves in the hydraulic system of the Hydra-Matic.

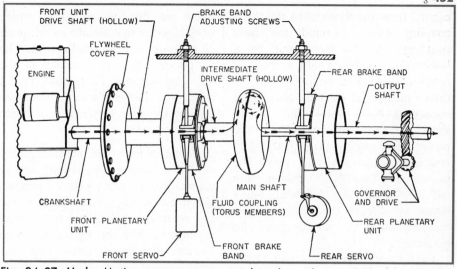

Fig. 24–37. Hydra-Matic components arranged in the order in which they actually transmit power from the engine to the transmission output shaft. Note that the power passes through the front planetary unit before it enters the fluid coupling (torus members). The reverse planetary unit is not shown. (*Oldsmobile Division of General Motors Corporation*)

Actually, the hydraulic system is rather complex. The additional valves function to smooth out the shifts and hasten the shifts at higher engine speeds (to prevent the engine from "running away" momentarily during shift). Also, they aid in downshifts, provide quick parking when the engine is turned off, etc. After we have discussed the operation of the power-transmitting units in the Hydra-Matic, we shall return to the valves and the hydraulic system.

§ **452. Hydra-Matic operation** We have seen how a shift valve can be used to cause an automatic upshift or downshift in a planetary-gear set. Now let us examine the operation of the two versions of the Hydra-Matic (the type with one fluid coupling as described in

§ 447 and the type with two fluid couplings as described in § 448). First, we will look at the type with one fluid coupling.

1. One-fluid-coupling unit. The transmission consists of the following components, listed in the order in which they transmit power (Fig. 24–37): flywheel, flywheel cover, front-planetary-unit drive shaft, front planetary unit, intermediate drive shaft, fluid coupling (torus), main shaft, rear planetary unit, reverse planetary unit, and output shaft.

Note that, in Fig. 24–37, the various units have been rearranged to show *the order in which power is transmitted.* These are not their positions in the actual transmission. Their actual positions are shown in Figs. 24–27 and 24–38. In the actual unit, the power is

515

carried from the flywheel to the fluid-coupling cover (around the fluid coupling), to the front unit by a hollow shaft, and then back to the fluid coupling by another hollow shaft. The driven member of the fluid coupling is connected by a solid shaft (main shaft) to the rear unit. Thus, the power, after passing through the fluid coupling, enters the rear unit. The power path through the transmission will be clarified on following pages when we discuss the action of the transmission in the various gear-ratio positions.

Each forward planetary unit (front and rear) has a separate servo for applying and releasing its brake band. Also, each of these two planetary units has a clutch operated by an annular piston as already described (§ 451). In addition, each planetary unit is controlled by a separate shift valve (Fig. 24–36). Thus, each planetary unit can upshift or downshift independently of the other. This arrangement gives the four forward gear ratios, as in Table 24–1.

As we mentioned above, each planetary unit has its own control system, servo, brake band, clutch, clutch piston, and shift valve. There are additional valves whose functions are described in the following article.

There are also two oil pumps which work together to maintain an adequate oil pressure in the control system. The oil pumps are also discussed in the following sections. First, however, let us see what happens with the transmission in the four forward gear ratios and in reverse.

NOTE: Names used interchangeably in the following discussion include planet gears and planet pinions, planet-pinion cage and planet-pinion carrier, fluid coupling and torus, driving member and driving torus, driven member and driven torus, ring gear and internal gear. These different names are used by different car companies, and thus you are likely to run into both names in the shop.

a. Neutral. In neutral with the engine running (Fig. 24–38), the power flows through the flywheel (1 in Fig. 24–38) and torus cover (2) and to the front-unit ring (internal) gear (3). Since the bands and clutches in both the front and rear planetary units are off, no power can be transmitted through the transmission.

b. First. In first (Fig. 24–39), the front band and the rear band are both on, and both the front and rear clutches are off, so that both planetary units are in reduction. The power flows

Table 24–1. FOUR FORWARD GEAR RATIOS

Front planetary	Rear planetary	Gear ratio
Downshifted (in reduction)	Downshifted (in reduction)	First
Upshifted (in direct drive)	Downshifted (in reduction)	Second
Downshifted (in reduction)	Upshifted (in direct drive)	Third
Upshifted (in direct drive)	Upshifted (in direct drive)	Fourth

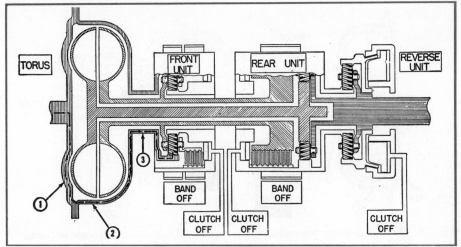

Fig. 24–38. Hydra-Matic transmission in neutral with engine running. (*Oldsmobile Division of General Motors Corporation*)

through the flywheel (1), torus cover (2), front-unit ring (internal) gear (3), and front-unit planet-pinion carrier and intermediate shaft (4) and to the driving torus (5). Power then flows through the torus (fluid coupling) to the driven torus (6), and from there to the main shaft (7) and sun gear of the rear unit (8). From there it passes into the planet-pinion carrier

(9) and to the output shaft (17). Note that, in the front unit, the sun gear is held stationary so that, when the ring gear rotates, the planet pinions must "walk around" the sun gear, carrying the planet-pinion carrier with them (at a reduced speed). In the rear unit, the ring gear is held stationary so that the planet pinions must "walk around" it when the sun gear rotates. This carries

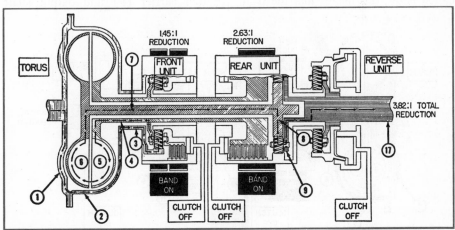

Fig. 24–39. Hydra-Matic transmission in first. (*Oldsmobile Division of General Motors Corporation*)

517

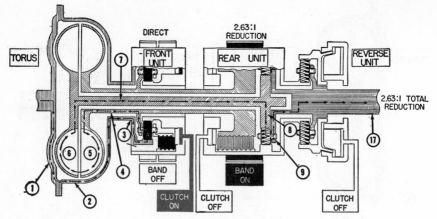

Fig. 24–40. Hydra-Matic transmission in second. (*Oldsmobile Division of General Motors Corporation*)

the planet-pinion carrier around (at a reduced speed). In both planetary units, gear reduction is achieved (§ 434).

The gear reduction in the front unit is 1.45:1. The gear reduction in the rear unit is 2.63:1. Thus, the total gear reduction in the transmission is 3.82:1 (1.45 × 2.63).

c. Second. In second (Fig. 24–40), the front band is off, and the front clutch is on; this means that the front

unit is in direct drive. The rear band is on, and the rear clutch is off; the rear unit is in reduction. The power flow is through the flywheel (1), torus cover (2), front-unit ring gear (3), and front unit in direct drive and to the intermediate shaft (4). From there, it flows through the torus (5 and 6), through the main shaft (7) to the rear sun gear (8) and to the planet-pinion carrier (9) and output shaft

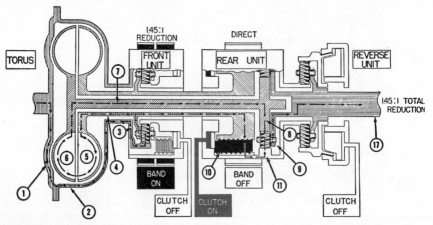

Fig. 24–41. Hydra-Matic transmission in third. (*Oldsmobile Division of General Motors Corporation*)

518

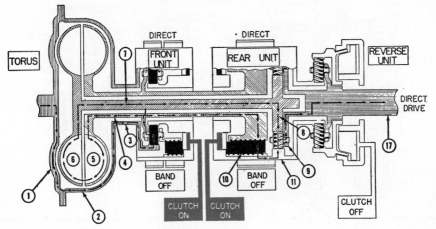

Fig. 24–42. Hydra-Matic transmission in fourth. (*Oldsmobile Division of General Motors Corporation*)

(17). Note that, in the front unit, the band is off and the clutch is on so that the sun gear and planet-pinion carrier are locked together; this means the planetary must turn as a unit or in direct drive. The rear unit functions exactly as it did in first (see above).

The gear reduction in the front unit is 1:1 (direct drive), while the gear reduction in the rear unit is 2.63:1. Thus, the total gear reduction in the transmission is $2.63:1$ (1×2.63).

d. Third. In third (Fig. 24–41), the front band is on, and the front clutch is off; this means that the front unit is in reduction. The rear band is off, and the rear clutch is on; the rear unit is in direct drive. The power flow is through the flywheel (1), torus cover (2), front planetary ring gear (3), and front-unit planet-pinion carrier and intermediate shaft (4). All

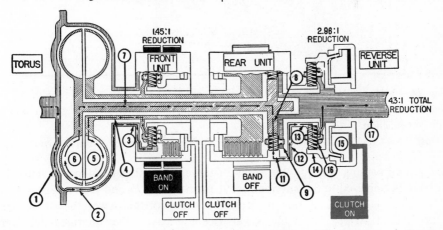

Fig. 24–43. Hydra-Matic transmission in reverse. (*Oldsmobile Division of General Motors Corporation*)

519

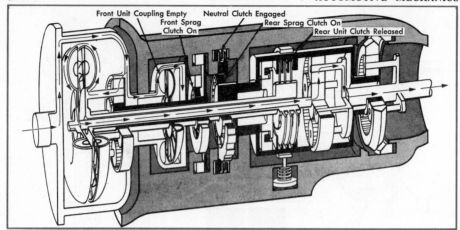

Fig. 24–44. Hydra-Matic with two fluid couplings in first. The front-unit coupling is empty and the front sprag clutch is on, so the front unit is in reduction. The rear sprag clutch is on and the rear clutch released, so the rear planetary is also in reduction. With both planetaries in reduction, the maximum gear reduction is achieved.

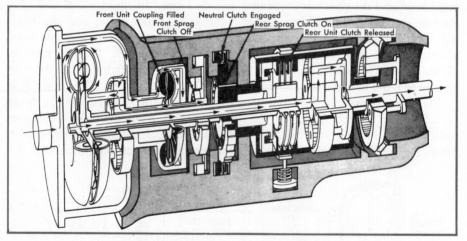

Fig. 24–45. Hydra-Matic in second. The front-unit fluid coupling has filled with oil, so that, with the front sprag clutch off, the front unit is in direct drive. The rear unit is still in reduction.

Figs. 24–44 to 24–47: Cadillac Motor Car Division of General Motors Corporation

the power passing through the transmission is delivered to the intermediate shaft (4). However, at this point it splits. About 40 percent of the power leaves the intermediate shaft and enters the torus (5 and 6). From there, this 40 percent passes into the main shaft (7) and rear sun gear (8). The rest of the power (about 60 percent) leaves the intermediate shaft through the rear clutch (10) and ring gear (11). This 60 percent (mechan-

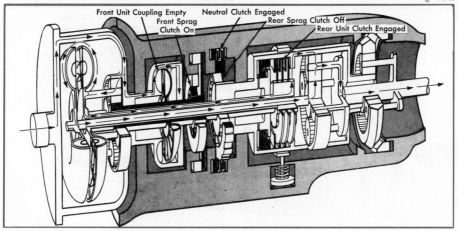

Fig. 24–46. Hydra-Matic in third. The front-unit fluid coupling has emptied and the front sprag clutch is on, so the front planetary is in reduction. The rear sprag clutch is off and the rear unit clutch is engaged, so the rear planetary is in direct drive, and the front unit supplies all the reduction in the transmission.

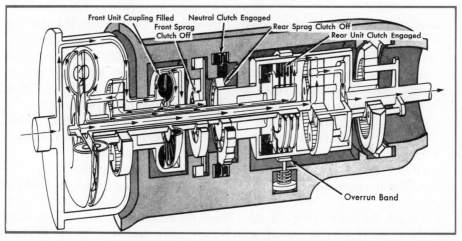

Fig. 24–47. Hydra-Matic in fourth. Both planetary gearsets are in direct drive. The band shown around the outside of the rear unit is an overrun brake band which comes into action when the car tries to drive the engine (for example, when coasting down-hill) to keep the output shaft from overrunning the rest of the transmission.

ical) then joins the 40 percent (hydraulic) at the planet pinions of the rear planet-pinion carrier (9). The reunited 100 percent then passes into the output shaft (17).

NOTE: It is more accurate to speak of splitting the *torque* leaving the intermediate shaft (4) than splitting the *power*. Torque (§ 77) is turning, or twisting, effort and is applied to the intermediate shaft. This torque splits between the torus and rear ring gear.

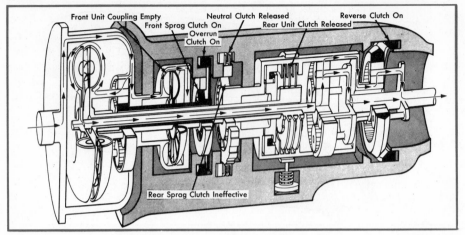

Front Unit Coupling Empty   Neutral Clutch Released   Reverse Clutch On
    Front Sprag Clutch On   Rear Unit Clutch Released
        Overrun
       Clutch On

Rear Sprag Clutch Ineffective

Fig. 24–48. Hydra-Matic in reverse. The front unit is in reduction, the rear unit is in neutral, and the reverse unit clutch is on. Note that the neutral clutch is released (it is engaged in all forward speeds), so that the rear sprag clutch becomes ineffective. (*Cadillac Motor Car Division of General Motors Corporation*)

With 60 percent of the power (torque) being mechanical and only 40 percent being hydraulic, there is less power lost due to slippage in the hydraulic fluid coupling. This increases the efficiency of the transmission in third (and fourth) speed.

The gear reduction in the front unit is 1.45:1, and in the rear unit it is 1:1 (direct drive). Thus, total gear reduction in the transmission is 1.45:1 (1.45×1).

e. Fourth. In fourth (Fig. 24–42), both front and rear bands are off, and both front and rear clutches are on. Both units are in direct drive. Power flow is through the flywheel (1), torus cover (2), front-unit ring gear (3), and front unit in direct drive to the intermediate shaft (4). There, the power splits as it does in third. About 40 percent enters the torus (5 and 6), and 60 percent enters the rear-unit ring gear (11) through the rear clutch (10). The 40 percent, after passing

through the torus, enters the rear sun gear (8) through the main shaft (7). The 60 percent joins the 40 percent at the planet pinions of the rear planet-pinion carrier (9). The total then passes into the output shaft (17).

With both units in direct drive, there is direct drive through the transmission (1:1 gear ratio).

f. Reverse. In reverse (Fig. 24–43), the front unit is in reduction, the rear unit has both band and clutch off, and the clutch is on in the reverse unit. The power flow is from the flywheel (1) through the torus cover (2), front planetary ring gear (3), intermediate shaft (4), torus (5 and 6), and main shaft (7), to the rear sun gear (8). The rear planet pinions act as idlers; interposing them into the gear train (as idlers) causes the rear ring gear (11) to turn in a reverse direction. The ring gear (11) is attached to the reverse sun gear (13) through a flange (12). The reverse ring gear (14) is

held stationary by the reverse clutch (15). Thus, the power entering the reverse sun gear (13) causes the reverse planet pinions (16) to "walk around" the stationary ring gear. They carry the reverse planet-pinion carrier and the output shaft (17) with them.

The front unit is in reduction (1.45:1), while the reverse unit provides a gear reduction of 2.96:1. Total gear reduction through the transmission is thus 4.3:1 (1.45 × 2.96). The output shaft revolves in the reverse direction so that the car will back.

2. *Two-fluid-coupling unit.* In the model with two fluid couplings, the front unit is controlled by the second fluid coupling and a sprag, or one way, clutch. See § 458 for an explanation of this type of clutch. The rear unit is controlled by a sprag clutch and a multiple-disk clutch actuated by an annular piston. Figures 24–44 to 24–48 show the actions in the transmission in the different gear speeds. Each planetary unit can shift separately to give four gear speeds, as in the transmission with one fluid coupling (see Table 24–1).

In first (Fig. 24–44), the front and rear planetary units are in reduction. The front coupling is empty, and the front-unit sprag clutch is on. The sprag clutch of the rear unit is on, and the rear clutch is off. The power flow is shown by the arrows. Since both planetary units are in reduction, maximum reduction is obtained through the transmission.

In second (Fig. 24–45), the hydraulic system has directed a flow of oil into the front-unit fluid coupling so that it has filled with oil. In ef-
fect, the two halves of the front coupling are locked together and turn at the same speed. This means that the front unit is in direct drive. However, the rear unit is still in reduction and furnishes the total amount of reduction through the transmission.

In third (Fig. 24–46), the valves in the hydraulic system have operated so that the oil is drained from the front fluid coupling. Now, the front unit drops down into reduction as it was in first. However, at the same time, the hydraulic system forces the annular clutch in the rear unit to engage. This causes the rear planetary set to lock up and turn as a unit so that there is no reduction in the rear unit. The front unit supplies all the reduction in the transmission.

In fourth (Fig. 24–47), the hydraulic system has again filled the front fluid coupling with oil so that the front unit is locked up and is in direct drive. At the same time, the annular clutch in the rear unit is engaged so that the rear unit is locked up. With both units locked up, the transmission furnishes no reduction; it is in direct drive.

In reverse (Fig. 24–48), the front unit is in reduction (the front fluid coupling is filled), the rear unit is in neutral, and the reverse unit is engaged. The neutral clutch is an annular clutch which is engaged in all forward speeds but is disengaged when a shift is made to reverse so that the rear unit, in effect, "gets out of the way" to permit the reverse unit to function.

§ 453. Hydraulic controls We have already described the shift control

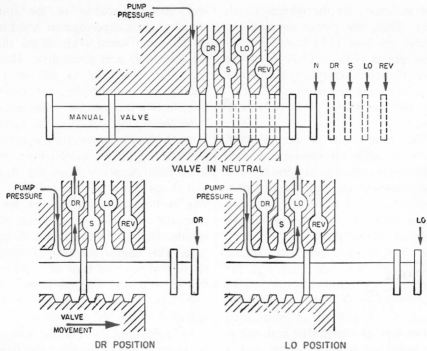

Fig. 24–50. Details of the manual valve, showing the valve in neutral (*at top*) and in the DR ("drive") and LO ("low") positions. In the upper illustration, the various positions of the valve are shown dotted.

(§ 451) which automatically produces upshifting or downshifting of the planetary unit. Figure 24–49* shows the complete control circuit, valves, servos, governor, etc., of the Hydra-Matic. At first glance, this circuit may seem rather complicated. However, the circuits, in essence, are no more complicated than the circuit shown in Fig. 24–36. Figure 24–36 illustrates the actions of the throttle valve, the shift valve, and the governor in controlling upshifting or downshifting. That is the function of the various circuits in Fig. 24–49. However, since the actual Hydra-Matic must have several shifts (instead of the two shown in Fig. 24–36), there must be several circuits. Each

*See inside back cover.

524

circuit handles one shift. All circuits must be interconnected so that only one shift at a time will occur. Also, the shifts must occur more rapidly at high engine speed in order to keep the engine from running away. They must occur more slowly at low engine speeds to prevent sudden grabbing and rough shifts. Then too, at wide-open throttle, when more power is being transmitted through the transmission, the pressure must be increased for heavier band application. This prevents band slippage. Various components in the circuit produce all these actions. Figure 24–50 shows the details of the manual valve that the driver positions as he moves the selector lever.

REVIEW QUESTIONS

1. Does increasing the area of the applying piston increase or decrease the pressure per square inch in the liquid?
2. If the area of the output piston is 2 square inches and the pressure in the liquid is 160 psi, what is the force on the output piston?
3. Explain how a pressure-regulating valve operates in a hydraulic system.
4. Explain the operation of a balanced valve.
5. Explain the operation of a servo.
6. Describe a fluid coupling. Explain briefly how it operates.
7. What is the purpose of the guide ring in the fluid coupling?
8. Explain how the transmission illustrated in Fig. 24–18 shifts.
9. Describe the actions of this transmission as it shifts from first to second. From third to fourth.
10. Describe the controls of this transmission in the "downshifted" position. During upshift. During downshift.
11. How many planetary sets are there in Hydra-Matic?
12. Describe the construction of the front-planetary-gear system in the Hydra-Matic (both the one-coupling and the two-coupling types).
13. Explain how hydraulic pressure is used to control the action of the front planetary.
14. Explain how the shift is controlled in the Hydra-Matic.
15. Describe and compare the operation of the two types of Hydra-Matic in first. In second. In third. In fourth. In reverse.
16. Describe the actions in the hydraulic system as the transmission shifts from neutral to first. From first to second. From second to third. From third to fourth.

STUDY QUESTIONS

1. Write an essay describing some of the properties of liquids so far as their ability to transmit pressures and movement is concerned.
2. Make a drawing of an input-output system. Show the areas of the input and output pistons and the pressures or forces on each.
3. Make a drawing of a pressure-regulator valve, and describe how it operates.
4. Make a drawing of a balanced valve, and describe how it operates.
5. Make a drawing of a servo, and describe how it operates.
6. Write an essay describing the operation of a fluid coupling.
7. Describe the controlling mechanisms for the front planetary set in the Hydra-Matic having one fluid coupling. In the unit having two fluid couplings.
8. Prepare a chart showing whether the front and rear planetaries are in direct or reduction in the four forward speeds of the Hydra-Matic.
9. Refer to a manufacturer's shop manual and write an essay describing the actions in the hydraulic system of the Hydra-Matic when a shift is made (both types).

THIS CHAPTER DESCRIBES THE construction and operation of torque converters, compares them with fluid couplings, and discusses the automatic transmissions with which torque converters are used. The fundamental principles of hydraulics and the operation of fluid couplings (§§ 442 and 443) were discussed in the previous chapter. Review those sections if the principles are not clear in your mind.

§ 454. Fluid couplings vs. torque converters At first glance, torque converters appear to be very similar to fluid couplings. Both have a driving member and a driven member. Both transmit torque (power) by passing oil from the vanes of the driving member to the vanes of the driven member. However, the fluid coupling is essentially a special form of clutch that transmits torque at maximum efficiency when both members are turning at close to the same speed. When the driving member turns appreciably faster than the driven member, then the efficiency with which torque is delivered to the driven member is lowered. Here's the reason:

When the driving member is turning considerably faster than the driven member, the oil is thrown onto the vanes of the driven member with con-

siderable force. It strikes the driven-member vanes and splashes, or "bounces back," into the driving member. In other words, this effect actually causes the oil to work against the driving member. Thus, when there is a big difference in driving and driven speeds, a good part of the driving torque is used in overcoming this "bounce-back" effect. Torque is lost; there is a torque reduction through the fluid coupling.

The situation is greatly different in the torque converter. This device is so designed as to prevent or reduce to a minimum the bounce-back effect. The result is that torque is not reduced when there is a large difference in driving and driven speeds. Quite the reverse. The torque is increased, or multiplied, in the torque converter.

§ 455. Torque converter The torque converter acts, in a sense, like a gear transmission with a large number of gearshift positions. That is, it can transmit torque at a 1:1 ratio. Or, under certain conditions, it can increase, or multiply, this torque so that more torque is delivered than is applied. This compares with a transmission in low gear. In low gear, the speed through the transmission is reduced; this increases the torque. (If the relationship between speed reduc-

tion and torque increase is not clear, reread § 426.)

In a like manner, speed reduction through the torque converter means a torque increase. That is, torque output is greater than the torque input; there is torque multiplication.

§ 456. Torque-converter action

The torque converter provides varying drive ratios between the driving and

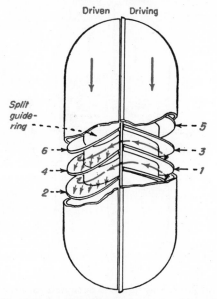

Fig. 25–1. Simplified cutaway view of two members of torque converter, showing, with heavy arrows, how oil circulates between driving and driven member vanes. In operation, the oil is forced by vane 1 downward toward vane 2, and thus it pushes downward against vane 2 as shown by small arrows. Oil then passes around behind split guide ring and into driving member again, or between vanes 1 and 3. Then it is thrown against vane 4 and continues this circulatory pattern, passing continuously from one member to the other.

driven members, thus providing varying amounts of torque increase. It accomplishes this by means of curved vanes in the driving and driven members and by the use of one or more extra members (between driving and driven members). These extra members act to reduce the splashing, or bouncing-back effect, mentioned in § 454. You will recall that this effect causes torque loss in a fluid coupling since the "bouncing" oil strikes the forward faces of the driving-member vanes and thereby tends to slow down the driving members.

NOTE: In the torque converter, the driving member is usually referred to as the *pump* (also called the impeller), while the driven member is called the *turbine.* In operation, the pump drives the turbine.

1. Curved vanes in torque converter. As already mentioned, the vanes in the driving and driven members of the torque converter are curved. This curvature is shown in Fig. 25–1. Note how the curving vanes allow the oil to change directions rather gradually as it passes from the driving to the driven member. The heavy arrows show the oil paths. The small arrows indicate the driving force with which the oil strikes the vanes of the driven member. It can be seen that the oil, which is moving round with the driving member, is thrown with a forward motion, or velocity, into the driven member. As the oil passes into the driven member, it "presses" forward all along the vanes, as shown by the small arrows. This produces the push which causes the driven member to rotate.

2. Bouncing-back effect without

527

additional members. When the two members are revolving at about the same speed, there is relatively little movement of oil between the two. This is similar to the action in the fluid coupling. However, when the driving member is revolving considerably faster than the driven member, the oil is thrown forward with considerable velocity into the driven member. You will recall the difficulty this produces in the fluid coupling because of the bouncing-back effect. You can see how this effect occurs in Fig. 25–2. In this figure, the front parts of the vanes and the guide ring have been cut away so that the inner ends of the vanes can be seen. Compare this illustration with Fig. 25–1.

NOTE: In actuality, the inner ends of the vanes are not as shown in Fig. 25–2. This figure is included merely to show what would happen if the vanes were continuous and if there were no additional members in the assembly.

As the oil passes through the driven member, as shown by the heavy arrows (Fig. 25–2), it moves along the curved vanes of the driven member. It is still moving rapidly as it leaves the trailing edges of the driven-member vanes. (The trailing edges are the back edges, or the edges that the oil passes last as it leaves the member.) However, note that the oil has changed directions. The curved vanes of the driven member have caused the oil to leave the trailing edges of the vanes so that it is thrown against the forward face of the driving-member vanes. This is shown by the small arrows in Fig. 25–2. The oil thus opposes the driving force of the driving member. With

a big difference in speeds between the driving and driven members, this opposing force would use up a good part of the power being applied by the driving member. Thus, some means of reducing this effect must be used if the torque converter is to function efficiently when the driving member is turning considerably faster than the driven member.

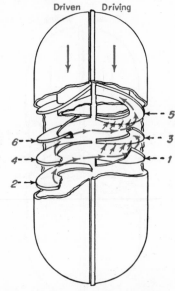

Fig. 25-2. This figure is designed to show what would happen if the vanes in Fig. 25–1 were continuous. Actually, the inner ends of the vanes are not as shown here but are as pictured in following figures. In this illustration, the split guide ring and the outer ends of the vanes have been cut away. If the vanes were as shown here, the oil leaving the trailing edges of the driven member would be thrown upward against the forward faces of the driving-member vanes, thus opposing the driving force. This effect, shown by the small arrows, would cause wasted effort and loss of torque.

Fig. 25-3. Effect of a jet of oil on a bucket attached to a wheel. If the oil enters and leaves as at A, the push imparted to the bucket, and wheel, is small. But if the oil jet is redirected into the bucket by a curved vane as at B, the push will be increased. (*De Soto Division of Chrysler Corporation*)

A simple method of overcoming this effect, and at the same time increasing the push (torque) on the driven member, is shown in Fig. 25-3. In Fig. 25-3A, a jet of oil is shown striking a hemispherical bucket attached to the rim of a wheel. This compares with the oil being thrown from the driving member into the curved vanes of the driven member in the torque converter. The jet of oil swirls around the curved surface of the bucket and leaves the bucket with almost the same velocity as it had when entering the bucket. In exactly the same way, the oil is thrown into the driven member (Fig. 25-2); the curved vanes of the driven member react against it, change its direction, and throw it back to the driving member.

In Fig. 25-3A, the oil will give up very little of its energy to the bucket, and there will be only a small push on the bucket. That is, there will be but little torque applied to the driven member.

Furthermore, it is this returning oil which bounces back into the driving member and causes the loss of torque, as already explained. However, we can prevent this effect if we install a stationary curved vane as shown in Fig. 25-3B. Now, the oil, as it comes out of the bucket, enters the stationary curved vane and will again be reversed in direction. That is, it will once more be directed into the bucket. Theoretically, the oil could make many complete circuits between the bucket and the vane. Each time it reentered the bucket, it would impart a further push (added torque) to the bucket. This effect is known as *torque multiplication*.

In an actual torque converter, there are stationary curved vanes which reverse the direction of the oil as it leaves the driven member. Thus, the oil enters the driving member in a "helping" direction, passes through, and then reenters the driven member where it gives the vanes of the driven member another push. In other words, the oil is repeatedly redirected into the driven member, each time adding torque to the driven member. Thus,

there will be an increase in torque: torque has been multiplied. Following paragraphs explain how this effect is achieved in actual torque converters.

3. Changing direction of oil flow. In an actual torque converter, one or more additional members are placed between the trailing edges of the driven-member vanes and the leading edges of the driving-member vanes. The trailing edges are the edges of the vane that the oil passes last as it leaves a member. The leading edges are the edges onto which the oil first flows. The additional members in the torque converter have curved vanes that change the direction of the oil into a *helping* direction instead of a hindering direction. The effect illustrated in Fig. 25–3*B* is thus achieved. Figure 25–4*a* is a cutaway view of a torque converter with a reaction member (called the stator). The stator vanes change the direction of oil flow into a helping direction before it reenters the driving member under certain operating conditions. This is shown by the curved arrows.

4. Number of members in torque converters. Torque converters used on passenger cars in recent years have three to five members. Several of these are discussed in following articles.

§ 457. Three-member torque converters Figure 25–4b is a partial cutaway view of the Ford Cruise-O-Matic transmission. This unit has a torque converter with three members, a pump, a stator, and a turbine. Figure 25–5 shows the three members detached from the assembly and separated. Figure 25–6 is a simplified drawing of the converter. The stator is mounted

on a freewheeling mechanism which permits it to run free when the torque members are both turning at about the same speed. This freewheeling mechanism is similar to the one used in overdrives (§ 433). However, it has a somewhat different purpose in the Fordomatic. In this transmission, the freewheeling mechanism permits the stator to freewheel, or run free during

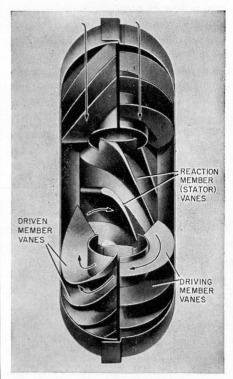

DRIVEN MEMBER VANES

REACTION MEMBER (STATOR) VANES

DRIVING MEMBER VANES

Fig. 25–4a. Cutaway view of a torque converter with three members. The third member, the stator, serves as a reaction member. It changes the direction of oil flow as shown by the curved arrows under certain operating conditions. Compare this illustration with Figs. 25–1 and 25–2. (*Chevrolet Motor Division of General Motors Corporation*)

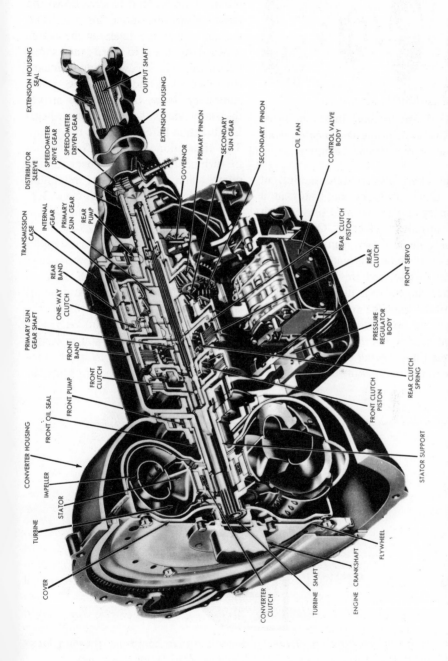

Fig. 25-4b. Partial cutaway view of the Ford Cruise-O-Matic transmission which has a three-member torque converter. This transmission is very similar to the Fordomatic transmission. (*Ford Division of Ford Motor Company*)

531

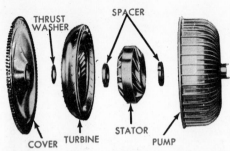

Fig. 25–5. The turbine, stator, and pump (impeller) used in the Fordomatic. (*Ford Division of Ford Motor Company*)

certain operating conditions. But, at other times, it locks the stator in a stationary position and prevents it from turning backward. Other free-wheeling devices (overrunning clutches) used on other automatic transmissions are described in § 458.

When the pump is turning considerably faster than the turbine, the tendency for a bounce-back effect exists, as explained in § 456. With this condition, the oil is leaving the trailing edges of the turbine vanes in a "hindering"

direction. That is, if its direction were not changed before it entered the pump, it would tend to slow down the pump. However, under this condition, the oil strikes the faces of the stator vanes and tries to turn the stator backward. The freewheeling mechanism locks up and holds the stator stationary. Now, the oil, as it strikes the stator vanes, is turned into a helping direction before it enters the pump. The circulation of the oil from pump to turbine to stator and back to the pump again can produce a maximum torque increase of slightly over 2:1. The stator thus produces the action shown in Figs. 25–3*B* and 25–4*a*.

As turbine speed approaches pump speed (car speed increases), the torque increase gradually drops off until it becomes 1:1 as the turbine and pump speeds reach a ratio of approximately 9:10. At this point, the oil begins to strike the backs of the stator vanes. This causes the stator to start free-wheeling, or turning ahead. Thus, in

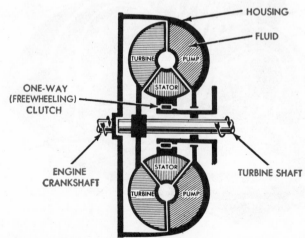

Fig. 25–6. Simplified drawing of the Fordomatic torque converter, showing locations of pump, stator, and turbine. (*Ford Division of Ford Motor Company*)

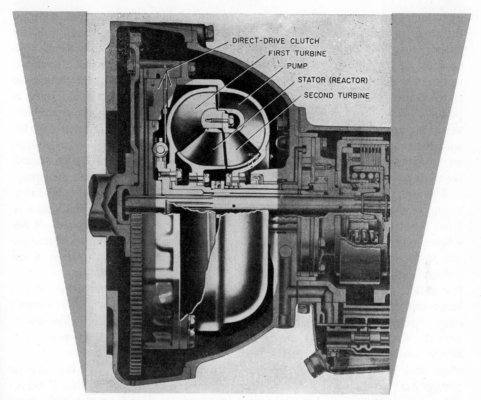

Fig. 25–7. Sectional view of a four-member torque converter. (*Studebaker-Packard Corporation*)

effect, the stator "gets out of the way" of the oil and thereby no longer enters into the torque-converter action. The converter then acts as a fluid coupling.

Three-member torque converters of a type similar to that described above have been used in late-model Chevrolet Powerglides and in the Studebaker automatic transmission, among others.

§ 458. **Four-member torque converters** Several torque converters have used four members. The additional member, the manufacturers indicate, is effective in the intermediate operating range, or during the time when the torque converter is approaching the fluid-coupling stage. These torque converters are described below.

1. Packard Ultramatic drive. The torque converter used with this automatic transmission is shown in Fig. 25–7. It contains four members, two of them rigidly bolted together so that they turn together at all times. The oil passes from the pump to the first turbine, from there to the stator, or reactor, and then to the second turbine, which is rigidly bolted to the first turbine. During acceleration, the stator (reactor) is held stationary by the force of the oil thrown into its vanes from the first turbine. The curved vanes of the reactor change the

direction of oil so that it is thrown into the vanes of the second turbine in the proper direction. There, the oil gives up most of its remaining velocity and so does not offer any great interference to the pump vanes as it moves into the pump. During steady running, the converter acts simply as a fluid coupling, with the reactor, which is mounted on an overrunning clutch, rotating with the mass of oil.

The overrunning clutch used in this torque converter is somewhat different from those previously described. It is a sprag-type overrunning clutch which acts in the same way but is differently constructed. The sprags are somewhat like flattened rollers (Fig. 25–8). The inner and outer races of the overrunning clutch are not notched but are smooth. A series of sprags are positioned between the inner and outer races and are held in place by two springs put into the sprag notches. The outer race is stationary, but the inner race is splined to the reactor hub and therefore turns with the reactor. During steady running, the reactor is not needed, as already mentioned. It rotates. The sprags, being at a slight

angle as shown in Fig. 25–8, have no effect on the forward rotation of the inner race. During acceleration, however, the oil must change directions, and it is thrown against the front faces of the reactor vanes, as mentioned in the previous paragraph. This produces a backward thrust, or pressure, on the reactor vanes that halts the reactor and attempts to turn it backward. However, as this happens, the sprags jam between the inner and outer races, thereby locking up the inner race so that it cannot turn backward. It becomes stationary so that its vanes can effectively change the direction of the oil flow.

This torque converter also contains a direct-drive clutch, which is mounted directly to the flywheel. The direct-drive clutch (Fig. 25–9) contains a driven plate centered between two driving plates. One of the driving plates can move back and forth a fraction of an inch. At the right time (according to the car speed and accelerator position), an oil passage is opened by a control valve to permit oil to flow to the clutch. This oil exerts pressure through a pressure passage

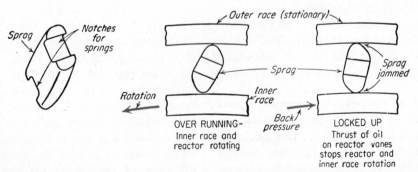

Fig. 25–8. The appearance and action of a sprag used in the overrunning clutch in the Packard Ultramatic.

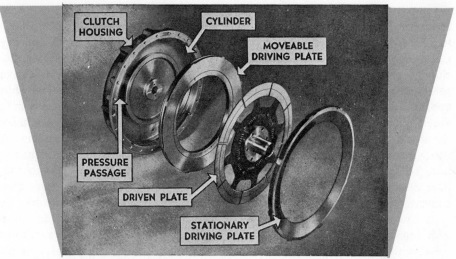

Fig. 25–9. Disassembled view of the direct-drive clutch in the torque converter shown in a previous figure. (*Studebaker-Packard Corporation*)

against the movable driving plate, forcing it toward the driven plate. As a result, the driven plate is clamped tightly between the two driving plates so that it turns with the driving plates.

Since the driven plate is splined to the transmission input shaft, the effect is to bypass the torque converter and thereby place the car in direct drive. With the car in direct drive, the driv-

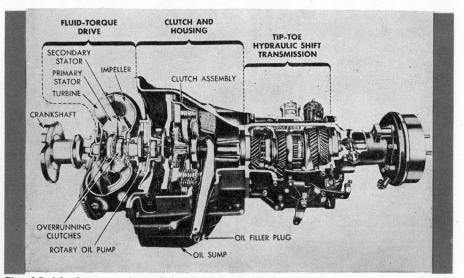

Fig. 25–10. Cutaway view of the Fluid-Torque Drive, clutch, and Tip-Toe hydraulic-shift transmission. (*De Soto Division of Chrysler Corporation*)

ing and driven members of the torque converter (pump and turbine) are locked together through the clutch. Clutching action of the direct-drive clutch, and thus direct drive, is achieved by operation of the hydraulic system as explained in a following article. The hydraulic system places the converter in direct drive during steady driving and during deceleration. In direct drive, there is no slippage or speed loss through the torque converter.

2. *Chrysler Fluid-Torque Drive.* This four-member torque converter is used with the Gyro-Matic, Presto-matic, and Tip-Toe transmission on Chrysler, Dodge, and De Soto cars. This torque converter has also been adapted for the Plymouth Hy-Drive, and a modification of it is used in the

Chrysler, De Soto, and Dodge Power-flite automatic transmission.

Figure 25–10 is a partial cutaway view of this torque converter. The figure shows it in combination with a clutch assembly and a Tip-Toe Shift transmission. It has supplanted a fluid coupling used with the transmission shown. This earlier fluid coupling, as well as the transmission and controls, is discussed in detail in §§ 444 to 446.

The Fluid-Torque Drive torque converter contains a driving member, or impeller (called the pump in other torque converters), and a driven member, plus a primary stator and a secondary stator. Each of these stators is mounted on a freewheeling device, or overrunning clutch, as shown in Fig. 25–11. The action in the torque converter when first starting is illus-

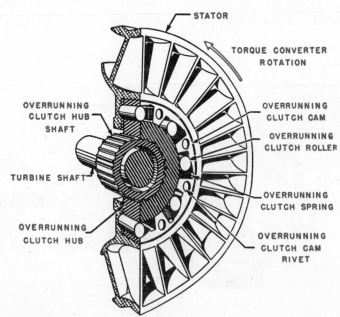

Fig. 25–11. Details of an overrunning clutch used to support a stator in a torque converter. (De Soto Division of Chrysler Corporation)

trated in Fig. 25–12. Under these conditions, the driving member is rotating much faster than the driven member. The two stators are stationary, and they redirect the oil as it leaves the driven member into a helping direction. This is shown by the arrows. In other words, as the oil comes off the driven-member vanes, it strikes the stationary stator vanes and is changed in direction. Then, it enters the driving member in a direction that does not hinder driving-member rotation.

When the car picks up speed, the driven-member speed increases until it nears the speed of the driving member. As this happens, the oil leaving the driven-member vanes gradually changes in direction until it begins to strike the back faces of the primary-stator vanes. This causes the primary stator to begin to rotate. It no longer enters into the action but simply rotates to get out of the way. The secondary stator still continues to change the direction of the oil, but it, alone,

does not change the direction as much as the two stators working together did. On the other hand, with the two converter members operating at more nearly the same speeds, the oil does not require so much change of direction.

When the car is cruising along at a steady speed, there is little difference in the speed of rotation of the two members. The oil now strikes the back faces of the secondary-stator vanes. This stator also begins to rotate so as to get out of the way. Neither stator now enters into the action; the drive acts simply as a fluid coupling.

The torque converter shown in Fig. 25–10 has its own oil pump and oil supply. The pump is the rotary type assembled on the impeller shaft. The oil is retained in a sump below the clutch housing. A variation of this same design, used on certain Chrysler and De Soto models, utilizes the engine oil and does not have an oil sump of its own. In this latter system, a greater amount of engine oil is required (13

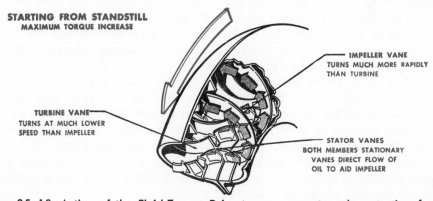

STARTING FROM STANDSTILL
MAXIMUM TORQUE INCREASE

IMPELLER VANE
TURNS MUCH MORE RAPIDLY
THAN TURBINE

TURBINE VANE
TURNS AT MUCH LOWER
SPEED THAN IMPELLER

STATOR VANES
BOTH MEMBERS STATIONARY
VANES DIRECT FLOW OF
OIL TO AID IMPELLER

Fig. 25–12. Action of the Fluid-Torque Drive torque converter when starting from a standstill. Both stators are stationary and are redirecting the oil from the turbine into the impeller (pump) in a helping direction. (De Soto Division of Chrysler Corporation)

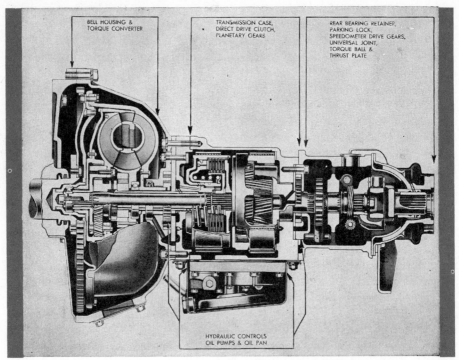

Fig. 25–13. Sectional view of the Buick Twin-Turbine Dynaflow transmission. (*Buick Motor Division of General Motors Corporation*)

quarts). However, with the larger volume of oil, it is necessary to change oil but twice a year, under normal driving conditions. The oil filter should be replaced every 5,000 miles. In operation, the engine oil pump supplies not only engine lubrication but also a flow of oil to the torque converter.

3. Buick Twin Turbine. The Buick Twin-Turbine torque converter contains two turbines, a stator, and a pump. The design is somewhat different from other four-member torque converters already described. This unit has two turbines which are interconnected by a planetary-gear set. A sectional view of the complete transmission and torque converter is shown in Fig. 25–13. The transmission itself is

a fully automatic unit; its construction and operation are described later in this chapter. Let us look more closely at the torque converter, however, and find out how the two turbines function under different operating conditions.

a. Twin-Turbine construction. Figure 25–14 is a cutaway view of the Twin-Turbine torque converter, showing the locations of the turbines, pump, and stator and the manner in which these four members are mounted. The pump is bolted to the engine flywheel and functions in the same manner as the pumps in the other torque converters already described. That is, it delivers oil to the turbines.

The first turbine is supported on a

BELL HOUSING
TURBINES
PUMP
STATOR

PUMP
COVER
FLYWHEEL

Fig. 25–14. Cutaway view of the Twin-Turbine torque converter, showing manner in which the turbines, stator, and pump are supported. (*Buick Motor Division of General Motors Corporation*)

disk and hub, which, in turn, are supported by needle bearings on the hub of the second turbine (Fig. 25–14). The first-turbine hub and the second-turbine hub are thus free to turn independently of each other. As part of the first-turbine disk, there is an internal, or ring, gear. This ring gear is the internal gear of the planetary-gear set. (If you are somewhat hazy about how planetary gears operate, reread § 434.)

The second turbine is bolted to the turbine carrier. The hub of the turbine carrier is splined to the input shaft (input to the transmission). Thus, the second turbine and transmission input shaft must turn together. The turbine carrier is also the planet-pinion carrier

of the planetary-gear set. This means that the planet-pinion carrier also rotates with the second turbine and input shaft.

The sun gear of the planetary-gear set is independent of the input shaft but is attached to the freewheel cam of the stator freewheeling clutch.

The stator is mounted on a freewheeling clutch. This clutch is very similar in construction and action to those already described. That is, when there is a big difference between turbine and pump speeds, oil is thrown from the turbine into the stator vanes in such a direction as to hold the stator stationary. However, when turbine and pump speeds are nearly equal, then the direction of the oil is

539

changed; it now strikes the vanes from the rear so that the stator is set into motion. Now, the stator simply rotates to keep out of the way of the moving oil; it no longer enters into the action of the torque converter.

Let us get back to the planetary-gear set again. We have noted that the ring gear is part of the first turbine, the planet-pinion carrier is part of the second turbine, and the sun gear is part of the stator freewheeling clutch cam. With these details in mind, let us find out how the torque converter operates.

b. Twin-Turbine action during acceleration. In accelerating from a standing stop, there is a big difference in pump and turbine speeds. Oil passes from the pump into the first and second turbines with considerable forward velocity and imparts considerable torque to the turbines. The first turbine starts to rotate in the same direction as the pump, carrying the ring gear around with it. Meantime, the sun gear is held stationary because the stator is stationary. This means that the ring gear (in the first-turbine disk) rotates the planet pinions and causes them to "walk around" the sun gear. This action carries the planet-pinion carrier around. The input shaft is splined to the planet-pinion carrier. Thus, torque, or turning effort, is imparted to the input shaft by the action of the first turbine; this action is carried through the planet pinions to the carrier.

Meantime, as the oil passes through the first turbine, it enters the second turbine, still moving with considerable velocity. Thus, torque is applied to the second turbine, and this torque adds to the torque from the first turbine (which is passing through the planet pinions and carrier). The two torques join at the planet-pinion carrier and enter the input shaft. This means a substantial torque increase through the converter.

Note that the first turbine imparts torque through the ring gear and planet pinions. The second turbine imparts torque directly since it is splined to the input shaft.

c. Twin-Turbine action as cruising speed is reached. As the car gains speed, the speed of the turbines approaches the speed of the pump. This means that the oil leaving the second turbine no longer strikes the forward faces of the stator vanes. Instead, the angle of the oil changes so that it begins to strike the rear faces of the stator vanes. Now, the stator is no longer held stationary. It begins to rotate so that, in effect, it moves out of the way of the oil. As the stator starts to rotate, the freewheeling clutch cam is no longer held. It rotates also and thus permits the sun gear to rotate. If the sun gear rotates, instead of being held, then the torque-adding effect of the first turbine is lost. That is, when the sun gear is free, then the ring gear can no longer cause the planetary gears to walk around it.

Thus, as turbine speed approaches pump speed, the stator and the first turbine no longer contribute anything to the torque-converter action. They merely spin on their bearings and are no longer effective. All torque now passes from the pump to the second turbine; the assembly acts as a fluid coupling.

Actually, there is no sudden change in the torque converter from the torque increase to the coupling stage. As turbine speed increases and approaches pump speed, the pressure on the stator vanes gradually slacks off. At the same time, the torque applied to the primary turbine slacks off (since oil begins to pass between primary-turbine vanes instead of striking them). Thus, the torque contributed by the primary turbine tapers off as the coupling stage is approached.

4. Buick variable-pitch Twin-Turbine torque converter. This converter is shown in cutaway view in Fig. 25–15. It is very similar to the Twin-Turbine torque converter described in the previous paragraph. One major difference is that the vanes, or blades, of the stator are mounted on crankshafts so that their angle, or pitch, can be changed. The stator does the same job as in other torque converters. That is, it changes the direction of the oil as it leaves the turbine so that it re-enters the pump in a helping direction. However, in this unit, the stator blades can be positioned in either of two positions (bottom in Fig. 25–15). In the high-angle, or "closed," position, as shown to the right, the blades are turned almost like the slats of a nearly closed venetian blind. This is the position they assume when the accelerator is opened wide for heavy acceleration. With this condition, the pump is turning much faster than the turbines. The oil leaves the turbines with a very heavy reaction force (bounce back). The high angle of the stator blades then changes the direction of the oil sharply so that it can re-enter the pump in a fully helping di-

rection. This action increases the torque multiplication in the torque converter.

As the car speed increases, the accelerator is eased up. This action causes the stator blades to change angles. They move into the "wide-open" position (left in Fig. 25–15). In this position, they still redirect the oil after it leaves the turbine into a helping direction. However, since the pump is not moving a great deal faster than the turbines, the direction does not have to be changed quite so much. Changing the blade angles reduces the amount that the oil is changed in direction.

Later, when the car attains road speed and the driver holds the accelerator steady, the turbine speed approaches pump speed. As it does this, the oil leaving the turbine blades strikes the back of the stator blades. Now, the stator starts to spin, or overrun. The torque converter now acts as a fluid coupling.

Control of the stator blades is achieved by an annular piston and by cranks on the inner ends of the shafts that support the blades. The shafts and cranks are shown dotted at the bottom of Fig. 25–15. The cranks are attached to the piston. When the piston moves, the cranks are turned (from the position shown dotted at left to the position shown dotted at right). This action turns the shafts and blades so that they move from low to high pitch (or from high to low pitch). The annular piston is controlled, in turn, by a linkage between the accelerator pedal and a valve in the valve body. When the accelerator is opened beyond a certain point, the valve is

541

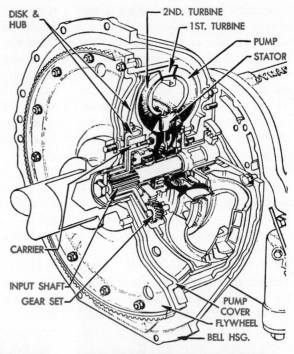

DISK & HUB

2ND. TURBINE

1ST. TURBINE

PUMP

STATOR

CARRIER

INPUT SHAFT

GEAR SET

PUMP COVER

FLYWHEEL

BELL HSG.

Fig. 25–15. *(Top)* Cutaway view of Twin-Turbine torque converter with variable pitch stator. *(Bottom)* Two positions of the stator blades for cruising *(left)* and acceleration *(right)*. *(Buick Motor Division of General Motors Corporation)*

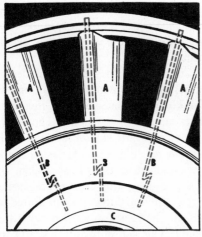
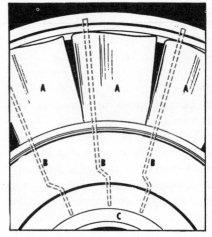

actuated. The valve then admits oil under pressure against the piston. This causes the piston to move and the stator blades to turn to the "high-pitch" position. Then, when the accelerator is released, the valve moves again. Now, it admits oil under pres-

sure to the other side of the piston. The piston moves back and turns the blades into their "low-pitch" position.

§ 459. Five-member torque converters Figures 25–16 and 25–17 are

sectional and cutaway views of a torque converter using five members. This torque converter was used on earlier models of the Powerglide and Dynaflow transmissions. The five members are the turbine, secondary stator, primary stator, secondary pump, and primary pump. The turbine, two stators, and primary pump operate in the manner already described. The secondary pump supplies some additional pumping effect during

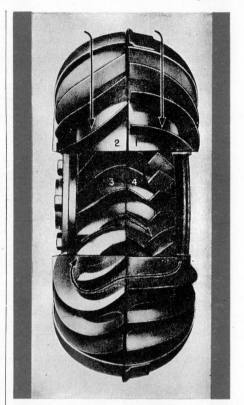

Fig. 25–17. Cutaway view of a torque converter using five members. Refer to Fig. 25–16 for names of numbered parts. Lower arrows show circulation of oil in torque converter. (*Chevrolet Motor Division of General Motors Corporation*)

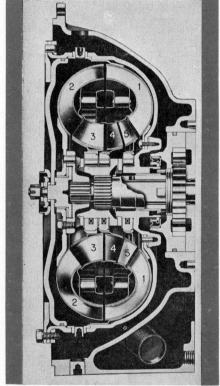

Fig. 25–16. Sectional view of a torque converter using five members. 1 to 5 show the vanes of 1, driving member, or primary pump; 2, driven member, or turbine; 3, secondary stator; 4, primary stator; 5, secondary pump. (*Chevrolet Motor Division of General Motors Corporation*)

light-load steady driving. Thus, it permits somewhat more efficient operation during the coupling stage, when the torque converter is functioning as a fluid coupling.

§ 460. Torque-converter transmissions
Torque converters have been used with a variety of transmissions, including the Chrysler Corporation's Powerflite and Torque-Flite, Ford's Fordomatic and Cruise-O-Matic, Buick's

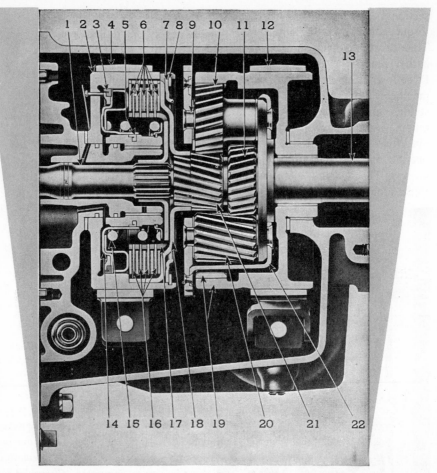

Fig. 25–18. Cross-sectional view of planetary system used in transmission for torque converter with five members. (*Chevrolet Motor Division of General Motors Corporation*)

1. Input shaft
2. Clutch drum
3. Clutch-piston outer ring seal
4. Low brake band
5. Clutch-piston inner ring seal
6. Clutch-driven plates
7. Clutch-flange retainer
8. Clutch-flange retainer ring
9. Planet-pinion pin
10. Planet short pinion
11. Reverse sun gear
12. Reverse brake band
13. Output shaft
14. Clutch piston
15. Clutch spring
16. Clutch drive plates
17. Clutch hub
18. Clutch flange
19. Reverse drum and ring gear
20. Planet long pinion
21. Low sun gear
22. Planet carrier

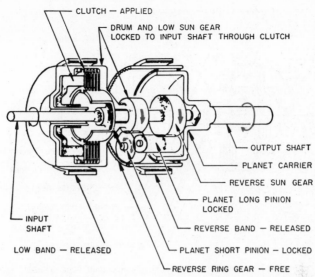

CLUTCH — APPLIED

DRUM AND LOW SUN GEAR
LOCKED TO INPUT SHAFT THROUGH CLUTCH

OUTPUT SHAFT

PLANET CARRIER

REVERSE SUN GEAR

PLANET LONG PINION
LOCKED

INPUT
SHAFT

REVERSE BAND — RELEASED

LOW BAND — RELEASED

PLANET SHORT PINION — LOCKED

REVERSE RING GEAR — FREE

Fig. 25–19. Simplified drawing of transmission, showing actions when transmission is in direct drive. (*Buick Motor Division of General Motors Corporation*)

Dynaflow, Chevrolet's Powerglide and Turboglide, and Packard's Ultramatic.

All transmissions are similar in action even though they have different designs. All have a selector lever or control buttons on the steering column or on the instrument panel. In most automatic transmissions, there are five selector positions, although some transmissions have only four. These are N (neutral), DR (drive), LO (low), R (reverse), and P (park) on many units. In park, the transmission is locked up so that the car cannot move. (There is no park position in some transmissions, the Powerflite, for example.) In neutral, no power flows through the transmission, but the locking effect is off. In LO, there is gear reduction through the transmission; this provides extra torque for a hard pull or for braking in going down a long hill. R is, of course, used to back the car. In the DR position, some

transmissions will automatically shift between reduction and direct drive according to car speed and throttle position. This gives extra torque at low speeds (when transmission is in reduction) for better pulling power and acceleration. Other transmissions have only direct drive through the transmission (no shift) in DR. Still other transmissions depend on a planetary gearset or a variable-pitch stator in the torque converter itself (as in the Buick Twin-Turbine Dynaflow) to provide extra torque during getaway and acceleration.

Other special features will be found in the various automatic transmissions. Let us examine these automatic transmissions in detail.

§ 461. Automatic transmissions with five-member torque converters As examples of automatic transmissions using five-member torque converters,

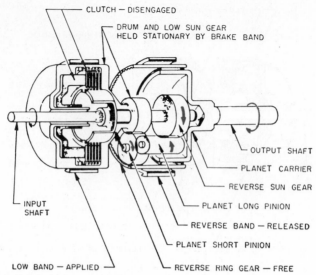

CLUTCH — DISENGAGED

DRUM AND LOW SUN GEAR
HELD STATIONARY BY BRAKE BAND

OUTPUT SHAFT

PLANET CARRIER

REVERSE SUN GEAR

PLANET LONG PINION

REVERSE BAND — RELEASED

PLANET SHORT PINION

INPUT
SHAFT

LOW BAND — APPLIED

REVERSE RING GEAR — FREE

Fig. 25–20. Simplified drawing of transmission, showing actions when transmission is in reduction, or low. (*Buick Motor Division of General Motors Corporation*)

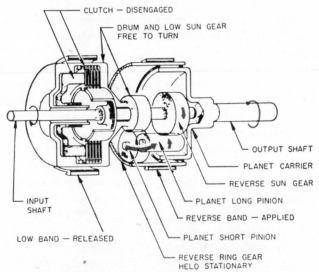

CLUTCH — DISENGAGED

DRUM AND LOW SUN GEAR
FREE TO TURN

OUTPUT SHAFT

PLANET CARRIER

REVERSE SUN GEAR

PLANET LONG PINION

REVERSE BAND — APPLIED

INPUT
SHAFT

PLANET SHORT PINION

LOW BAND — RELEASED

REVERSE RING GEAR
HELD STATIONARY

Fig. 25–21. Simplified drawing of transmission, showing actions when transmission is in reverse. (*Buick Motor Division of General Motors Corporation*)

we shall use the Chevrolet Powerglide (earlier version) and the Chevrolet Turboglide. They are similar in many respects to the Buick Dynaflow. A later-model Powerglide uses a three-member torque converter (§ 463).

1. Powerglide. Figures 25–16 and 25–17 show the torque converter used with the Powerglide. Figure 25–18 shows the planetary system. It has an extra sun gear (reverse, No. 11) and two sets of planet pinions (short, No.

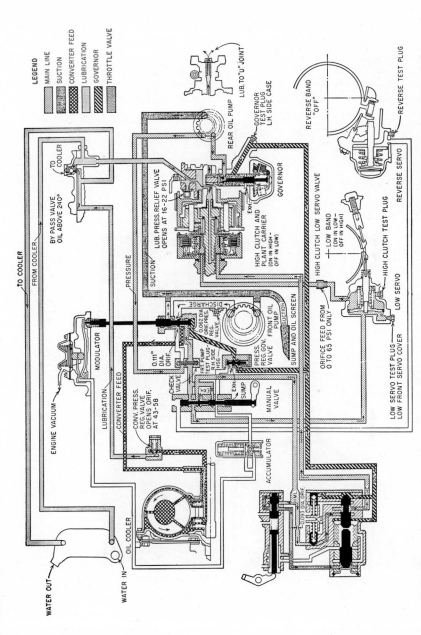

Fig. 25-22. Oil circuits in the transmission shown in the previous figures. (*Chevrolet Motor Division of General Motors Corporation*)

547

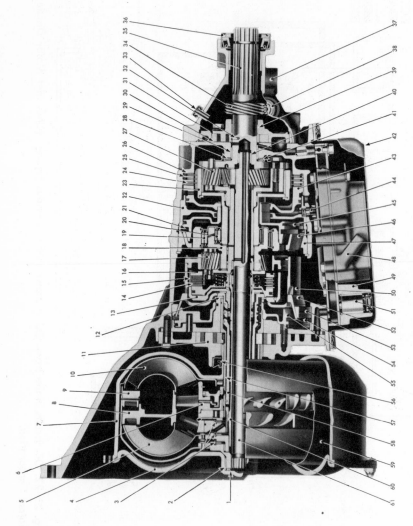

Fig. 25-23.

Fig. 25–23. Cross-sectional view of Turboglide transmission. (Chevrolet Motor Division of General Motors Corporation)

1. Needle bearing and races
2. Converter cover hub bushing
3. Caged needle bearings
4. Converter cover
5. Third turbine assembly
6. Stator assembly
7. Converter
8. Second turbine assembly
9. First turbine ring
10. Converter pump
11. Front pump assembly
12. Selective thrust washer
13. Neutral clutch hub
14. Neutral clutch drive plate (3)
15. Neutral clutch driven plate (3)
16. Neutral clutch driven drive plate
17. Front planetary gearset
18. Front sun gear
19. Front-sun-gear freewheeling assembly (outer sprag)
20. Forward piston return spring
21. Forward piston return spring
22. Forward and brake piston support
23. Rear planet ring gear
24. Brake plate (3)
25. Thick reaction plate (2)
26. Thin reaction plate (2)
27. Rear planetary gearset
28. Caged needle thrust washer
29. Transmission case bushing
30. Rear pump spacer
31. Rear pump assembly
32. Rear pump drive pin
33. Extension vent
34. Speedometer drive gear
35. Output shaft (part of rear planetary gearset)
36. Extension oil seal
37. Transmission extension
38. Speedometer driven gear
39. Rear oil-pump bushing
40. Output shaft inner bushing
41. Pinion shaft lock plate
42. Oil pan
43. Brake piston
44. Oil-pressure tube (2)
45. Forward piston
46. Forward cone
47. Forward-cone ring
48. Main valve body assembly
49. Hydraulic modulator valve assembly
50. Front ring gear hub
51. Hydraulic accumulator
52. Reverse cone
53. Reverse-cone ring
54. Return spring
55. Reverse piston
56. Front pump oil seal
57. Stator support shaft
58. Second turbine shaft (integral with front ring gear hub)
59. Turbine shell
60. Third turbine shaft (integral with neutral clutch hub)
61. First turbine shaft (integral with turbine shell)

549

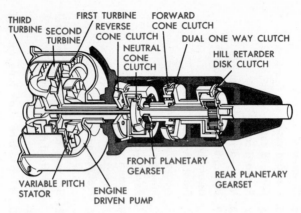

Fig. 25–24. Simplified cutaway drawing of the Turboglide showing the major components of the converter and transmission. (*Chevrolet Motor Division of General Motors Corporation*)

10, and long, No. 20). Figures 25–19 to 25–21 show the transmission in drive, low, and reverse, while Fig. 25–22 shows the oil circuits which provide the control.

2. Turboglide. Figure 25–23 is a sectional view of the Turboglide, and Fig. 25–24 shows the major elements of the unit. It has three turbines and two planetary gearsets. The first turbine, which is active from stall to about 30 mph (wide-open throttle), is connected to the rear planetary sun gear by a shaft (Fig. 25–25). During acceleration at low speeds and open throttle, the first turbine drives the rear sun gear. The internal gear is held stationary by the two overrunning clutches and the cone clutch. Therefore, the planetary carrier and output shaft are rotated at reduced speed (with a gear reduction of 2.67:1). At higher speed and at part throttle, less torque and higher output speed are desirable. Under these conditions the first turbine freewheels, or over-

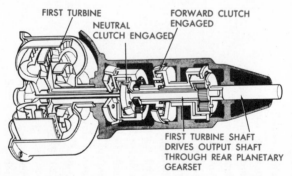

Fig. 25–25. Operation of first turbine and clutches during the first turbine phase. Unshaded portion shows power path through transmission. (*Chevrolet Motor Division of General Motors Corporation*)

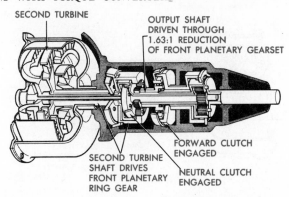

SECOND TURBINE

OUTPUT SHAFT
DRIVEN THROUGH
1.63:1 REDUCTION
OF FRONT PLANETARY GEARSET

FORWARD CLUTCH
ENGAGED

SECOND TURBINE
SHAFT DRIVES
FRONT PLANETARY
RING GEAR

NEUTRAL CLUTCH
ENGAGED

Fig. 25–26. Operation of clutches and planetary gearsets during second turbine phase. Unshaded parts show power path through transmission. (*Chevrolet Motor Division of General Motors Corporation*)

runs, and thus no longer enters the converter action. This action is permitted by the overrunning clutch which holds the internal gear.

At intermediate speed the second turbine begins to contribute torque (Fig. 25–26). It drives the output shaft through the internal gear of the secondary planetary gearset. At light throttle and intermediate speed, the second turbine also begins to freewheel

and thus no longer enters into the converter action. An overrunning clutch permits this action.

The third turbine (Fig. 25–27) comes into operation during cruising and light road-load conditions. With the first two turbines overrunning or freewheeling, the third turbine delivers torque directly to the output shaft through the cone clutch. Actually, there is no sudden shift from one tur-

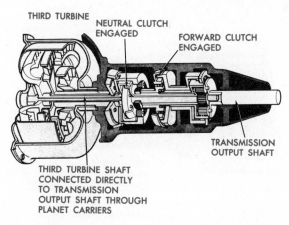

THIRD TURBINE

NEUTRAL CLUTCH
ENGAGED

FORWARD CLUTCH
ENGAGED

TRANSMISSION
OUTPUT SHAFT

THIRD TURBINE SHAFT
CONNECTED DIRECTLY
TO TRANSMISSION
OUTPUT SHAFT THROUGH
PLANET CARRIERS

Fig. 25–27. Operation of clutches and planetary gearsets during third turbine phase or direct drive. (*Chevrolet Motor Division of General Motors Corporation*)

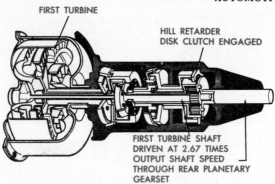

Fig. 25–28. Operation of clutches, planetary gearsets, and converter when hill-retarder is in action. (*Chevrolet Motor Division of General Motors Corporation*)

bine to another. There is some overlap so that the transmission shifts smoothly from one phase to another.

The hill-retarder (Fig. 25–28) provides braking by the engine through the transmission on steep downgrades. When the transmission lever is shifted to the hill-retard position (HR), the first turbine is geared to the output shaft at a gear ratio of 2.67:1. Both the second and third turbines freewheel.

In reverse (Fig. 25–29) the reverse clutch engages and the first turbine

shaft drives the rear planetary gearset. With the reverse clutch engaged, the front internal gear is held so that the front planet gears are interposed in the gear train to reverse the direction of motion. The output shaft thus turns in the opposite direction to back the car.

Hydraulic controls for the Powerglide are shown in Fig. 25–22. Positioning of the shift lever operates the manual valve which, in turn, directs oil to the servos. The servos then operate to provide the desired drive position.

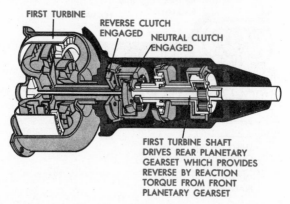

Fig. 25–29. Operation of clutches, planetary gearsets, and converter in reverse. (*Chevrolet Motor Division of General Motors Corporation*)

§ 462. Four-member torque-converter transmissions Two different automatic transmissions with four-member torque converters are described in the following pages. In one (the Ultramatic), there is an arrangement to lock up the torque converter (with a direct-drive clutch) under the appropriate car-speed and throttle-opening conditions. In the other (the Powerflite), there is an automatic shifting arrangement in DR (shifting between reduction and direct drive).

1. Packard Ultramatic drive. Figure 25–7 illustrates the torque converter used with the automatic transmission described in this article. The operation of the torque converter itself has already been discussed (§ 458). Figure 25–30 is a partial cutaway view of the planetary-gear system. This gear

system is quite similar in construction and practically identical in operation to the planetary-gear system of the transmission discussed in the previous article. In the high, or drive, range, the multiple-disk clutch in the transmission is engaged, and the two brake bands are released. In the low range, the low brake band is applied, and the clutch and reverse brake band are released. In reverse, the clutch and low band are released, while the reverse band is applied. (Refer to § 461 for detailed explanations of how the planetary-gear system behaves under each of these conditions.)

Application of, or release of, the clutch and brake bands is secured by movement of the selector lever on the steering column to the various "drive" positions. This action operates the

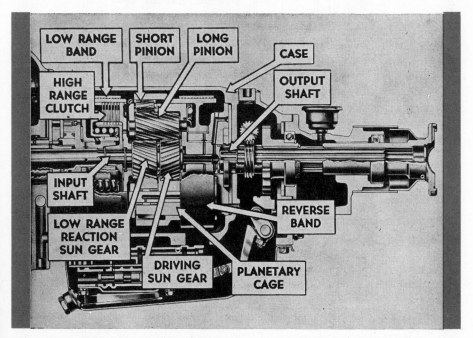

Fig. 25–30. Sectional view of the planetary system used with the torque converter illustrated in Fig. 25–7. (*Studebaker-Packard Corporation*)

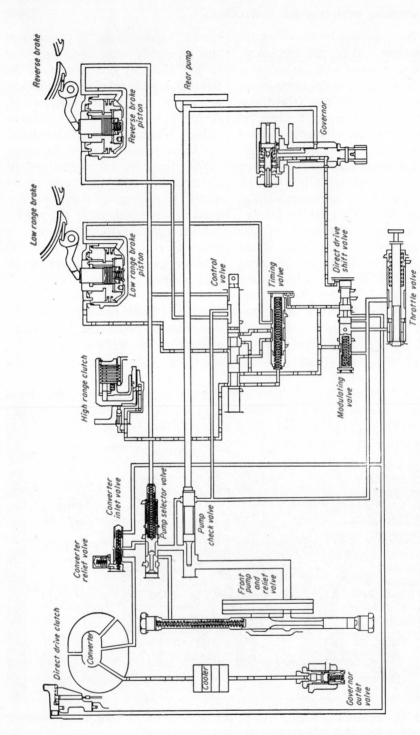

Fig. 25–31. Oil circuits in transmission shown in Fig. 25–30. (Studebaker-Packard Corporation)

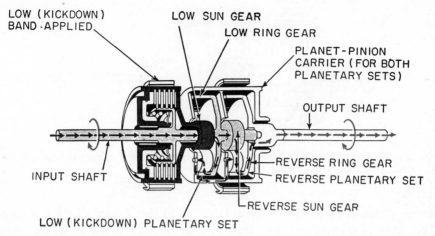

LOW (KICKDOWN)
BAND-APPLIED

LOW SUN GEAR

LOW RING GEAR

PLANET-PINION
CARRIER (FOR BOTH
PLANETARY SETS)

OUTPUT SHAFT

INPUT SHAFT

REVERSE RING GEAR
REVERSE PLANETARY SET
REVERSE SUN GEAR

LOW (KICKDOWN) PLANETARY SET

Fig. 25–32. Power flow through Powerflite transmission in L (low). (*De Soto Division of Chrysler Corporation*)

control valve in the transmission, which then directs oil to, or relieves oil pressure from, the servos that operate the bands and clutch.

In addition to these actions, the hydraulic system of this transmission also includes a governor which functions, in conjunction with car speed and throttle opening, to actuate the direct-drive clutch (Fig. 25–9), which is part of the torque converter. The purpose of this clutch is to lock up the driving and driven members of the torque converter under certain conditions so as to eliminate all slippage and thereby improve performance. The conditions under which this clutch will engage to produce lockup include steady driving and also decelerating at speeds above 13 mph (miles per hour).

Figure 25–31 shows, schematically, the hydraulic system of this transmission. You will note that it is much like the hydraulic system shown in Fig. 25–22. Although the parts are some-

what differently constructed, they perform the same jobs of applying or releasing the brake bands and clutch. The system shown in Fig. 25–31 contains the governor mentioned above. It is driven from the output shaft of the transmission. The system also has a direct-drive shift valve which is interconnected with a throttle valve that is actuated by throttle opening. The purpose of these parts is to control the operation of the direct-drive clutch in the torque converter. Increasing car speed increases the oil pressure from the governor, and this oil pressure is applied to one end of the shift valve. Increased throttle opening opens the throttle valve so that increased oil pressure is applied to the *other* end of the shift valve. These two pressures (from the governor and from the throttle valve) oppose each other in attempting to move the shift valve. When governor pressure exceeds throttle-valve pressure (as during steady light-throttle driving or decel-

555

DIRECT CLUTCH APPLIED

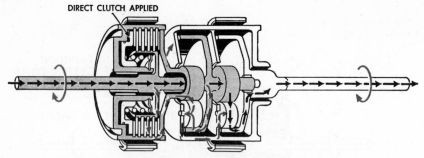

Fig. 25–33. Power flow through Powerflite transmission in D (direct drive). (*De Soto Division of Chrysler Corporation*)

erating), then the shift valve is moved. This opens an oil passage to the direct-drive-clutch piston, causing the direct-drive clutch to engage. These parts are very much like the governor, throttle valve, and shift valve used in the Hydra-Matic transmission; they are described in detail in § 451 and illustrated schematically in Fig. 24–36.

2. *Powerflite automatic transmission.* The Powerflite automatic transmission described in this article is supplied on cars built by the Chrysler Corporation, including Chrysler, De Soto, Plymouth, and Dodge. The four-member torque converter (called the Fluid-Torque Drive by the manufacturer) used with this transmission has already been described (§ 458).

The selector lever in this transmission has four positions, R, N, D, and L (R is reverse, N is neutral, D is drive, and L is low). In drive, the transmission starts out (on breakaway or acceleration) in reduction and then automatically shifts into direct drive. The shifting point is determined by car speed and throttle position. In low, the transmission remains in reduction. Let us examine the actions in the transmission in these various gear positions.

a. In low. Figure 25–32 is a simple diagrammatic drawing of the clutch and planetary gearsets in the transmission, showing the power flow in low, or reduction. The low (kickdown) band is on, the clutch and reverse band off. Reduction (low) is attained in the transmission under any of three conditions: (1) when first pulling away (breakaway) in D; (2) in accelerating hard below a specified maximum speed (this gives a forced downshift or *kick-down*); (3) in the L selector-lever position.

In low, the power flow is as shown in Fig. 25–32. It is through the torque converter, through the input shaft to the ring gear of the low planetary set (also called the *kick-down* planetary set by the manufacturer). The low (*kick-down*) band is applied, and this holds the low sun gear stationary. Thus, the low ring gear, as it rotates, forces the low planet pinions to "walk around" the low sun gear. They carry the planet-pinion carrier around with them (but at a speed slower than the input shaft is turning). Note that the low planet-pinion carrier and the reverse planet-pinion carrier must rotate with the low planet-pinion carrier.

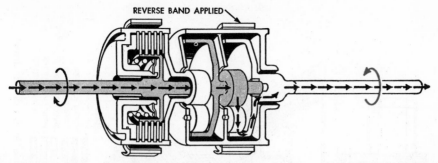

Fig. 25–34. Power flow through Powerflite transmission in R (reverse). (*De Soto Division of Chrysler Corporation*)

Notice also that the reverse sun gear is splined to the input shaft and must turn with the input shaft.

Now let us see what we have. The reverse sun gear is rotating at input-shaft speed. The reverse planet-pinion carrier is rotating slower than input-shaft speed. As a result, the planet pinions drive the reverse ring gear, *but at a speed slower than input-shaft speed*. Direction of all members is forward (not reverse) except for the planet pinions. The planet pinions rotate backward since the sun gear is turning faster than the pinion carrier. The gear reduction through the transmission under these conditions is 1.72:1 (input shaft turns 1.72 times for every revolution of the output shaft).

If the above is hard for you to understand, look at it this way: Suppose the planet-pinion carrier turned at the same speed as the sun gear. The ring gear would then turn at the same speed also, in the same direction. But, at the other extreme, suppose the planet-pinion carrier were held stationary. This means the planet pinions would act as idlers; the ring gear would turn in the reverse direction from the sun gear. Now, suppose we

rotated the planet-pinion carrier at a speed about halfway between full stop and full speed. If we chose this speed correctly, we should find that the ring gear would not turn at all. That is, the forward speed of the sun gear would be balanced by the reverse speed of the planet pinions. The ring gear would remain stationary. But if we increased the speed of the planet-pinion carrier a little, then the ring gear would start moving forward. The more we increase carrier speed, the faster the ring gear turns, until, when the carrier turns at sun-gear speed, the ring gear also turns at sun-gear speed. In low, carrier speed is somewhat slower than sun-gear speed so that the 1.72:1 gear reduction is achieved.

b. In direct drive. In direct drive, the power flow is as shown in Fig. 25–33. The direct clutch is applied, and both bands are off. With the clutch on, the input shaft is locked to the low sun gear. Since the low ring gear is splined to the input shaft, this means that the low sun gear and ring gear turn together. Thus, the planet pinions and carrier also turn with the sun and ring gears. The planetary set turns as a unit. The same condition exists in the

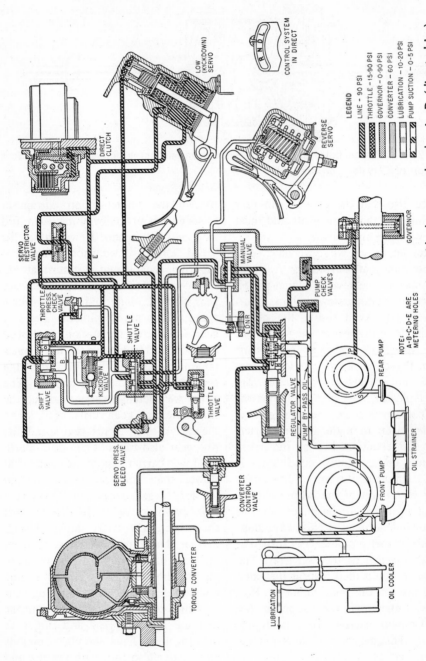

Fig. 25-35. Hydraulic circuit of the Powerflite automatic transmission with the manual valve in D (direct drive). (De Soto Division of Chrysler Corporation)

LOW (KICKDOWN) SERVO

CONTROL SYSTEM IN DIRECT

R N D L

REVERSE SERVO

DIRECT CLUTCH

LEGEND
LINE - 90 PSI
THROTTLE - 15-90 PSI
GOVERNOR - 0-90 PSI
CONVERTER - 60 PSI
LUBRICATION - 10-20 PSI
PUMP SUCTION - 0-5 PSI

SERVO RESTRICTOR VALVE

E

MANUAL VALVE

GOVERNOR

THROTTLE PRESS. CHECK VALVE

SHUTTLE VALVE

PUMP CHECK VALVES

D

L D N R

A   B

SHIFT VALVE

KICKDOWN VALVE

THROTTLE VALVE

REGULATOR VALVE

PUMP BY-PASS OIL

REAR PUMP

NOTE: A-B-C-D-E ARE METERING HOLES

SERVO PRESS. BLEED VALVE

OIL STRAINER

FRONT PUMP

CONVERTER CONTROL VALVE

TORQUE CONVERTER

LUBRICATION

OIL COOLER

reverse planetary set. The sun gear is splined to the input shaft and must turn at input-shaft speed. Since the planet-pinion carrier is also turning at input-shaft speed (through the low planetary set), then the reverse ring gear must also turn at input-shaft speed. This ring gear is splined to the output shaft. Thus, the output shaft turns at the same speed as the input shaft; there is direct drive through the transmission.

c. In reverse. Figure 25–34 shows the power flow through the transmission in reverse. The direct clutch and the low band are off, and the reverse band is applied. This holds the planet-pinion carrier stationary. Now drive is from the input shaft through the reverse sun gear (which is splined to the input shaft), through the reverse planet pinions (which act as idlers), and through the reverse ring gear. Since the reverse planet pinions are interposed, as idlers, between the sun and ring gear, the ring gear turns in the reverse direction. The gear reduction in reverse is 2.39:1. That is, the input shaft turns 2.39 times for every rotation of the output shaft (with output shaft turning in reverse direction).

d. Hydraulic circuit. The hydraulic circuit for the Powerflite is shown in Fig. 25–35. The conditions illustrated are for D (direct drive). You will note that this circuit is very similar to the circuits for other automatic transmissions previously shown (Figs. 25–22 and 25–31). However, there are several differences. The major difference is that this circuit has a throttle valve, a governor, and a shift valve to provide upshifting or downshifting when proper car speed and throttle

opening are reached. This part of the hydraulic circuit is very much like the shifting arrangement in the Hydra-Matic described in § 451 and illustrated in Fig. 24–36. The throttle valve, a balanced valve, is described in § 442, 5. With increasing throttle opening, the output pressure of the throttle valve goes up. This output pressure is called throttle pressure. The governor is driven by the output shaft of the transmission, and thus governor pressure goes up with car speed. Let us see how these, and other, components in the system function.

e. In low and upshifting. When the car first pulls away from a standing stop with selector in D, the transmission is in low. Pump (line) pressure is passing through the manual valve (positioned at D by the selector lever). The pump pressure is admitted by the manual valve to the shift valve, throttle valve, and "apply" side of the low servo. The servo is applying the low band, the clutch is off, and the transmission is in low, as shown in Fig. 25–32. As car speed increases, increasing governor pressure, working against the end of the shift valve, puts an increasing pressure on the shift valve. Opposing this pressure is throttle pressure applied on the other end of the shift valve. As soon as car speed increases enough, however, governor pressure will be sufficient to overcome throttle pressure, move the shift valve, and cause the transmission to upshift.

The car speed required depends on throttle opening. With a light throttle and thus low throttle pressure, the upshift will take place at a relatively low speed [as low as 15 mph (miles per

hour)]. But with a wide-open throttle and high throttle pressure, the upshift will not occur until car speeds of 60 to 75 mph are reached.

As the shift valve moves, pump (line) pressure is admitted to the release side of the low servo and also to the direct clutch. Thus the low band is released and the clutch is applied to put the transmission into direct drive (Fig. 25–33).

f. Kick-down. There is a kick-down arrangement in this transmission to permit the driver to downshift into reduction (Fig. 25–32) for rapid acceleration under certain circumstances. This action results if the throttle is pushed to "wide-open" position. As the throttle nears the "wide-open" position, the driver feels a sudden increase in pressure required for further throttle movement. This increased pressure is due to an arm on the throttle cam forcing the kick-down valve to open. As the kick-down valve opens, it admits additional pressure to the shift valve. This kick-down pressure forces the shift valve to overcome governor pressure and then move. As it moves, it cuts off pump pressure from the direct clutch and the release side of the low servo. Thus, the clutch releases, and the low servo applies. Now, the transmission is in low. The other components of the hydraulic system provide regulation of pump pressure and proper timing of the clutch and brake band on application and release.

g. Reverse. As the selector is moved to R, the entire hydraulic circuit from the manual valve on up (except to the reverse servo) is cut off. There is no pressure to the throttle valve, shift valve, shuttle valve, direct clutch, or low servo. These are all inoperative. Pump pressure is applied to the reverse servo so that the transmission shifts into reverse (Fig. 25–34). An exceptionally high band pressure is required because of the large torque reduction (and thus torque increase on the output shaft). To attain this high band pressure, the pump pressure is temporarily stepped up to a maximum of 250 psi. This is done as the manual valve is shifted to R since this cuts off line pressure from the secondary reaction area in the regulator valve. With this action, line (pump) pressure must go considerably higher before the regulator valve begins to regulate.

§ 463. Three-member torque-converter transmissions As examples of automatic transmissions with three-member torque converters, we shall discuss the Ford Cruise-O-Matic, a late-model Chevrolet Powerglide, a Chrysler Torque-Flite, and a Studebaker automatic transmission. All these have an automatic shift in the DR (drive) range.

1. Cruise-O-Matic. Figure 25–4b is a partial cutaway view of the Cruise-O-Matic automatic transmission. The Fordomatic is very similar in construction. The transmission uses a three-member torque converter. The same assembly, with some modifications, is used on the Mercury. If you will study Fig. 25–4b and Figs. 25-36 to 25–42, you will note that this transmission has a gear and clutch arrangement that is somewhat different from the automatic transmissions previously described. It uses short and long pinions (called

primary and *secondary* pinions in the Fordomatic) such as the Powerglide uses (see § 461). But it has two multiple-disk clutches. The arrangement provides an additional forward gear ratio, and so the transmission has three (low, intermediate, and high). Let us see how this transmission operates.

a. Selector lever positions and gear ratios. The Fordomatic selector lever has four positions: N, DR, LO, and R. The Cruise-O-Matic has five: N, D1, D2, L, and R. Table 25–1 shows the clutch and band action and the gear ratios in these selector-level positions.

b. Gears, clutches, and bands. Figure 25–36 is a simplified cutaway showing the transmission elements. Compare this with Fig. 25–4b. The arrangement is similar for the two transmissions except that the Cruise-O-Matic has a one-way or overrunning clutch (see Fig. 25–40).

c. Neutral. In neutral (Fig. 25–37), none of the gear-train members are held or driven, so no power can pass through.

d. Second. In second (Fig. 25–38), the secondary sun gear is held stationary by the front band and the primary sun gear is driven. The primary pinions drive the secondary pinions, so they must "walk around" the secondary sun gear. They carry the internal gear and output shaft around with them.

e. Third. In third (Fig. 25–39), both sun gears are locked together and are driven as a unit. The pinions cannot rotate, and the gear train turns as a unit to provide a 1:1 ratio.

f. First (Fordomatic, Fig. 25–40). Power is transmitted as shown. The secondary sun gear turns free and does not enter into the action.

g. First (Cruise-O-Matic, Fig. 25–41). Here, the pinion carrier is held against rotation by the one-way clutch instead of the rear band as in the Fordomatic.

h. Reverse. Reverse is obtained by driving the secondary sun gear and holding the pinion carrier (Fig. 25–42).

i. Hydraulic control system. The various units in the hydraulic system which control the front and rear clutches and bands in the transmission are shown in Fig. 25–43. In this figure,

Table 25–1

Gear	Selector-lever position		Clutch applied	Band applied	Gear ratio
	Fordomatic	Cruise-O-Matic			
Neutral	N	N	None	None	. . . . .
Second	DR	D1 or D2	Front	Front	1.47:1
Third	DR	D1 or D2	Front and rear	None	1.00:1
First	LO	D1 or L	Front	Rear	2.40:1
Reverse	R	R	Rear	Rear	2.00:1

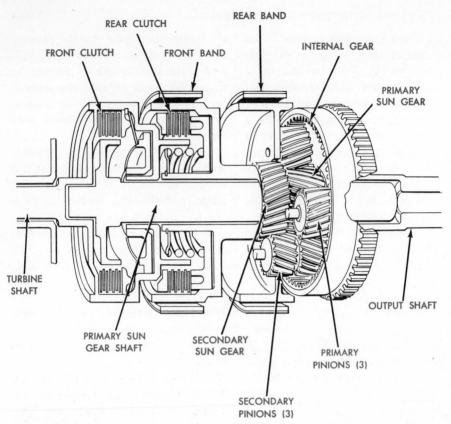

Fig. 25–36. Arrangement of the planetary-gear-train elements in the Fordomatic. Cruise-O-Matic is similar except it also has a one-way clutch. (*Ford Division of Ford Motor Company*)

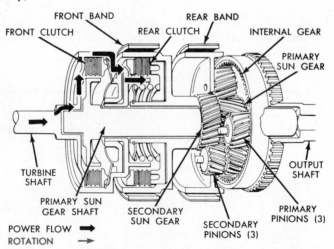

Fig. 25–37. Clutch and band action in neutral. (*Ford Division of Ford Motor Company*)

562

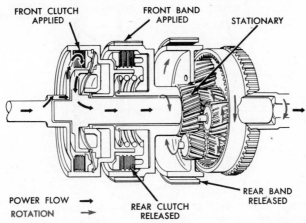

Fig. 25–38. Power flow in second gear. (*Ford Division of Ford Motor Company*)

the transmission is in high. The manual valve has been positioned by movement of the selector lever to the DR position, and the car speed and throttle position are such as to cause the system to place the transmission into high (see Fig. 25–39).

The transmission will downshift from high to intermediate below 55 mph if the driver pushes the accelerator all the way down (Fig. 25–44).

This action moves the throttle valve so that pressure is admitted to the spring side of the shift valve. This moves the shift valve to cut off pressure to the rear clutch so that it releases. At the same time, a drain port is opened; this drains the oil from the release side of the front-servo piston so that the front servo applies the front band. Now, the transmission is in intermediate (see Fig. 25–38).

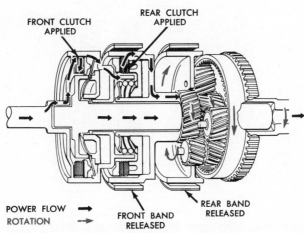

Fig. 25–39. Power flow in third gear. (*Ford Division of Ford Motor Company*)

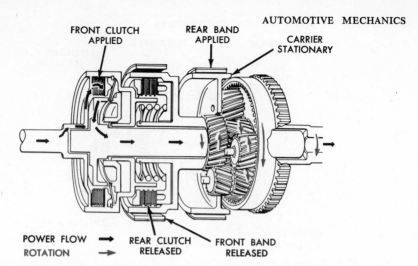

FRONT CLUTCH
APPLIED

REAR BAND
APPLIED

CARRIER
STATIONARY

POWER FLOW ➡
ROTATION ➡

REAR CLUTCH
RELEASED

FRONT BAND
RELEASED

Fig. 25–40. Power flow in first gear in Fordomatic. (*Ford Division of Ford Motor Company*)

In low, the manual control valve is moved to the position shown in Fig. 25–45. This changes the pattern of control pressure application so that the front clutch and rear band are applied while the rear clutch and front band are released (see Fig. 25–40).

2. Powerglide with three-member torque converter. The Powerglide automatic transmission which uses a three-member torque converter has five selector-lever positions ("drive," "low," "reverse," "neutral," and "park") as in the earlier-model Power-

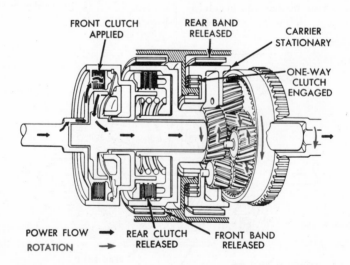

FRONT CLUTCH
APPLIED

REAR BAND
RELEASED

CARRIER
STATIONARY

ONE-WAY
CLUTCH
ENGAGED

POWER FLOW ➡
ROTATION ➡

REAR CLUTCH
RELEASED

FRONT BAND
RELEASED

Fig. 25–41. Power flow in first gear in Cruise-O-Matic. (*Ford Division of Ford Motor Company*)

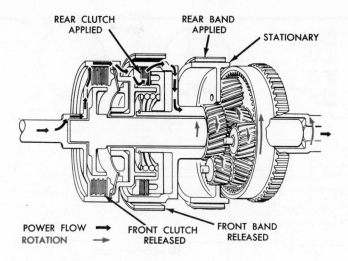

Fig. 25–42. Power flow in reverse. (*Ford Division of Ford Motor Company*)

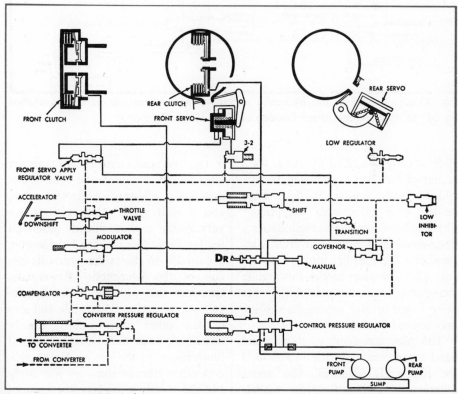

Fig. 25–43. Simplified drawing of the Fordomatic hydraulic control circuit, showing circuit with transmission in high. (*Ford Division of Ford Motor Company*)

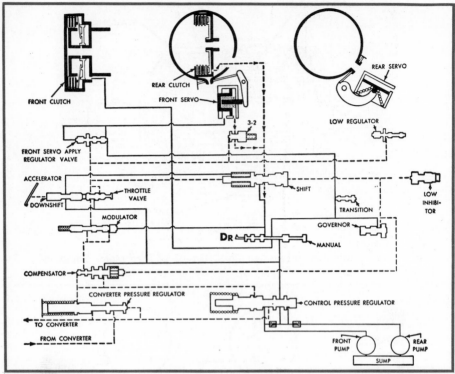

Fig. 25–44. Actions in the hydraulic circuit when the transmission is downshifted (in DR) to intermediate. (*Ford Division of Ford Motor Company*)

glide already described (§ 461). As a matter of fact, the later-model Powerglide is very similar to the earlier model, with these two exceptions: (1) The later-model Powerglide uses a three-member torque converter (instead of a five-member torque converter). (2) The later-model Powerglide incorporates an automatic shift in the drive range to give automatic shifting between low and direct.

The planetary-gearing, clutch, and band arrangements in the two models are practically identical. The major difference between the two models (aside from the torque converter) lies in the hydraulic control circuit. In the later model, the hydraulic control circuit has a governor, a throttle valve, and a shift valve. Their actions are very similar to those already described for the Powerflite and the Fordomatic. Figure 25–46 shows the hydraulic circuit of the later-model Powerglide. Compare this with the hydraulic circuits of the earlier Powerglide and also of the other transmissions already described. Refer to the discussions and illustrations of the earlier Powerglide and other transmissions as you study Fig. 25–46 to learn how the components in this circuit function.

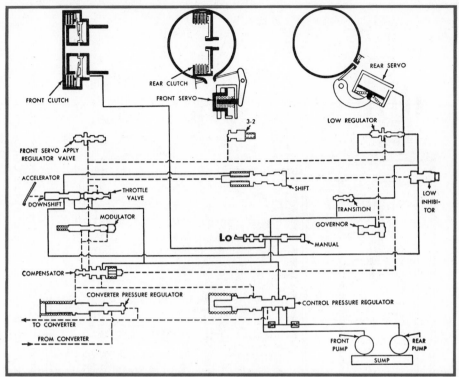

Fig. 25–45. Actions in the hydraulic circuit when the transmission is in low. (*Ford Division of Ford Motor Company*)

3. Studebaker automatic transmission. Figure 25–47 shows the Studebaker automatic transmission. This transmission incorporates many features of other transmissions previously described. It also has an air-cooling system to prevent the development of excessive temperatures in the torque converter. In addition, it has an anti-creep feature which keeps the car from creeping forward when the selector lever is in low or direct and the engine is running. The transmission uses a three-member torque converter, a double-planetary system with three brake bands, and one multiple-disk clutch. Also, it uses a direct-drive clutch of the type incorporated in the Packard Ultramatic (§ 462, 1). Figure 25–48 will provide a key to the operation of the various components. For example, in reverse, the reverse band (1) is on, but the multiple-disk clutch (2), low band (3), forward band (4), and direct-drive clutch (5) are all off. It will be noted that this transmission has an intermediate gear position, which is brought into play when the car is operated at low speed in DR. However, an automatic shift is made from intermediate into direct (governed by throttle opening and car and

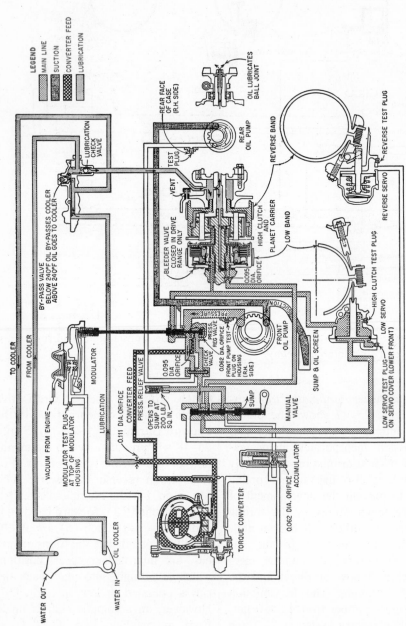

LEGEND
MAIN LINE
SUCTION
CONVERTER FEED
LUBRICATION

OIL LUBRICATES BALL JOINT

REAR FACE OF CASE (R.H. SIDE)

LUBRICATION CHECK VALVE

REVERSE BAND

REAR OIL PUMP

REVERSE TEST PLUG

REVERSE SERVO

BY-PASS VALVE
BELOW 240°F OIL BY-PASSES COOLER
ABOVE 240°F OIL GOES TO COOLER

TEST PLUG

VENT

BLEEDER VALVE
CLOSED IN DRIVE RANGE ONLY

HIGH CLUTCH AND PLANET CARRIER

LOW BAND

HIGH CLUTCH TEST PLUG

LOW SERVO

TO COOLER

FROM COOLER

0.095 DIA. ORIFICE

MODULATOR

SUCTION

PRESSURE

FRONT OIL PUMP

LOW SERVO TEST PLUG ON SERVO COVER (LOWER FRONT)

VACUUM FROM ENGINE

MODULATOR TEST PLUG AT TOP OF MODULATOR HOUSING

LUBRICATION

0.111 DIA. ORIFICE

CONVERTER FEED

PRESS. RELIEF VALVE

0.095 DIA ORIFICE

CHECK VALVE

PRESS. REG VALVE

0.062 DIA. ORIFICE

FRONT PUMP TEST PLUG ON HOUSING (R.H. SIDE)

SUMP & OIL SCREEN

OPENS TO SUMP AT 200 LB./SQ. IN.

SUMP

MANUAL VALVE

WATER OUT

WATER IN

OIL COOLER

TORQUE CONVERTER

ACCUMULATOR

0.062 DIA. ORIFICE

Fig. 25–46. Hydraulic circuit of the Powerglide automatic transmission, using the three-member torque converter and having the automatic shift in D. (Chevrolet Motor Division of General Motors Corporation)

568

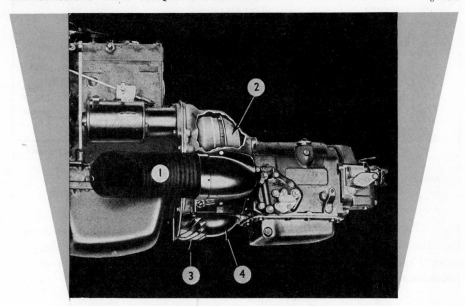

Fig. 25–47. Partial cutaway view of the Studebaker automatic transmission mounted on the engine, showing the air-circulating system: 1, air duct; 2, blower; 3, louvers; 4, cover. (*Studebaker-Packard Corporation*)

engine speed) under the proper conditions. For instance, this will occur at about 18 mph with a light accelerator. With full throttle, it will occur at about 35 mph. This action is much like that occurring in the Hydra-Matic transmission and the other transmissions described on the past few pages.

This transmission incorporates an anticreep feature (Fig. 25–49), which makes use of a spring-loaded solenoid-operated check valve in the rear-wheel brake system. The solenoid circuit is completed through a pressure switch and a throttle-control switch. The pressure switch is operated off the rear pump, which in turn operates only when the car is in motion. With the car stationary, there is no oil pressure and

the pressure-switch contacts are closed. Likewise, with the throttle closed, the throttle-control switch is closed. Since both switches are closed, the solenoid is in operation, closing the solenoid valve so that pressure is trapped in the rear-wheel brake cylinders. The rear brakes are therefore on and hold the car stationary. However, as soon as the throttle is opened, the solenoid circuit opens, to release the brakes.

4. *Torque-Flite* (*Fig. 25–50*). This transmission has two multiple-disk clutches, an overrunning clutch, two brake bands, and two planetary gearsets. When first starting (in D, or drive), the power flow is as shown in Fig. 25–51, that is, through the front

569

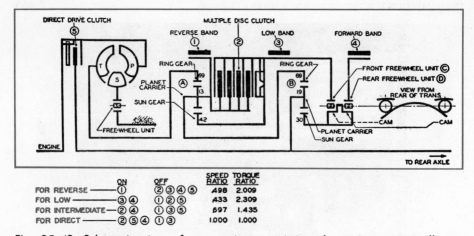

	ON	OFF	SPEED RATIO	TORQUE RATIO
FOR REVERSE	①	②③④⑤	.498	2.009
FOR LOW	③④	①②⑤	.433	2.309
FOR INTERMEDIATE	②④	①③⑤	.697	1.435
FOR DIRECT	②⑤④	①③	1.000	1.000

Fig. 25–48. Schematic view of automatic transmission shown in previous illustration. The table shows the clutches and bands which become engaged in the three forward speeds and in reverse, as well as the drive and torque ratios achieved. (*Studebaker-Packard Corporation*)

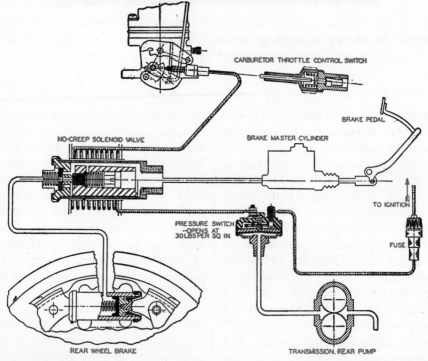

Fig. 25–49. Schematic diagram of anticreep feature of transmission shown in Figs. 25–47 and 25–48. This feature prevents creeping of the car when it is standing with the transmission in the drive range and the engine is idling. (*Studebaker-Packard Corporation*)

570

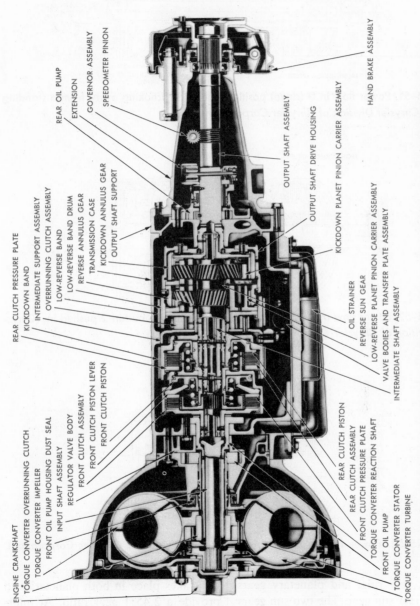

ENGINE CRANKSHAFT
TORQUE CONVERTER OVERRUNNING CLUTCH
TORQUE CONVERTER IMPELLER
FRONT OIL PUMP HOUSING DUST SEAL
INPUT SHAFT ASSEMBLY
REGULATOR VALVE BODY
FRONT CLUTCH ASSEMBLY
FRONT CLUTCH PISTON LEVER
FRONT CLUTCH PISTON

REAR CLUTCH PRESSURE PLATE
KICKDOWN BAND
INTERMEDIATE SUPPORT ASSEMBLY
OVERRUNNING CLUTCH ASSEMBLY
LOW-REVERSE BAND
LOW-REVERSE BAND DRUM
REVERSE ANNULUS GEAR
TRANSMISSION CASE
KICKDOWN ANNULUS GEAR
OUTPUT SHAFT SUPPORT

REAR OIL PUMP
EXTENSION
GOVERNOR ASSEMBLY
SPEEDOMETER PINION

OUTPUT SHAFT ASSEMBLY

OUTPUT SHAFT DRIVE HOUSING

HAND BRAKE ASSEMBLY

KICKDOWN PLANET PINION CARRIER ASSEMBLY

OIL STRAINER
REVERSE SUN GEAR
LOW-REVERSE PLANET PINION CARRIER ASSEMBLY
VALVE BODIES AND TRANSFER PLATE ASSEMBLY
INTERMEDIATE SHAFT ASSEMBLY

REAR CLUTCH PISTON
REAR CLUTCH ASSEMBLY
FRONT CLUTCH PRESSURE PLATE
TORQUE CONVERTER REACTION SHAFT
FRONT OIL PUMP
TORQUE CONVERTER STATOR
TORQUE CONVERTER TURBINE

Fig. 25–50. Sectional view of Torque-Flite transmission. (Chrysler Division of Chrysler Corporation)

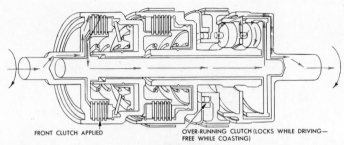

Fig. 25–51. Power flow in D (drive) position when first breaking away from a standing start. (*Chrysler Division of Chrysler Corporation*)

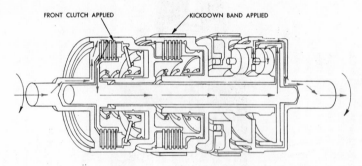

Fig. 25–52. Power flow in intermediate and also with push button 2 pushed in. (*Chrysler Division of Chrysler Corporation*)

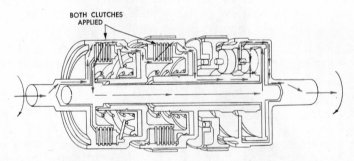

Fig. 25–53. Power flow in direct drive. (*Chrysler Division of Chrysler Corporation*)

clutch, rear ring, and planetary gears to the rear sun gear. The two sun gears turn together, causing the front planetary gears to drive the front ring gear and thus the output shaft. Gear reduc- tion takes place in both planetaries to provide a 2.45:1 gear ratio. At intermediate speed (Fig. 25–52), the front clutch and kick-down band are applied and gear reduction takes place

572

FRONT CLUTCH APPLIED LOW AND REVERSE BAND APPLIED

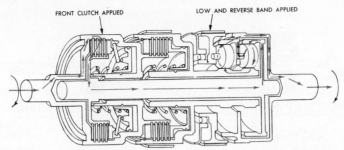

Fig. 25–54. Power flow with push button 1 pushed in. (*Chrysler Division of Chrysler Corporation*)

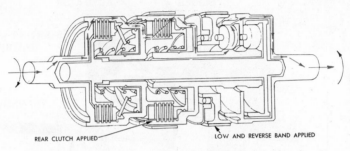

REAR CLUTCH APPLIED LOW AND REVERSE BAND APPLIED

Fig. 25–55. Power flow in reverse. (*Chrysler Division of Chrysler Corporation*)

only in the rear planetary set for a gear ratio of 1.45:1.

In the direct-drive position (Fig. 25–53), both multiple-disk clutches are applied and both bands are released. As a result, the two planetary gearsets are locked up and no gear reduction can take place. The gear ratio therefore is 1:1.

Additional selector positions (1 and 2) are available (see Fig. 25–56) so that the low and intermediate speed gear ratios can be held. For instance, if button 1 is pressed, the situation shown in Fig. 25–54 will result. This is the same as shown in Fig. 25–51 except that the low and reverse band is applied to hold the front planet carrier stationary and thus provide engine braking.

In reverse (Fig. 25–55), the rear clutch and low and reverse bands are applied. The power flow is now through the rear clutch and front sun gear, planet pinions, and ring gear. Since the planet pinions are interposed in the gear train, they act as idlers to reverse the direction of rotation. Thus, the output shaft turns in the reverse direction to back the car. A gear ratio of 2.20:1 results.

5. *Push-button controls.* Figure 25–56 shows one type of push-button control used with the Torque-Flite transmission just described. The control is mounted on the instrument panel. It is connected by a push-pull control cable to the manual control-valve lever in the transmission. When a button is pushed, the slide moves the cable ac-

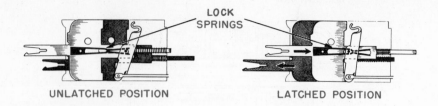

LOCK
SPRINGS

UNLATCHED POSITION   LATCHED POSITION

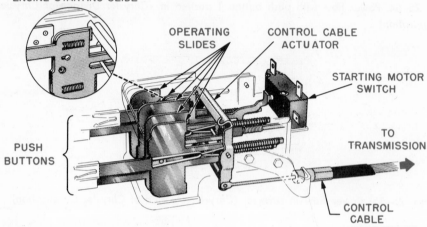

NEUTRAL OPERATING AND
ENGINE STARTING SLIDE

OPERATING   CONTROL CABLE
SLIDES   ACTUATOR

STARTING MOTOR
SWITCH

PUSH
BUTTONS

TO
TRANSMISSION

CONTROL
CABLE

Fig. 25–56. Push-button control unit, external and operating views. (*Chrysler Division of Chrysler Corporation*)

tuator. A lock spring holds the button in until another button is pushed. A backup light switch is used on many models; this switch is closed when the R (reverse) button is pushed. Also, the assembly has a starting-motor switch which is closed when the N (neutral) button is pushed in. As soon as the engine starts, a vacuum switch on the engine opens the starting-motor circuit and cranking ends. The starting-motor switch is closed only when the N button is depressed. Thus, no starting-motor operation is possible when any of the other buttons are pushed in, even though the engine might die.

REVIEW QUESTIONS

1. Name some differences between a fluid coupling and a torque converter.
2. Describe the "bouncing-back" effect resulting when there are only two members in the coupling.
3. Explain how adding a third member to the torque converter permits the torque converter to multiply torque when there is speed reduction.
4. Describe a torque converter with three members. With four members. With five members.
5. Explain how the direct-drive clutch used in the Ultramatic operates.
6. Explain how the Twin Turbine operates.
7. Explain how the variable-pitch Twin-Turbine torque converter operates.
8. Describe the operation of the transmission used with the Powerglide. The Turboglide.
9. Describe the operation of the Ultramatic transmission.
10. Describe the operation of the Powerflite transmission. The Torque-Flite.
11. Describe the operation of the Fordomatic transmission. The Cruise-O-Matic.

STUDY QUESTIONS

1. Write an essay describing the construction and operation of a torque converter. Cover only the essentials, and show how torque is multiplied.
2. Write an essay describing the construction and operation of one of the automatic transmissions which has an automatic shift.

THIS CHAPTER DISCUSSES GENERAL trouble-shooting and servicing procedures on automatic transmissions. The instructions that follow apply, in general, to all automatic transmissions. However, the manufacturer's shop manual applying to the specific model transmission being serviced should be carefully followed when any work is done on an automatic transmission.

§ 464. Automatic-transmission trouble-shooting The manufacturer usually supplies a diagnosis guide such as is shown in Figs. 26–1 and 26–2. As you will see when you study the guide sheet, it lists the various checks and adjustments to be made and relates various abnormal conditions with possible causes. As an example, suppose you found a case of severe engagement in LO (low), DR (drive), or R (reverse). You would find this condition under "Operating Conditions." Components to check, as indicated by the letters, would be K, B, W, E, and F. Being underlined, K and B are the most likely causes.

Also, the manufacturer may supply trouble-shooting information in the form shown in Figs. 26–3 and 26–4. Figure 26–3 is a list of possible troubles, and Fig. 26–4 is an index of possible causes. To use the list and index, first locate the trouble in the list, and then refer to the numbered causes in the index of causes. For example, suppose the trouble is erratic shifting. First, find the entry "Shifts erratically" in the list (under "Shift Pattern Abnormalities"). After this entry, you will find the numbers 1, 13, 21, 35. Now refer to these numbers in the index of possible causes (Fig. 26–4). There, you will find that erratic shifting could be caused by "1, oil level"; "13, valve-body mating surface"; "21, shift valve, spring"; or "35, output-shift support gaskets." In other words, erratic shifting could be caused by troubles with any of these four. By studying Figs. 26–3 and 26–4, you can relate other troubles and their causes in a similar manner.

§ 465. Automatic-transmission service For specific servicing procedures on automatic transmissions, always refer to the applicable shop manual that covers the model being worked on. Further, use the special service tools that the shop manual calls for. General points of transmission testing and servicing, and precautions to observe, are noted below.

1. Road tests. If you road-test a car

Fordomatic Diagnosis Guide

Owner_____ Date_____

Address_____City_____State_____

Vehicle Code No._____License No._____Trans. Serial No._____

Mileage_____Mechanic_____

IMPORTANT: Begin diagnosis with the steps listed under, "Preliminary Checks and Adjustments," then road test the vehicle to check the adjustments made. If the road test indicates the need for further adjustments, refer to "Final Diagnosis."

PRELIMINARY CHECKS AND ADJUSTMENTS

These five checks, when made before road test, will avoid possible further damage and will correct the majority of difficulties.

$\boxed{V}$ Found Satisfactory; $\boxed{X}$ Adjustment Made

1. ☐ Fluid Level—If low, refill, then immediately turn to Final Diagnosis table of External Fluid Leakage and correct cause before proceeding.

2. ☐ Engine Idle—Adjust idle, then set anti-stall dashpot.

3. ☐ Throttle Linkage—Check free operation and specifications.

4. ☐ Manual Linkage—Check linkage and starter neutral switch.

5. ☐ Stall Test—With engine at operating temperature, attach tachometer and set selector lever in desired position. Apply hand and foot brakes firmly, then accelerate engine to wide open throttle. Read engine R.P.M. and record results in the table.

CAUTION: Do not hold throttle open longer than five seconds. Release throttle immediately if slippage is indicated.

ENGINE R.P.M.	DR	R	PROCEDURE
Normal*			Proceed to Road Test.
Low			Tune engine and repeat stall test. If still low check one-way clutch.
High			Slippage—Perform pressure test.**

*6-cyl. Engine 1300-1500 R.P.M.; 8-cyl. Engine 1365-1565 R.P.M.
**If pressures meet specifications—check band adjustment.

ROAD TEST CHECKS

Make *all* of these checks (State speed laws permitting) to determine the exact operating conditions of the transmission. Record the results opposite each specification.

1. Initial engagements at closed throttle are $\boxed{V}$ Smooth; $\boxed{X}$ Rough.
   ☐ Low (L); ☐ Intermediate (DR); ☐ Reverse (R).

2. Reverse start at light throttle. ☐ Smooth; ☐ Chatters; ☐ Slips.

3. Shift points on smooth level road "DR" range (write in Actual M.P.H.).
   a. _____ Intermediate to High, minimum throttle -15-20 M.P.H.
   b. _____ Intermediate to High, full throttle -56-67 M.P.H.
   c. _____ High to Intermediate, minimum throttle—10-3 M.P.H.
   d. _____ High to Intermediate, forced downshift—20-62 M.P.H.

4. Manual shift from DR to LO range (write in Actual M.P.H.).
   a. _____ High to Intermediate above 21-27 M.P.H.
   b. _____ High to Low below 21-27 M.P.H.

5. Noise occurs in ☐ Neutral; ☐ Low; ☐ Int.; ☐ Reverse; ☐ Neutral (Coasting at 20-30 M.P.H. with Engine Off).

Fig. 26—1. Fordomatic diagnosis guide, page 1. (*Ford Division of Ford Motor Company*)

FINAL DIAGNOSIS

Final Diagnosis of Operating Conditions, Noise, and External Fluid Leakage will indicate final repairs and adjustments to be made. Components to check are shown in logical sequence with the most probable causes underlined. Checking component symbols against the Legend will point out the items to correct. After immediate corrections have been made, be sure that cause of difficulty has been corrected. *Always follow sequence* for quickest results.

OPERATING CONDITIONS

CONDITION	√	COMPONENTS TO CHECK*		CONDITION	√	COMPONENTS TO CHECK*
Severe Engagement LO, DR, or R		KB WEF		Slippage or Chatter in Rev. Ratio		ABH WEFlbc
Rough R Start		KBH WEF		No Drive in DR		GEJac
INT.-HI Shift MPH Low, High or Erratic		BD WEc		No Drive in LO or R		H IE
Severe INT.-HI Shift		B GEJF		No Drive in Any Range		AC EFc
Engine Overspeeds, INT.-HI Shift		B GEc		Lockup in R		ag
No INT.-HI Shift		D Ebc		Lockup in LO or DR		bg
No Forced Downshift HI-INT.		B WE		Parking Lock Will Not Hold		C g
Severe HI-INT. Shift (Closed Throttle)		BK E		Unable to Start Engine by Pushing		Fec
Excessive Creeping		K		Transmission Overheating		XH FnG
Slippage or Chatter in INT. Ratio		ABG WEFJac		Engine Runaway on Forced Downshift		E
Slippage or Chatter in LOW Ratio		ABH WEFlac				

NOISE

LOCATION	√	COMPONENTS TO CHECK*		LOCATION	√	COMPONENTS TO CHECK*
In Neutral		L dia		Coasting in N 20-30 MPH, Engine Off		e
In LOW, INT. or REVERSE Ratio		hab		In Converter		L i

EXTERNAL FLUID LEAKAGE

WHERE NOTICED	√	POSSIBLE CAUSES*		WHERE NOTICED	√	POSSIBLE CAUSES*
Converter Housing or Air Duct		MZ jkmo		Front of Extension Housing		SV
Transmission Oil Pan		NO		Rear of Extension Housing		U
Left Side of Case		PQT		Speedometer Gear Boss		Y
Right Side of Case		QRT				
IMPORTANT: Inoperative vent on right hand side of case can cause general leakage.						

LEGEND*

A. Fluid Level	J. Front Servo	S. Ext. Housing to Case Lock Washers
B. Throttle Linkage	K. Engine Idle Speed	T. Center Support Bolt Lock Washers
C. Manual Linkage	L. Converter Cover Bolts Striking	U. Extension Rear Oil Seal
D. Governor	M. Converter Drain Plugs	V. Governor Insp. Cover Gasket
E. Valve Body	N. Oil Pan Gasket	W. Perform Pressure Check
F. Pressure Regulator	O. Oil Pan Drain Plug Gasket	X. Converter Cooling Air Passages
G. Front Band	P. Manual or Throt. Lever Shaft Seal	Y. Speedo, Driven Gear Seal
H. Rear Band	Q. 1/8 Pipe Plug in Side of Case	Z. Converter Cover Bolt Torque
I. Rear Servo	R. Filler Cap	
a. Front Clutch	f. Fluid Distributor Sleeve	k. Converter Cover Gasket
b. Rear Clutch	g. Parking Linkage	m. Front Pump Oil Seal
c. Leakage in Hydraulic System	h. Planetary Assembly	n. Converter One-Way Clutch
d. Front Pump	i. Interference in Converter	o. Converter Impeller Hub Seal
e. Rear Pump	j. Engine Rear Oil Seal	p.

*Capitalized legends denote repairs not requiring transmission removal from car. Non-capitalized legends denote repairs requiring transmission removal.

Repairs Made:_____   Parts Replaced:_____

_____   _____

_____   _____

Remarks:_____

Fig. 26—2. Fordomatic diagnosis guide, page 2. (*Ford Division of Ford Motor Company*)

Operation Difficulty	Possible Causes
Improper response to shift lever positions	
No detent feel	14
Det. not with pointer	2-14
Gate not with pointer	2
Moves forward in N	4-13-21-23-33 34-38-43-44-50
Moves forward in N at high engine speed	46
Moves backward in N	2-14-25-26-27 51
No drive	1-2-8-12-14-30 31-32-33-50-51
No drive in D and L	15-51
Excessive slip indications	
Slip in all ranges	1-8-9-13-30-32 33-38
Kick-down band slips	3-4-13-15-19-22 23-24
KD band slips over 25 mph	19-22
Slips in D (direct)	13-23-40-44-45 46
Reverse band slips	13-25-26-27
Slips on steep grades	1
Dragging, bands, clutch, or brakes	
Drag in all ranges	7-21-43
Drag in D and L	25-26-27-51
Drag in R, D, and L	13-33-34-38-44 45
Drag in D (direct)	13-41
Drag in R, D (direct)	23
Shift Pattern Abnormalities	
No upshift	1-2-13-14-21-23 36-37-46
Upshift pattern low	3-13-15-21-36 37
Upshift pattern low at heavy throttle only	8
All upshifts 10-15 mph	15-17
Upshift pattern high	3-13-15-21-36 37
Shifts erratically	1-13-21-35
No downshift	21-36
Low downshift speed	21
High downshift speed	2-13-14-20
KD at part throttle	2-13-14-20
No kick-down	3-13-15-20-21
KD limit low	8-13-36-37

Operation Difficulty	Possible Causes
Poor shift quality	
Harsh shift N to R	25-26-27
Harsh shift N to D	3-23
Delayed shift N to D	4-24
Runaway on upshifts	1-3-8-13-15-23 33-34-38-40-44 45-46
Runaway on upshifts light throttle only	32
Harsh upshifts	3-8-13-15-23-33 42-43
Harsh lift foot shifts	3-13-15-16-22
Runaway on downshifts at part throttle	1-2-3-13-14-18
Harsh downshift	3-13-15-18-44 45-47
Runaway on kick-downs	4-8-13-18-22-23 36-37
Harsh kick-downs	4-8-16-22-23-33 34-36-37-38-42 43-44-45
Shudder during shifts	21
Noises	
Grating (car moving)	10-28
Buzzing	1-33
Squealing after trans. Installation	30-31
Whistling (R, D and L)	9-30
Rubbing	32-47
Rubbing in D (direct)	41
Excessive gear noise	37-48-50-51-52
Grinding	49
Other difficulties	
Starter will not energize	2-5-14
Hard to shift into N	5
Hard to shift into R	6
Accel. pedal sticks at closed throttle	3-15
Hard to fill trans.	11-35
Oil foams from filler	1-11-35
Oil leaks at seals	11-29-35
Transmission overheats	4-9-25-26-27-33 34-37-38-39-41 43-44-47
Impossible to push start the engine	35-37

Fig. 26—3. Powerflite transmission trouble-diagnosis chart. N. neutral; D, drive; **L**, low; R, reverse; KD, kick-down or low. (*De Soto Division of Chrysler Corporation*)

1. Oil level
2. Gearshift-linkage adjustment
3. Throttle-linkage adjustment
4. Kick-down band adjustment
5. Neutral starter switch
6. Back-up switch
7. Handbrake adjustment
8. Regulator valve, spring
9. Converter control valve
10. Speedometer pinion
11. Breather
12. Oil strainer
13. Valve-body mating surface
14. Manual valve, lever
15. Throttle valve, cam, spring
16. Servo pressure bleed valve
17. Throttle pressure check ball
18. Servo restrictor valve
19. Valve-body end-cover plug
20. Kick-down valve ball, rod
21. Shift valve, spring
22. Shuttle valve, plug, etc.
23. KD piston, guide, etc.
24. KD band, lever, strut, etc.
25. Reverse band adjustment
26. Reverse piston, sleeve, etc.
27. Reverse band, lever, strut, etc.
28. Rear bearing, snap ring
29. External seals
30. Front pump drive sleeve
31. Front pump pinion
32. Front pump assembly (worn)
33. Regulator body mating surfaces
34. Reaction shaft seal
35. Output shaft support gaskets
36. Governor assembly
37. Rear-pump assembly
38. Input-shaft seal rings
  Reaction-shaft bore
39. Plugged lubrication holes
40. Clutch-retainer bushing
  Reaction-shaft seal rings
41. KD sun-gear snap ring
42. Direct clutch spring
43. Clutch-spring-retainer snap ring
44. Clutch disks, plates
45. Clutch piston, seal rings
46. Clutch check valve ball
47. Thrust washers
48. KD-carrier bushing
49. Oil-collector rings
50. Planet pinion shafts
51. Output-shaft support
52. Output-shaft bushing

Fig. 26–4. Index of possible causes of trouble in the Powerflite transmission. (De Soto Division of Chrysler Corporation)

580

to check the transmission operation, be sure to observe all traffic laws. If a chassis dynamometer is available, it can be used and it will not be necessary to take the car out on the road to check shift points and other operating characteristics of the transmission.

2. *Towing or pushing a car to start it.* With a run-down battery, it is often the practice to push or tow the car to start the engine. If this is done, the special instructions supplied by the manufacturer should be observed. For instance, Chevrolet says the car should be pushed, with the selector lever in neutral, until a speed of about 16 mph (miles per hour) is reached. Then a shift should be made into low. After the engine starts, the selector lever should be returned to neutral until the engine warms up. It is better to push, rather than tow, a car to start it. If the car is towed, the engine might start and cause the car to ram the car ahead of it before it could be brought under control.

3. *Towing a disabled car.* If a car with an automatic transmission is disabled, it can usually be towed short distances without danger. However, towing speed should be low. Selector lever should be in neutral. On some cars, the recommendation is to use a rear-end pickup truck or else remove the propeller shaft if the car is to be towed any distance. When the car is towed, the transmission may not be furnished normal lubrication. Thus it could be ruined in fairly short distances, particularly if the car were towed at fairly high speeds.

4. *Engine performance.* Before the automatic transmission is checked, the engine should be tested to make sure it is in good condition. A sluggish engine will not give the transmission a chance to perform normally. Shifting may be delayed. Further, the engine might not have enough power to pull the car and accelerate normally. This might lead to wrong guesses about the transmission.

5. *Throttle and control linkages.* For the transmission to function properly, the linkages between the throttle pedal and transmission, and between the selector lever and transmission, must be correctly adjusted. Incorrect throttle linkages will throw off the shift points and may prevent shifting entirely. Incorrect selector-lever-linkage adjustment could keep the transmission from functioning in the operating range selected by the lever.

6. *Oil level and cleanliness.* The oil level must be correct in the transmission and the fluid coupling or torque converter. If the fluid level is low, transmission parts may not be adequately lubricated and may thus fail. Further, inadequate oil may cause the fluid coupling or torque converter to function below par and not transmit the power fed into it. Servos may not work properly if they are oil-starved. Thus, the oil level must be maintained properly. Naturally, the oil must be clean and of the proper type. Any trace of dirt in the oil is likely to cause a valve to hang up, and this could throw the operation of the transmission completely off. Also, if the wrong type of oil is used, it might foam or prove otherwise unsuitable. In such a case, transmission malfunctioning and damage could be expected.

7. *Oil-pressure checks.* One of the checks commonly made on automatic

transmissions measures the oil pressures in various parts of the hydraulic circuit. These measurements will disclose whether or not oil pressures are getting through to the valves and servos as they should. If they are not, then there is some fault in the hydraulic system. If they are, and yet valve or servo action is not correct, then the cause of trouble is pin-pointed at the valve or servo.

8. Stall test. Another test to be made on many automatic transmissions is to apply the car brakes so that the car cannot move, put the selector lever in a "drive" position, and open the throttle wide. If engine speed increases excessively, this is a sign that brake bands are slipping in the transmission. If the engine does not come up to speed, the chances are the engine is not in good condition and should be tuned up.

9. Brake-band adjustments. Brake bands are adjusted in different ways on the various automatic transmissions. When correct, they will not slip on the stall test but will release fully under the proper operating conditions.

10. Automatic-transmission overhaul. Always follow the instructions given in the applicable manufacturer's shop manual when overhauling, adjusting, or otherwise servicing an automatic transmission. These mechanisms, while very sturdy, must be serviced correctly to provide normal operation. Of special importance in the disassembly-reassembly procedure is cleanliness. It must be remembered that many parts in the automatic transmission are fitted with extremely close tolerances. Thus, even tiny particles of dirt or grit can cause serious malfunctioning and damage to the unit. For example, a particle of dirt in the valve body could cause valves to hang up so that the transmission would not shift normally.

REVIEW QUESTIONS

1. Explain the purpose of the diagnosis guides manufacturers supply for their automatic transmissions.
2. Discuss the various precautions to observe when engaged in automatic-transmission service.

STUDY QUESTIONS

1. Select an automatic transmission, and write an overhaul story on it. Base your story on both the shop manual and actual shopwork, if possible. Be sure to cover details of adjustments.

THIS CHAPTER DESCRIBES THE purpose, construction, operation, and servicing of drive lines. Drive lines, in automobiles, are the driving connection between the transmission and the driving mechanism at the rear wheels (the differential). The purpose of the drive line is to carry the driving power from the transmission to the rear wheels. It consists of the propeller shaft, a universal joint (or joints), and a slip joint.

§ 466. Function of propeller shaft
The propeller shaft is a driving shaft that connects the transmission main, or output, shaft to the differential at the rear axles. Rotary motion of the trans-

mission main, or output, shaft carries through the propeller shaft to the differential, causing the rear wheels to rotate. The propeller-shaft design must take into consideration two facts. First, the engine and transmission are more or less rigidly attached to the car frame. Second, the rear-axle housing (with wheels and differential) is attached to the frame by springs. As the rear wheels encounter irregularities in the road, the springs compress or expand. This changes the angle of drive between the propeller and transmission shafts. It also changes the distance between the transmission and the differential (see Fig. 27–1). In order that the propeller shaft may take care of

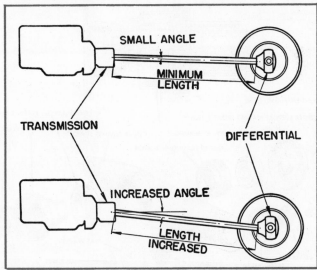

Fig. 27–1. As the rear-axle housing, with differential and wheels, moves up and down, the angle between the transmission output shaft changes and the length of the propeller shaft also changes.

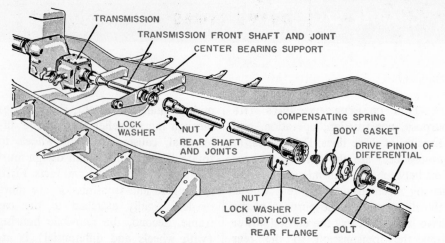

Fig. 27–2. One type of propeller shaft, partly disassembled so that the component parts can be seen. (*Willys Motors, Inc.*)

these two changes, it must incorporate two separate types of device. There must be one or more universal joints to permit variations in the angle of drive. There must also be a slip joint that permits the effective length of the propeller shaft to change.

The propeller shaft may be solid or hollow, protected by an outer tube or exposed. Some applications include

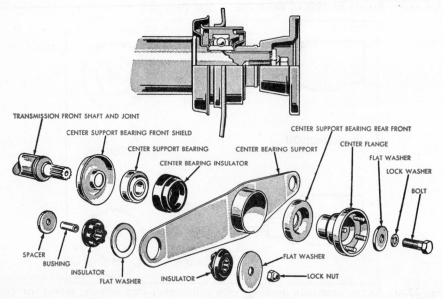

Fig. 27–3. Details of propeller-shaft center support and bearing. (*Willys Motors, Inc.*)

bearings at or near the propeller-shaft center to support the shaft. Figures 27–2, 27–7, and 27–9 illustrate various types of propeller shaft. On some applications, the propeller shaft is in two or more sections (see Fig. 27–2), often supported by bearings and coupled together by universal joints. The two-section shaft shown in Fig. 27–2 has a center support as shown in Fig. 27–3.

§ 467. Universal joints   A simple universal joint is illustrated in Fig. 27–4. It is essentially a double-hinged joint consisting of two Y-shaped yokes, one on the driving shaft and the other on the driven shaft, and a cross-shaped member called the spider. The four arms of the spider, known as *trunnions,* are assembled into bearings in the ends of the two shaft yokes. The driving shaft causes the spider to rotate, and the other two trunnions of the spider cause the driven shaft to rotate. When the two shafts are at an angle to each other, the bearings in the yokes permit the yokes to swing round on the trunnions with each revolution. A variety of universal joints have been used on automobiles, but the two types now in most common use are the spider and two-yoke design and the ball-and-trunnion design.

The spider and two-yoke design is essentially the same as the simple universal joint discussed above, except that the bearings are often of the needle type (Fig. 27–5). As will be noted, there are four needle bearings, one for each trunnion of the spider. The bearings are held in place by snap rings that drop into undercuts in the yoke-bearing holes. A variation of this

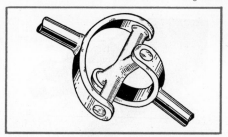

Fig. 27–4. A simple universal joint.

design makes use of separately mounted bearing housings on the yokes (Fig. 27–6). Figure 27–7 shows a propeller shaft with two universal joints, one at each end.

The ball-and-trunnion type of universal joint combines both the universal and the slip joint in one assembly. A universal joint of this design is shown in Fig. 27–8 in exploded view and in sectional view in Fig. 27–9. The shaft has a pin pressed through it, and around both ends of the pin are placed balls drilled out to accommodate needle bearings. The other member of the universal joint consists of a steel casing, or body, that has two longitudinal channels into which the balls fit. The body is bolted to a flange on the mating shaft (not shown in Fig. 27–8 or 27–9). The rotary motion is carried through the pin and balls. The balls can move back and forth in the channels of the body to compensate for varying angles of drive. At the same time, they act as a slip joint by slipping in or out of the channels.

§ 468. Slip joint   A slip joint is illustrated in Fig. 27–10. As previously explained, the slip joint consists of outside splines on one shaft and matching internal splines on the mating hollow shaft (see parts 8 and 17 in Fig. 27–10). The splines cause the two shafts

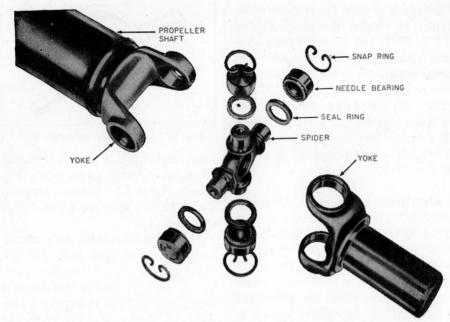

Fig. 27–5. Two-yoke and cross universal joint in disassembled view, with parts shown in their order of assembly. (*Studebaker-Packard Corporation*)

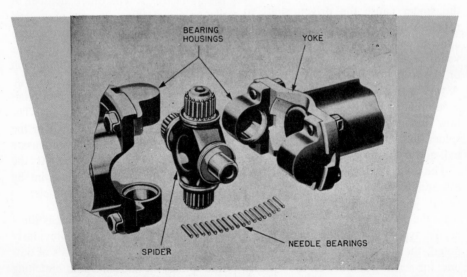

Fig. 27–6. Two-yoke and cross universal joint disassembled. The bearing housings are separately bolted to the yokes. (*Cadillac Motor Car Division of General Motors Corporation*)

586

to rotate together but permit the two to move endwise with each other. This accommodates any effective change of length of the propeller shaft as the rear axles move toward or away from the car frame.

§ 469. Types of drive   The rotation of the propeller shaft transmits torque through the differential to the rear wheels, causing them to rotate and move the car. The wheels rotate because torque is applied to them. This torque not only rotates the wheels in one direction; it also attempts to rotate the differential housing in the opposite direction. To understand why this occurs it is necessary to review briefly the construction of the differential (Fig. 28–2). The ring gear is connected through other gears to the rear-wheel axles; the torque applied through the drive pinion forces the ring gear and wheels to rotate. It is the side thrust of the drive-pinion teeth against the ring-gear teeth that makes the ring gear rotate. This side thrust also causes the drive-pinion shaft to push against the shaft bearing. The thrust against the shaft bearing is in a direction opposite to the thrust of the pinion teeth against

the ring-gear teeth. Since the drive-pinion bearings are held in the differential housing, the housing tries to rotate in a direction opposite to the ring-gear and wheel rotation. This action is termed *rear-end torque,* and, to prevent excessive movement of the differential housing from this action, several methods of bracing the housing are used. The two most common types of bracing found on modern automobiles are the torque-tube drive and the Hotchkiss drive (Fig. 27–11).

In the torque-tube drive, the propeller shaft is incased in a hollow tube. The tube is rigidly bolted to the differential housing at one end and is fastened at the other end to the transmission case through a somewhat flexible joint. On many cars, a pair of truss rods are attached between the rear-axle housings and the transmission end of the torque tube. The torque tube and the truss rods brace the differential housing to prevent excessive differential-housing movement. In other words, these members absorb the rear-end torque.

In the Hotchkiss drive, the rear-end torque is absorbed by the rear springs. The rear springs are attached to

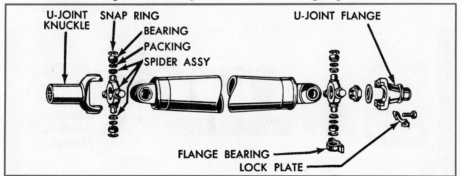

Fig. 27–7. Disassembled view of a propeller shaft (drive line) using two universal joints. (*Ford Division of Ford Motor Company*)

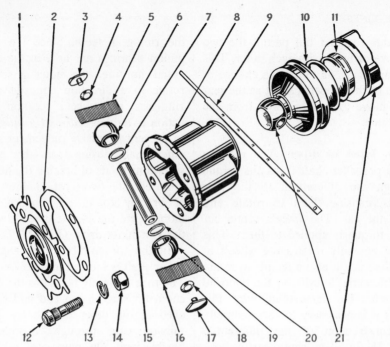

Fig. 27–8. Disassembled view of ball-and-trunnion type of universal joint. (*Plymouth Division of Chrysler Corporation*)

1. Grease cover
2. Gasket
3. Centering button
4. Centering-button spring
5. Rollers
6. Ball
7. Thrust washer
8. Body
9. Dust-cover clamp (long)
10. Dust cover, or boot
11. Dust-cover clamp (short)
12. Propeller-shaft bolt (front only)
13. Propeller-shaft bolt-nut lock washer
14. Propeller-shaft bolt nut
15. Pin
16. Rollers
17. Centering button
18. Centering-button spring
19. Ball
20. Thrust washer
21. Propeller shaft

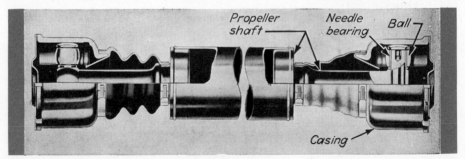

Fig. 27–9. Propeller shaft with two universal joints of the ball-and-trunnion design. (*Plymouth Division of Chrysler Corporation*)

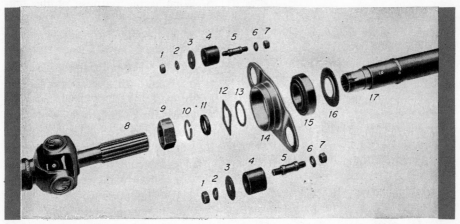

Fig. 27–10. Propeller shaft and support bearing partly disassembled so that the slip joint can be seen. External splines are on universal-joint yoke (8), and internal splines are in shaft (17). (*Studebaker-Packard Corporation*)

1. Nut	7. Nut	13. Spacer
2. Lock washer	8. Slip yoke	14. Support
3. Plain washer	9. Grease-washer nut	15. Support bearing
4. Support cushion	10. Washer retainer	16. Dust shield
5. Stud	11. Grease washer	17. Front shaft
6. Lock washer	12. Lock plate	

brackets bolted to the rear-axle housing so that the springs themselves act as the torque-absorbing members. Thus, when the car is moving forward, the rear-end torque causes the front halves of the springs to be compressed while the rear halves of the springs are expanded. Two universal joints are required on the propeller shaft in the Hotchkiss drive, one at each end of the shaft (see Fig. 27–7). The reason for this is obvious: the differential housing does rotate as a result of rear-end torque within the limits imposed by car springs.

§ 470. **Universal-joint service** Little maintenance of universal joints is required aside from periodic lubrication. When disassembly is required, it may take 1 hour, when only one universal joint is to be overhauled, to approximately 4 hours, when the propeller shaft is removed and replaced. On many cars, the propeller-shaft and universal-joint parts are carefully balanced during original assembly. To assure reassembly in the correct relationship, so that the balance will be maintained, the parts are marked. If the marks cannot be found, new marks should be made, so that the parts can be reassembled correctly. Refer to the applicable car shop manual for service procedures on specific models.

REVIEW QUESTIONS

1. What function does the propeller shaft perform?

589

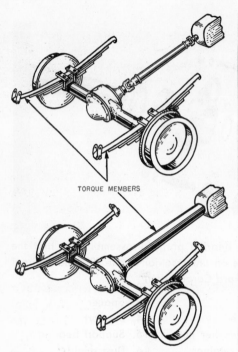

TORQUE MEMBERS

Fig. 27–11. Hotchkiss drive (*top*) compared with torque-tube drive (*bottom*).

2. What two actions take place as the rear springs compress and expand, in so far as the propeller shaft is concerned? What two devices are used to take care of these actions?

3. Describe the action of a two-yoke and cross universal joint.

4. Describe the action of a ball-and-trunnion type of universal joint.

5. What is the purpose of the universal joint?

6. What is the purpose of a slip joint?

7. What is rear-end torque? Describe in detail what causes rear-end torque.

8. How many universal joints are used with a torque-tube drive?

9. What absorbs the rear-end torque in the torque-tube drive?

10. What absorbs the rear-end torque in the Hotchkiss drive?

11. How many universal joints are required on the Hotchkiss drive? Why that number?

STUDY QUESTIONS

1. Make a sketch of a universal joint, and write an explanation of its operation.

2. Make a sketch of a slip joint, and write an explanation of its operation.

3. Write a brief article explaining why rear-end torque occurs.

4. Make sketches of a torque tube and a Hotchkiss drive, indicating the members that absorb rear-end torque.

5. Write a service story on one propeller shaft, including the universal joints. Base your story on a shop manual and also on actual shopwork, if possible.

CHAPTER 28

REAR AXLES AND DIFFERENTIALS

THIS CHAPTER DISCUSSES THE purpose, construction, operation, and servicing of differentials and rear axles. The differential is part of the rear-axle-housing assembly, which includes the differential, rear axles, wheels, and bearings.

§ 471. Function of differential

If the car were to be driven in a straight line without having to make turns, then no differential would be necessary. However, when the car rounds a turn, the outer wheel must travel farther than the inner wheel. If a right-angle turn is made with the inner wheel turning on a 20-foot radius, this wheel travels about 31 feet (Fig. 28–1). The outer wheel, being nearly 5 feet from the inner wheel, turns on a 24 2/3-foot radius (in the car shown), and it travels nearly 39 feet.

If the propeller shaft were geared rigidly to both rear wheels so that they would both have to rotate together, then each wheel would have to skid an average of 4 feet in making the turn discussed above. On this basis, tires would not last long. In addition, the skidding would make the car hard to control on turns. The differential eliminates these troubles because it allows the wheels to rotate different amounts when turns are made.

To study the construction and action of the differential, let us build up, in effect, a simple differential (Fig. 28–2). The two rear wheels are attached, through the axles, to two small bevel gears (Fig. 28–2a). There is a differential case assembled around the left axle (Fig. 28–2b). The case has a bearing that permits it to turn independently of the left axle. Inside the case is a shaft that supports a third bevel gear (Fig. 28–2c). This third bevel gear, called the *differential-pinion* gear, is meshed with the two axle bevel gears. Thus, when the differential case is rotated, both axle bevel

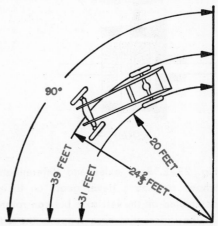

Fig. 28–1. Difference of wheel travel as car makes a 90-degree turn with inner rear wheel on a 20-foot radius.

591

gears rotate and thus both wheels turn. However, let us suppose that one wheel is held stationary. Then, when the differential case is rotated, the differential-pinion gear will also rotate as it "runs round" on the stationary axle bevel gear. As it rotates in this manner, it carries rotary motion to the other axle bevel gear, causing it, and the wheel, to rotate.

It can be seen that, when one rear wheel turns more rapidly than the other, the differential-pinion gear spins on its shaft, transmitting more rotary motion to one rear wheel than to the other. When both turn at the same speed, the differential-pinion gear does not rotate on its shaft.

The differential case is rotated by means of a ring gear attached to it. This ring gear is meshed with a drive pinion on the end of the propeller shaft

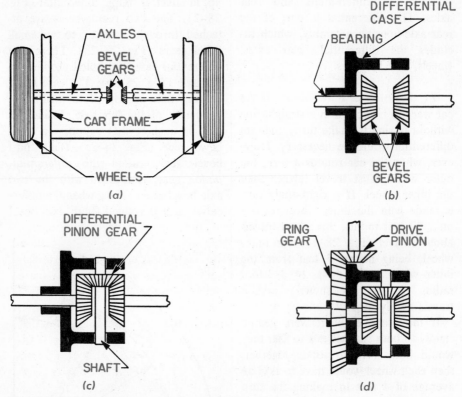

Fig. 28–2. Rear axles and differential: (a) The rear axles are attached to the wheels and have bevel gears on their inner ends; (b) the differential case is assembled on the left axle but can rotate on a bearing independently of the axle; (c) the differential case supports the differential-pinion gear on a shaft, and this gear meshes with the two bevel gears; (d) the ring gear is attached to the differential case, so that the case rotates with the ring gear when the latter is driven by the drive pinion.

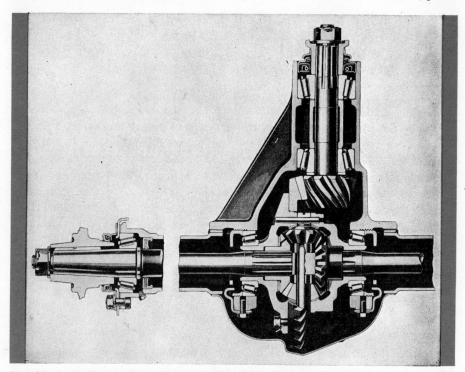

Fig. 28–3. Sectional view of differential and rear axle (see Fig. 28–4 for names of parts). (*Plymouth Division of Chrysler Corporation*)

(Fig. 28–2*d*). When the car is on a straight road, the ring gear, differential case, differential-pinion gear, and two axle bevel gears all turn as a unit without any relative motion. However, when the car begins to round a curve, the differential-pinion gear rotates on its shaft to permit the outer rear wheel to turn more rapidly than the inner rear wheel.

1. Standard differential. The actual differential is more complicated than that in Fig. 28–2. An actual differential, partially cut away to show the parts, is illustrated in Fig. 28–3. The driving power enters the differential through the drive pinion on the end of the propeller shaft (No. 45 in Fig. 28–4). The drive pinion is meshed with a large ring gear (No. 46) so that the ring gear revolves with the pinion. Attached to the ring gear (through the differential case) is a differential-pinion shaft (No. 1), on which are assembled two differential-pinion gears (No. 3). Each rear car wheel has a separate axle, and there are two side gears (No. 4) splined to the inner ends of the two wheel axles (Nos. 10 and 47). The two differential-pinion gears mesh with these two side gears. When the car is on a straight road, the two differential-pinion gears do not rotate on the pinion shaft but they do exert pressure on the two side gears so that the side gears turn at the same speed as the ring gear, causing both rear wheels to turn at the same speed, also.

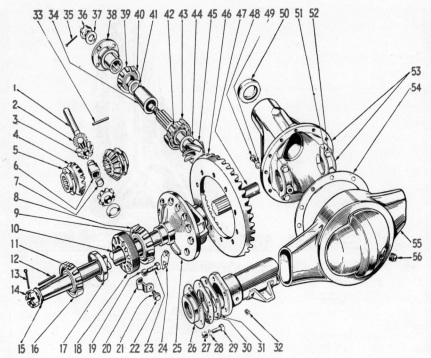

Fig. 28–4. Exploded view of differential and rear axle shown in sectional view in previous illustration. (*Plymouth Division of Chrysler Corporation*)

1. Differential-pinion shaft
2. Differential-pinion thrust washer
3. Differential-pinion gear
4. Differential side gear
5. Differential-gear thrust
6. Axle thrust block
7. Axle-thrust-block spacer
8. Differential-bearing cap
9. Differential-bearing cone and rollers
10. Axle
11. Axle-bearing cone and rollers

12. Axle key
13. Axle-nut cotter pin
14. Axle nut
15. Axle-nut washer
16. Axle-bearing cap
17. Axle oil washer
18. Differential-bearing adjuster
19. Axle-gear bolt nut
20. Differential-bearing adjuster lock
21. Differential-bearing-adjuster lock-screw lock washer
22. Differential-bearing-adjuster lock screw
23. Axle-gear bolt
24. Axle-bolt nut lock
25. Differential case

26. Axle-bearing oil seal
27. Rear-wheel brake-support-to-axle-housing ball nut
28. Rear-wheel brake-support-to-axle-housing bolt-nut lock washer
29. Rear-wheel brake-support-to-axle-housing bolt
30. Axle-bearing oil-seal retainer gasket
31. Axle-bearing shim
32. Axle-bearing oilhole plug
33. Differential-pinion-shaft lockpin, or screw

594

When the car rounds a curve, the outer wheel must turn faster than the inner wheel. To permit this, the two pinion gears rotate on their pinion shaft, transmitting more turning movement to the outer side gear than to the inner side gear. Thus, the side gear on the outer-wheel axle turns more rapidly than the side gear on the inner-wheel axle. This permits the outer wheel to turn more rapidly while the car is rounding the curve.

2. *Nonslip differential.* The conventional differential delivers the same amount of torque to each rear wheel. If one wheel slips on ice, then the other wheel cannot deliver torque. To prevent this, many cars are now equipped with a nonslip differential (Figs. 28–5 and 28–6). This differential is very similar in construction to conventional types except that it has two sets of clutch plates and, in addition, the ends of the pinion shafts lie rather loosely in notches in the two halves of the differential case. During normal straight-road driving, power flow is as shown in Fig. 28–7. The turning effort passes from the drive pinion, through the axle drive gear and the differential case to the pinion shafts, and through the differential pinions and differential side pinions to the axle shaft. Note that the turning differential case carries the pinion shafts around with it. Since there is considerable side thrust, the pinion shafts tend to slide up the sides of the notches in the two halves of the differential case (these notches can be seen in Fig. 28–5). As they slide up, they are forced outward, and this force is transmitted to the clutch plates. The clutch plates thus lock the axle shafts to the differential case. Then, if one wheel should encounter a patch of ice or mud that causes it to lose traction temporarily, it will not spin since it cannot turn faster than the other wheel.

When rounding a curve (Fig. 28–8), the differential acts in the conventional manner to permit the outer wheel to rotate a little faster than the inner wheel. This action is permitted by slipping of the clutches.

34. Drive-pinion-bearing spacer
35. Drive-pinion flange-nut cotter pin
36. Drive-pinion flange nut
37. Drive-pinion flange-nut washer
38. Drive-pinion flange
39. Drive-pinion front-bearing cone and rollers
40. Drive-pinion front-bearing cup
41. Drive-pinion front-bearing adjusting shims
42. Drive-pinion rear-bearing cone and rollers
43. Drive-pinion rear-bearing cup
44. Drive-pinion rear-bearing washer, or shims
45. Drive pinion
46. Ring gear
47. Axle
48. Carrier screw
49. Carrier-screw lock washer
50. Drive-pinion-bearing oil seal
51. Differential-bearing cap-screw lock washer
52. Differential-bearing cap screw
53. Carrier and cap
54. Gasket
55. Housing
56. Housing-cover plug

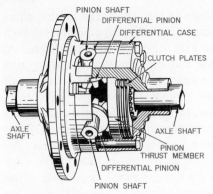

Fig. 28–5. Cutaway view ot a nonslip differential. (*Dodge Division of Chrysler Corporation*)

§ **472. Differential gearing** Since the ring gear has many more teeth than the drive pinion, a considerable gear reduction is effected in the differential. The gear ratios vary somewhat on different cars, depending on car and engine design. Ratios of 3.36:1 upward to about 5:1 are used on passenger cars. This means that the ring gear has 3.36 to 5 times as many teeth as the drive pinion, so that the drive pinion has to rotate 3.36 to 5 times (according to gear ratio) in order to cause the ring gear to rotate once. For heavy-duty applications, such as large trucks, ratios about 9:1 may be used. Such high ratios are secured by use of double-reduction gearing (Fig. 28–12).

The gear ratio in the differential is usually referred to as the *axle ratio* although it would be more accurate to call it the differential ratio.

Early cars used simple spur-gear-type drive pinions and ring gears (Fig. 28–10). In this type of gearing, the

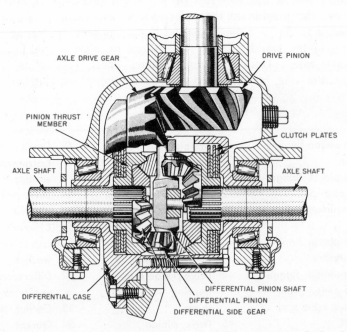

Fig. 28–6. Sectional view of a nonslip differential. (*Dodge Division of Chrysler Corporation*)

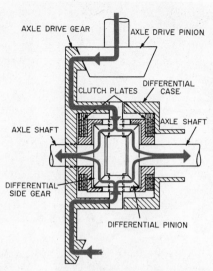

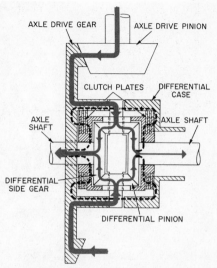

Fig. 28-7. Power flow through nonslip differential on straightaway. (*Dodge Division of Chrysler Corporation*)

Fig. 28-8. Power flow through nonslip differential when rounding a turn. (*Dodge Division of Chrysler Corporation*)

lines of the gear teeth are straight, and all point toward the center of the gear. The center line of the drive-pinion shaft, if extended, would intersect the center line of the axles.

A later design made use of spiral bevel gears (Fig. 28-10), in which the teeth have a curved or spiral shape. This permits contact between more than one pair of teeth at a time; more even wear and quieter operation result. Extension of the center line of the drive-pinion shaft would intersect the axle center line.

Modern car design features lower bodies, and this has brought up the problem of interference between the propeller shaft and the floor of the car body. In order to permit further lowering of the car body without interference with the propeller shaft, hypoid differential gears have come into use (Figs. 28-9 and 28-10). These gears are somewhat similar to the spiral bevel gears, except that the tooth formation allows the drive-pinion shaft to be lowered. In this type of gear, a wiping action takes place between the teeth as the teeth mesh and unmesh. This wiping action, which is characteristic of hypoid gears, makes the use of special hypoid-gear lubricants necessary.

Figure 28-11 illustrates gear-tooth nomenclature. The mating teeth to the left illustrate clearance and backlash, while the tooth to the right has the various tooth parts named. Clearance is the distance between the top of the tooth of one gear and the valley between adjacent teeth of the mating gear. Backlash is the distance between adjacent meshing teeth in the driving and driven gears; it is the distance one gear can rotate backward, or backlash, before it will cause the other gear

597

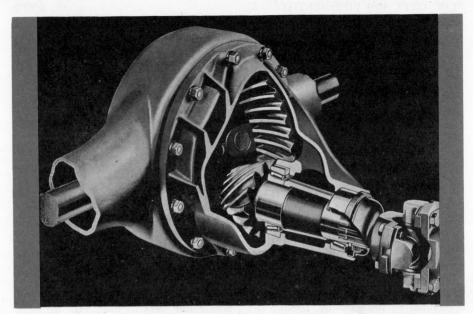

Fig. 28–9. Partial cutaway view of differential, showing drive pinion and ring gear. These are hypoid gears. (*Cadillac Motor Car Division of General Motors Corporation*)

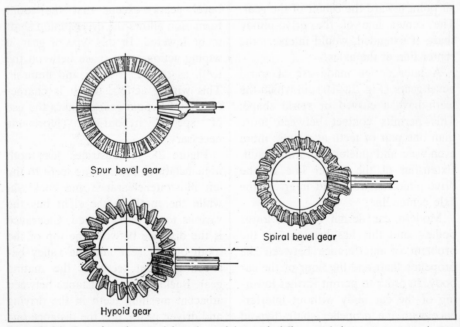

Spur bevel gear

Spiral bevel gear

Hypoid gear

Fig. 28–10. Spur bevel, spiral bevel, and hypoid differential-drive pinions and ring gears.

to move. The toe is the smaller section of the gear tooth; the heel is the larger section.

§ 473. **Double-reduction differentials** In order to secure additional gear reduction through the differential and thus provide a higher gear ratio between the engine and the rear wheels, some heavy-duty applications use double-reduction differentials (Fig. 28–12). In this type of differential, the drive pinion meshes with a ring gear assembled to a straight shaft on which there is a reduction-drive gearset. The reduction-drive gearset drives a driven gearset that has a greater number of gear teeth. Gear reduction is thus obtained between the drive pin-

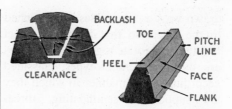

Fig. 28–11. Gear-tooth nomenclature. (*Plymouth Division of Chrysler Corporation*)

ion and the ring gear and also between the two-reduction gearsets.

§ 474. **Types of rear axle** There are two basic types of axle: dead axles and live axles. The dead axle does not rotate; the wheel rotates on it. A common example is the axle on a horse-

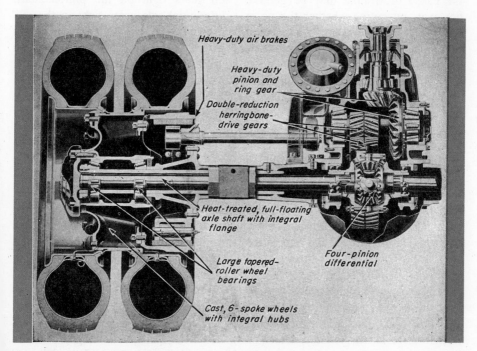

Fig. 28–12. Double-reduction differential in sectional view. (*International Harvester Company*)

drawn wagon. Live axles are attached to the wheel so that both the wheel and the axle rotate together. Live axles are of three general types, classified according to the manner in which they are supported: semifloating, three-quarter-floating, and full-floating.

§ 475. Diagnosis differential troubles

Most often, it is noise that draws attention to trouble existing in the rear axles or differential. It is not always easy, however, to diagnose the trouble by determining the source of noise and the operating conditions under which noise is obtained. Such conditions as defective universal joints, rear-wheel bearings, or muffler or tire noises may be improperly diagnosed as differential or rear-axle trouble. Some clue as to the cause of trouble may be gained, however, by noting whether the noise is a hum, growl, or knock; whether it is obtained when the car is operating on a straight road or on turns only; and whether the noise is most noticeable when the engine is driving the car or when the car is coasting.

A humming noise in the differential is often caused by improper drive-pinion or ring-gear adjustment, which prevents normal tooth contact between the gears. This produces rapid gear-tooth wear, so that the noise will gradually take on a growling characteristic. Correction should be made before the trouble progresses to this extent, since abnormal tooth wear will require pinion and gear replacement.

If the noise is most evident when the car is being accelerated, the probability is that there is heavy heel contact on the gear teeth; the ring gear must be moved near the drive pinion. If the noise is most evident when the car is coasting with the car in gear and the throttle closed, it is probable that there is heavy toe contact on the gear teeth; the ring gear must be moved away from the drive pinion.

NOTE: Tire noise may sometimes be mistaken for differential noise. Since tire noise varies considerably according to the type of pavement, while differential noise does not, the car may be driven over various types of pavement to determine whether or not the noise is resulting from tires or differential.

If the noise is present only when the car is rounding a curve, the trouble is due to some condition in the differential-case assembly. Differential-pinion gears tight on the pinion shaft, differential side gears tight in the differential case, damaged gears or thrust washers, or excessive backlash between gears could produce noise when the car turns.

A knocking noise will result if bearing or gears are damaged or badly worn.

The *axle ratio* of a car may be easily determined when the propeller shaft is exposed (Hotchkiss drive) by marking one rear tire and the propeller shaft with chalk and then pushing the car forward, counting at the same time the revolutions the propeller shaft makes for one wheel revolution. Car transmission should be in neutral. If, for example, the propeller shaft makes 4.4 revolutions while the wheel is making 1 revolution, the axle ratio is 4.4:1.

Backlash in the differential and power train may be checked by placing

the transmission in high gear, raising one rear wheel off the floor, and noting the amount of free rotary motion the raised wheel has.

§ 476. Differential repair Repair
and overhaul procedures on rear axles and differentials vary somewhat from one car to another. Always consult the applicable car shop manual before attempting to service these mechanisms.

REVIEW QUESTIONS

1. What is the purpose of the differential?
2. Name in order the various parts in the differential through which power is carried, from the drive pinion to the axle shafts.
3. When the car is being operated on a straight road, do the differential-pinion gears rotate on their shafts?
4. What occurs to the differential-pinion gears when the car rounds a curve?
5. About what gear reduction is obtained in the differential on passenger cars? Does it vary from car to car?
6. Name three types of gearing that have been used in differentials. Give advantages of each.
7. Mention one reason why hypoid differential gears have come into use. Does this type of gearing require special lubricants? Why?

8. In gears, what is clearance? Backlash? Face? Flank?
9. What are double-reduction differentials?
10. What are the two basic types of axle? In what way do they differ?
11. What are the three general types of live axle?
12. What is it that most often draws attention to trouble existing in the differential?
13. What does a humming noise in the differential often indicate?
14. When differential noise is most evident during car acceleration, what is the probable trouble?
15. If the noise is most evident when the car is coasting in gear, what is the probable trouble?
16. If the noise is present only when the car rounds a turn, what is the probable location of the trouble?
17. On a Hotchkiss-drive car, how can the axle ratio be determined? What is the meaning of the term "axle ratio"?
18. How is backlash in the power train checked?

STUDY QUESTIONS

1. List the parts in a differential in the order in which they transmit power from the propeller shaft.
2. Describe the operation of a standard differential.
3. Describe the operation of a non-slip differential.

CHAPTER 29

AUTOMOTIVE SPRINGS AND SUSPENSION

THIS CHAPTER DESCRIBES THE various springs and suspension systems used in automotive vehicles, including shock-absorber construction and operation.

§ 477. Function of spring The car frame supports the weight of the engine, power-train components, body, and passengers. The frame, in turn, is supported by the springs. The springs are placed between the frame and the wheel axles. Figure 29–1 shows an automotive chassis using coil springs at the front and leaf springs at the rear. Regardless of the type of spring, all work in a similar manner. The weight of the frame, body, etc., applies an initial compression to the springs. The springs will further compress, or will expand, as the car wheels encounter irregularities in the road. Thus, the wheels can move up and down somewhat independently of the frame. This allows the springs to absorb a good part of the up-and-down motion of the car wheels. The motion therefore is not transmitted to the car frame and from it to the passengers. Figures 2–11 and 2–12 show how coil springs compress and expand as the wheels encounter bumps or holes in the road.

§ 478. Types of springs The automobile uses four basic types of spring: coil, leaf, torsion bar, and air (in air-

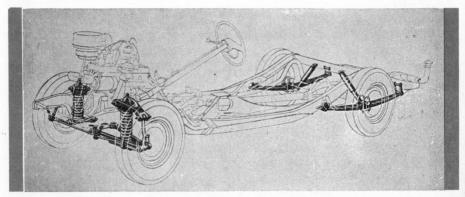

Fig. 29–1. Phantom view of an automotive chassis, showing locations of the coil *springs (at left, or front of car)* and leaf springs *(at right, or rear of car).*

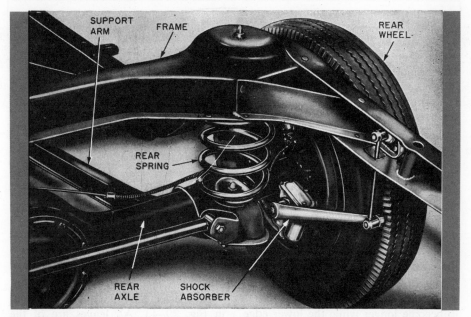

Fig. 29–2. Coil spring placed between the frame and the rear axle housing supports the weight of the frame and vehicle. (*Buick Motor Division of General Motors Corporation*)

suspension systems). Most cars use coil springs at the two front wheels. Some cars use coil springs at the rear wheels (Fig. 29–2 shows a coil spring at a rear wheel). Other cars use leaf springs at the rear wheels. A few cars (and many heavy-duty vehicles) also use leaf springs at the front wheels. The other two types of spring, torsion-bar suspension and air suspension, have been introduced into this country in recent years.

1. *Coil springs.* The coil spring is made of a length of special spring steel (usually round in cross section) which is wound in the shape of a coil. The spring is formed at high temperature (the steel is white-hot), and it is then cooled and properly heat-treated so as to give it the proper characteristics of elasticity and "springiness." Spring characteristics are discussed in a following article.

2. *Leaf spring.* The leaf spring is made up of a series of flat steel plates of graduated length, placed one on top of another as shown in Fig. 29–3. The plates, or leaves, are held together at the center by a center bolt which passes through holes in the leaves. Clips placed at intervals along the spring keep the leaves in alignment. Instead of clips, as shown in Fig. 29–3, some leaf springs are sheathed in a metal cover. The longest, or master, leaf is rolled at both ends to form spring eyes through which bolts are placed to attach the spring ends. On some springs, the ends of the second leaf are also rolled part way around the two spring eyes to reinforce the master leaf.

603

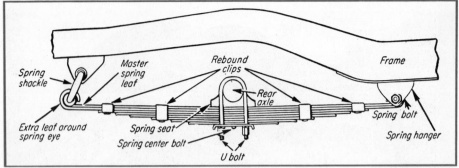

Fig. 29–3. A typical leaf spring showing attachments to frame and also method of attachment to axle.

In operation, the leaf spring acts much like a flexible beam. An ordinary solid beam strong enough to support the car weight would not be very flexible. This is because, as the beam bends (Fig. 29–4), the top edge tries to become longer while the lower edge tries to become shorter. There is a pull-apart effect at the top, or elongating, edge. There is a push-together, or shortening, effect along the lower edge. The result is that the upper edge pulls apart (if the beam is overloaded) and the beam breaks. However, there would be a different action if the beam were made of a series of thin leaves, one on top of another (right in Fig.

29–4). The leaves would slip on each other to take care of the pull-apart and push-together tendencies of the two edges of the beam. You can see how much the leaves will slip on each other if the beam is sharply bent (lower right in Fig. 29–4). All leaves are of the same length, and the amount that the inner leaves project beyond the outer leaves (when curved) indicates the amount of slippage.

In the actual leaf spring, the leaves are of graduated length. To permit them to slip, various means of applying lubricant between the leaves are used. In addition, some leaf springs have special inserts of various materials,

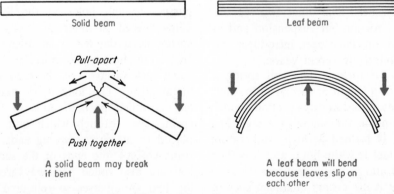

Fig. 29–4. Comparing the effects of bending a solid beam and a leaf spring.

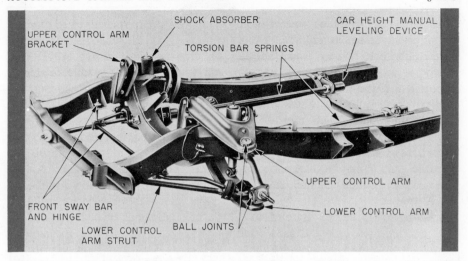

Fig. 29–5. Passenger-car front suspension using torsion rods. The rods are locked at the rear to the frame and are attached at the front to the inner or pivot ends of the lower control arms. They twist varying amounts as varying loads are applied to permit the front wheels to move up and down. This action is similar to that of other springs. (*Chrysler Division of Chrysler Corporation*)

placed between the leaves, to permit easier slipping. The clips shown on the spring in Fig. 29–3 are called *rebound* clips because they prevent excessive leaf separation during rebound, or after the wheel has passed over an obstruction in the road. In addition, springs may be covered with a metal sheath as shown in Fig. 29–11 to retain lubricant and prevent the entrance of moisture and dirt.

3. Torsion-bar suspension. Figure 29–5 shows a torsion-bar front-suspension system using two torsion bars. The rear end of each torsion bar is attached to a frame cross member through a car-leveling device. This car-leveling device can be adjusted to level up the car in case any sag occurs in the suspension after long mileage. The rear ends of the torsion bars are kept from turning by this attachment. The

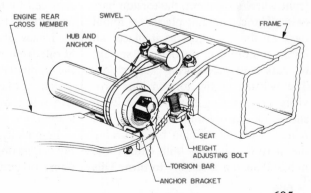

Fig. 29–6. Method of attaching rear of torsion bar to frame. Hub and anchor, swivel, and adjusting bolt are for adjusting height of car. (*Chrysler Division of Chrysler Corporation*)

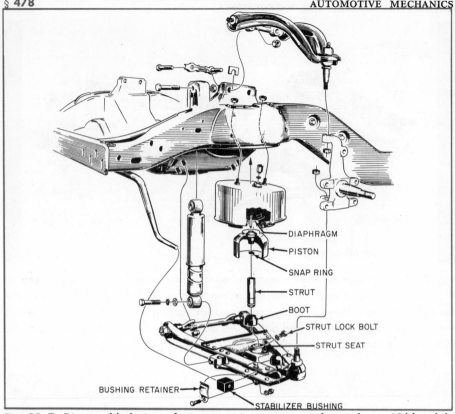

DIAPHRAGM
PISTON
SNAP RING
STRUT
BOOT
STRUT LOCK BOLT
STRUT SEAT
BUSHING RETAINER
STABILIZER BUSHING

Fig. 29–7. Disassembled view of air-suspension system on front of car. (*Oldsmobile Division of Chrysler Corporation*)

front ends of the torsion bars are attached to the lower control arms at the pivot points of the arms. Thus, as the lower control arms move up and down in response to up-and-down front-wheel movement, the torsion bars twist. The car weight places an initial twist on the bars, just as it places an initial compression on the coil springs of cars with coil-spring suspension. The twisting of the torsion bars provides the springing effect. Figure 29–6 shows the car-leveling device at one rear end of one torsion bar. Turning the height adjusting bolt causes the hub and anchor assembly to turn. This

rotates the rear end of the torsion bar so that the front end of the car is raised or lowered.

4. Air suspension. In air suspension, the four conventional springs are replaced by four air bags or air-spring assemblies. Figure 29–7 is a disassembled view of an air-suspension system at one front wheel. Figure 29–8 shows the components of an air-suspension system at one rear wheel. Figure 29–9 is a schematic diagram of a complete system.

Essentially, each air-spring assembly is a flexible bag enclosed in a metal dome or girdle. The bag is filled with

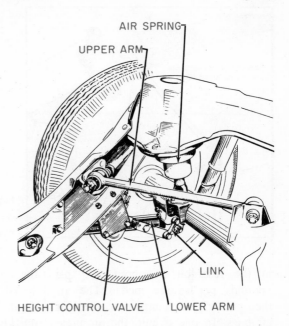

AIR SPRING
UPPER ARM

LINK

HEIGHT CONTROL VALVE   LOWER ARM

Fig. 29–8. Air-suspension system on rear of car. (*Oldsmobile Division of General Motors Corporation*)

compressed air which supports the weight of the car. When a wheel encounters a bump in the road, the air is further compressed and absorbs the shock.

An air compressor, or pump, supplies air to the system (Fig. 29–9). On the system shown, the compressor is driven by a belt from the water-pump pulley. Pressure is maintained

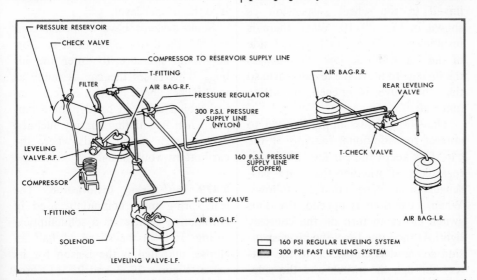

PRESSURE RESERVOIR
CHECK VALVE
COMPRESSOR TO RESERVOIR SUPPLY LINE
T-FITTING
FILTER   AIR BAG-R.F.
AIR BAG-R.R.
PRESSURE REGULATOR
REAR LEVELING VALVE
300 P.S.I. PRESSURE SUPPLY LINE (NYLON)
160 P.S.I. PRESSURE SUPPLY LINE (COPPER)
LEVELING VALVE-R.F.
T-CHECK VALVE
COMPRESSOR
T-FITTING
T-CHECK VALVE
AIR BAG-L.F.
SOLENOID
AIR BAG-L.R.
LEVELING VALVE-L.F.

☐ 160 PSI REGULAR LEVELING SYSTEM
▨ 300 PSI FAST LEVELING SYSTEM

Fig. 29–9. Schematic diagram of an air-suspension system. (*Mercury Division of Ford Motor Company*)

607

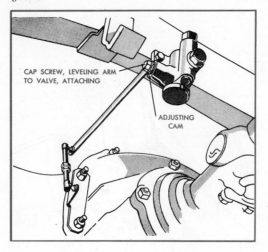

CAP SCREW, LEVELING ARM
TO VALVE, ATTACHING

ADJUSTING
CAM

Fig. 29–10. Rear leveling valve on air-suspension system. (*Mercury Division of Ford Motor Company*)

in the reservoir at about 300 psi (pounds per square inch). The air then passes by two circuits to the four air bags. In one circuit, the air pressure is reduced to 160 psi by a pressure regulator. This pressure is admitted to the four air bags through height control or leveling valves. These valves are attached to the frame and linked to the wheel suspension as shown in Fig. 29–10. When there is insufficient air in an air bag, that side of the car will ride low. This causes the linkage to move the leveling arm so that the valve is opened, admitting more air.

The 300 psi air supply is used to correct for additional loading of the car. This keeps the car level the same regardless of whether there are passengers or not. The action is as follows. When a car door is opened, the door switch closes to turn on the courtesy light. At the same time, the air-suspension solenoid is connected to the battery through the switch and the solenoid valve opens. Now, air at 300 psi is admitted to the leveling valves. If

the air bag has been compressed by added weight, as when a passenger climbs in, then the leveling valve quickly feeds additional air pressure to the low air bag and it is brought up to the proper level. On the other hand, if a passenger has gotten out, then the air bag is high. Now, the leveling valve releases air from the air bag to lower it to the proper level.

Some systems have a special control that the driver can operate to allow additional pressure to enter the air bags. This raises the car as much as four inches above normal. Such a control would come in handy, for example, when negotiating sharply inclined driveways or rutted roads where the car bottom would drag.

§ 479. Leaf-spring installation The leaf spring most commonly used in automotive vehicles is a semielliptical spring. It is in the shape of half an ellipse, and that is the reason for its name. Figures 29–3 and 29–11 show springs of this type. The method of attachment in these figures is a com-

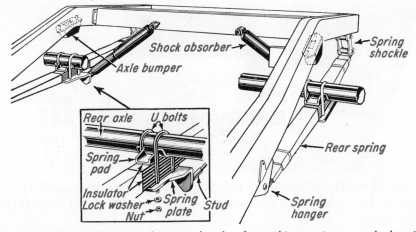

Fig. 29–11. Rear leaf springs showing details of attaching spring to axle housing.

mon one for leaf springs. The center of the spring is attached to the axle housing with two U bolts so that the spring is, in effect, hanging from the axle housing. A spring plate or straps are used at the bottom of the spring, while a spring pad is used between the axle and spring. There may also be an insulating strip of rubber or similar material to reduce noise transference between the axle and spring.

1. Spring hanger. One end of the spring is attached to a hanger on the frame by means of a bolt and bushing in the spring eye (Fig. 29–12). The

Fig. 29–12. Details of attaching spring to hanger of spring suspension shown in Fig. 29–11.

spring, as it bends, causes the spring eye to turn back and forth with respect to the spring hanger. The attaching bolt and bushing must permit this rotation. Some applications (Fig. 29–13)

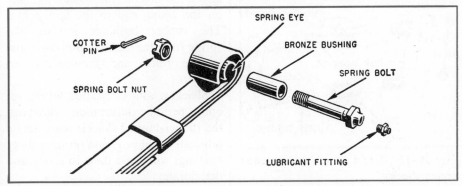

Fig. 29–13. Bushing and bolt for attaching spring eye to hanger on frame.

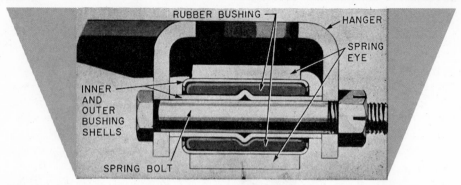

Fig. 29–14. Details of bushing in spring eye through which the spring eye is attached to the hanger on the car frame. (*Chevrolet Motor Division of General Motors Corporation*)

have a hollow spring bolt with a lubricating fitting. This permits lubrication of the bushing. Other designs do not require lubrication. Many designs have a bushing made up of an inner and an outer metal shell. Between these two shells is a molded rubber bushing. The weight is carried through the rubber bushing. The rubber acts to dampen vibration and noise and thus prevents them from entering the car frame. Figure 29–14 shows one type of rubber-bushed mounting.

2. *Spring shackle.* As the spring bends, the distance between the two

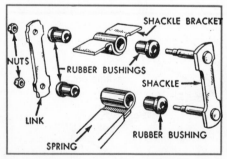

Fig. 29–15. Details of a rubber-bushed spring shackle.

spring eyes changes. If both ends of the spring were fastened rigidly to the frame, then the spring would not be able to bend. To permit bending, the spring is fastened at one end to the frame through a link called a shackle. The shackle is a swinging support attached at one end to the spring eye and at the other end to a supporting bracket on the car frame. Spring shackles can be seen in Figs. 29–3 and 29–11. A spring shackle is shown in disassembled view in Fig. 29–15. The two links provide the swinging support that the spring requires, while the bolts attach the links to the shackle bracket on the frame and to the spring eye. The rubber bushings insulate the spring from the frame to prevent transference of noise and vibration between the two.

Shackles with lubrication fittings require periodic lubrication. However, the rubber-bushed shackle must not be lubricated. Oil or grease on the rubber bushings will cause them to soften and deteriorate.

§ 480. Sprung and unsprung weight

In the automobile, the terms "sprung weight" and "unsprung weight" refer to the part of the car that is supported on springs and the part that is not. The frame and the parts attached to the frame are sprung. That is, their weight is supported on the car springs. However, the wheels and wheel axles (and rear-axle housing and differential) are not supported on springs; they represent unsprung weight. Generally speaking, unsprung weight should be kept as low as possible. The reason for this is, as unsprung weight increases, so does the roughness of the ride. For example, consider a single wheel. If it is light, it can move up and down as road irregularities are encountered without causing much reaction to the car frame. But if the weight of the wheel is increased, then its movement would become more noticeable to the car occupants. To take a ridiculous example, suppose the unsprung weight at the wheel is equal to the sprung weight above the wheel. In such a case, the sprung weight would tend to move about as much as the unsprung weight. The unsprung weight, which must move up and down as road irregularities are encountered, would tend to cause a like motion of the sprung weight. This is the reason for keeping the unsprung weight as low as possible so that it represents only a small portion of the total weight of the car.

§ 481. Characteristics of springs

The ideal spring for automotive suspension would be one which would absorb road shock rapidly and then return to its normal position slowly. Such an ideal is not possible, however. An extremely flexible, or soft, spring would allow too much movement, while a stiff, or hard, spring would give too rough a ride. However, satisfactory riding qualities are attained by using a fairly soft spring in combination with a shock absorber (§ 488).

Softness or hardness of a spring is referred to as its *rate*. The rate of a spring is the weight required to deflect it one inch. The rate of automotive springs is about constant through their operating range, or deflection, in the car. This is stated by Hooke's law, as applied to coil springs: The spring will compress in direct proportion to the weight applied. Thus, if 600 pounds will compress the spring 3 inches, 1,200 pounds will compress the spring 6 inches.

§ 482. Hotchkiss and torque-tube drives

Before we discuss rear-suspension systems further, we should note that the rear springs may have an additional job to do besides supporting the car load. This additional job may be to absorb *rear-end torque* (see § 469). Whenever the rear wheel is being driven, through the power train, by the engine, it rotates as shown in Fig. 29–16 (for forward car motion). At the same time, the wheel-axle housing tries to rotate in the opposite direction, as shown (Fig. 29–16). The twisting motion thus applied to the axle housing is called rear-end torque. Two different rear-end designs are used to combat this twisting motion of the axle housing. They are the Hotchkiss drive and the torque-tube drive (Fig. 27–16).

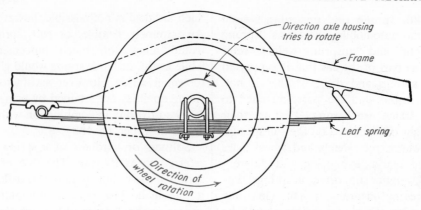

Fig. 29–16. Axle housing tries to rotate in direction opposite to wheel rotation.

§ **483. Rear suspension** We have illustrated and discussed rear-suspension systems in some detail. Figures 29–3 and 29–11 show rear-suspension systems using leaf springs. Methods of attaching the springs through hangers and shackles have also been shown and described (§ 479). No additional bracing is needed with leaf springs.

However, with coil springs, the rear-suspension system requires some method of holding the axle housing in place. Figure 29–17 is a disassembled view of a rear suspension using coil springs. The coil springs are assembled between spring mounting plates on the axle housing and spring seats in the car frame. The two rear-axle support arms are attached between the rear-axle housing and the car frame and permit upward or downward movement of the axle housing with respect to the car frame. They prevent relative forward or backward movement. The track bar (to upper left) is connected between the axle housing and the car frame and prevents sideward movement of the housing assembly with respect to the car frame. The shock absorbers are

attached to the rear wheels through shields bolted to the brake-backing-plate assembly and are linked to the car frame. The stabilizer shaft is connected between the two rear-axle support arms and helps to reduce rolling action of the car on turns.

§ **484. Front suspension** The suspension of the front wheels is more complicated than the suspension for the rear wheels. Not only must the front wheels move up and down with respect to the car frame (for spring action), but also they must be able to swing at various angles to the car frame for steering. In the pages that follow, we discuss the various types of suspension systems used on modern cars. Chapter 30 covers steering systems.

In order to permit the front wheels to swing to one side or the other for steering, each wheel is supported on a spindle which is part of a steering knuckle. The steering knuckle is then supported, through a kingpin, by the front axle beam or by a steering-knuckle support.

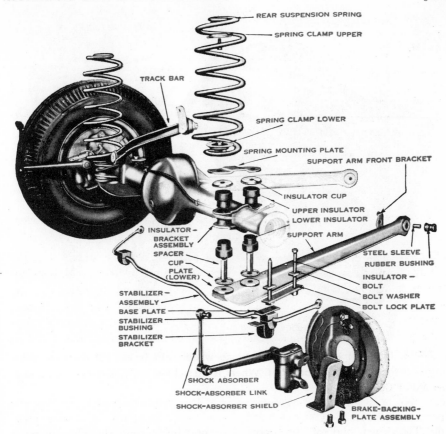

Fig. 29–17. Disassembled view of a rear-suspension system using coil springs. (*Oldsmobile Division of General Motors Corporation*)

§ 485. Independent front suspension Practically all passenger cars now use the independent type of front suspension in which each front wheel is independently supported by a coil or leaf spring. The coil-spring arrangement is most common. Figure 29–1 shows, in phantom view, essential parts of an independent front-suspension system using coil springs. Figure 29–18 shows the details of a similar front suspension for one wheel. Figure 29–19 shows another front-suspension system in disassembled view. All these operate in a similar manner. The coil spring is retained between an upper spring seat in the car frame and a lower spring seat that is part of the lower suspension arm (also called the lower *control* arm). One end of the lower suspension arm is attached to the car frame through a pivot. The other end of the lower suspension arm is attached to the lower end of the steering-knuckle support, also through a pivot. The upper end of the steering-knuckle support is attached to the upper suspension (control) arm, by a

513

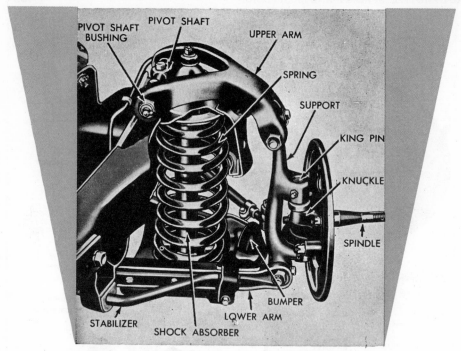

Fig. 29–18. Front-suspension systems at one wheel with frame cut away to show spring and shock-absorber locations. Wheel is assembled on, and turns on, spindle. (*Ford Motor Company*)

pivot. The inner end of the upper suspension arm is attached, through a pivot, to the frame. On some cars, the upper suspension arm is part of the shock absorber. On many cars, the shock absorber is of the telescoping type (which expands or shortens in operation) and is placed inside the coil spring as shown in Figs. 29–18 and 29–19.

The steering-knuckle support carries the steering knuckle; the two are attached by the kingpin (see Figs. 29–18 and 29–19). The wheel mounts on, and rotates on, the spindle which is part of the steering knuckle. This arrangement keeps the wheel in vertical alignment with the steering-knuckle

support but permits the wheel to pivot about the kingpin for steering the car (see Chap. 30).

Figure 29–20 is a simplified line drawing showing the action that takes place as the wheel, and steering-knuckle support, move up and down. The upper and lower suspension arms swing up or down on the frame pivots, thereby causing the coil spring to compress or expand.

Note that the steering-knuckle support is maintained in nearly vertical alignment as it moves up and down. This keeps the wheel in almost vertical alignment, which is desirable from the standpoint of steering control and tire wear. This maintenance of alignment

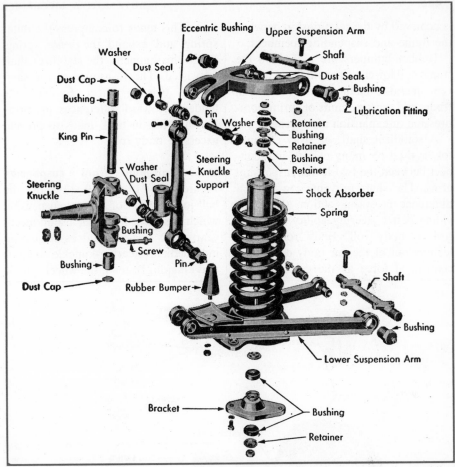

Fig. 29–19. Disassembled view of a front suspension for one wheel. (*Cadillac Motor Car Division of General Motors Corporation*)

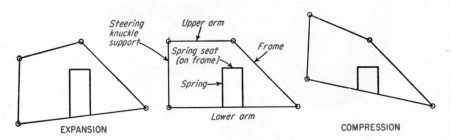

Fig. 29–20. Geometry of front-suspension system. As steering-knuckle support (and wheel) move up and down, upper and lower arms pivot on frame, causing the spring to expand or compress.

is achieved by the relationship between the frame and suspending members.

Rubber bumpers are placed on the frame and lower suspension arm to prevent metal-to-metal contact between frame and arms as limits of spring compression or expansion are reached.

A stabilizer shaft, or sway eliminator, is used on many cars to interconnect between the two lower suspension arms. The shaft prevents too great a difference in spring action, thus providing better steering ability and control of body roll. Body roll is the leaning out of the car body caused by centrifugal force as the car rounds a

turn. This tends to compress the outer spring and expand the inner spring. When this happens, the stabilizer shaft is twisted. The resistance of the shaft to the twisting effect combats the tendency toward differences in spring length. This, in turn, tends to prevent excessive body roll.

§ 486. Ball-joint front suspension

Figures 29–21 and 29–22 show the ball-joint type of front suspension which has come into wide use in recent years. This suspension does not use an intermediate steering-knuckle support and kingpin. Instead, the wheel spindle

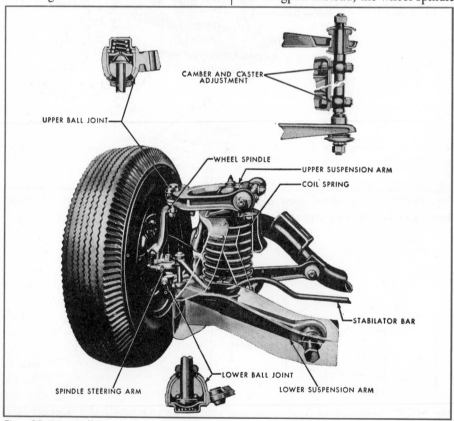

Fig. 29–21. Ball-joint type of front-suspension system. Note camber and caster adjustment method. (*Ford Motor Company*)

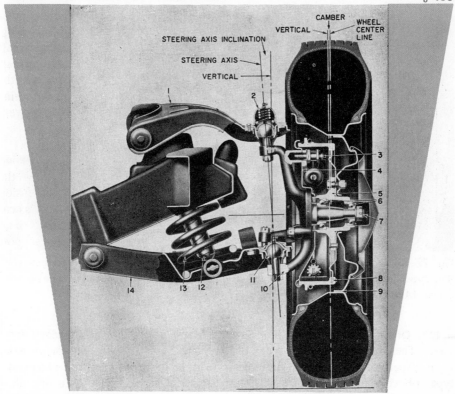

Fig. 29–22. Spherical or ball-joint front-suspension system. (*Chevrolet Motor Division of General Motors Corporation*)

1. Upper control arm	6. Front-wheel bearings	10. Steering knuckle
2. Upper spherical joint	7. Front-wheel spindle	11. Lower spherical joint
3. Brake anchor pin	(part of knuckle)	12. Shock absorber
4. Brake backing plate	8. Brake drum	13. Front spring
5. Front-wheel hub	9. Wheel	14. Lower control arm

is elongated and is attached directly to the upper and lower suspension arms by means of ball joints. Adjustment for wheel camber and caster (see §§ 496 and 499) is made by installing or removing shims from between the inner shaft attaching the upper suspension arm and the support bracket or frame. On this suspension, the inner ends of the suspension arms are attached to the frame through rubber bushings or sleeves which are sandwiched between two steel shells. The inner shells are held stationary on the frame. The outer shells are locked to the suspension arms. All pivoting at these points occurs by deflection of the rubber. Thus, there is no metal-to-metal contact or movement. As the arms pivot up and down, the rubber in the sleeves deflects to permit the movement.

Fig. 29–23. Front-suspension system in which the coil springs are located between the upper ends of the steering-knuckle pins and seats in the outer wheelhouse panel. (*American Motors Corporation*)

§ 487. Other types of front suspension   There are many other types of front suspension. A somewhat different type of coil-spring front-suspension system is shown in Fig. 29–23. The coil springs are located between upper ends of steering-knuckle pins and seats in outer wheelhouse panel. Direct-acting shock absorbers are also used.

Many trucks and other heavy-duty vehicles use a solid, one-piece axle beam at the front (and not independent wheel suspension). As a rule, this arrangement makes use of leaf springs, one at each wheel. Figure 29–24 shows the manner in which the steering knuckle is supported on the end of the axle beam.

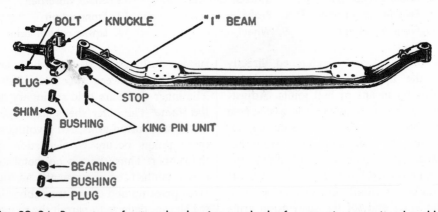

Fig. 29–24. Beam-type front axle showing method of supporting steering knuckle on end of beam. (*Chevrolet Motor Division of General Motors Corporation*)

618

§ 488. Purpose of shock absorbers

Springs alone are not satisfactory for a car suspension system. As has already been mentioned (in § 481), the spring must be a compromise between flexibility and stiffness. It must be flexible so that it can absorb road shocks. But if it is too flexible, it will flex and rebound excessively and repeatedly, giving a rough ride. A stiff spring will not flex and rebound so much after a bump has been passed. But on the other hand it will also give a hard ride because it will transmit too much of the road shock to the car. By using a relatively flexible, or soft, spring and a shock absorber, a satisfactorily smooth ride will be achieved.

You can demonstrate to yourself why a spring alone would be unsatisfactory for a vehicle suspension. Hang a weight on a coil spring as shown in Fig. 29–25. Then lift the weight and let it drop. It will expand the spring as it drops. Then, it will rebound, or move up. The spring, as it expands and contracts, will keep the weight moving up and down (oscillating) for some time.

On the car, a very similar action will take place with a flexible spring. The spring is under an initial compression because of the car weight. Then, as the wheel passes over a bump, the spring is further compressed. After the bump is passed, the spring attempts to return to its original position. But it overrides this position and expands too much. This action causes the car frame to be thrown upward. Now, having overexpanded, the spring compresses. Again it overrides and compresses too much. As this happens, the wheel may be raised clear of the road,

Fig. 29–25. If a weight hanging from a coil spring is set into up-and-down motion, it will oscillate for some time, the distance it moves up and down gradually shortening as indicated by the curve. Finally, the motion will die out.

and the frame may drop. Now, the spring expands again, and so the oscillations continue, gradually dying out. But every time the wheel encounters a bump or hole in the road, the same series of oscillations will take place.

Such spring action on a vehicle produces a rough and unsatisfactory ride. On a bumpy road, and especially on a curve, the oscillations might become serious enough to cause the driver to lose control of the car. Therefore, it is necessary to use some device to dampen out the spring oscillations quickly once the wheel has passed the hole or bump in the road. The shock absorber is the device universally used today. There have been many types of shock absorber, operating on friction, on compressed air, and hydraulically. The hydraulic shock absorber is the only type in common use at present. It contains a fluid that is forced through restricting orifices as the shock absorber is operated by spring flexure. The resistance to the movement of the

619

fluid through the restricting orifices imposes a drag on spring movement, thus quickly dampening out spring oscillations. Several designs of shock absorbers are discussed below.

§ 489. Direct-acting shock absorber

The direct-acting, or telescope, shock absorber is the most widely used shock absorber and is found on both front- and rear-suspension systems. Several of the illustrations in this chapter show methods of mounting the shock absorber at front and rear wheels. Figures 29–26 and 29–27 show

the details of front- and rear-mounting direct-acting shock absorbers.

Regardless of the method of mounting, the shock absorber is attached in such a way that, as the wheel moves up and down, the shock absorber shortens and lengthens (telescopes and extends). Since the shock absorber imposes a restraint on this movement, excessive wheel and spring movements as well as spring oscillation are prevented.

A direct-acting shock absorber is shown in sectional view in Fig. 29–28, with the internal parts illustrated. Figure 29–29 shows the operation of the shock absorber during compression and

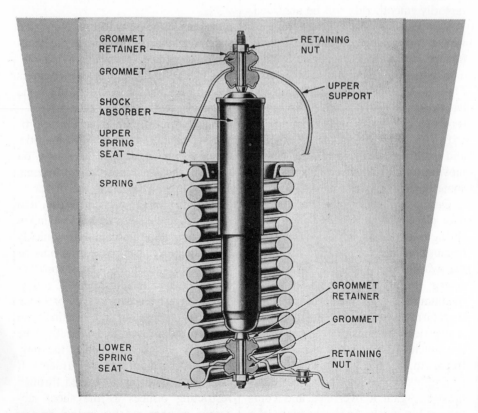

Fig. 29–26. Method of attaching direct-acting shock absorber in front-suspension system. (*Chevrolet Motor Division of General Motors Corporation*)

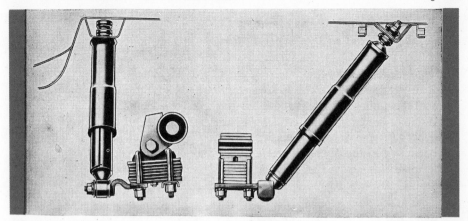

Fig. 29–27. Front and side views showing method of attaching direct-acting shock absorber in rear-suspension system using leaf springs. (*Chevrolet Motor Division of General Motors Corporation*)

extension (rebound). With either action, the fluid in the shock absorber moves one way or the other through small passages in the piston. This imposes a restraint on the spring and wheel action as noted in the previous section.

§ 490. Parallel-cylinder shock absorber

This unit, no longer used, has two cylinders side by side, one for compression and one for rebound. Each has a separate piston.

§ 491. Opposed-cylinder shock absorber—external-valve type

This unit has opposed cylinders with a cam between working two pistons in the cylinders. The valves are outside the housing. It is no longer used.

§ 492. Opposed-cylinder shock absorber—internal-valve type

This unit is the same as the one in the previous paragraph except that the valves are internal.

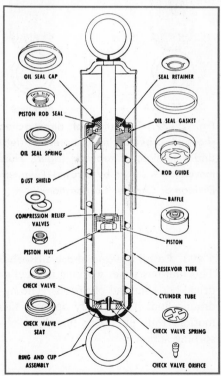

Fig. 29–28. Direct-acting shock absorber in sectional view, with internal parts illustrated and their positions in the assembly shown. (*Plymouth Division of Chrysler Corporation*)

621

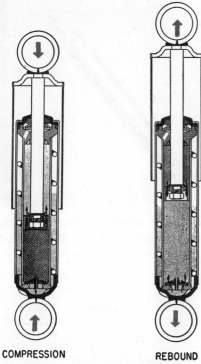

COMPRESSION   REBOUND

Fig. 29–29. Operation of direct-acting shock absorber during compression (*left*) and extension, or rebound (*right*). Fluid movement is shown by arrows. (*Plymouth Division of Chrysler Corporation*)

§ **493. Rotating-vane shock absorber** This unit has vanes working in a cylindrical body instead of pistons. The hydraulic fluid in the body opposes this motion, thus providing the shock-absorbing action.

REVIEW QUESTIONS

1. What is the purpose of the car springs?
2. Describe a coil spring.

3. Describe the construction of a leaf spring.
4. Describe a torsion-bar-suspension system.
5. Describe the construction and operation of an air-suspension system.
6. Describe one method of attaching a leaf spring to a car.
7. What is the purpose of the spring shackle? Describe a spring shackle.
8. What is meant by sprung and unsprung weight?
9. What absorbs rear-end torque in the Hotchkiss drive? In the torque-tube drive?
10. What is the purpose of the stabilizer shaft? Describe how this shaft functions.
11. In a rear suspension using coil springs, between what two members is the coil spring retained?
12. What is the purpose of the two rear-axle support arms in a coil-spring rear suspension? What is the purpose of the track bar?
13. Between what two members is the coil spring retained on most front-suspension systems?
14. Describe the ball-joint front-suspension system, and explain how it differs from other suspension systems.
15. Why are shock absorbers desirable?
16. Describe the action of a spring on a car without shock absorbers as a wheel encounters a bump in the road. Why is this action troublesome?
17. What is the hydraulic principle on which most modern shock-absorber action is based?

18. What is another name for the direct-acting shock absorber? Describe briefly the actions that take place in this shock absorber when it is telescoped because of spring compression. Describe briefly the actions that take place when it is extended because of spring expansion.

STUDY QUESTIONS

1. What is Hooke's law as applied to coil springs?
2. Make a sketch of a rear-suspension system using a leaf spring, and show the actions that take place when the wheel encounters a hole. When it encounters a bump.
3. Make a sketch of a front-suspension system using coil springs, and show the actions that take place when the wheel encounters a hole. When it encounters a bump.
4. Write a story explaining what takes place when a direct-acting shock absorber goes into operation.

OPPORTUNITIES IN THE AUTOMOTIVE BUSINESS

About nine million people in the United States owe their jobs to the automotive industry. Naturally, some of these jobs are much better paying than others. But one thing you can be sure of—those higher-paying jobs were earned by hard workers who applied themselves. What are the opportunities open to the young man who takes a job in the automotive field?

The automotive mechanic today is a skilled, well-paid, well-respected worker. His services are always in demand. For many men, a job as an automotive mechanic becomes a steppingstone to greater things. Chances are the service manager, parts manager, or sales manager in the automotive shop or dealer agency started out as an automotive mechanic. The good automotive mechanic may some day be able to open his own shop and have others work for him. If he is outstanding and has a good personality, he might become an automotive jobber salesman or a field representative of a parts manufacturer. He might become a factory representative working out of a zone office or out of the factory. Perhaps he might have the chance to go into the factory and work up through the office or manufacturing department.

But one thing is demanded of the successful man: he must work and study hard. The man who works and studies hard is bound to go up the ladder of success to better and better jobs. Apply yourself—let this man be you.

THIS CHAPTER COVERS THE various types of steering systems used in automotive vehicles. The requirements of a steering system as well as types of steering gears and linkages are described. The discussion of steering gears takes up most of the chapter since there are many varieties of steering gears, both manually and hydraulically operated. The latter type is known as *power steering*.

§ **494. Function of the steering system** A simplified drawing of a steering system is shown in Fig. 2–14. We have already described the various methods of supporting the front-wheel spindle (Chap. 29) so that the wheels can be swung to the left or right for steering. This movement is produced by gearing and linkage between the steering wheel in front of the driver and the steering knuckle (or wheel). The complete arrangement is called the steering system. Actually, the steering system is composed of two elements, a steering gear at the lower end of the steering column, and linkage between the gear and the wheel steering knuckles. Before we discuss linkages and steering gears in detail, let us take a look at the steering system from the standpoint of geometry, or of the angles involved.

§ **495. Front-end geometry** The term "front-end geometry" refers to the angular relationship between the front wheels, the front-wheel attaching parts, and the car frame. The angle of the kingpin away from vertical, the pointing in, or toe-in, of the front wheels, the tilt of the front wheels from vertical — all these are involved in front-end geometry. Every one of them influences the steering ease, steering stability, and riding qualities of the car and has a direct effect on tire wear. The various factors that enter into front-end geometry are classified under the following terms: camber, kingpin inclination, caster, toe-in, and toe-out on turns. These are discussed in detail below.

§ **496. Camber** Camber is the tilting of the front wheels from the vertical (Fig. 30–1). When the tilt is outward, so that the wheels are farther apart at the top than at the bottom, the camber is positive. Positive camber is shown in Fig. 30–1. When the tilt is inward, so that the wheels are closer together at the top than at the bottom, the camber is negative. The amount of tilt is measured in so many degrees from the vertical, and this measurement is called the camber angle. The purpose of camber is to give the wheels a slight outward tilt to start with. Then, when the vehicle is loaded and rolling along on the road, the load will just about bring the wheels to a vertical position. If you started with no camber angle

(wheels vertical), then loading the car might give them a negative camber. Any amount of camber (positive or negative) tends to cause uneven or more rapid tire wear since the tilt puts more of the load on one side of the tread than on the other.

§ **497. Kingpin inclination** Kingpin inclination (KPI) is the inward tilt of the kingpin from the vertical (Fig. 30–1). KPI is desirable for several reasons. In the first place, it helps provide steering stability by tending to return the wheels to the "straight-ahead" position after any turn. It also reduces steering effort, particularly when the car is stationary. In addition, it reduces tire wear.

The inward tilt, or inclination, of the kingpin (KPI) tends to keep the wheels straight ahead. It helps recovery, or the return of the wheels to the straight-ahead position after a turn has been made. You can make a table-top demonstration of why this is so with a pencil, a rubber band, a cardboard disk, and a piece of cardboard

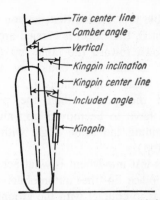

Fig. 30–1. Camber angle and kingpin inclination. Positive camber is shown. (*Plymouth Division of Chrysler Corporation*)

(Fig. 30–2). Put them together as shown in Fig. 30–2. The cardboard disk represents the wheel, the pencil the kingpin, and the cardboard brace at the top holds the two apart at the top so as to get kingpin inclination. Needless to say, the angle is greatly exaggerated in the figure. Now, hold the pencil at an angle with the table top so that the wheel is vertical as shown in Fig. 30–3. Then rotate the pencil, but do not change its angle with

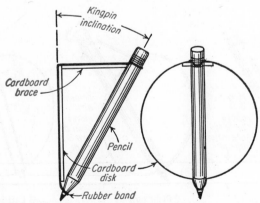

Fig. 30–2. A cardboard disk, a rubber band, a pencil, and a cardboard brace will demonstrate the effect of kingpin inclination.

625

the table top. Notice that, as you turn the pencil, the wheel is carried around and down toward the table top (Fig. 30–3). If the wheel could not move down, what would happen? As you turned the pencil, then the pencil would have to be moved up (always maintaining the same angle with the table top).

This last movement is what actually takes place in the automobile. The wheel is in contact with the ground. It cannot move down. Therefore, as it is swung away from straight-ahead, the kingpin and supporting parts are moved upward. This means that the car body is actually lifted. In other words, kingpin inclination causes the car to be raised every time the front wheels are swung away from straight ahead. Then, the weight of the car tends to bring the wheels back to straight-ahead after the turn is completed and the steering wheel is released.

§ **498. Included angle** The included, or combined, angle is the camber angle plus the KPI angle (Fig. 30–1).

The included angle is important because it determines the point of intersection of the wheel and the kingpin center lines (Fig. 30–4). This, in turn, determines whether the wheel will tend to toe out or toe in. "Toe-out" is a term used to describe the tendency for the wheel to point outward. A soldier standing at attention has his feet "toed out." Toe-in" is just the opposite; a pigeon-toed person turns the toes of his feet inward. Likewise, a wheel that toes in tries to point inward as it rolls. Figure 30–9 shows what toe-in is on a vehicle. The tire on a wheel that is toed in or toed out will wear more rapidly. The tire has to go in the direction in which the car is moving. But since it is not pointed in that direction (it is toed out or toed in), it is dragged sideways as it rolls forward. The more toe-out or toe-in, the more it is dragged sideways and the faster the tire wears.

When the point of intersection (Fig. 30–4) is below the road surface, then the wheel will tend to toe out. This is because the forward push (which is through the kingpin) is inside the tire

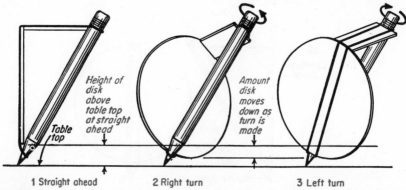

1 Straight ahead   2 Right turn   3 Left turn

Fig. 30–3. The cardboard disk represents the left front wheel as viewed from the driver's seat: 1, the "straight-ahead" position; 2, a right turn; 3, a left turn.

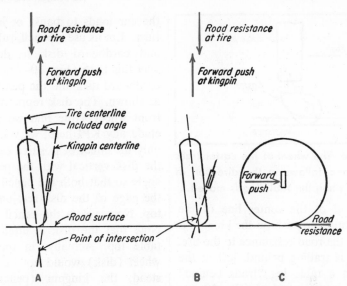

Fig. 30–4. Effect when point of intersection is below road surface (A), and above road surface (B). Left front wheel as viewed from driver's seat shown in A and B C is a side view of the wheel to show two forces acting on wheel and kingpin.

center line at the road surface. In the right-hand picture in Fig. 30–4, the two opposing forces working on the wheel are shown. One is the forward push through the kingpin; the other is the road resistance to the tire. If these two forces are exactly in line, then the wheel will have no tendency to toe out or toe in. The two forces will be in line with each other only when the point of intersection is at the road surface. When it is below the road level as shown at *A* in Fig. 30–4, then the wheel attempts to swing outward, or toe out. When the point of intersection is above the road level as shown at *B* in Fig. 30–4, then the wheel attempts to swing inward, or toe in.

§ **499. Caster** In addition to being tilted inward toward the center of the car (KPI), the kingpin may also be tilted forward or backward from the vertical (Fig. 30–5). Backward tilt from the vertical is called positive caster. Positive caster aids directional stability since the center line of the kingpin passes through the road sur-

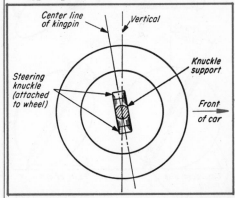

Fig. 30–5. Left front wheel (as viewed from driver's seat), shown from inside so that backward tilt of kingpin from vertical can be seen. This backward tilt is called positive caster.

627

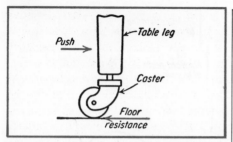

Fig. 30–6. The wheel of the caster trails behind and follows in the direction of the push when the table leg is moved.

face ahead of the center line of the wheel. Thus, the push on the kingpin is ahead of the road resistance to the tire. The tire is trailing behind, just as the caster on a table leg "trails behind" when the table is pushed (Fig. 30–6).

Caster has another effect that is important. When both front wheels have positive caster, the car tends to roll out or lean out on turns. But if the front wheels have negative caster, then

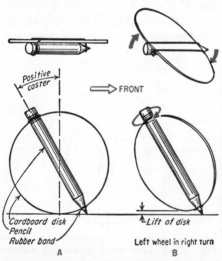

Fig. 30–7. Using a cardboard disk, a pencil, and a rubber band to show the effects of positive caster in a right turn. The disk represents the left front wheel.

the car tends to bank, or lean in, on turns. Let us use a pencil, rubber band, and cardboard disk to demonstrate why this is so (Fig. 30–7). Fasten the cardboard disk and the pencil together as shown. The disk represents the left front wheel. Note that we do not include any KPI here; we want to show only the effect of positive caster. Hold the disk vertical with the pencil at an angle so that both the pencil point and the edge of the disk rest on the table top. Now, rotate the pencil as shown. Note that the disk is lifted from the table top. Actually, in the car, the wheel (disk) would not be lifted. Instead, the kingpin (pencil) would move down. In other words, on a right turn, the left side of the car would drop.

Now, let us see what happens at the right front wheel (Fig. 30–8). As the right turn is made, the wheel pivots on the road surface, causing the kingpin (pencil) to be lifted. The right side of the car is lifted.

When the left side of the car is low-

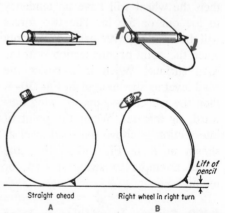

Fig. 30–8. The effect of positive caster on the right front wheel during a right turn.

ered and the right side of the car is lifted as a right turn is made (as described above), then the car rolls, or leans out, on the turn. This is just the opposite of what would be the most desirable since it adds to the effect of centrifugal force on the turn. By using negative caster (tilting kingpins forward), the car can be made to lean in on a turn (and thus decrease the effect of centrifugal force). For instance, with negative caster, the left side of the car would lift during a right turn, while the right side of the car would drop. This would combat the roll-out effect of centrifugal force.

There is another important effect that caster has. Positive caster tries to make the front wheels toe in. With positive caster, the car is lowered as the wheel pivots inward. Thus, the weight of the car is always trying to make the wheel toe in. With negative caster, the wheels would try to toe out.

Note that positive caster increases the effort required to steer. Positive caster tries to keep the wheels straight ahead. To make a turn, this tendency must be overcome. Note, too, that KPI also tries to keep the wheels straight ahead. Thus, to make a turn, the effects of both caster (when positive) and KPI must be overcome. Late-model vehicles, and particularly heavy-duty trucks, tend toward a negative caster. This makes steering easier and there is still sufficient tendency toward recovery, or the return of the wheels to straight-ahead (provided by KPI).

§ **500. Toe-in**   As we have already mentioned, toe-in is the turning in of the front wheels; they attempt to roll inward instead of straight ahead. On a car with toe-in (Fig. 30–9), the distance between the front wheels is less at the front *(A)* than at the rear *(B)*. The actual amount of toe-in is normally only a fraction of an inch. The

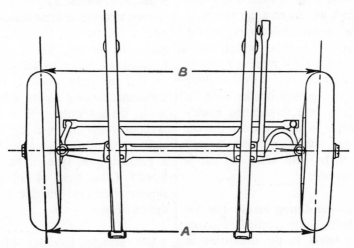

Fig. 30–9. Toe-in. The wheels are viewed from the top with front of car at lower edge of illustration. A is less than B. (*Chevrolet Motor Division of General Motors Corporation*)

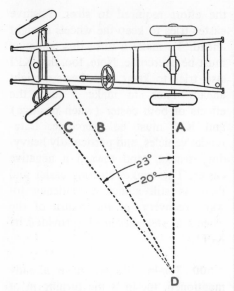

Fig. 30–10. Toe-out on turns. (*Chevrolet Motor Division of General Motors Corporation*)

lowing a smaller radius than the outer wheel when the car is rounding a curve, its axle must be at a sharper angle with the car frame, that is, it must toe out more. This condition is shown in Fig. 30–10. When the front wheels are steered to make the turn illustrated, the inner wheel turns to an angle of 23 degrees with the car frame. But the outer wheel turns only 20 degrees with the car frame. This permits the inner wheel to follow a shorter radius than the outer wheel, and the circles on which the two front wheels turn are concentric, that is, their centers are at the same place, *D*. Toe-out is secured by providing the proper relationship between the steering-knuckle arms, tie rods, and pitman arm. This relationship is such that the inner wheel on a curve always toes out more than the outer wheel. Figure 30–11 illustrates the manner of securing this condition. When the tie rod is moved to the left during a right turn, it pushes at almost a right angle against the left steering-knuckle arm. The right end of the tie rod, however, not only moves to the left, but it also swings forward, as shown by the dotted line, so that the right wheel is turned an additional amount. When a left turn is made, the left wheel will be turned an additional amount over that which the right wheel turns. Figure 30–11 shows a parallelogram type of linkage (see § 502). Other types of linkage give a similar effect and provide a like toe-out on turns.

purpose of toe-in is to ensure parallel rolling of the front wheels, to stabilize steering, and to prevent sideslipping and excessive wear of tires. The toe-in on the front wheels of a car serves to offset the small deflections in the wheel-support system which come about when the car is moving forward. These deflections are due to the rolling resistance of the tires on the road. In other words, even though the wheels are set to toe in slightly when the car is standing still, they tend to roll parallel on the road when the car is moving forward.

§ 501. **Toe-out during turns** Toe-out during turns, also called *steering geometry,* refers to the difference in angles between the two front wheels and the car frame during turns. Since the inner wheel is rotating on or fol-

§ 502. **Steering linkages** Many types of steering linkage have been made to connect between the steering knuckles of the front wheels and the pitman arm

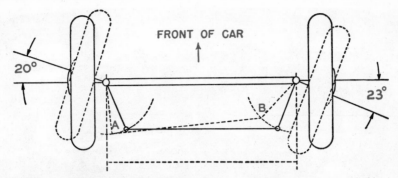

FRONT OF CAR

20°

23°

A

B

Fig. 30–11. Manner in which toe-out on turns is obtained. (*Chevrolet Motor Division of General Motors Corporation*)

of the steering gear. You will recall that the pitman arm swings from one side to the other (or forward and backward on some cars) as the steering wheel is turned. This movement must be carried to the steering knuckles at the wheels by some form of linkage. All have some means of adjusting the lengths of the tie rods or links so that proper alignment can be established between the front wheels.

This alignment gives the front wheels a slight toe-in when the car is at rest. Then, when the car begins to move forward, this toe-in practically disappears as all looseness, or "sloppage," in the steering system is taken up.

Figure 30–12 shows one form of parallelogram linkage with the connecting-rod assembly connected at one end to the pitman arm and at the other end to the steering idler arm.

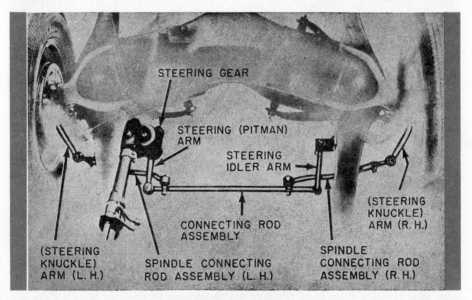

STEERING GEAR

STEERING (PITMAN) ARM

STEERING IDLER ARM →

(STEERING KNUCKLE) ARM (R. H.)

(STEERING KNUCKLE) ARM (L. H.)

CONNECTING ROD ASSEMBLY

SPINDLE CONNECTING ROD ASSEMBLY (L. H.)

SPINDLE CONNECTING ROD ASSEMBLY (R. H.)

Fig. 30–12. One form of parallelogram steering linkage. (*Ford Motor Company*)

Fig. 30–13. Steering system with center-arm steering and traverse drag link. (*Willys Motors, Inc.*)

The steering-knuckle (spindle) arms are connected to the connecting-rod assembly by two secondary connecting-rod assemblies.

Figure 30–13 shows a center-arm steering linkage with a traverse drag link. The traverse drag link is connected between the pitman arm and the center arm. The center arm is attached through a bushing to the car frame so that it can swing back and forth. As the pitman arm swings back and forth, it causes the traverse link to swing the center arm back and forth. This motion is carried through the two tie rods to the steering-knuckle arms.

Figure 30–14 illustrates the details of a connecting-rod assembly used in a parallelogram steering linkage. Note that the pitman arm, idler arm, and tie rods are attached to the connecting rod by means of ball sockets. This type of joint offers very low friction and a minimum of free play so that steering is easier and, at the same time, there is little free play in the system.

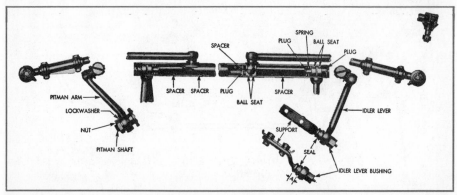

Fig. 30–14. Steering connecting-rod assembly, of type used in parallelogram steering linkage, showing details of ball sockets by which it is attached to pitman arm, idler lever, and tie rods. (*Pontiac Motor Division of General Motors Corporation*)

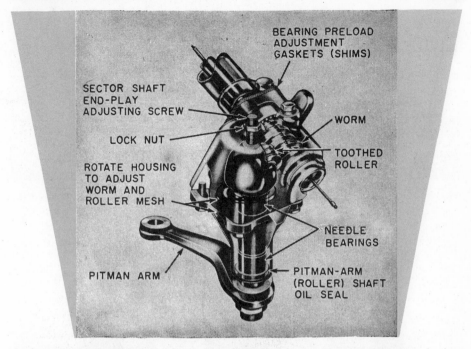

Fig. 30–15. Phantom view of a steering gear using a toothed roller attached to the pitman-arm shaft. Worm and roller teeth mesh. (*Ford Motor Company*)

§ 503. **Steering gears** The steering gear is a device for converting the rotary motion of the steering wheel into straight-line motion (of linkage). Essentially, the steering gear consists of two parts, a worm on the end of the steering shaft, and a pitman-arm shaft on which there is a gear sector, toothed roller, or stud. The gear sector, toothed roller, or stud meshes with the worm as shown in Figs. 30–15 and 30–16. In these two figures, the steering gear uses a toothed roller. The roller and worm teeth mesh. When the worm is rotated (by rotation of the steering wheel), the roller teeth must follow along and this action causes the pitman-arm shaft to rotate. The other end of the pitman-arm shaft carries the

pitman arm; rotation of the pitman-arm shaft causes the arm to swing in one direction or the other. This motion is then carried through the linkage to the steering knuckles at the wheels.

NOTE: The pitman-arm shaft is also called the cross shaft, pitman shaft, roller shaft, steering-arm shaft, and sector shaft.

A somewhat different type of steering gear is shown in Fig. 30–17. In this unit, friction is kept exceptionally low by interposing balls between the major moving parts, or between the worm teeth and grooves cut in the inner face of a ball nut. The rotation of the worm gear causes the balls to roll in the worm teeth. The balls also roll in

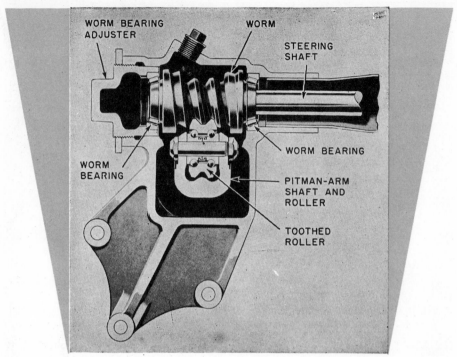

Fig. 30–16. Sectional view of a steering gear similar to one shown in Fig. 30–15. Different adjustment procedures are required for the two. (*Chevrolet Motor Division of General Motors Corporation*)

grooves cut in the inner face of the nut. Thus, as the worm rotates, the balls cause the nut to move up or down along the worm. This up-or-down motion is carried to the gear sector by teeth on the side of the ball nut. This then forces the gear sector to move along with the ball nut so that the pitman-arm shaft rotates.

The balls are called recirculating balls because they can continuously recirculate from one to the other end of the ball nut through a pair of ball return guides. For example, suppose that the driver makes a right turn. The worm gear is rotated in a clockwise direction (viewed from the driver's seat), and this causes the ball nut to move upward. The balls roll between the worm and ball nut, and as they reach the upper end of the nut, they enter the return guide and then roll back to a lower point, where they re-enter the groove between the worm and ball nut.

§ 504. **Power steering** Power steering has been used for a number of years on heavy-duty applications, but it is only in recent years that power steering has been applied to any extent on passenger cars. The principle of power steering is very simple. A booster arrangement is provided which is set into operation when the steering-wheel shaft is turned. The booster then takes over and does most of the work of steering. Power steering has

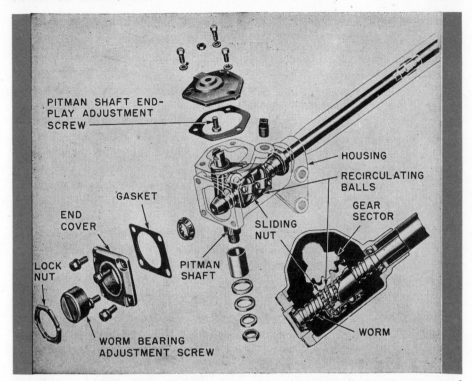

PITMAN SHAFT END-
PLAY ADJUSTMENT
SCREW

HOUSING

RECIRCULATING
BALLS

GASKET

GEAR
SECTOR

END
COVER

SLIDING
NUT

LOCK
NUT

PITMAN
SHAFT

WORM

WORM BEARING
ADJUSTMENT SCREW

Fig. 30–17. Sectional and phantom views of a recirculating ball-and-nut type of steering gear. (*Buick Motor Division of General Motors Corporation*)

used compressed air, electrical mechanisms, and hydraulic pressure. Hydraulic pressure is used on the vast majority of power-steering mechanisms today. You will recall that we discussed hydraulic pressure in some detail (§ 442) and learned that pressure, and movement, can be transferred from one part of a hydraulic system to another.

In the hydraulic power-steering system, a continuously operating pump provides hydraulic pressure when needed. As the steering wheel is turned, valves are operated that admit this hydraulic pressure to a cylinder. Then, the pressure causes a piston to move, and the piston does most of the steering work. Specific power-steering

systems are described in the articles that follow. There are actually two general types of power-steering systems. In one, the integral type, the power operating assembly is part of the steering gear. In the other, the linkage type, the power operating assembly is part of the linkage.

§ 505. General Motors power steering There are several General Motors models, including the offset, the in-line, and the torsion bar. Although much alike in action, they are somewhat different in construction. All are integral units and mount on the lower end of the steering shaft (Fig. 30–18). The steering unit consists of a recirculating ball-and-nut steering gear (such

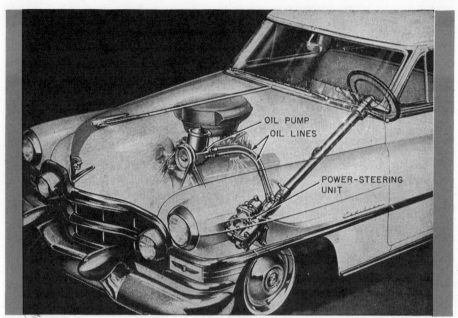

Fig. 30–18. Hydraulic power-steering system. Oil pump is driven by a V belt from the engine crankshaft pulley. (*Cadillac Motor Car Division of General Motors Corporation*)

as is illustrated in Fig. 30–17), to which has been added a hydraulic booster cylinder. Before we discuss the tie-in between the two, let us first talk about the hydraulic part of the system.

1. Hydraulic system. Figure 30–19 shows the hydraulic circuits in the off-set unit. The oil pump is mounted on the front of the engine and is driven by a V belt from the engine crankshaft pulley. Whenever the engine is running, the oil pump supplies oil to the system. The position of the valve spool then determines where the oil will be directed in the system, and what effect, if any, it will have on the steering of the car. The valve spool is shown, by itself, removed from the housing, at the bottom of Fig. 30–19. Essentially, it is a solid cylinder in which two

grooves have been cut (or you could say it is a shaft with three collars on it). The valve spool is a close sliding fit within the hole in the valve housing. The housing has three internal grooves which are concentric. The two internal grooves at the two ends of the valve housing are connected to the reservoir. The center internal groove is connected to the pump. There are two additional openings from the two internal collars in the housing to the two sides of the power cylinder, as shown.

When the valve spool is in the position shown in Fig. 30–19, the oil flows from the pump, into the center part of the valve housing, and then splits evenly and flows back to the reservoir, as shown by the arrows. Oil pressure is not built up, and the same pressure

636

(very low) is applied to both sides of the piston in the cylinder. Thus, there is no tendency for the piston to move one way or the other in the cylinder.

However, if the valve spool is moved in the valve body, oil pressure will build up and the piston will move in the cylinder. When the valve spool is moved (for instance, to the right as in Fig. 30–20), then the collars on the valve spool close off the openings, or ports, connecting the pressure line to the return line. When these ports are closed, the oil can no longer return to the pump reservoir. It must now flow into the cylinder as shown by the arrows in Fig. 30–20. Thus, the full hydraulic pressure developed by the oil pump is applied to one side of the piston in the cylinder. The piston must

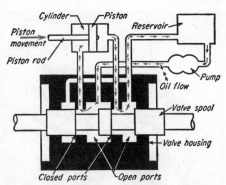

Fig. 30–20. When the valve spool is moved to the right, ports are closed so that oil can no longer flow from the oil pump, past the valve spool, and into the return passages to the pump reservoir. Instead, it flows to the cylinder as shown by the arrows, forcing the piston to move to the right. (*Saginaw Steering Gear Division of General Motors Corporation*)

move (to the right in Fig. 30–20). Oil on the other side of the piston is free to discharge from the piston and pass through the valve housing and into the pump reservoir as shown by the arrows.

If the valve spool is moved in the opposite direction (to the left in Fig. 30–20), then the oil flow to the cylinder would be reversed. Oil pressure would be applied to the right-hand side of the piston, forcing it to the left. At the same time, the circuit would be open to permit the oil in the left-hand side of the cylinder to return to the pump reservoir.

2. Power cylinder. Figure 30–21 shows a simple cutaway view of the offset steering assembly. Note that the piston rod has a toothed rack on its end (called the power rack). This rack is meshed with a gear sector on the

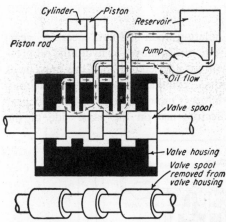

Fig. 30–19. In the position shown, the valve spool directs the oil flow from the pump into the two return passages to the pump reservoir, as shown by the arrows. Thus, oil pressure is the same on both sides of the piston. (*Saginaw Steering Gear Division of General Motors Corporation*)

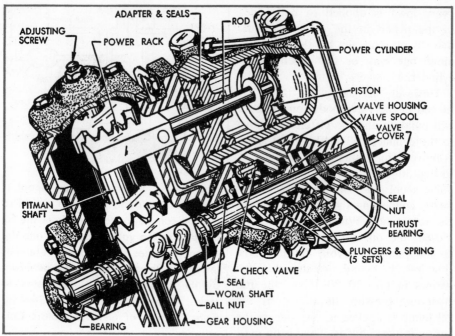

Fig. 30–21. Cutaway view of power-steering-gear assembly. (*Buick Motor Division of General Motors Corporation*)

end of the pitman shaft. There is another gear sector on the pitman shaft that is meshed with the ball nut. Compare this figure with Fig. 30–17. Note that the power cylinder and power rack are simply additions to the cir-culating ball-and-nut steering gear. The piston moves as hydraulic oil pressure is applied to it, and this movement then provides most of the steering effort. On some models, the two gear sectors are on the same side of the

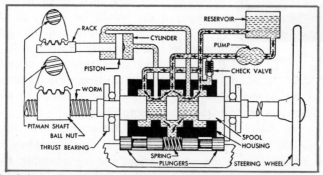

Fig. 30–22. Schematic drawing of the power-steering-gear assembly, showing hydraulic circuits with the steering wheel in the straight-ahead position. (*Buick Motor Division of General Motors Corporation*)

638

pitman shaft as shown in Fig. 30–21. On other models, the two gear sectors are on opposite sides of the pitman shaft. Operation is identical, however.

3. *Valve action.* We have noted that moving the valve spool from the centered position causes oil to be directed into one or the other side of the cylinder. This, in turn, causes the piston to move and thereby turn the pitman shaft in one direction or the other. The valve spool is forced to move as the steering wheel is turned.

In Fig. 30–22, note that turning the steering wheel to make a left turn would cause the worm to turn in the ball nut and would, in effect, tend to back the worm up and out of the nut. You would get the same effect if you backed a screw out of a nut and at the same time held the nut stationary. The screw would rise upward as it was backed out. There is resistance to ball-nut movement from the ball nut to the front wheels. This tends to hold the ball nut stationary. If the ball nut is held stationary, then the worm, and steering shaft, will move upward (actually only a small amount). This upward movement will carry the valve

spool upward, also, so that the valve spool is moved into the position shown in Fig. 30–23. In this position, oil pressure is directed to one side of the piston cylinder, and the other side of the cylinder is connected to the pump reservoir. This means that the piston is moved to the left (in Fig. 30–23), and this assists in turning the pitman shaft so that a left turn is made.

The valve spool is maintained in its centered position, during straight-ahead driving, by five sets of plungers and springs. These plungers and springs are evenly spaced around the valve housing, and the plunger ends are in contact with two thrust bearings. You can see one set of plungers with its springs in the lower part of Fig. 30–21. Note how the spring must be compressed as the valve spool moves (Fig. 30–23). Actually, the five springs provide a considerable pressure tending to hold the valve spool in its centered position. In one application, for example, the five springs will not compress unless 300 pounds or more is applied. This 300 pounds of end thrust will result if about 4 pounds pull is exerted on the rim of the steering

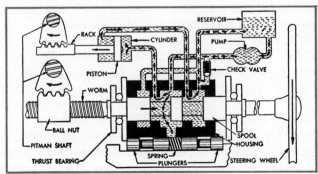

Fig. 30–23. Schematic drawing of the power-steering-gear assembly, showing hydraulic circuits with the steering wheel being turned to make a left turn. (*Buick Motor Division of General Motors Corporation*)

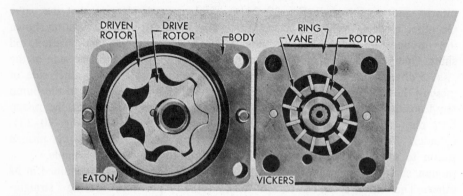

Fig. 30–24. End views, with covers removed, of two types of pump used with the Saginaw power-steering gear. (*Left*) Eaton pump. (*Right*) Vickers pump. (*Buick Motor Division of Generals Motors Corporation*)

wheel. Owing to the mechanical advantage of the worm and nut, the comparatively light twisting effort on the steering wheel produces a heavy end thrust on the worm. This causes the valve spool to overcome the pressure of the five plunger springs and move so that the power piston is brought into action.

Note that under easy steering conditions, when steering can be accomplished with less than 4 pounds of pull at the rim of the steering wheel, there will be no power-steering action. It is only when steering requires more than 4 pounds of pull at the rim that enough end thrust is developed to move the valve spool. When this happens, the power cylinder supplies any effort above the 4-pound pull needed for steering.

4. Check valve. The check valve shown in Figs. 30–22 and 30–23 (close to the pump) is provided to prevent excessive pressures in the system. Since movement of the valve spool shuts off all return passages so that

oil cannot return to the pump reservoir, there is a good chance that excessive oil pressures would develop. If this happens, the check valve opens and relieves the excessive pressure by bypassing some of the oil from the pump into the return line to the pump reservoir.

5. Oil pump. Figure 30–24 shows two types of pump used with the Saginaw power steering gear. In the Eaton pump, an inner drive rotor causes the driven rotor to rotate with it. As they rotate, the pockets between the rotors increase and then decrease in size. During increase, oil flows into the pockets through an inlet port from the pump reservoir. Then, during decrease, this oil is forced out of the pump through an exit port. In the Vickers pump, there is a slotted driving rotor in which 12 vanes are assembled. These vanes slide outward to contact the inner face of the pump body. The inner face is so shaped (oval) as to provide two pumping chambers. As the rotor rotates, the vanes slide out

and in to increase and then decrease the pockets between the vanes. During increase, oil enters the pockets from the pump reservoir. During decrease, the oil is forced from the pockets through exit ports. Both pumps have an overload relief valve set to open when the pressure goes above about 750 psi (pounds per square inch).

6. *In-line power steering.* This unit has been used in late-model General Motors cars, among others. It is much like the Saginaw offset power-steering unit. The major differences are that, in the in-line unit, the positions of the power piston and the control valve have been reversed. In the in-line unit, the power piston is in line with the steering shaft while the valve is off to one side. Figure 30–25 is a cutaway view of the unit. The piston has a rack

on it as shown in Fig. 30–26. The rack meshes with the sector on the pitman shaft. When the steering wheel is turned, the worm at the lower end of the steering shaft turns. This action causes the ball nut and the piston to move endwise. The sector therefore turns the pitman shaft for steering.

The assisting action of the unit comes into effect whenever more than about three pounds is required to turn the wheel. When this occurs, because of the resistance of the wheels to turning, the worm shifts endwise slightly to cause the valve to operate. This admits oil at high pressure from the pump to one side or the other of the piston, and the piston is moved to assist in the turning effort.

For instance, on a right turn (Fig. 30–27a), the worm moves downward a small amount. This movement car-

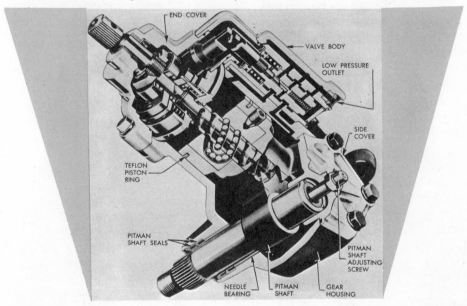

Fig. 30–25. Cutaway view of Saginaw in-line power-steering unit. (*Buick Motor Division of General Motors Corporation*)

641

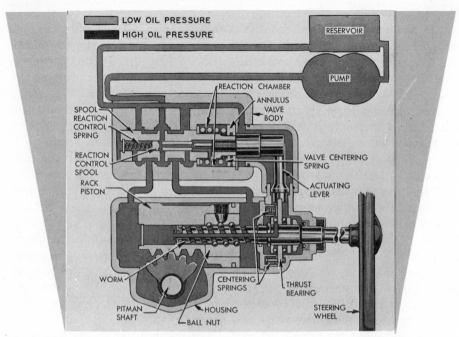

Fig. 30–26. Circulation of oil through power-steering unit in straight-ahead position. (*Buick Motor Division of General Motors Corporation*)

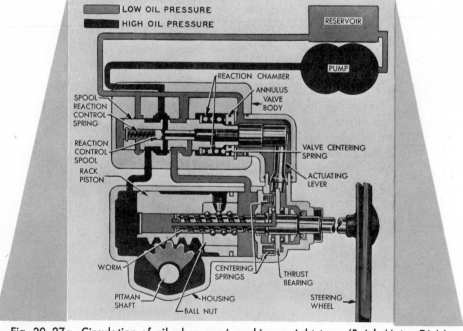

Fig. 30–27a. Circulation of oil when car is making a right turn. (*Buick Motor Division of General Motors Corporation*)

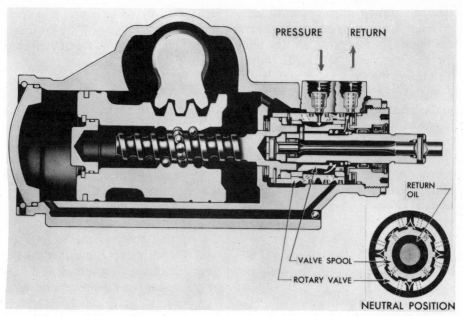

PRESSURE RETURN

RETURN
OIL

VALVE SPOOL
ROTARY VALVE

NEUTRAL POSITION

Fig. 30–27b. Torsion-bar power-steering unit in straight-ahead position. (*Pontiac Motor Division of General Motors Corporation*)

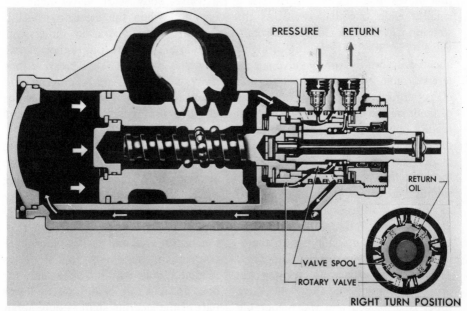

PRESSURE RETURN

RETURN
OIL

VALVE SPOOL
ROTARY VALVE

RIGHT TURN POSITION

Fig. 30–27c. Torsion-bar power-steering unit during a right turn. (*Pontiac Motor Division of General Motors Corporation*)

ries the thrust bearing downward, also. As the thrust bearing moves downward (to the left in Fig. 30–27a), it causes the actuating lever to tilt, as shown. This brings the spool valve to the right. Now, oil at high pressure is admitted to the left side of the piston. The piston is moved to the right. The higher the turning resistance, the more the valve spool is moved, and the higher the oil pressure on the piston. Thus, a proportional effect is at work. Most of the turning effort is handled by the oil pressure on the piston.

When a left turn is made, the valve spool is moved to the left and oil under pressure is admitted to the right side of the piston.

7. Torsion-bar power steering. This unit is similar to others previously discussed. However, instead of using spiral centering springs and a valve that moves in a straight line, it uses a small torsion bar that twists as the steering wheel is turned, and a rotary valve (Fig 30–27b). In the straight-ahead position, the rotary valve is centered around the valve spool so that oil is permitted to flow past both sides of lands on the spool. The oil can thus readily flow to the oil return, and no oil pressure builds up. When a turn is made, the turning effort is applied through the torsion bar; it twists slightly and causes the valve spool to move slightly with respect to the rotary valve. Now, oil is forced to flow to one end of the piston; oil pressure therefore assists the turn (Fig. 30–27c). The more resistance to turning the driver encounters, the more the valve spool is displaced and the higher the oil pressure is applied to the piston. Thus, while most of the steering effort

is handled by oil pressure, a proportional amount is "sensed" by the driver so that he is always aware of variations in steering effort.

§ **506. Gemmer power steering** The Gemmer Hydraguide power-steering unit has been used on Chrysler Corporation cars, including Chrysler and De Soto. Its steering-assist action is very similar to that of the Saginaw unit although the construction and operation of the two units are quite different. The power-steering unit is part of the steering gear, as in the Saginaw unit. The oil pump is mounted on the back end of the generator; it is driven by a coupling from the generator shaft. The generator is driven by a V belt from the engine crankshaft pulley.

1. Power-steering operation. The Gemmer power-steering unit contains a valve body with valves that are operated when the steering wheel is turned. Valve operation directs hydraulic oil pressure into either of two power cylinders. The oil pressure then moves a piston assembly; movement of the piston assembly supplies the major effort in turning the steering wheel and in steering the car.

Figure 30–28 shows the complete layout of the system. Note that the steering shaft (on which the steering wheel is mounted) consists of two parts. The upper part, which is several feet long, carries the steering wheel at the upper end and a flexible rubber coupling at the lower end. It is so mounted that it can rotate only. It does not move up or down. The lower part of the steering shaft is only about a foot long; its upper end is attached to the upper steering shaft by the flex-

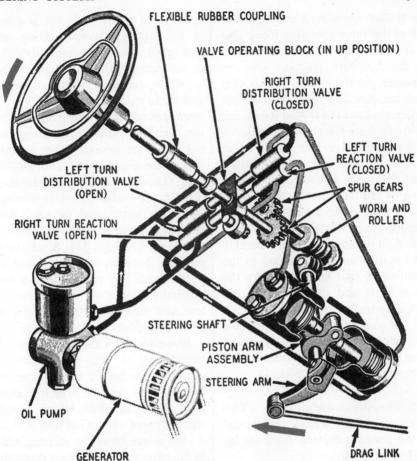

FLEXIBLE RUBBER COUPLING

VALVE OPERATING BLOCK (IN UP POSITION)

RIGHT TURN
DISTRIBUTION VALVE
(CLOSED)

LEFT TURN
REACTION VALVE
(CLOSED)

LEFT TURN
DISTRIBUTION VALVE
(OPEN)

SPUR GEARS

WORM AND
ROLLER

RIGHT TURN REACTION
VALVE (OPEN)

STEERING SHAFT

PISTON ARM
ASSEMBLY

STEERING ARM

OIL PUMP

GENERATOR

DRAG LINK

Fig. 30–28. Left turn being made with Gemmer power-steering unit. The spur gear on the short steering shaft climbs the spur gear on the worm. This moves the valve operating block upward, closing the two upper valves as shown and opening the two lower valves wide-open. Oil now flows to and from the two cylinders as shown by the arrows to cause the power pistons to move and assist the steering. (*De Soto Division of Chrysler Corporation*)

ible rubber coupling. There is a spur gear on its lower end. At an intermediate point, there is a single spherical bearing which supports it.

2. *Operation during left turn.* Figure 30–28 shows the actions in the system during a left turn. Reaction between the two spur gears causes the

steering-shaft spur gear to climb upward; this lifts the valve-operating block. Movement of the block closes the right-turn distribution valve and the left-turn reaction valve. Thus, flow of oil to the right cylinder is halted. At the same time, closing of the left-turn reaction valve halts the flow of oil

645

from the left cylinder. Upward movement of the valve-operating block also moves the left-turn distribution valve and the right-turn reaction valve to wide-open positions. This means that the oil can now flow freely *into* the left cylinder (but not out). And it can also flow freely from the right cylinder.

Oil pressure therefore builds up in the left cylinder, and the left piston causes the piston assembly to move as shown by the large arrow. Since there is no oil pressure in the right cylinder, no resistance to this motion is offered by the right piston. The piston assembly works against an arm fastened to the pitman shaft, thus helping to turn the pitman shaft and thereby swing the steering (pitman) arm.

3. Oil pump. The oil pump is the inner-outer rotor type such as shown to the left in Fig. 30–24 and operates as already explained (§ 505, 4).

§ 507. Chrysler power steering Two models are discussed here, the coaxial and the constant control. Both are integral units.

1. Coaxial power steering. The term "coaxial" is used because the center lines, or axes, of the major working parts all coincide. The operating piston, spool valve, and steering shaft are all in line. Figure 30–29 is a cutaway view of the steering gear. Following paragraphs describe the operation of the unit.

a. Construction. Oil pressure is provided by an oil pump mounted on the generator. This is the arrangement used with the Gemmer power-steering system (§ 506). The oil is directed, under pressure, to a spool valve centered in the piston (Fig. 30–30). This

spool valve is similar to the one used in the Saginaw power-steering unit. The spool valve is mechanically linked to the steering wheel through a valve-operating rod, the worm connector, and worm shaft (see Fig. 30–29). The worm connector is a recirculating ball nut similar to the recirculating ball nut used on several other steering gears (see Figs. 30–17 and 30–21).

b. Operation. During straight-ahead driving, the valve spool is centered inside the piston, and the same pressure is directed against both ends of the piston (Fig. 30–31). Since the oil passages between the valve and the piston lands are open, there is little restriction to the oil. The pressure is low, and there is no tendency for the piston to move.

However, when the driver turns the steering wheel away from straight-ahead, the hydraulic system goes into operation to provide steering assistance. As an example, let us consider what happens when a left turn is made. As the driver turns the steering wheel to the left, the worm threads down into the worm connector (or recirculating ball nut) since it has a left-hand thread. This causes the nut to move upward. The first effect of this movement is that the valve-operating rod moves upward, carrying the valve spool with it. This displaces the valve spool slightly with respect to the piston as shown in Fig. 30–32. Now, note that oil flow is restricted at points *A* and *B*. Oil pressure therefore builds up on one end of the piston. At the same time, the oil ahead of the other end of the piston is released to the low-pressure side of the hydraulic system. This means that the piston and rack assembly is moved (to

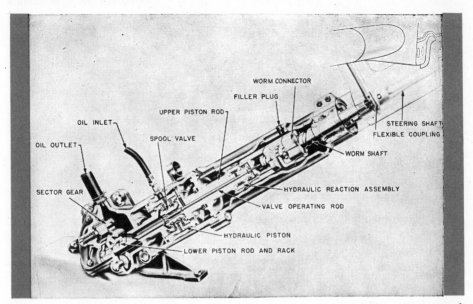

Fig. 30–29. Cutaway view of coaxial-power-steering gear. (*De Soto Division of Chrysler Corporation*)

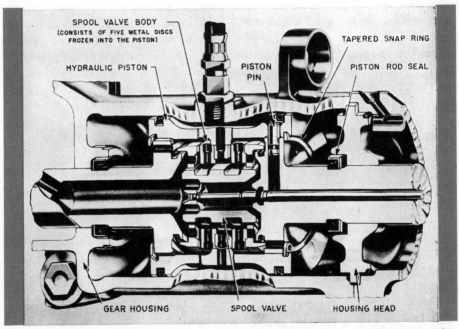

Fig. 30–30. Piston and spool valve in coaxial-power-steering gear. (*De Soto Division of Chrysler Corporation*)

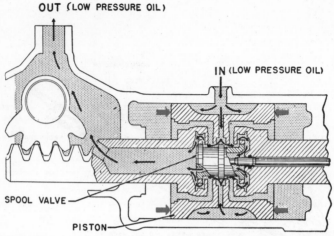

Fig. 30–31. Oil flow with spool valve centered in the piston. (*De Soto Division of Chrysler Corporation*)

the right as shown by the heavy arrows in Fig. 30–32). The rack causes the sector and pitman shaft to rotate so that the front wheels are turned for a left turn. As long as the driver continues to rotate the steering wheel, he keeps the valve moving slightly ahead of the piston so that hydraulic pressure continues to assist him.

If the driver should stop turning the wheel and hold it stationary, then the valve is also held stationary. The piston moves up slightly so that it is approximately centered with re-

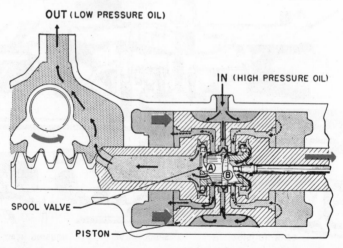

Fig. 30–32. Oil flow during left turn. Valve is shifted to right, and oil flows and builds up pressure against the left end of the piston so that piston is moved to right as shown by heavy arrows. (*De Soto Division of Chrysler Corporation*)

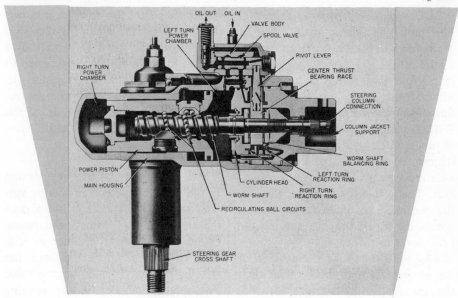

Fig. 30–33. Cutaway view of constant-control power-steering unit. (*Chrysler Division of Chrysler Corporation*)

spect to the valve as shown in Fig. 30–31.

c. Steering feel. Steering feel is produced by the reaction seal which is located in the hydraulic reaction assembly (Fig. 30–29). This device applies a reaction to the steering wheel that is proportional to steering effort.

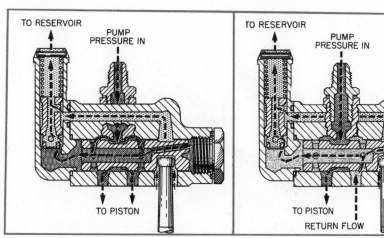

Fig. 30–34. Position of steering-gear valve in straight-ahead driving. (*Chrysler Division of Chrysler Corporation*)

Fig. 30–35. Position of steering-gear valve when car makes left turn. (*Chrysler Division of Chrysler Corporation*)

2. Constant-control power steering.
This unit is similar in many ways to
the Saginaw in-line power-steering unit.
Figure 30–33 is a cutaway view of the
unit. Note that it has a pivot lever
which forms a linkage between the
thrust bearing and the spool valve.

The operation of the unit is similar
to others already described. When the
steering wheel is turned, a slight endwise movement of the worm shaft occurs. This is due to end thrust through
the worm. The endwise movement
moves the thrust bearing, causing the
pivot lever to pivot.

Figure 30–34 shows the position of
the pivot lever and spool valve when
the car is moving straight forward.
Figure 30–35 shows their positions
when a left turn is made. Here, the
worm shaft has been thrust upward
(to the right in Fig. 30–33) so that

the upper end of the pivot lever moves
downward (to the left in Fig. 30–35).
This moves the spool valve as shown
so that high-pressure oil is directed to
the lower side of the power piston (to
the left in Fig. 30–33) while the return line from the upper side of the
power piston is opened. The oil pressure therefore assists the turn.

§ 508. Linkage-type power steering
In the linkage-type power-steering system, the power cylinder is not part of
the steering gear. Instead, the power
cylinder (or booster cylinder as it is
also called) is connected into the
steering linkage. In addition, the valve
assembly is included in the steering
linkage, either as a separate assembly
or integral with the power cylinder.
Figure 30–36 shows one linkage-type
power-steering system in which the

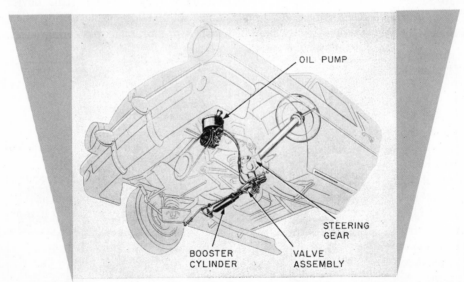

Fig. 30–36. Phantom view of car from underneath, showing arrangement of a linkage-type power-steering system which has separate valve assembly and power
(booster) cylinder. (*Lincoln-Mercury Division of Ford Motor Company*)

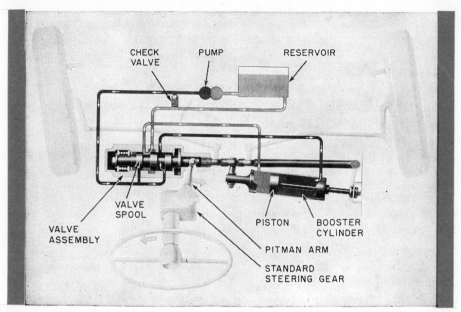

CHECK VALVE   PUMP   RESERVOIR

VALVE SPOOL

VALVE ASSEMBLY

PISTON   BOOSTER CYLINDER

PITMAN ARM

STANDARD STEERING GEAR

Fig. 30–37. Schematic view of linkage-type power steering shown in Fig. 30–36. Arrows show direction of oil flow when a left turn is being made. Large arrows show directions in which steering wheel, pitman arm, and front wheels turn. (*Lincoln-Mercury Division of Ford Motor Company*)

booster cylinder and valve assembly are separate units. In operation, the steering gear works in exactly the same way as the mechanical types described in § 503. However, the swinging end of the pitman arm is not directly connected to the steering linkage. Instead, it is connected to a valve assembly. As the end of the pitman arm swings when a turn is made, it actuates the valve assembly. Then, the valve assembly directs hydraulic oil pressure from the oil pump to the booster cylinder. Inside the booster cylinder, pressure is applied to one or the other side of a piston. Movement then takes place (actually, in this unit, the cylinder moves instead of the piston), and this movement is transferred to the connecting rod in the steering linkage. Thus, most of the effort required to move the connecting rod and steer the car is furnished by the booster cylinder.

1. Valve-assembly operation. In many ways, the valve assembly is very similar to that used in the Saginaw power-steering unit (Figs. 30–18 to 30–24). The operating part consists of a valve spool that looks much like the valve spool shown at the bottom of Fig. 30–19. The valve spool is assembled into the valve body as shown in Fig. 30–37. The ball on the end of the pitman arm fits a socket in the stem of the valve spool. During neutral, or straight-ahead, operation, the valve spool is centered in the valve

651

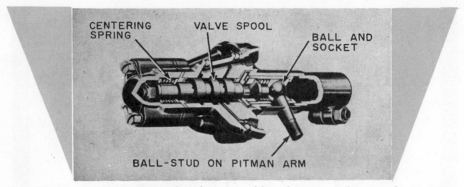

Fig. 30–38. Cutaway view of valve assembly, showing valve spool, centering springs, and ball-and-socket attachment of pitman arm to valve-spool stem. (*Lincoln-Mercury Division of Ford Motor Company*)

assembly by one or more centering springs. In this position, the oil circuits through the valve will impose equal pressure on both sides of the piston in the booster cylinder. Thus, there is no tendency for the booster cylinder to exercise any action.

Figure 30–38 is a cutaway view of the valve assembly, showing the centering springs for holding the valve spool in the centered position during straight-ahead driving.

When a turn is made, the pitman arm swings in one direction or the other, thus causing valve action as already mentioned. Figure 30–37 shows what happens when a left turn is made. Turning the steering wheel to the left, as shown, makes the pitman arm swing to the right. The ball on the end of the pitman arm moves the valve spool to the right. Now, oil under pressure from the pump can flow through the valve body to only one side of the piston in the booster cylinder. In the figure, oil flows into the cylinder on the right side of the piston as shown by the arrows. Since the piston is fastened to the car frame by the piston rod, it cannot move. Therefore, the hydraulic pressure in the cylinder causes the cylinder itself to

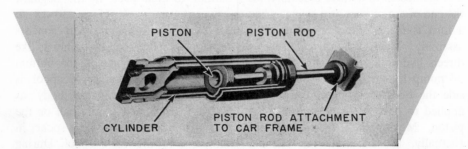

Fig. 30–39. Cutaway view of booster cylinder, showing relationship of piston, rod, cylinder, and rod attachment. (*Lincoln-Mercury Division of Ford Motor Company*)

move. The cylinder is fastened to the connecting rod. Thus, the major effort of steering is supplied by the booster cylinder. As the cylinder moves to the right (in the figure), the oil in the left-hand side flows back to the reservoir through the valve body as shown by the arrows. Note that movement of the valve spool to the right has connected the left-hand side of the cylinder to the reservoir.

2. Booster cylinder. Figure 30–39 is a cutaway view of the booster cylinder. The cylinder is made up of two concentric shells. Oil flows between the two shells to enter the piston-rod end of the cylinder. The end of the piston rod is attached to the car frame by a flexible connection so that some movement of the rod can take place to permit alignment of the rod with the cylinder as the cylinder moves back and forth during steering.

§ **509. Integral valve and power cylinder** Figure 30–40 shows the linkage-type power-steering unit in which the valve assembly and power cylinder are one unit. The piston rod of the power cylinder is attached to the car frame. The cylinder is linked to the steering linkage, forming a part of the linkage. Note that this assembly is called the *power link* since it is a part of the linkage and, at the same time, supplies steering power.

Figure 30–40 shows the actions during a left turn. When the steering wheel is turned, the ball on the end of the pitman arm shifts the valve spool to the right. This permits oil to flow from the pump under pressure, through the ports in the valve section of the assembly, and into the right-hand side of the power cylinder. The high-pressure oil then forces the cylinder to move to the right. It is this move-

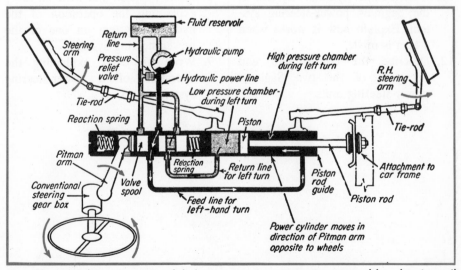

Fig. 30–40. Schematic view of linkage-type power-steering assembly, showing oil flow and movement of parts when a left turn is made. (*Monroe Auto Equipment Company*)

ment of the cylinder which provides the major mechanical steering effort within the car.

REVIEW QUESTIONS

1. What does the term "front-end geometry" mean?
2. What is camber? What is positive camber? Negative camber?
3. What is kingpin inclination? What is its purpose?
4. What is the included angle?
5. When the point of intersection is below the pavement, will the wheel tend to toe in or toe out?
6. What is caster? What is its purpose? What is negative caster?
7. What is meant by toe-in?
8. What is meant by toe-out on turns? How is it achieved?
9. Describe typical steering linkages.
10. Describe the construction and operation of a typical steering gear.
11. Describe the hydraulic system in the Saginaw power-steering system. Explain how it works when a turn is made.
12. Describe the construction and operation of the two Saginaw power-steering units.
13. Describe the construction and operation of the Gemmer power-steering unit.
14. Describe the construction and operation of the two Chrysler power-steering units.
15. Describe the construction and operation of a linkage-type power-steering system.

STUDY QUESTIONS

1. Make a sketch showing front wheels with positive camber.
2. Make a sketch showing front wheels with toe-in.
3. Make a sketch showing the meaning of included angle.
4. Write an essay explaining the purpose of camber, caster, kingpin inclination, toe-in, and toe-out on turns.
5. Write an essay explaining the operation of a typical steering gear and linkage.
6. Make a sketch and write an essay explaining the operation of the hydraulic system on one of the power-steering systems.
7. Write an essay explaining the operation of a power-steering system.

CHAPTER 31

STEERING AND SUSPENSION SERVICE

THIS CHAPTER DISCUSSES VARIOUS steering and suspension troubles and relates them to possible causes. It also outlines the various servicing and overhauling procedures required on steering gears and suspension systems and discusses different front-alignment checks and adjustments.

§ 510. Need for logical procedure

If you are able to relate various steering and suspension complaints with the conditions that cause them, you are much better off than the fellow who seeks blindly to find what is causing the trouble. You will know what items to check and correct to eliminate the trouble. You can save a great deal of time and effort when you know where to look.

The following sections tell you where to look when various complaints are made regarding the steering or suspension.

§ 511. Trouble-shooting

A variety of steering and suspension troubles will bring the driver to the mechanic, but it is rare that the driver will have a clear idea of what causes his trouble. He can detect an increase in steering difficulty, hard steering, or excessive play in the steering system. But he probably would not have a very good idea of what would cause those conditions. The following sections describe various steering and suspension troubles and discuss their causes and corrections.

§ 512. Excessive play in system

Excessive play, or looseness in the steering system means that there will be excessive free movement of the steering wheel without corresponding movement of the front wheels. A small amount of steering-wheel play is desirable in order to provide easy steering. But when the play becomes excessive, it is considered objectionable by most drivers. Excessive play can be due to wear or improper adjustment of the steering gear, to wear or improper adjustments in the steering linkage, to worn steering-knuckle parts, or to loose wheel bearings.

The tie rods and linkage may be checked for looseness by jacking up the front end of the car. Then grasp both front wheels, push out on both at the same time, and then pull in on both at the same time (Fig. 31–1). Excessive relative movement between the two wheels means that the linkage connections are worn or out of adjustment.

Worn steering-knuckle parts and loose wheel bearings may be detected

655

Fig. 31–1. Checking tie rods and linkage for looseness. (*Bear Manufacturing Company*)

Fig. 31–2. Checking for wear in steering knuckle and wheel bearing. (*Bear Manufacturing Company*)

by jacking up the front end of the car. Then grasp the wheel top and bottom, and check it for side play (Fig. 31–2). Try to see how much you can wobble the wheel. Excessive looseness indicates worn or loose parts, either in the steering knuckle or in the wheel bearing. The bearing should be readjusted to see whether the looseness is in the bearing or in the knuckle.

A rough check for looseness in the steering gear can be made by watching the pitman arm while an assistant turns the steering wheel one way and then the other with the front wheels on the floor. If, after reversal of steering-wheel rotation, considerable initial movement of the steering wheel is required to set the pitman arm in motion, then the steering gear is worn or in need of adjustment.

§ 513. Hard steering If hard steering occurs just after the steering system has been worked on, the chances are that this is due to excessively tight adjustments in the steering gear or linkages. If hard steering develops at other times, this could be due to low or uneven tire pressure, to abnormal friction in the steering gear or linkage or at the kingpin, or to improper wheel or frame alignment.

On a car equipped with power steering, failure of the power-steering mechanism will cause the steering system to revert back to straight mechanical operation and to require a considerably greater steering effort. In such a case, the power-steering unit and hydraulic pump should be checked.

The steering system may be checked for excessive friction by jacking up the front end of the car. Then turn the steering wheel, and observe the steering-system components to locate the source of excessive friction. Disconnect the linkage at the pitman arm. If this eliminates the frictional drag that makes it hard to turn the steering wheel, then the friction is either in the linkage itself or at the steering knuckles. If the friction is not eliminated when the linkage is disconnected at the pitman arm, then the steering gear is probably at fault.

If the trouble does not seem to be due to excessive friction in the steering system, the chances are it is due to incorrect front-wheel alignment or to a misaligned frame or sagging springs. Excessive caster, especially, will cause hard steering.

§ 514. Car wander Car wander is experienced as difficulty in keeping the car moving straight ahead; frequent steering-wheel movements are necessary to prevent the car from wandering from one side to the other of the road. An inexperienced driver may sometimes complain of car wander. This is because he tends to oversteer so that he has to keep moving the wheel back and forth unnecessarily to stay on his side of the road.

A considerable variety of conditions can cause car wander. Low or uneven tire pressure, binding or excessive play in the linkage or steering gear, or improper front-wheel alignment will cause car wander. Any condition that causes tightness in the steering system will keep the wheels from automatically seeking the "straight-ahead" position. The driver therefore has to correct the wheels constantly. This

condition would probably also cause hard steering (§ 513). Looseness, or excessive play, in the steering system might also cause car wander; this would tend to allow the wheels to waver somewhat and permit the car to wander.

Excessively low caster, uneven caster, or a point of intersection too far above or below the road surface (from wrong camber angle) will tend to cause the wheels to swing away from straight-ahead so that the driver must steer continually. Excessive toe-in will cause the same condition.

§ 515. Car pulls to one side (normal driving)

If the car persistently pulls to one side so that pressure must more or less constantly be applied to the steering wheel to maintain forward movement, the trouble could be due to any of the following: uneven tire pressure, uneven caster or camber, a tight wheel bearing, uneven springs, or the wheels not tracking (rear wheels not following in the tracks of the front wheels). Anything that would tend to make one wheel drag or toe in or toe out more than the other will make the car pull to that side.

§ 516. Car pulls to one side (during braking)

The most likely cause of this condition is grabbing brakes. This could be due to the brake linings becoming soaked with oil or brake fluid, to brake shoes unevenly or improperly adjusted, to a brake-backing plate loose or out of line, or to other causes that would cause the brake at one wheel to apply harder than the brake at the corresponding wheel on the other side. The other conditions listed in § 515 could also cause pulling to one side during braking since the condition, from whatever cause, tends to become more noticeable when the car is braked.

§ 517. Front-wheel shimmy (low speed)

Front-wheel shimmy and front-wheel tramp (§ 518) are sometimes confused. Low-speed shimmy is the rapid oscillation of the wheel on the knuckle pin. The wheel tries to turn in and out alternately. The action causes the front end of the car to shake from side to side. On the other hand, front-wheel tramp, or high-speed shimmy, is a tendency for the wheel and tire assembly to move up and down and, under severe conditions, actually to leave the pavement. Even when the tire does not leave the pavement, tramp can be observed as a rapid flexing-unflexing action of the part of the tire in contact with the pavement. That is, the bottom of the tire first appears deflated (as the wheel moves down) and then inflated (as the wheel moves up).

Low-speed shimmy can result from low or uneven tire pressure, loose linkage, excessively soft springs, incorrect or uneven wheel camber, or irregularities in the tire treads.

§ 518. Front-wheel tramp

As explained in the previous article, front-wheel tramp is often called high-speed shimmy. This condition causes the front wheels to move up and down alternately. One of the most common causes of front-wheel tramp is unbalanced wheels, or wheels that have too much run-out. An unbalanced wheel is heavy at one part; as it rotates, the

heavy part sets up a circulating outward thrust that tends to make the wheel hop up and down. A similar action occurs if the wheel has too much run-out. Run-out is the amount the wheel is out of line with the axle so that one part of the wheel "runs out," or moves to the side, more than other parts of the wheel. Defective shock absorbers, which fail to control natural spring oscillations, will also cause wheel tramp. Any of the causes described in the previous article may also cause wheel tramp. Following articles describe the servicing of the wheel and tire so that they can be restored to proper balance and alignment.

§ 519. **Steering kickback** Steering shock, or kickback, becomes evident as sharp and rapid movements of the steering wheel when the front wheels encounter obstructions in the road. Normally, some kickback to the steering wheel will always occur. But when it becomes excessive, an investigation should be made. This condition could result from incorrect or uneven tire inflation, sagging springs, defective shock absorbers, or looseness in the linkage or steering gear. Any of these defects could permit road shock to carry back excessively to the steering wheel.

§ 520. **Tires squeal on turns** If the tires skid or squeal on turns, this may be due to excessive speeds on the turns. If this is not the cause, then it is probably due to low or uneven tire pressure or to misalignment of the front wheels (particularly camber and toe-in).

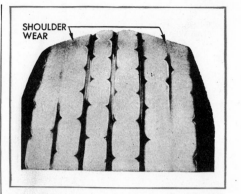

Fig. 31–3. Wear of treads along sides, or shoulders, due to underinflation. (*Buick Motor Division of General Motors Corporation*)

§ 521. **Improper tire wear** Various types of abnormal tire wear can be experienced. The type of tire wear found is often a good indication of a

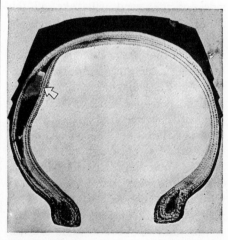

Fig. 31–4. Separation of plies in side wall of tire resulting from operation of tire in underinflated condition. A piece of wood (arrowed) has been inserted between the plies to show clearly where separation has occurred. (*Studebaker Corporation*)

Fig. 31–5. Center-tread wear due to overinflation. (*Buick Motor Division of General Motors Corporation*)

definite defect in the suspension or steering system or of improper operation or abuse. For example, if the tire is operated with insufficient air pressure (underinflated), the sides will bulge over and the center of the tread will be lifted clear of the road. The sides of the tread will take all the wear, the center being hardly worn (Fig. 31–3). Uneven tread wear shortens tire life. But even more damaging is the excessive flexing of the tire side walls that takes place as the underinflated tire rolls on the pavement. The repeated flexing causes the fabric in the side walls to crack or break and the plies to separate (Fig. 31–4). Naturally, this seriously weakens the side walls and may soon lead to complete tire failure. Aside from all this, the tire that is underinflated is unprotected against rim bruises. That is, if the tire should strike a rut or stone on the road, or if it should bump a curb a little too hard, the tire will flex so much under the blow that it will actually be pinched on the rim. This breaks plies and leads to early tire failure.

Overinflation causes the tire to ride on the center of its tread so that only the center of the tread wears (Fig. 31–5). This uneven tread wear shortens tire life. But more damaging than this is the fact that the overinflated tire does not have normal "give" when it meets a rut or bump in the road. Instead of giving normally, the tire fabric takes the major shock of the encounter. This may cause the fabric to crack or break so that the tire will soon fail.

Excessive camber of the wheel causes one side of the tire tread to wear more rapidly than the other, as shown in Fig. 31–6.

Excessive toe-in or toe-out on turns causes the tire to be dragged sideways while it is moving forward. The tire on a front wheel that toes in 1 inch from straight-ahead will be dragged sideways about 150 feet every mile. This sideward drag scrapes off rubber as shown in Fig. 31–7. One characteristic of this type of wear is the featheredges of rubber that appear on one side of the tread design. If both

Fig. 31–6. Tire-tread wear from excessive camber. (*Buick Motor Division of General Motors Corporation*)

Fig. 31–7. Tire-tread wear due to excessive toe-in or toe-out on turns. (*Buick Motor Division of General Motors Corporation*)

front tires show this type of wear, the front system is misaligned. But if only one tire shows this type of wear (and if both front tires have been on the car for some time), then this indicates a bent steering arm. This causes one wheel to toe in more than the other.

Cornering wear (Fig. 31–8), caused by taking curves at excessively high speeds, may be mistaken for camber wear or toe-in or toe-out wear. Cornering wear is due to centrifugal force acting on the car and causing the tires to roll as well as skid on the road. This produces a diagonal type of wear, which rounds the outside shoulder of the tire and roughens the tread surface near the outside shoulder. In severe cornering wear, fins or sharp edges will be found along the inner edges of the tire treads. There is no adjustment that can be made to correct the steering system for this type of wear. The only preventive is for the driver to slow down on curves.

Uneven tire wear such as shown in Fig. 31–9, where the tread is unevenly or spottily worn, can result from a number of mechanical conditions. These include misaligned wheels, unequal or improperly adjusted brakes, unbalanced wheels, and incorrect linkage adjustments.

High-speed operation causes much more rapid tire wear because of the high temperature and greater amount of scuffing and rapid flexing to which the tires are subjected. The chart (Fig. 31–10) shows how tire wear increases with car speed. According to the chart, tires wear more than three times as fast at 70 mph (miles per hour) than they do at 30 mph. More careful, slower driving and correct tire inflation will increase tire life greatly.

§ 522. **Hard or rough ride** A hard or rough ride could be due to excessive tire pressure, improperly operating shock absorbers, or excessive friction in the spring suspension. Make correction by lubricating springs, shackles, and bushings (on types where lubrication is specified) and by loosening the shock-absorber arm linkages, shackle bolts, and U bolts. Then

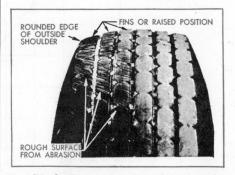

Fig. 31–8. Cornering wear of tire treads. (*Buick Motor Division of General Motors Corporation*)

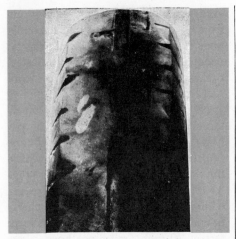

Fig. 31–9. Uneven tire-tread wear caused by mechanical troubles. (*Chevrolet Motor Division of General Motors Corporation*)

retighten the U bolts, shackle bolts, and shock-absorber linkages in that

order. This procedure permits realignment of parts that might have slipped to cause excessive friction.

Shock-absorber action on cars giving a hard or rough ride may be roughly checked by bouncing each corner of the car in turn. This is done by seizing the bumper, pulling up and pushing down on it several times so that the car bounces, and then releasing the bumper.* If the shock absorber is operating normally, the car will come to rest immediately. If the car continues to bounce after the bumper is released, the shock absorber is probably defective. A more accurate check can be made by disconnecting the

* Some direct-acting shock absorbers, as, for instance, those used on Plymouth, cannot be tested in this way since they are valved to permit slow spring oscillations in the interest of smoother riding.

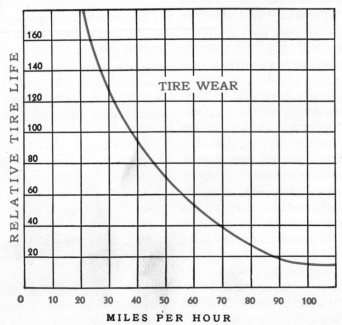

Fig. 31–10. Manner in which tire wear increases with speed. (*Studebaker Corporation*)

shock-absorber linkage so that the shock absorber can be operated. Then note the resistance to shock-absorber movement. If the resistance is small or is not uniform through the full stroke, or if the movement is very stiff, the shock absorber will require service. As a rule, shock absorbers are serviced by complete replacement. Special tools are required for shock-absorber repair.

NOTE: The shock-absorber arm should not be disconnected on front-suspension systems on which the arm forms the upper control, or suspension, arm unless the wheel alignment is to be adjusted or parts are to be replaced. Disconnecting this arm will change wheel alignment.

§ 523. Sway on turns

Sway of the car body on turns or on rough roads may be due to a loose stabilizer bar or shaft. The attachments of such bars or shafts to the frame, axle housing, or suspension arms should be checked. Weak or sagging springs could also cause excessive sway. If the shock absorbers are ineffective, they may permit excessive spring movement which could cause strong body pitching and sway, particularly on rough roads. If the caster is excessively positive, it will cause the car to roll out, or lean out, on turns (see § 499). This requires front-wheel realignment.

§ 524. Spring breakage

Breakage of leaf springs can result from excessive overloading; loose U bolts which cause breakage near the center bolt; loose center bolt, which causes breakage at the center-bolt holes; an improperly

operating shock absorber, which causes breakage of the master leaf; or tight spring shackle, which causes breakage of the master leaf near or at the spring eye. Determining the point at which breakage has occurred will indicate the cause.

§ 525. Sagging springs

Springs will sag from overloading or if they have become weak (as, for example, from habitual overloading). Loss of the shim from the coil-spring seat on the coil-spring suspension (from failure to return it during overhaul) will cause the spring to seem shorter and to sag. Not all coil springs require or use shims. Defective shock absorbers may tend to restrict spring action and thus make them appear to sag more than normal.

§ 526. Noises

Noises produced by spring or shock-absorber difficulties will usually be either a rattle or a squeak. Rattling noises can be produced by looseness of such parts as spring U bolts, metal spring covers, rebound clips, spring shackles, or shock-absorber linkages or springs. These can generally be located by a careful examination of the various suspension parts. Spring squeaks can result from lack of lubrication in the spring shackles or at spring bushings (on the type requiring lubrication) or in the spring itself (leaf type requiring lubrication). Shock-absorber squeak could result from tight or dry bushings. Steering-linkage rattles may develop if linkage components become loose. Under exceptional circumstances, squeaks during turns could develop owing to lack of lubrication in steer-

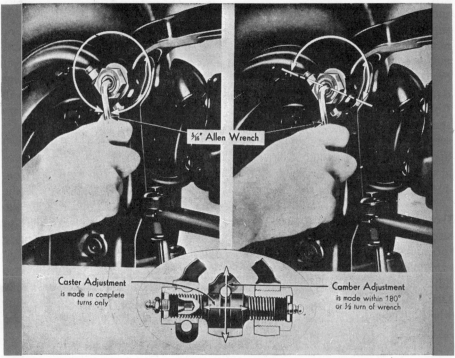

Fig. 31–11. Adjusting caster and camber by turning the pivot pin. (*Cadillac Motor Car Division of General Motors Corporation*)

ing-linkage joints or bearings. This would, of course, also produce hard steering.

§ 527. **Servicing steering linkages and suspensions** Steering and suspension service includes removal, replacement, and adjustment of tie rods, removal and replacement of other linkage parts such as the steering idler and the upper and lower control arms, removal and replacement of springs, removal and replacement of wheel hub and drum, and so on. In addition, the steering gear may require adjustment or removal, overhaul, and reinstallation. Also, the front wheels may require alignment (adjustment of caster, camber, toe-in, and so on).

For service on any of these components, refer to the shop manual on the model and make of car being worked on. Discussions of front-end alignment, wheel balance, steering-gear adjustments and service follow.

§ 528. **Front-end alignment** A variety of aligning equipment is in use. The purpose of this equipment is to measure the caster, camber, kingpin inclination, toe-in, and toe-out on turns. Adjusting procedures to correct these various factors vary with different cars. For instance, on Chevrolet (pre-ball-joint type), caster and camber are adjusted together by turning the upper control-arm pivot with an Allen wrench (Fig. 31–11). On this

664

Fig. 31–12. Camber being adjusted by turning the upper-control-arm-pin eccentric bushing: 1, lock screw; 2, upper-control-arm-pin eccentric bushing; 3, steering-knuckle support; 4, adjusting tool. (*Plymouth Division of Chrysler Corporation*)

design, incorrect kingpin inclination or toe-out on turns means bent parts that will require replacement. On Plymouth, caster is originally adjusted when the upper-control-arm-pin eccentric bushing is installed. Camber is adjusted by turning this bushing (Fig. 31-12). Incorrect kingpin inclination or toe-out on turns means there are bent parts that must be replaced. On the ball-joint type of suspension shown in Figs. 29–16*a* and *b* caster and camber are adjusted by removing or installing shims between the upper suspension-arm shaft and support

bracket or frame. Figure 31–13 shows the installation of an adjusting shim.

§ 529. Preliminary checks   Before front alignment is checked, the following items must be checked and corrected if necessary:

1. Tire inflation
2. Wheel bearings
3. Wheel run-out
4. Steering knuckles
5. Steering linkages
6. Wheel balance
7. Shock absorbers
8. Tracking

665

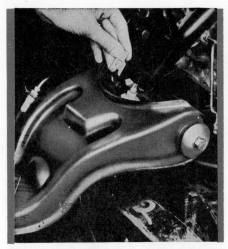

Fig. 31–13. Installing an adjusting shim between the upper suspension-arm shaft and support bracket to adjust camber and caster. (*Chevrolet Motor Division of General Motors Corporation*)

If tires are incorrectly inflated, if wheel bearings, steering knuckles, or steering linkages are worn or out of adjustment, then alignment of the wheels cannot be accurately checked. Likewise, if the wheel is bent or out of balance, alignment adjustments would mean little; as soon as the car went out on the highway, the bent or out-of-balance condition would cause steering trouble. If the shock absorbers are faulty, they could cause steering trouble. Also, failure to track (failure of rear wheels to follow in the tracks of the front wheels) because of a bent frame or other parts would cause steering trouble that could not be corrected by alignment adjustments.

§ **530. Steering-gear service** Manual steering gears have two basic adjustments, one for taking up the worm-gear and steering-shaft end play, and

the other for removing backlash between the worm and sector (or roller or lever studs). In addition, some designs have a means of adjusting the sector-shaft (pitman-arm-shaft) end play. In addition, on power-steering units, various other adjustments may be required. Always follow the instructions in the applicable shop manual when adjusting or overhauling a steering gear.

REVIEW QUESTIONS

1. What could cause excessive play in the steering system?
2. What could cause hard steering?
3. What could cause car wander?
4. What could cause the car to pull to one side during normal driving?
5. What could cause the car to pull to one side during braking?
6. What could cause front-wheel shimmy at low speeds?
7. What could cause front-wheel tramp (high-speed shimmy)?
8. What could produce steering kickback?
9. What causes tires to squeal on turns?
10. Describe various types of abnormal tire wear, and explain what could cause each.
11. What could cause a hard ride?
12. What might cause the car to sway on turns?
13. What are causes of spring breakage?
14. What causes springs to sag?
15. Explain how to check the steering linkage for looseness.
16. Explain how to check front-wheel bearings for wear or improper adjustment.

17. Explain how to check the steering system for excessive friction.
18. Describe a method of checking shock-absorber action.
19. Describe two methods of making caster adjustments.
20. What are the preliminary checks to be made before front alignment is checked?

STUDY QUESTIONS

1. Make a list of various steering and suspension troubles, their causes and corrections.
2. Refer to a manufacturer's shop manual, and write a service story on steering-linkage service, including removal, replacement, and adjustment.
3. Refer to a manufacturer's shop manual, and write a service story on aligning a front end, including the preliminary checks such as balancing wheels, adjusting front-wheel bearings, and so on.
4. Refer to a manufacturer's shop manual, and write a service story on a manual steering gear, including removal, disassembly, reassembly, replacement, and adjustment.
5. Write a similar service story on a power-steering unit.

THIS CHAPTER DESCRIBES THE construction and operation of the various types of brakes used on automobiles. Since most automotive brakes in use today are hydraulically actuated, the chapter contains a review of hydraulic principles and explains their application to brakes. Also, since brakes operate by friction, some of the principles of friction are reviewed. Brakes have already been discussed briefly (in § 43).

§ 531. **Friction** As already noted (§ 78), friction is the resistance to motion between two objects in contact with each other. Three types of friction were discussed in § 78—dry, greasy, and viscous. Generally, we are concerned only with dry friction in brakes (but sometimes we have greasy friction if the brake linings are greasy or oil-soaked). Friction varies according to the pressure applied between the sliding surfaces, the roughness of the surfaces, and the material of which the surfaces are made. Suppose, for example, that a platform and its load weigh 100 pounds and it takes 50

pounds of pull to move it along the floor (Fig. 32–1). If you reduced the load so that the platform and load weighed only 10 pounds, you would find that it required only 5 pounds pull to move it along the floor. *Friction varies with the load.*

If you went over the floor and the sliding part of the platform with sandpaper and smoothed them off, you would find that it would require less pull to move the platform on the floor. *Friction varies with the roughness of the surfaces.*

Friction varies with the type of material, too. For example, if you dragged a 100-pound bale of rubber across a concrete floor, you might find that it required a pull of 70 pounds (Fig. 32–2). But to drag a 100-pound cake of ice across the same floor might require a pull of only 2 pounds.

§ 532. **Friction of rest and motion** It requires more force to start an object to moving than it does to keep it in motion (Fig. 32–3). In the example shown, it takes two men to get the object started, but once it is

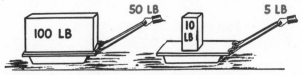

Fig. 32–1. Friction varies with the load applied between the sliding surfaces. (*Pontiac Motor Division of General Motors Corporation*)

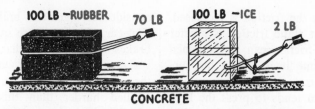

Fig. 32–2. Friction varies with the type of material. (*Pontiac Motor Division of General Motors Corporation*)

started, only one man can keep it moving. Thus, the friction of an object at rest is greater than the friction of an object in motion.

Engineers do not usually refer to these two kinds of friction as friction of rest and friction of motion. Instead, they call them *static friction* and *kinetic friction*. The word "static" means at rest. The word "kinetic" means in motion, or moving. Thus, static friction is friction of rest, and kinetic friction is friction of motion.

§ 533. Causes of friction One explanation of friction is that it is caused by surface irregularities. That is, it is caused by high spots on the two surfaces in contact that tend to catch on each other and hinder the motion between the two objects. When the surfaces are smoothed off, the high spots are cut down and there is less tendency for them to catch on each other; friction is reduced. On the other hand, if the force between the two surfaces is increased, then the high spots are pressed harder against each

Fig. 32–3. Friction of rest is greater than the friction of motion. In the example shown, it takes two men to overcome the friction of rest, but only one to overcome the friction of motion (after object starts moving). (*Pontiac Motor Division of General Motors Corporation*)

other so that the friction is increased. The fact that static friction is greater than kinetic friction can be explained along the same lines. When the surfaces are at rest, the force, or weight, between them tends to press the high spots of one surface into the other surface. Then, it takes more pull to move all the high spots of one surface up and out of the low spots of the other surface. But, once moving, the high spots do not have a chance to "settle" into the opposing surface; less force is required to keep the surfaces moving. That is, kinetic friction is less than static friction.

§ 534. Friction in the car brakes We have mentioned that friction is used in the car braking system. The friction between the brake drum and brake shoes slows or stops the car. This friction slows the rotation of the wheels, and then friction between the tires and road slows the motion of the car. Note that it is the friction between the tires and road that results in the stopping of the car. That being the case, would the car stop more quickly if the wheels were locked (so that the tires skidded on the road)? The answer is that the car would not. If the brakes are applied so hard that the wheels lock, then the friction between the tires and road is kinetic friction (friction of motion as the tires skid on the road). When the brakes are applied a little less hard, so that the wheels are permitted to continue rotating, then it is static friction that works between the tires and road. The tire surface is not skidding on the road but is rolling on it. Since this produces static friction between the road and tires, there is

considerably greater braking effect. The car will stop more quickly if the brakes are applied just hard enough to get maximum static friction between the tires and road. If the brakes are applied harder than this, then the wheels will lock, the tires will slide, and the lower kinetic friction will result.

§ 535. Hydraulic principles Since most brakes are hydraulically operated, we might review briefly the hydraulic principles that cause them to operate. Article 442 describes the manner in which motion and pressure can be transmitted by liquid. Since liquid is not compressible, pressure on a liquid will force it through a tube and into chambers or cylinders where it can force pistons to move. This is shown graphically in Fig. 24–6, where a piston in a cylinder applies a pressure of 100 psi (pounds per square inch). In the figure, liquid is shown being forced through lines or tubes to three other cylinders. The force the liquid applies to the pistons in the three cylinders is proportional to the size of the pistons. When the piston has an area of 1 square inch, then there will be a force of 100 pounds on it (100 psi, in other words). If the piston has an area of 0.5 square inch, then the force on it will be 50 lb (100 psi $\times$ 0.5 square inch). If the piston has an area of 2 square inches, the force on it would be 200 lb (100 psi $\times$ 2 square inches). You might wish to review Article 442 if these fundamentals are not clear in your mind.

§ 536. Brake action Now that we have reviewed friction and hydraulic

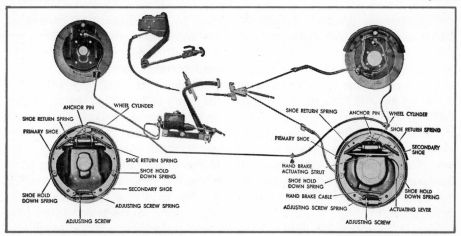

ANCHOR PIN   WHEEL CYLINDER
SHOE RETURN SPRING
PRIMARY SHOE
SHOE RETURN SPRING
SHOE HOLD DOWN SPRING
SECONDARY SHOE
SHOE HOLD DOWN SPRING
ADJUSTING SCREW SPRING
ADJUSTING SCREW

SHOE RETURN SPRING   ANCHOR PIN   WHEEL CYLINDER
SHOE RETURN SPRING
PRIMARY SHOE
SECONDARY SHOE
HAND BRAKE ACTUATING STRUT
SHOE HOLD DOWN SPRING
HAND BRAKE CABLE
ADJUSTING SCREW SPRING
SHOE HOLD DOWN SPRING
ACTUATING LEVER
ADJUSTING SCREW

Fig. 32–4. Schematic layout of a hydraulic-brake system. (*Pontiac Motor Division of General Motors Corporation*)

principles, let us see how these principles are applied in the braking system. Figure 32–4 shows, schematically, a typical hydraulic braking system. The system includes two essentials, the master cylinder with brake pedal, and the wheel brake mechanism, together with the connecting tubing, or brake lines, as well as the supporting arrangements.

In operation, movement of the brake pedal forces a piston to move in the master cylinder. This applies pressure to liquid ahead of the piston, forcing

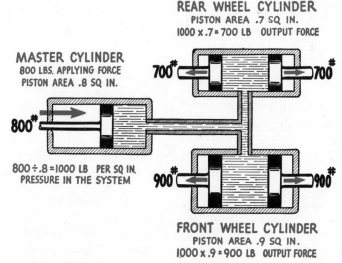

REAR WHEEL CYLINDER
PISTON AREA .7 SQ IN.
1000 x .7 = 700 LB   OUTPUT FORCE

MASTER CYLINDER
800 LBS. APPLYING FORCE
PISTON AREA .8 SQ IN.

700#   700#

800#

800 ÷ .8 = 1000 LB PER SQ IN.
PRESSURE IN THE SYSTEM

900#   900#

FRONT WHEEL CYLINDER
PISTON AREA .9 SQ IN.
1000 x .9 = 900 LB   OUTPUT FORCE

Fig. 32–5. As the brake pedal is moved, the piston in the master cylinder applies pressure to the liquid, forcing it, under pressure, into the wheel cylinders. (*Pontiac Motor Division of General Motors Corporation*)

671

the liquid, under pressure, through the brake lines to the wheel cylinders (Fig. 32–5). Each wheel cylinder has two pistons, as shown. Each piston is linked to one of the brake shoes by an actuating pin (or the end of the shoe rests on the piston). Thus, when the liquid is forced into the wheel cylinders, the two wheel-cylinder pistons are pushed outward. This outward movement forces the brake shoes outward and into contact with the rotating brake drum.

The brake shoes are lined with a tough asbestos material that can withstand the heat and dragging effect imposed when they are forced against the drum. During hard braking, the shoe may be pressed against the drum with a pressure as great as 1,000 pounds. Since friction increases as the load (pressure) increases, this produces a strong frictional drag on the brake drum and a strong braking effect on the wheel.

A great deal of heat is produced, also, by the frictional effect between the brake shoes and drum. When you rub your hands together vigorously, they become warm. In like manner, when the drum rubs against the shoe, the drum and shoe get warm. In fact, under extreme braking conditions, temperatures may reach 500°F. Some of this heat goes through the brake linings to the shoes and backing plate, where it is radiated to the surrounding air. But most of it is absorbed by the brake drum. Some brake drums have cooling fins to provide additional radiating surface for getting rid of the heat more quickly. Excessive temperatures are not good for brakes since they may char the brake linings. Also, with the linings and drums hot, less effective braking action results. This is the reason that brakes "fade" when they are used continuously for relatively long periods, as, for instance, in coming down a mountain or a long hill.

Note that, in Fig. 32–5, piston sizes

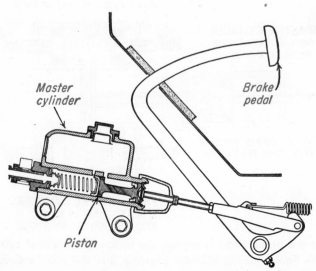

Fig. 32–6. Relationship between brake pedal and master cylinder. (*Pontiac Motor Division of General Motors Corporation*)

and hydraulic pressures are given as examples of the pressures involved. The piston in the master cylinder has an area of 0.8 square inch. A push of 800 pounds is being applied to the piston. This gives a pressure of 1,000 psi in the system. This pressure at the rear wheels gives an outward force of 700 pounds on each piston. The pistons are 0.7 square inch in area. At the front wheels, the piston area is shown as 0.9 square inch; so a pressure of 900 pounds is applied by the pistons to the front brake shoes.

The pistons are usually larger at the front wheels because, when the brakes are applied, the forward momentum of the car throws more of the weight on the front wheels. A stronger braking effort at the front wheels is therefore necessary to achieve balanced braking effort.

§ 537. Master cylinder Figures 32–6 and 32–7 show sectional and disassembled views of the master cylinder. The piston in the master cylinder is linked to the brake pedal through a lever arrangement which provides a considerable mechanical advantage. That is, the push on the brake pedal is multiplied several times by the lever

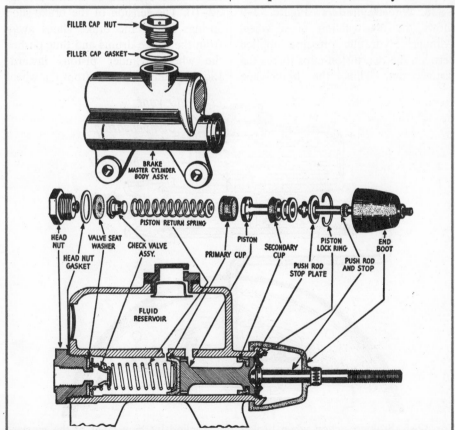

Fig. 32–7. External, disassembled, and sectional views of master cylinder. (Pontiac Motor Division of General Motors Corporation)

673

arrangement. For example, in the arrangement shown in Fig. 32–6, a push of 100 pounds on the brake pedal will produce a push of 750 pounds at the piston (as brakes are first applied).

As the piston in the master cylinder moves in (from the position shown in Fig. 32–6 to the position shown in Fig. 32–8), it moves past the compensating port. This traps the liquid in the cylinder that is ahead of the piston. Pressure rises rapidly, and liquid is forced through the brake lines to the wheel cylinders. This action is shown in Fig. 32–8.

§ 538. Wheel cylinders Figure 32–9 shows the construction of a wheel cylinder. Hydraulic pressure applied between the two piston cups forces the pistons out. Thus, the brake-shoe

actuating pins force the brake shoes into contact with the brake drums. The piston cups are so formed that the hydraulic pressure forces them tightly against the cylinder wall of the wheel cylinder. This produces a good sealing action that holds the liquid in the cylinder.

§ 539. Return stroke On the return stroke, spring tension on the brake linkage and spring pressure against the master-cylinder piston force the piston to move back in its cylinder. Liquid now flows from the wheel cylinders to the master cylinder as shown in Fig. 32–10. The tension of the brake-shoe springs forces the brake shoes away from the brake drums and thus pushes the wheel cylinder pistons inward. Liquid is thus returned from the wheel

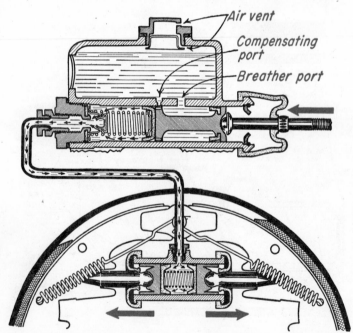

Fig. 32–8. Braking action when brakes are applied by movement of the master-cylinder piston. (*Pontiac Motor Division of General Motors Corporation*)

674

cylinders to the master cylinder as shown by the arrows. However, in the system shown, some pressure is trapped in the lines by the check valve at the end of the master cylinder (see Fig. 32–7). As the pressure drops, the check valve closes, trapping a few pounds of pressure in the lines and wheel cylinders. This pressure has the purpose of keeping the wheel cylinders from leaking and also of reducing the chances of air leaking into the system.

§ 540. Two-wheel-cylinder arrangement Figure 32–11 shows an arrangement which makes use of two wheel cylinders at the wheel. Each cylinder has a single piston, operating only one of the brake shoes.

§ 541. Disk brakes Disk brakes have a different construction and operate in a somewhat different manner from the shoe-type brake described above. The principle of the disk brake can be illustrated by two disks mounted on a shaft (Fig. 32–12). One of the disks is held stationary so that it cannot rotate. The other disk can rotate freely. However, if the two disks are brought together, the friction between them will bring the rotating disk to a stop.

The disk brake contains two pressure plates on which lining segments

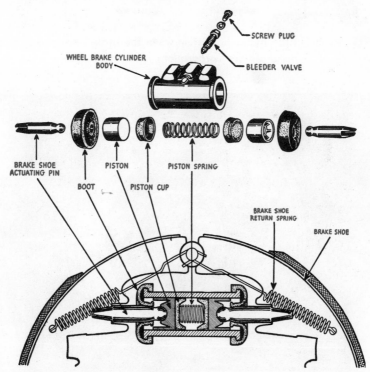

Fig. 32–9. Disassembled and sectional views of wheel cylinder. (*Pontiac Motor Division of General Motors Corporation*)

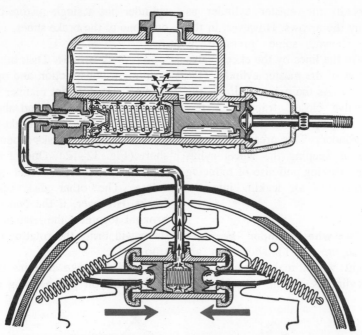

Fig. 32–10. Action in the hydraulic system when the brakes are released. (*Pontiac Motor Division of General Motors Corporation*)

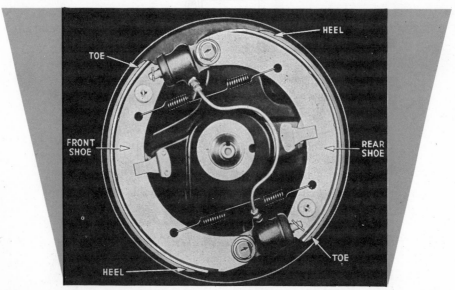

Fig. 32–11. Hydraulic brake using two wheel cylinders, one for each brake shoe. (*Chrysler Sales Division of Chrysler Corporation*)

676

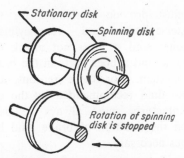

Fig. 32–12. The principle of the disk brake is that, if a spinning disk is brought into frictional contact with a stationary disk, the spinning disk will be brought to a stop. (*Chrysler Sales Division of Chrysler Corporation*)

are bonded (Fig. 32–13). These pressure plates are semistationary and are positioned between an inner and an outer housing. Figure 32–14 is a sectional view of the assembly. The pressure plates are held in position by a spider which is rigidly attached to the steering knuckle (at front wheels) or to the axle housing (at rear wheels).

Notches in the pressure plates index with anchors on the spider to prevent rotation of the pressure plates.

Braking occurs when the two pressure plates are pushed away from each other so that they are forced into contact with the inside faces of the rotating inner and outer brake housings. A series of steel balls located between the two pressure plates causes the plates to push away from each other when the brakes are applied. This action is shown in Fig. 32–15, which illustrates one of the steel balls in position. When the brakes are released, the steel ball is in the bottom of the ramps in the two pressure plates. The pressure plates are held in the "released" position by a series of short coil springs that tend to pull the plates toward each other.

When the brakes are applied, the wheel cylinders (there are two at each wheel) force the two pressure plates to rotate a few degrees in opposing direc-

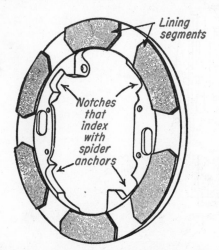

OUTER PRESSURE PLATE

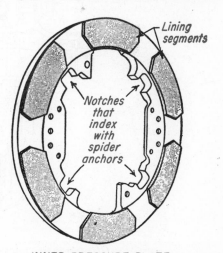

INNER PRESSURE PLATE

Fig. 32–13. The two pressure plates used in the disk brake. (*Chrysler Sales Division of Chrysler Corporation*)

677

tions as shown in the lower illustration in Fig. 32–15. As this happens, the steel ball rides up both ramps and forces the two pressure plates away from each other. They move out and into contact with the inner faces of the brake housing, thus producing the braking action.

§ 542. **Brake fluid** The liquid used in the hydraulic breaking system is called brake fluid. Brake fluid must have very definite characteristics. It must be chemically inert. It must be little affected by high or low temperatures.

It must provide lubrication for the master-cylinder and wheel-cylinder pistons. And it must not attack the metallic and rubber parts in the braking system. For these reasons, the brake fluid recommended by the car manufacturer must always be used when the addition of brake fluid becomes necessary.

▶ *CAUTION:* Mineral oil must never be put into the brake system. Mineral oil will cause the rubber parts in the system, including the piston cups, to swell and disintegrate. This would, of

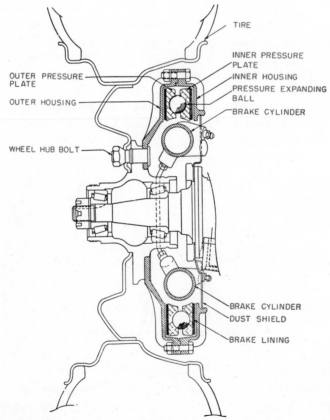

TIRE

INNER PRESSURE PLATE
INNER HOUSING
PRESSURE EXPANDING BALL
BRAKE CYLINDER

OUTER PRESSURE PLATE
OUTER HOUSING

WHEEL HUB BOLT

BRAKE CYLINDER
DUST SHIELD
BRAKE LINING

Fig. 32–14. Sectional view of disk-brake assembly. (*Chrysler Sales Division of Chrysler Corporation*)

course, cause faulty braking action and possibly complete brake failure. Nothing except the fluid recommended by the manufacturer must be put into the hydraulic brake system.

§ **543. Brake lines** Steel pipe is used between the master cylinder and the frame connections and between the rear-axle T fitting and the rear-wheel cylinders. Flexible hose connects the brake pipe to the front-wheel cylinders and to the rear-axle fitting. These various hoses and pipes can be seen in Fig. 32–4. If a section of pipe or a hose becomes damaged, be sure to replace

it with the proper pipe or hose as specified by the manufacturer. Since these lines are required to withstand considerable pressure, they are special. Ordinary copper tubing, for example, would not be satisfactory. The steel pipe, or tubing, must be double-flared, as explained in the following chapter, when it is installed.

§ **544. Hand brakes** Hand, or parking, brakes are operated by a lever, or pull, in the driving compartment. The lever, or pull, is connected by linkage and cables to the rear-wheel brake shoes or to a separate brake on

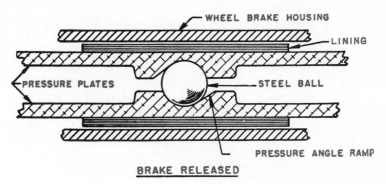

BRAKE RELEASED

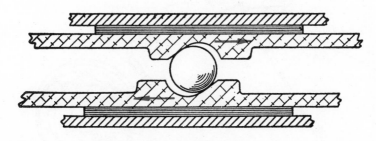

BRAKE ENERGIZED

Fig. 32–15. Action of steel ball as brakes are applied. Relative rotation of pressure plates as shown by arrows in lower illustration causes ball to roll up ramps, forcing the pressure plates apart and into contact with the brake housing. (Chrysler Sales Division of Chrysler Corporation)

679

the transmission shaft. Figure 32–16 illustrates a parking brake using the rear-wheel brake shoes. As the hand lever is pulled, the brake shoes are forced into contact with the brake drum. Figure 32–17 illustrates a transmission-shaft parking brake.

§ 545. **Power brakes** For hard-braking and fast stops, considerable pressure must be exerted on the brake pedal with the braking system described above. Also, the heavier the vehicle, the greater the braking effort required. For many years, buses and trucks have used special equipment that assists the driver to brake the vehicle. This equipment may use either compressed air or vacuum. When the driver applies the brake, the compressed air or vacuum then supplies most of the effort required for braking. There is another system that uses an electrical means of braking.

In recent years, passenger cars have been supplied with vacuum-assisted braking systems, called *power brakes*. Essentially, they all operate in a similar manner. When the brake pedal is moved to apply the brakes, a valving

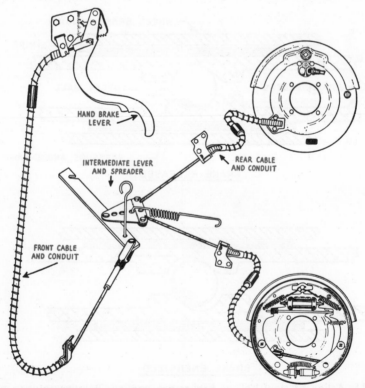

Fig. 32–16. Schematic layout of a parking-brake system. Operation of the hand-brake lever causes the intermediate lever to pivot forward. This pulls on the two rear cables so that the rear brakes are mechanically applied. (*Pontiac Motor Division of General Motors Corporation*)

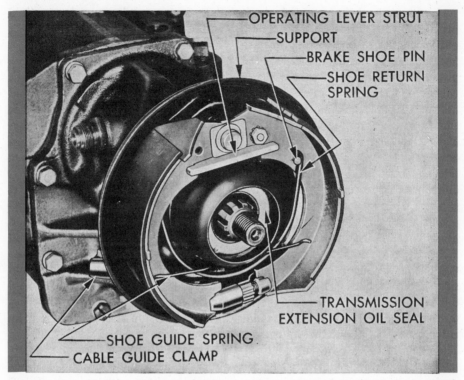

OPERATING LEVER STRUT
SUPPORT
BRAKE SHOE PIN
SHOE RETURN SPRING
TRANSMISSION EXTENSION OIL SEAL
SHOE GUIDE SPRING
CABLE GUIDE CLAMP

Fig. 32–17. Internal-expanding type of transmission-shaft hand brake assembled on transmission. Drum is not shown. (*Dodge Division of Chrysler Corporation*)

arrangement is actuated. The valves admit atmospheric pressure on one side of a piston or diaphragm and apply vacuum to the other side. The piston or diaphragm then moves toward the vacuum side; this movement supplies most of the hydraulic pressure, through the brake fluid, to the wheel cylinders.

§ 546. Atmospheric pressure and vacuum Atmospheric pressure is about 15 psi at sea level (§ 63). Vacuum is an absence of air. If we arranged a simple cylinder and piston as shown in Fig. 32–18 and then applied atmospheric pressure to one side and vacuum to the other, the

piston would move toward the vacuum side, as shown. If we held the piston stationary, we could figure the pres-

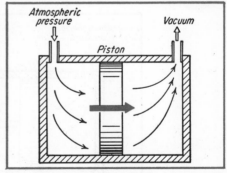

Atmospheric pressure   Vacuum
Piston

Fig. 32–18. If atmospheric pressure is applied on one side of a piston and vacuum on the other side, the piston will move toward the vacuum side, as shown.

681

sure, or push, being exerted on it provided we knew the area of the piston and the atmospheric pressure and amount of vacuum. Suppose the piston had an area of 50 square inches (about 8 inches in diameter). We'll assume also that the atmospheric pressure is 15 psi and the vacuum is great enough to have brought the pressure down to only 5 psi. With 15 psi on one side and only 5 psi on the other, the difference in pressure is 10 psi. That is, there is an effective pressure of 10 pounds on every square inch of the piston area. Since there is 50 square inches of piston area, then the push on the piston, urging it to the vacuum side, is 500 pounds (50 × 10). It is this effective pressure, or push, that is utilized in power brakes. The vacuum is supplied by the automobile engine. The engine is a vacuum pump in one sense of the word. With every intake stroke, the downward-moving piston produces a partial vacuum in the cylinder and thus in the intake manifold (see § 69). The vacuum side of the power-brake cylinder (Fig. 32–18) is connected to the intake manifold so that it can utilize intake-manifold vacuum.

§ 547. Putting the vacuum to work

If we add a hydraulic device to the cylinder and piston of Fig. 32–18 as shown in Fig. 32–19, we can utilize the push on the piston to produce hydraulic pressure. All the pressure on the piston is carried through the piston rod and into the hydraulic cylinder. Thus, in the example described above, the piston rod would push into the hydraulic cylinder with a 500-pound force. If the end of the piston rod had an area of 0.5 square inch, then the pressure in the hydraulic fluid would be 1,000 psi (or 500 pounds divided by the area, 0.5 square inch). The hydraulic pressure can be altered by changing the sizes of the piston and rod (with the same pressure differential acting on the piston). For instance, a piston with an area of 100 square inches and a rod of 0.2 square inch area, would result in a hydraulic pressure of 5,000 psi (or 1,000 pounds divided by 0.2 square inch).

If the hydraulic cylinder is con-

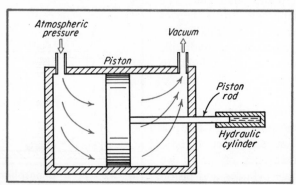

Fig. 32–19. If the piston rod is placed in a hydraulic cylinder, the pressure on the piston in the atmospheric-pressure chamber will be translated into hydraulic pressure.

nected to the wheel cylinders, as shown in Fig. 32–20, the hydraulic pressure produced will result in braking action. Note that the hydraulic cylinder has been increased in diameter (Fig. 32–20). However, the piston rod entering it still displaces liquid and produces the same pressure increase as though the cylinder were the same size as the rod (as shown in Fig. 32–19).

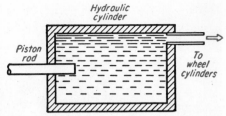

Fig. 32–20. If the hydraulic cylinder is connected by tubes to the wheel cylinders, movement of the piston rod into the cylinder will produce braking action.

§ 548. **Bendix power brakes** Let us discuss one type of power-braking system (the Bendix Treadle-Vac) in detail. This power-brake system is used on many cars made by General Motors and the Ford Motor Company. Figure 32–21 shows a schematic layout of this unit as installed on a car, while Figs. 32–22 and 32–23 are cutaway and sectional views of the unit. Vacuum is supplied by the engine intake manifold, and a special reservoir tank is used for vacuum reserve

in case brakes are applied with the engine off. The vacuum reserve is, however, limited. Vacuum assistance will not continue indefinitely if brakes are applied, released, and reapplied repeatedly with the engine off. However, braking can still be achieved although the brake-pedal pressure will have to be considerably increased (since no vacuum assistance will take place). In the following discussion, refer to Fig. 32–23 for the names of parts and to Figs. 32–24 to 32–26 for

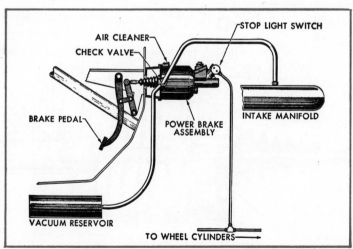

Fig. 32–21. Schematic layout of power-brake installation. Application of brake pedal causes power-brake unit to utilize engine vacuum to apply brakes. (*Lincoln-Mercury Division of Ford Motor Company*)

683

Fig. 32–22. Cutaway view of power-brake unit. (*Lincoln-Mercury Division of Ford Motor Company*)

illustrations of the actions taking place.

1. Operation — brakes off. Figure 32–24 is a sectional view of the power-brake assembly with the brakes released. In this position, the slide valve shuts off the vacuum port and opens

the atmospheric port. Atmospheric pressure is admitted through the atmospheric port and through the piston to the forward side of the vacuum piston. Atmospheric pressure is shown by the dark shading in the

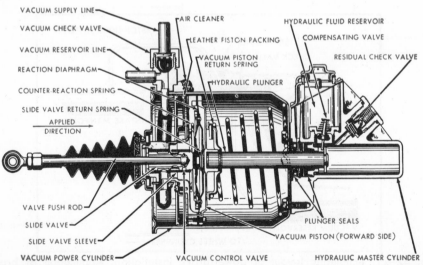

VACUUM SUPPLY LINE
VACUUM CHECK VALVE
VACUUM RESERVOIR LINE
REACTION DIAPHRAGM
COUNTER-REACTION SPRING
SLIDE VALVE RETURN SPRING
APPLIED DIRECTION

AIR CLEANER
LEATHER PISTON PACKING
VACUUM PISTON RETURN SPRING
HYDRAULIC PLUNGER

HYDRAULIC FLUID RESERVOIR
COMPENSATING VALVE
RESIDUAL CHECK VALVE

VALVE PUSH ROD
SLIDE VALVE
SLIDE VALVE SLEEVE
VACUUM POWER CYLINDER

VACUUM CONTROL VALVE

PLUNGER SEALS
VACUUM PISTON (FORWARD SIDE)
HYDRAULIC MASTER CYLINDER

Fig. 32–23. Sectional view of power-brake assembly. (*Lincoln-Mercury Division of Ford Motor Company*)

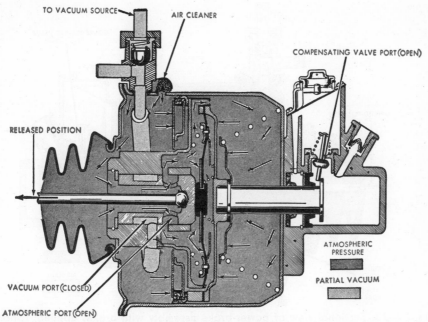

TO VACUUM SOURCE

AIR CLEANER

COMPENSATING VALVE PORT(OPEN)

RELEASED POSITION

ATMOSPHERIC PRESSURE

PARTIAL VACUUM

VACUUM PORT(CLOSED)

ATMOSPHERIC PORT(OPEN)

Fig. 32–24. Sectional view of power-brake assembly with brakes released. (*Lincoln-Mercury Division of Ford Motor Company*)

figure; the movement of the air is shown by the arrows. With atmospheric pressure acting on both sides of the piston, there is no tendency for the piston to move. A ring on the end of the hydraulic plunger is in contact with the stem of the compensating valve, holding this valve open. With the compensating-valve port open, hydraulic brake fluid can flow freely between the reservoir and the hydraulic master cylinder. No pressure develops in the brake system, and the brakes are not applied.

2. *Operation — brakes applied.* As the brake pedal is depressed to apply the brakes, the valve push rod moves inward, forcing the slide valve to move (Fig. 32–25). Movement of the slide valve closes off the atmospheric port and opens the vacuum port, as shown.

Now, vacuum is connected to the forward side of the vacuum piston (and also to the rear side of the reaction diaphragm). Atmospheric pressure is still being applied to the rear side of the vacuum piston. The difference in pressure on the two sides of the vacuum piston forces it to move forward as shown in Fig. 32–25. Atmospheric pressure is shown by the dark shading and vacuum by the light shading. As the vacuum piston is forced forward, the hydraulic plunger is forced into the master cylinder. The compensating valve therefore closes, and a high hydraulic pressure develops in the master cylinder. This forces brake fluid through the brake lines to the wheel cylinders; the brakes are therefore applied.

3. *Brake feel.* The driver should be

685

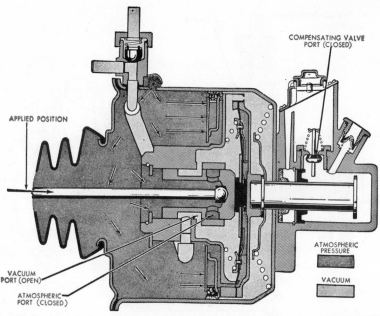

Fig. 32–25. Sectional view of power-brake assembly with brakes applied. (*Lincoln-Mercury Division of Ford Motor Company*)

able to apply the brakes by pedal-resistance feel. That is, he should be able to relate the amount of braking with the amount of pedal pressure he applies. The driver wants light braking when he applies the brake pedal lightly, and he wants heavy braking when he applies the brake pedal hard. To give this brake feel, there is a reaction diaphragm in the vacuum piston. There is atmospheric pressure between the forward part of the reaction diaphragm and the front plate of the vacuum piston (see dark shading in Figs. 32–24 and 32–25). This gives a reaction through the valve push rod to the brake pedal. When the driver brakes lightly, the push rod does not move the slide valve very far. Thus, only a small amount of vacuum is produced at the forward end of the

vacuum piston (because the vacuum valve is opened only slightly). This means that the vacuum piston is not pushed forward very hard; the pressure differential between the two sides of the piston is not very large. Only light breaking will result. Since there is not much vacuum produced, the vacuum back of the reaction diaphragm will be small. Thus, the backward push of the reaction diaphragm will be small. On the other hand, if the vacuum is high, owing to strong braking, then the backward push of the reaction diaphragm will be high. This is because there is a large pressure differential on the two sides of the reaction diaphragm.

4. Operation — brakes holding, or poised. As the brakes are applied, the forward motion of the brake pedal

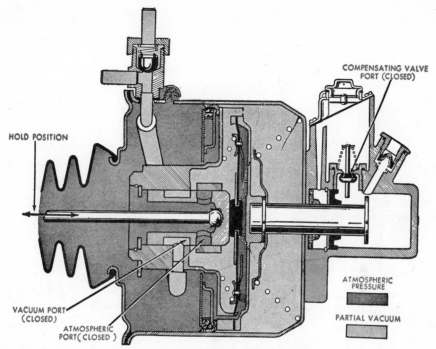

Fig. 32–26. Sectional view of power-brake assembly with slide valve in hold (poised) position. (*Lincoln-Mercury Division of Ford Motor Company*)

causes a forward motion of the slide valve. The amount that the slide valve advances is determined by the brake-pedal pressure. As the brake-pedal pressure is increased, the slide valve moves farther, the vacuum piston moves farther, and the hydraulic plunger therefore moves farther into the hydraulic master cylinder to produce a further increase of braking effort. There comes a time, however, in the braking cycle when the driver may stop increasing the pressure and, instead, simply holds the brake pedal in a poised position (not increasing or decreasing the pressure). At this point, the vacuum piston and slide-valve sleeve (which is attached to the piston) assume the position shown in

Fig. 32–26 with relation to the slide valve. Note that both the vacuum port and the atmospheric port are closed. The brakes are therefore held in the position shown (the amount of braking effort selected by the driver being maintained). This holding action continues until the brake-pedal pressure is increased or decreased.

5. Operation—brakes released. When the brakes are released, the slide valve is returned to its "released" position as shown in Fig. 32–24. This closes the vacuum port and opens the atmospheric port. Now, with atmospheric pressure on both sides of the vacuum piston, there is no pressure differential. The vacuum-piston return spring moves the vacuum piston into

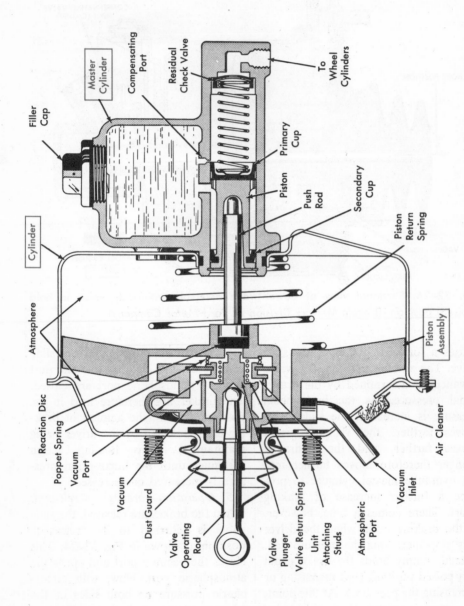

AUTOMOTIVE REPAIR

Fig. 32–27. Bendix Master-Vac power brake. (Cadillac Motor Car Division of General Motors Corporation)

the "released" position (Fig. 32–24). As the hydraulic plunger follows this movement, the hydraulic pressure in the brake lines and wheel cylinders is relieved so that the brakes are released. Then, when the hydraulic plunger nears the end of its return travel, it opens the compensating valve so that any remaining pressure is released and brake fluid can flow between the reservoir and hydraulic cylinder, as required.

6. *Bendix Master-Vac.* This model (Fig. 32–27), used on many late-model cars, is very similar in construction and operation to the model discussed above. Compare Fig. 32–27

with Fig. 32–23 to note points of similarity and difference between the two models.

§ 549. Other power brakes Two other widely used power brakes are Kelsey-Hayes and Moraine.

1. *Kelsey-Hayes.* This power-brake system is used on Buick and other cars. It is similar, in many ways, to the unit described in the preceding article. This unit, however, is the "vacuum-suspended" type. That is, when the brakes are not applied, then vacuum is being applied to both sides of the power piston. In other words, the piston is suspended in vacuum (vacuum

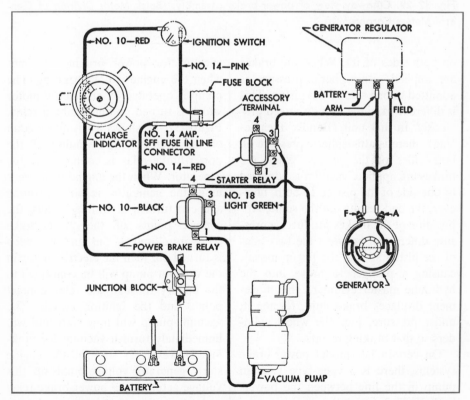

Fig. 32–28. Wiring circuit of power-brake vacuum pump and relay. (*Buick Motor Division of General Motors Corporation*)

689

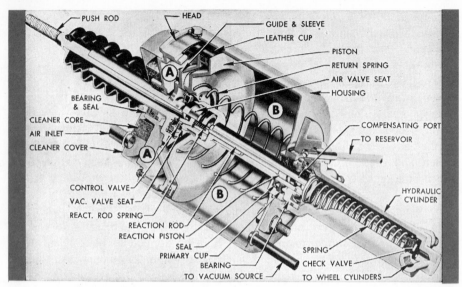

Fig. 32–29. Cutaway view of power-brake assembly. (*Buick Motor Division of General Motors Corporation*)

on both sides of it). When the brakes are applied, atmospheric pressure is admitted to one side of the piston. This is different from the unit discussed previously. In that unit (Bendix Treadle-Vac), there is atmospheric pressure on both sides of the piston. When the brakes are applied, vacuum is admitted to one side of the piston. In both, however, the end results are the same. Application of the brakes produces a pressure differential between the two sides of the piston so that the piston moves, causing a plunger to move into the hydraulic master cylinder. This movement displaces brake fluid, forcing it, under pressure, into the wheel cylinders so that braking results.

On certain late-model power-brake systems, there is a vane-type vacuum pump in the line between the power-brake cylinder and the engine intake manifold. This vacuum pump furnishes

vacuum for power braking at times when the engine is not operating. The pump is operated by an electric motor which is turned on and off by a relay. Figure 32–28 shows a wiring diagram of the system. The winding of the power-brake relay is connected to the generator. When the engine is not running, the generator is not operating and can furnish no voltage. Thus, the contact points of the power-brake relay are closed. If the ignition switch is turned on, then the electric motor in the vacuum pump will be connected to the battery through the relay contact points and the ignition switch. The vacuum pump will now start and will immediately furnish vacuum for braking. However, as soon as the engine starts, generator voltage builds up; this voltage actuates the power-brake relay and causes the relay contact points to separate. Now, the circuit between the

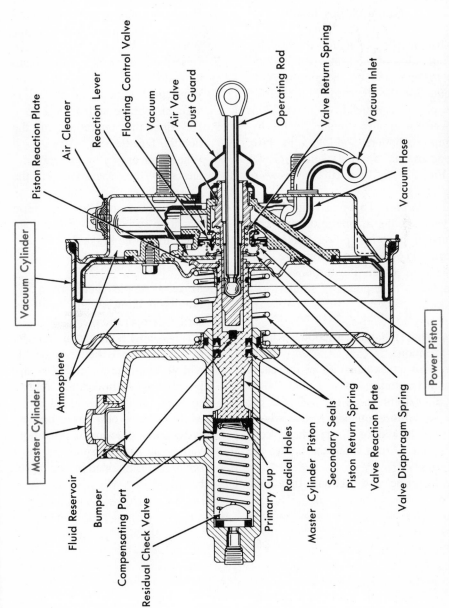

Vacuum Cylinder

Master Cylinder -

Atmosphere

Piston Reaction Plate
Air Cleaner
Reaction Lever
Floating Control Valve
Vacuum
Air Valve
Dust Guard
Operating Rod
Valve Return Spring
Vacuum Inlet
Vacuum Hose

Power Piston

Fluid Reservoir
Bumper
Compensating Port
Residual Check Valve
Primary Cup
Radial Holes
Master Cylinder Piston
Secondary Seals
Piston Return Spring
Valve Reaction Plate
Valve Diaphragm Spring

Fig. 32–30. Moraine power brake. (Cadillac Motor Car Division of General Motors Corporation)

691

vacuum-pump motor and the battery is broken, and the vacuum pump stops operating.

The operation of this power brake is very similar to the Bendix unit described in the preceding article. That is, operation of the brake pedal admits air to one side of the piston. With vacuum on the other side of the piston, the piston is forced to move. This movement applies pressure to the hydraulic cylinder, and this, in turn, produces the braking action. (Refer to Fig. 32–29 for a cutaway view of the unit.)

2. Moraine. This unit (Fig. 32–30) is very similar in operation and construction to other power-brake units previously discussed. Compare Fig. 32–30 to other illustrations in the chapter to note points of similarity.

Review Questions

1. What is static friction? Kinetic friction?
2. Give an explanation of the cause of friction.
3. Generally speaking, will the car stop more quickly if the wheels are locked or if the wheels continue to turn when the brakes are applied?
4. Describe the actions that take place in the master cylinder when the brakes are applied. In the wheel cylinders.
5. How hot may brake shoes and drum get during extreme braking?
6. What is brake fade?
7. Describe a disk brake, and explain its action.
8. Why must mineral oil never be used in a brake system?
9. Describe the operation of the Bendix Treadle-Vac.
10. What is meant by brake feel?
11. Describe the operation of the Kelsey-Hayes power brake.
12. What is meant by the term "vacuum-suspended" when applied to power brakes?

Study Questions

1. Make a simple sketch of a hydraulic braking system, and describe its operation.
2. Write a short essay explaining why braking action is better when the wheels continue to roll (as opposed to when brakes are applied so hard that the wheels skid).
3. Make a sketch of a power braking system, and describe its operation.
4. Write an essay explaining how brake feel is attained in one power brake.

THIS CHAPTER DISCUSSES THE trouble-shooting, adjusting, removal, repair, and reinstallation of the various hydraulic-brake-system components.

§ 550. Trouble-shooting brakes The section that follows relates various braking troubles with their possible causes and corrections. This information gives you a means of logically tracing down troubles to their actual causes. This permits quick location of causes and quick correction. If the cause is known, the trouble is usually relatively easy to correct. Following the trouble-shooting section are several sections that discuss the adjusting and repair procedures on different types of hydraulic brakes.

§ 551. Trouble diagnosis This section gives you a good idea of the types of trouble that might be found in hydraulic braking systems, their causes, and corrections. Let us discuss these troubles in more detail. Following sections will explain how to make corrections.

1. Brake pedal goes to floor board. When this happens, it means that there is no pedal reserve since full pedal movement does not provide adequate braking. This may be due to the pedal or linkage being out of adjustment, to brake shoes being out of adjustment, or to linings being worn. It could also be due to lack of brake fluid or to air in the system. Air prevents normal braking since it will compress when hydraulic pressure is applied and thus hydraulic pressure will not be carried to the wheel cylinders. Another condition that would allow the brake pedal to go to the floor board without normal brake application is a defective master cylinder. For example, the piston cup may be cracked so that it allows the brake fluid to bypass instead of building up hydraulic pressure.

2. One brake drags. This means that the brake shoes are not moving away from the brake drum when the brakes are released. This could be due to incorrect shoe adjustment, to a clogged brake line which does not release pressure from the wheel cylinder, to sticking pistons in the wheel cylinder, to weak or broken brake-shoe return springs, or to a loose wheel bearing which permits the wheel to wobble so that the brake drum comes in contact with the brake shoes even though they are retracted.

3. All brakes drag. When all brakes drag, it may be that the brake pedal does not have sufficient play so that the piston in the master cylinder does not fully retract. This would prevent the lip of the piston cup from clearing the compensating port so that hydraulic pressure would not be relieved as it should be (see Figs. 32–8 and

693

32–10). As a result, the wheel cylinders would not release the brake shoes. A similar condition could result if mineral oil had been added to the system since this would be likely to cause the piston cup to swell. If it swelled enough, it would not clear the compensating port even with the piston in the "fully retracted" position (Fig. 33–1). A clogged compensating port would have the same result. Do not use a wire or drill to clear the port; this might produce a burr that would cut the piston cup. Instead, clear it with alcohol and compressed air. Clogging of the reservoir vent might cause dragging brakes since this could

trap pressure in the reservoir which would prevent release of pressure. But this would be just as likely to cause leakage of air into the system (see item 9 below).

4. Car pulls to one side. If the car pulls to one side when the brakes are applied, this means that more braking pressure is being applied to one side than to the other. This happens if some of the brake linings have become soaked in oil or brake fluid (so that they lose braking effectiveness), if brake shoes are unevenly or improperly adjusted, if tires are not evenly inflated, or if defective wheel cylinders or clogged brake lines are preventing

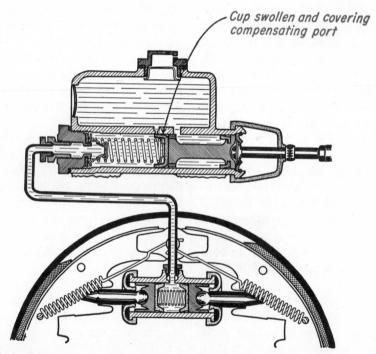

Cup swollen and covering compensating port

Fig. 33–1. If the primary piston cup swells badly, it can close off the compensating port to the reservoir with the piston fully retracted, as shown. This causes dragging or locked brakes since hydraulic pressure will not release. (*Pontiac Motor Division of General Motors Corporation*)

uniform braking action at all wheels. In addition, a loose brake backing plate or the use of two different types of brake lining will cause the car to pull to one side when the brakes are applied.

Linings will become soaked with oil if the lubricant level in the differential and rear axle is too high since this usually causes leakage past the oil seal (Fig. 33–2). The oil leaks onto the brake linings and soaks them. At the front wheel, brake linings may become oil-soaked if the front-wheel bearings are improperly lubricated or if the oil seal is defective or not properly installed. Wheel cylinders will leak brake fluid onto the brake linings if they are defective or if an actuating pin has been improperly installed (see item 10 below). If the linings at a left wheel become soaked with brake fluid or oil, for example, the car will tend to pull to the right. This is because the brakes would be more effective on the right side.

5. Soft, or spongy, pedal. If the pedal action is soft, or spongy, the chances are there is air in the system although out-of-adjustment brake shoes could cause this. Refer to item 9 below for conditions that could allow air to get into the system.

6. Poor braking action requiring excessive pedal pressure. If the brake linings are soaked with oil or brake fluid, they will not hold well and excessive pedal pressure is required for braking action. Improper brake-shoe adjustment or the use of the wrong brake lining could cause the same trouble. Sometimes, when brake linings have become wet after a hard rain or after driving through deep water puddles, they will not hold very well. In this case, normal braking action will be restored after the brake linings have dried out. But if the linings are soaked with oil or brake fluid, they must be replaced since it is not feasible to cleanse the linings of these contaminants. Another possible cause of poor braking action is excessive temperature. After the brakes have been applied for long periods, as in coming down a long hill, they begin to overheat. This overheating reduces braking effectiveness so that the brakes "fade." Often, if brakes are allowed to cool, braking efficiency will be

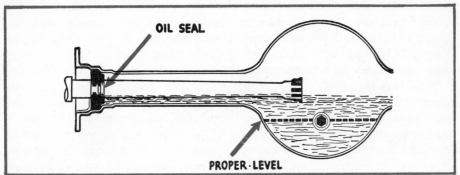

Fig. 33–2. A high lubricant level in the differential and rear-axle housing may cause leakage past the oil seal. This would result in soaked brake linings. (*Pontiac Motor Division* of General Motors Corporation)

695

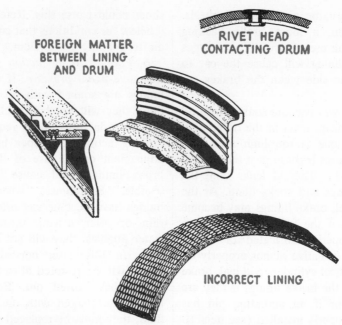

FOREIGN MATTER
BETWEEN LINING
AND DRUM

RIVET HEAD
CONTACTING DRUM

INCORRECT LINING

Fig. 33–3. Brake drums can be scored by foreign matter, such as dirt particles between the lining and drum, by worn linings that permit the rivet head to contact the drum, or by use of very harsh linings (especially on steel drums). (*Pontiac Motor Division of General Motors Corporation*)

restored. However, excessively long periods of braking at high temperature may char the brake linings so that they must be replaced. Further, this may glaze the brake drum so that it becomes too smooth for effective braking action. In this case, the drum must be ground or turned to remove the glaze. Glazing may also take place even though the brakes are not overheated.

7. *Brakes too sensitive or grab.* When the brakes are too sensitive and brake hard or grab with slight brake-pedal pressure, it may be that the linings have become greasy (if linings are greasy, the brakes are apt to grab, but if they are soaked with oil, they will not produce much braking effect at all). If the brake shoes are out of

adjustment, if the wrong lining is being used, or if drums are scored or rough (Fig. 33–3), grabbing may result as the linings come into contact with the drum. A loose backing plate may cause the same condition; as the linings come into contact with the drum, the backing plate shifts to give hard braking.

8. *Noisy brakes.* Brakes will become noisy if the brake linings wear so much that the rivets come into contact with the brake drum (see Fig. 33–3), if the shoes become warped so that pressure on the drum is not uniform, if shoe rivets become loose so that they contact the drum, or if the drum becomes rough or worn. Any of these conditions is likely to cause a squeak

or squeal when the brakes are applied. Also, loose parts, such as the brake backing plate, may rattle.

9. *Air in system.* If air gets into the hydraulic system, poor braking and a spongy pedal will result. Air can get into the system if the filler vent becomes plugged (Fig. 33–4) since this might tend to create a partial vacuum in the system on the return stroke of the piston. Air could then bypass the rear piston cup as shown by the arrows and enter the system. It is possible accidentally to plug the vent (by wrench action) when the filler plug is removed. Always check the vent and clean it when the plug is removed and replaced. Air can also get into the system if the master-cylinder valve is leaky and does not hold pressure in the system. This could allow air to seep in around the wheel-cylinder piston cups since there would be no pressure holding the cups tight against the cylinder walls. Probably the most common cause of air in the braking system is low brake fluid in the master cylinder. If the brake fluid drops below the compensating port, then the hydraulic system will draw air in as the piston moves forward on the braking stroke.

Air in the system must be removed by adding brake fluid and bleeding the system as described in a following article.

10. *Loss of brake fluid.* Brake fluid can be lost if the master cylinder leaks, if the wheel cylinder leaks, if the line connections are loose, or if the line is damaged. One possible cause of wheel-cylinder leakage is incorrect installation of the actuating pin (Fig. 33–5). If the pin is cocked, as shown, then the side thrust on the piston may permit leakage past the piston. Leakage from other causes at the master cylinder or wheel cylinder requires removal and repair, or replacement, of the defective parts.

§ 552. **Brake service** Whenever you encounter a complaint of faulty braking action, always try to analyze it and determine its cause, as noted in the previous article. In many cases, a minor adjustment of the brakes is all that will be required. However, at times, the brakes must have a major adjustment, addition of brake fluid, bleeding of the system, possibly repair or replacement of the master or wheel cylinders, and replacement of the

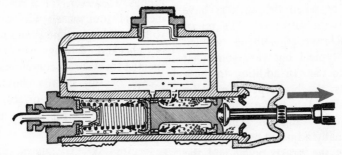

Fig. 33–4. If the filler vent becomes plugged, air may be drawn into the system on the return stroke of the piston, past the rear piston cup, as shown by the small arrows and bubbles. (*Pontiac Motor Division of General Motors Corporation*)

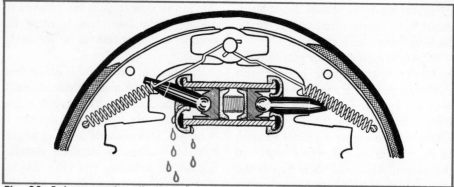

Fig. 33–5. Incorrect installation of the actuating pin will cause a side thrust on the piston which will permit leakage of brake fluid from the wheel cylinder. Pin must always align in the notch in the brake shoe. (*Pontiac Motor Division of General Motors Corporation*)

brake linings. Also, brake drums may require grinding or turning. Following articles describe these various services.

§ 553. Adjustment of brakes

Brake adjustments are divided into two classifications, minor adjustments and major adjustments. Minor adjustments compensate for brake-lining wear and are made without removing the car wheels. Major adjustments require aligning of the brake shoes by moving both toe and heel ends of the shoes. This latter adjustment is required after removal and installation of brake shoes or drums or when the anchors have been otherwise disturbed. The minor and major brake adjustments detailed below are typical but vary somewhat from car to car. In addition to these adjustments, the brake pedal must be adjusted after the brake shoes have been correctly aligned. The brake pedal is usually adjusted by turning the rod linking the brake pedal and the piston in the master cylinder. Before brake adjustment is attempted on any particular car, the car manufacturer's shop manual should be consulted.

Before any adjustment is attempted, the fluid in the master cylinder, the brake-pedal toeboard clearance, and brake-lining and brake-drum condition should be checked. Fluid should be added (§ 559) and the brake-pedal linkage adjusted, as necessary. For minor brake adjustments, it is not necessary to remove all four wheels to check the brake-lining condition, since similar conditions should be found at each wheel. Thus, as a rule, only one drum and wheel need be removed. Remove a front wheel since front-wheel linings wear faster than rear-wheel linings. However, for a major adjustment, all four wheels will be removed, so that all brake linings and drums can be checked. Linings should be inspected for wear or contamination with grease or oil. Drums should be inspected for roughness or scoring. (See §§ 554 and 555 for lining and drum service.)

▶ *CAUTION:* Handle brake linings with care to avoid getting grease on them. Even slight amounts of grease, as from greasy fingers, may cause uneven brake action.

698

Before the major brake adjustment is made, wheel-cylinder clamps should be installed, if specified, and the shoe return springs and shoes should be removed so that all dirt and rust can be cleaned from metal parts. Then all metal contact points should be lubricated with special lubricant (keep lubricant from brake linings) and the shoes and springs reinstalled. Make sure that the return springs have normal tension. Replace weak springs.

Refer to the applicable shop manual for details of making minor and major adjustments.

§ 554. Brake lining As a first step in replacing brake linings, the brake shoes must be removed. Brake linings can be checked by removing one front wheel and noting their condition (the brake drum can be checked at the same time). It can normally be assumed that the brake linings at the other three wheels will be in about the same condition. If the linings are oil- or brake-fluid-soaked or if they are worn down to the replacement point, then linings at all wheels should be replaced.

1. Shoe inspection. When the shoes have been removed, they should be cleaned and checked for distortion, cracks, or other defects (Fig. 33–6).

2. Lining replacement. Brake linings are either riveted or cemented (bonded) to the brake shoes. Some manufacturers recommend that on the bonded type no attempt should be made to install new linings on the shoes. The shoes should be replaced when the linings have become worn. Other manufacturers supply information on the bonding procedure. Typical

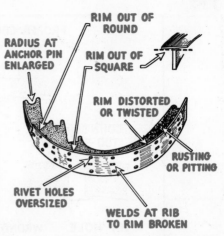

Fig. 33–6. Various types of brake-shoe defects. (*Pontiac Motor Division of General Motors Corporation*)

replacement procedures on both riveted and bonded types follow.

a. Riveted type. On the riveted type, drill out the rivets to remove the old lining. Do not punch them out since this may distort the shoe. Avoid using too large a drill because this would enlarge the rivet holes in the shoe and make it hard to do a good reinstallation job. Clean the shoe surfaces, and file off any burrs or rough spots. Wash the shoe in degreasing compound, and wipe dry. Then put the new lining in place, and attach it with the two center rivets. Use a roll-type set to set the rivets. A pointed punch might split the rivets. Figure 33–7 shows the right and several wrong ways to install rivets.

▶*CAUTION:* Be sure your hands are dry and free of grease or oil. Remember, even a slight trace of grease on a brake lining may cause erratic braking action that would require installation of another lining.

With the center rivets set, use a

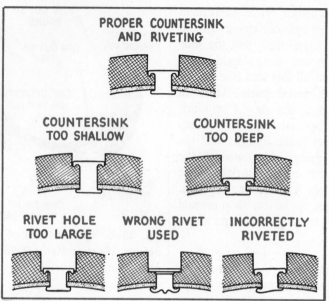

Fig. 33–7. The right and several wrong methods of installing brake-shoe rivets. (*Pontiac Motor Division of General Motors Corporation*)

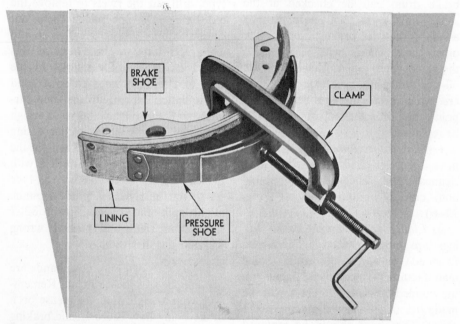

Fig. 33–8. Using brake-lining clamp to hold the brake lining tightly against the brake shoe during the riveting operation. (*Chevrolet Motor Division of General Motors Corporation*)

700

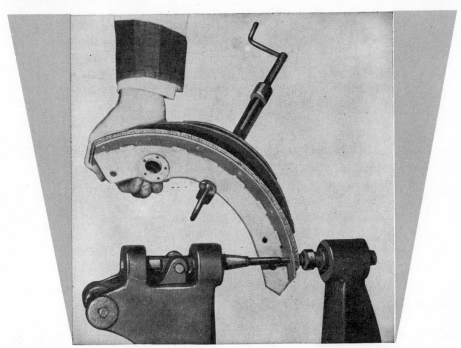

Fig. 33–9. Riveting the brake lining to the brake shoe. (*Chevrolet Motor Division of General Motors Corporation*)

brake-lining clamp if necessary (Fig. 33–8) to hold the lining against the shoe, and install the outer rivets. If it is available, a special riveting press should be used (Fig. 33–9).

b. Bonded type. On the bonded type of shoe, the shoe should be put in a vise and a hammer and chisel used to chip off the old lining. Be careful to avoid damaging or distorting the shoe. Next, the shoe should be cleaned in degreasing compound and the face sanded off smooth and bright. The new precemented lining should be put into position on the shoe and clamped into place with a special lining clamp as shown in Fig. 33–10.

NOTE: If the lining is old or of the type requiring cement, apply cement before the clamping operation.

Put the shoe, with the lining in place, into an oven at the specified temperature, and leave it for the specified time. Then use asbestos gloves to remove the shoe. Take off the clamp, and allow the shoe to cool slowly. Do not dip the shoe in water or blow air on it. This might cause the shoe to warp.

This job may also be done with an anvil-type bonder. The anvil has an internal heating element and is curved to conform to the shape of the shoe. There is a slot in which the shoe web fits. To use the anvil-type bonder, the shoe is clamped on the anvil (web in slot) and the heating element turned on for the specified time.

▶*CAUTION:* It is extremely important to follow the bonding procedure

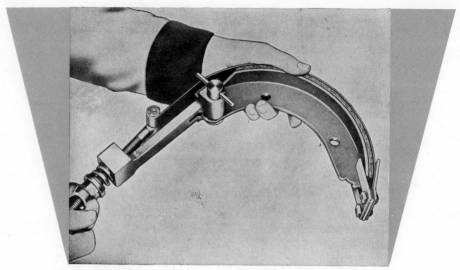

Fig. 33–10. Using clamping tool to clamp bonded-type shoe lining to brake shoe. (*Dodge Division of Chrysler Corporation*)

exactly. Any trace of dirt or oil on the bonding surfaces will prevent the formation of a satisfactory bond. Also, if the curing time is incorrect or the curing temperature too high or too low, a poor bond will result.

3. Grinding linings. To assure more perfect brake operation with new linings, some manufacturers recommend the use of a brake-lining grinder, such as shown in Fig. 33–11. The grinder shown is used after the brake shoes are reinstalled and adjusted. The grinding disk is then adjusted to take a light cut on the linings. Then, when the grinder is rotated about the axle, it removes high spots or irregularities from the linings that would tend to cause poor braking action. Of course, after the brakes are used for a while, these high spots would be worn down so that good braking action would be attained. The grinder simply assures

that good braking will result immediately.

Another method of grinding new brake-shoe linings makes use of a special off-the-car fixture in which the shoe is assembled. The shoe is then brought into contact with a rotating grinding wheel so that high spots on the lining are eliminated. It is also possible, on this type of grinder, to take a slightly heavier cut at the toe and heel ends of the lining. The advantage of this is that heavy toe or heel contact will be prevented during braking and consequently the center part of the lining can become effective. This assures good braking action.

§ 555. Brake drum Brake drums should be inspected for distortion, cracks, scores, roughness, or excessive glaze or smoothness (glaze lowers friction and braking efficiency). Drums that are distorted or cracked should be

702

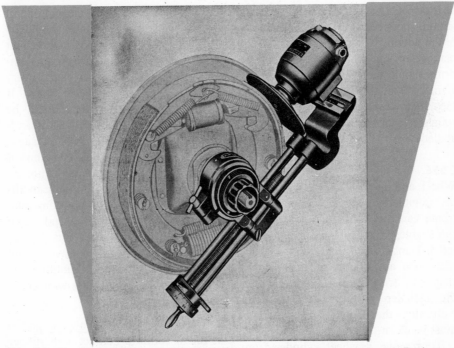

Fig. 33–11. Brake-lining grinder installed on wheel spindle. (*Barrett Equipment Company*)

discarded and new drums installed. Light score marks can be removed with fine emery cloth. All traces of emery must be removed after smoothing the drum. Deeper scores and roughness, as well as glaze, can be removed by turning or grinding the drum.

▶*CAUTION:* After grinding or turning a drum, be sure that all traces of cuttings or abrasives are removed. Do not touch the finished surface or get any oil or grease on it. This would prevent normal braking action.

Cast-iron drums can be either turned or ground, but steel drums, because of their hardness, usually require grinding. Many automobile manufacturers recommend turning in prefer-

ence to grinding, since a ground drum does not wear in as readily as a turned drum and is more apt to cause uneven braking when new.

In the servicing of drums, only enough material should be removed to smooth up the braking surface. However, if it is necessary to take off considerable material, the drum should be turned oversize and oversize brake linings be installed. For instance, one car manufacturer recommends that, if the drum has to be turned to more than 0.010 inch oversize, it be turned to 0.030 inch oversize, so that the regularly supplied 0.030 inch oversize linings can be installed.

▶*CAUTION:* Removing excessive amounts of material will result in over-

703

heating of the drum during braking action, possible warping, and faulty brake action. Not more than about 25 percent of the total thickness of the drum should be removed, in any event. If more than this amount must be removed to take out deep scores or roughness, new drums should be installed.

§ 556. **Wheel and master cylinders** Wheel and master cylinders must be disassembled and assembled with extreme care, in order to avoid getting the slightest trace of grease or dirt in them. Hands must be clean — washed with soap and water, not gasoline — since any trace of oil or gasoline on the cylinder parts may ruin them. Naturally, the bench and the tools must be clean.

To remove a wheel cylinder from the car, the wheel and the drum must be off, and the brake pedal should be blocked up to prevent its operation. Then, the tube or hose should be disconnected from the cylinder and the cylinder removed by taking out the attaching bolts. The tube end at the wheel should be taped closed, to prevent entrance of dirt. The cylinder can be disassembled by rolling off the rubber boots or taking off the covers (see Fig. 33–12). All parts should be washed in brake-system cleaning fluid. Old boots and piston cups should be discarded if they are not in excellent condition. Some manufacturers recommend replacement of these parts every time the cylinder is disassembled. If the cylinder is scored, it should be polished with crocus cloth (not sandpaper or emery cloth). Some manufacturers permit the use of a hone if the diameter of the cylinder is not increased more than a few thousandths of an inch. If scores do not come out, the cylinder should be replaced. Also, cylinder and pistons should be replaced if the clearance between them is excessive. When reassembling the cylinder, lubricate all parts with brake fluid.

▶ *CAUTION:* Never allow any grease or oil to come in contact with rubber parts of the brake system, since this would cause them to swell so that braking action might be destroyed.

To remove a master cylinder, detach the brake pedal and the brake line, and take out the bolts holding the cylinder to the frame. Then, drain out the brake fluid, and disassemble the cylinder by taking off the boot and removing the push rod, snap ring, or stop plate, so that piston, cup, spring, valve and other parts will come out (see Fig.

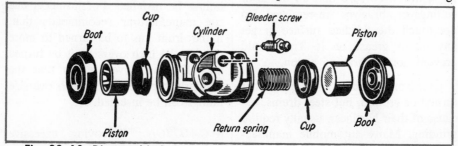

Fig. 33–12. Disassembled view of a wheel cylinder. (Ford Motor Company)

33–13). Use extreme care to keep all parts clean and free of grease or oil. All old rubber parts that appear at all deteriorated should be discarded. Some manufacturers supply master-cylinder repair kits and recommend that the parts in such a kit be used to replace the old parts whenever a master cylinder is disassembled.

All parts should be washed in brake-system cleaning fluid. If the cylinder is scored, it should be polished with crocus cloth (not sandpaper or emery cloth). Some manufacturers permit the use of a hone provided the diameter of the cylinder is not increased more than a few thousandths of an inch. However, if light polishing or honing does not remove scores, the cylinder should be replaced.

Check the fit of the piston to the cylinder, and if they are not within specifications, replace them.

On reassembly, lubricate the parts with brake fluid. Never allow grease or oil to come in contact with any rubber parts of the brake system.

§ 557. Installing brake tubing Special steel tubing must be used for hy-draulic brakes since it is best able to withstand the high pressures developed in the system. Tubing must be cut off square with a special tube cutter. Tubing must not be cut with a jaw-type cutter or with a hack saw. Either of these methods may distort the tube and leave heavy burrs that would prevent normal flaring of the tube. After the tube has been cut off, a special flaring tool must be used to flare the tube. This is a three-step operation (Fig. 33–14). First, the tubing is installed in the flaring fixture after the new coupling nuts have been installed on the tubing and the end of the tubing has been dipped into brake fluid (for lubrication during flaring). Then the clamping nut or handle is tightened to hold the tubing at the proper depth in the fixture. Next, a forming tool is inserted and driven down with a few light hammer blows. This bows out the end of the tubing as shown at the center in Fig. 33–14. Finally, the second forming tool is inserted and driven down with light hammer blows. This laps over the flare as the flare is final-formed as shown to the right in Fig. 33–14.

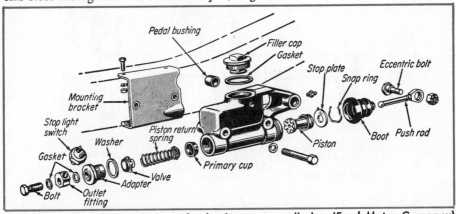

Fig. 33–13. Disassembled view of a brake master cylinder. (Ford Motor Company)

§ 558. Flushing hydraulic system If dirt or damaging liquid has been introduced into the hydraulic system, it will be necessary to flush out the system. We should like to repeat here that mineral oil should never be put into the system since this will cause the rubber parts to swell and deteriorate so that braking action may be completely lost. In flushing the system, only the special flushing compound recommended by the car manufacturer should be used. Anything else is likely to cause damage to the rubber, fabric, or metal parts in the system.

To flush the system, remove the bleeder-valve screws at all wheel cylinders, and attach bleeder drains.

▶*CAUTION:* Clean dirt and grease from around the valves so as to avoid getting any dirt into the cylinders. Any dirt at a valve or in a drain tube may get sucked into the cylinder on the brake-pedal return stroke. This could cause subsequent failure of the wheel cylinder and brakes at the wheel.

Put the lower ends of the drain tubes into clean glass jars (one tube in a jar is shown in Fig. 33–15). Unscrew the bleeder valves about 3/4 turn. Then operate the brake pedal full strokes to force all fluid from the system. When all fluid is out, fill the master cylinder with brake-system cleaning fluid (use only recommended brake-system cleaning fluid). Use a master-cylinder filler such as is shown in place in Fig. 33–15 so that the reservoir will be replenished as the cleaning fluid passes through the system. Operate the brake pedal full strokes until all the cleaning fluid in the reservoir and in the filler has passed through the system. Then use dry, clean air, applied through the master cylinder, to blow out all the liquid from the system. Do not apply too much air pressure. Finally, add new brake fluid, and bleed the system as outlined in the following article.

§ 559. Filling and bleeding brake system Whenever a hydraulic-brake system has been flushed, when the

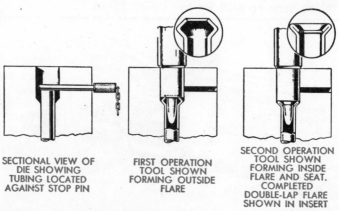

SECTIONAL VIEW OF DIE SHOWING TUBING LOCATED AGAINST STOP PIN

FIRST OPERATION TOOL SHOWN FORMING OUTSIDE FLARE

SECOND OPERATION TOOL SHOWN FORMING INSIDE FLARE AND SEAT. COMPLETED DOUBLE-LAP FLARE SHOWN IN INSERT

Fig. 33–14. The three steps in double-lap flaring hydraulic-brake tubing. (*Ford Motor Company*)

fluid has become low, or when air has leaked into the system, the system must be bled to eliminate the air. Air in the system will cause a soft, or spongy, brake-pedal action; the air will compress when the brakes are applied, and poor braking action will result. Air is eliminated by adding brake fluid and bleeding off a little of the fluid from each wheel cylinder. To add brake fluid, first make sure that the bleeder valves are closed at all cylinders. Then, either a master-cylinder reservoir filler such as shown in Fig. 33–15 or a pressure tank such as shown in Fig. 33–16 can be used. In either case, the reservoir filler or pressure tank should contain approved brake fluid.

When the reservoir is filled and the filler is in place (or pressure tank connected), install a bleeder drain and jar at one wheel cylinder (make sure dirt is cleaned from around connection so that dirt will not get into wheel cylinder). Open the bleeder drain. When using the reservoir, have someone get into the car and pump the brake pedal full strokes, allowing it to return slowly (Fig. 33–15). Continue until the fluid flows from the drain tube into the glass jar in a solid stream that is free of air bubbles. Make sure the end of the tube is below the liquid level in the jar. This prevents air from being sucked into the system on the brake-pedal return strokes. Tighten the bleeder valve, remove the drain tube, and replace the screw in the valve. Repeat the operation at the other wheel cylinders. Be sure to maintain proper fluid level in the master-cylinder reservoir. When the bleeding operation is complete, remove the master-cylinder filler. Make sure the fluid level in the reservoir is cor-

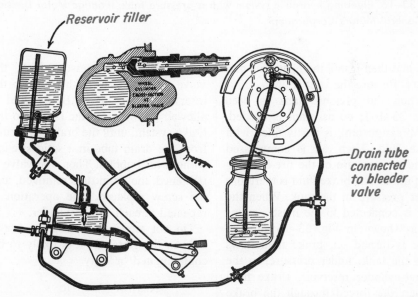

Fig. 33–15. Bleeding hydraulic system with a master-cylinder reservoir filler. (Pontiac Motor Division of General Motors Corporation)

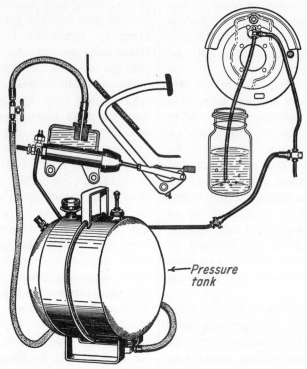

Fig. 33–16. Bleeding hydraulic system with a pressure tank. (Pontiac Motor Division of General Motors Corporation)

rect, and then install the filler plug and gasket. Be sure the vent is open.

When the pressure tank is used (Fig. 33–16), no assistant is needed. The pressure tank is partly filled with brake fluid. Then, air is compressed in the tank by use of the tire-inflating equipment. The brake fluid is therefore under pressure in the tank. When the tank is connected to the master cylinder as shown in Fig. 33–16 and the valve is turned on, brake fluid flows from the tank, under pressure, to the master-cylinder reservoir. Brake fluid is therefore forced through the brake line and wheel cylinder to which the drain tube has been connected, as

shown. With the pressure tank, the valve in the line from the tank to the reservoir is turned on. Brake fluid is allowed to flow from the tank into the brake system, until the brake fluid runs from the drain tube in a solid stream, without air bubbles. Then, the valve is tightened, the drain tube removed, and the screw replaced. The operation is repeated at each wheel cylinder.

Do not attempt to reuse the brake fluid in the glass jar. It is likely to be contaminated or dirty.

REVIEW QUESTIONS

1. What conditions could cause the brake pedal to go all the way to

the floor board when depressed?

2. What could cause one brake to drag?
3. What could cause all brakes to drag?
4. What could cause the car to pull to one side when the brakes are applied?
5. What causes a soft, or spongy, pedal?
6. What is the cause when excessive pedal pressure is required to produce braking action?
7. What causes the brakes to become too sensitive?
8. What causes noisy brakes?
9. Into what two classifications are brake adjustments divided? Generally speaking, what does each involve?
10. Describe the procedure of installing new brake linings.
11. How is the brake drum serviced if it is only slightly scored? If it is deeply scored and rough? How much material can be removed from the brake drum?

12. Describe the procedure of flushing the hydraulic system.
13. What would be the effect of introducing mineral oil into the hydraulic braking system?
14. What is the purpose of bleeding the hydraulic system? How is this procedure carried out?

STUDY QUESTIONS

1. Make a list of various types of braking difficulty, noting under each the possible causes and corrections.
2. Select a particular brake requiring minor and major adjustments, refer to the shop manual, and write a sequence story listing the steps required to make these adjustments.
3. Write a sequence story on the procedure for flushing a hydraulic system.
4. Write a sequence story on the procedure of bleeding the hydraulic system.

THIS CHAPTER DESCRIBES TIRES and tire service, including tire removal and replacement and tire and tube repair.

§ 560. Construction of tires   Tires have two functions. First, they interpose a cushion between the road and the car wheels to absorb shocks result-

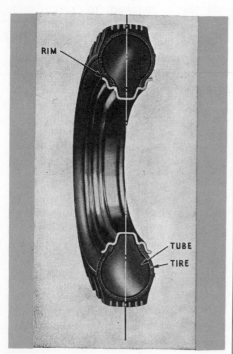

Fig. 34–1. Tire rim and tire cut away so that tube can be seen. (*Plymouth Division of Chrysler Corporation*)

710

ing from irregularities in the road. The tires flex, or give, as bumps are encountered, thus reducing the shock effect to the passengers in the car. Second, the tires provide frictional contact between the wheels and the road so that good traction is secured. This permits the transmitting of power through the tires to the road for rapid accelerating, combats the tendency of the car to skid on turns, and allows quick stops when the brakes are applied.

Tires are of two basic types, solid and pneumatic (air-filled). Solid tires have very limited usage, being confined largely to specialized industrial applications. Only pneumatic tires will be considered here. Pneumatic tires are of two types, those using an inner tube and the tubeless type. On the type with an inner tube, both the tube and the tire casing are mounted on the wheel rim, with the tube inside the casing (Fig. 34–1). The inner tube is inflated with air, and this causes the tire casing to resist any change of shape. The tubeless tire does not use an inner tube. This tire is mounted on the rim in such a way that the air is retained between rim and tire casing.

The amount of air pressure used depends on the type of tire and operation. Passenger-car tires are inflated about 22 to 30 pounds [actually

pounds per square inch (psi)]. Heavy-duty tires on trucks or buses may be inflated up to 100 psi.

Tire casings (and tubeless tires) are made up of layers of cord impregnated with rubber over which the rubber side walls and tread are applied (Fig. 34–2). The layers of cord (called the *plies*) are formed over a spacing device and rubberized, and the sidewall and tread material are applied and vulcanized into place. The term "vulcanizing" pertains to a process of heating the rubber under pressure. This process both molds the rubber into the desired form and gives it the characteristics required. The number of layers of cord (plies) varies according to the use to which the tire will be put. Passenger-car tires usually have 4 plies. Heavy-duty truck and bus tires may have up to 14 plies, whereas tires for extremely heavy-duty service, such as earth-moving machinery, have been made with 32 plies.

Various shapes of treads are used. The tread designs provide traction and reduce the possibility of skidding.

Air is introduced into the tire (or inner tube) through a valve that opens when the chuck on the air hose is applied as shown to the left in Fig. 34–3. On the tire with an inner tube, the valve is mounted on the tube. On the tubeless tire, the valve is mounted on the wheel rim. Figure 34–3 illustrates one type of tire valve in the "opened" and "closed" positions. In the closed position, the valve is held against its seat by spring pressure and the air pressure in the tube. Air can be released from the tube by pressing on the end of the valve stem. A cap is normally screwed down tightly over

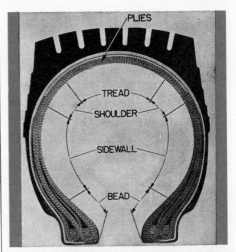

Fig. 34–2. Tire casing in sectional view to show construction. (B. F. Goodrich Company)

the end of the valve stem to provide an added safeguard against air leakage and to keep dirt from entering the valve.

§ 561. Types of tires and tubes We have already mentioned that the number of plies in tires varies according to the type of service for which the tires are built. Of course, the heavy-duty truck tire is much larger than the passenger-car tire. The typical passenger-car tire today (the low-pressure type) is designed for use on a rim 15 inches in diameter. They are called low-pressure tires (or *extra*-low-pressure tires) because they are normally inflated 22 to 28 psi.

1. Tire sizes. Tire sizes are marked on the side of the casing. A tire might be marked 8.00 × 15, for example. This means that the tire fits on a 15-inch rim and that it is 8 inches larger in radius than the rim (when properly inflated but without load). Thus, the

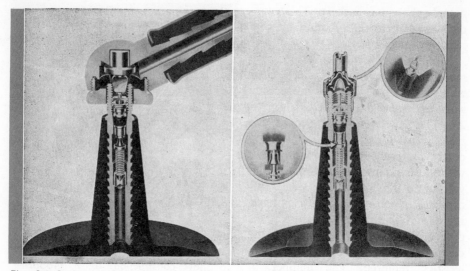

Fig. 34–3. Inner-tube valve in the "opened" (*left*) and "closed" (*right*) positions. (A. Schrader's Son Division of Scovill Manufacturing Company, Inc.)

diameter of the tire, when inflated but unloaded, is 31 inches (8 + 15 + 8).

2. Tubeless tires. Many late-model cars are equipped with tires that do not use tubes. The rim used with this type of tire must be sealed, and it must have a sealed-in tire valve. The tire bead is so constructed that it seals tightly against the rim flange; thus the air pressure will be retained when the tire is inflated.

3. Puncture-sealing tires. Some tubeless tires have a coating of plastic material in the inner surface. When the tire is punctured, this plastic material is forced, by the internal air pressure, into the hole left when the nail or other object is removed. The plastic material then hardens to seal the hole.

4. Tubes. Three types of rubber, one natural and two synthetic, have been used to make tubes. Today, the most common tube material is butyl.

You can identify a butyl tube by its blue stripe. The other synthetic rubber tube (GR-S) has a red stripe. Natural rubber is not striped.

5. Puncture-sealing tubes. Some tubes have a coating of plastic material which acts like the plastic material used in the puncture-sealing tire. It flows into and seals any holes left by punctures. In some tubes, the plastic material coats the inside of the tube. In others, the material is retained between an inner rubber diaphragm and the tube in a series of cells. This latter construction prevents the material from flowing as a result of centrifugal force and thereby from building up in certain spots in the tube. If the material were allowed to build up, it would cause an unbalanced condition.

6. Safety tube. The safety tube is really two tubes in one, one smaller than the other, and joined at the rim edge. When the tube is filled with air,

the air flows first into the inside tube. From there it passes through an equalizing passage into the space between the two tubes. Thus both tubes are filled with air. Now let us see what happens if a puncture or blowout occurs. In this case, the air is lost from between the two tubes. But the inside tube, which has not been damaged, retains its air pressure. It is sufficiently strong to support the weight of the car until the car can be slowed and stopped. Usually, the inside tube is reinforced with nylon fabric so that it can take the suddenly imposed weight of the car, when a blowout occurs, without giving way.

§ 562. Tire service Tire service includes periodic inflation to make sure the tire is kept at the proper pressure, periodic tire inspection so that small damages can be detected and repaired before they develop into major defects, tire removal, repair, and replacement. These services are covered in detail below.

§ 563. Tire inflation As we have noted in previous chapters, incorrect tire inflation can cause many types of steering and braking difficulty. Low pressure will cause hard steering, front-wheel shimmy, steering kickback, and tire squeal on turns. Uneven tire pressure will tend to make the car pull to one side. Article 521 covers, in detail, the effects of improper tire inflation on the tires themselves. Low pressure wears the sides of the treads (Fig. 31–3), causes excessive flexing of the side walls, and results in ply separation. A tire with insufficient

pressure is also subject to rim bruises; this could break plies and lead to early tire failure. Excessive pressure likewise causes uneven tread wear; the tread wears in the center. Also, a tire that is excessively inflated will give a hard ride and is subject to fabric rupture since the pressure may be so high that the tire does not give normally. Thus, when the tire meets a rut or bump, the fabric takes the shock and cannot give, or flex, in a normal manner.

For these reasons, it is very important to maintain proper pressure in the tires. There are a few points you should remember when inflating tires:

1. Don't inflate a tire when it is hot, as, for instance, after hard driving on the highway. This increase in temperature increases the air pressure in the tire. If you check pressure with the tire hot, you may find it is high and your first impulse might be to bleed some of the air out to reduce the pressure. But if you did this, you might excessively reduce cold-tire pressure. That is, when the tire cools off, the pressure drops. If you adjust the pressure to the proper value with the tire hot, then when the tire cools, the pressure will be too low. Pressures specified by the manufacturers are for cold tires.

2. Always replace the cap after checking air pressure or inflating a tire. The cap helps maintain the air pressure in case the tube valve is leaky. Also, it protects the valve from dirt. If dirt gets into the valve, it may cause the valve to leak. If you release air pressure when you take a cap off, it may be that the valve has become dirty. A new valve core should be installed if the old valve leaks. This

simply requires screwing out the old core and screwing in a new one.

§ **564. Tire inspection** There are certain types of damage and wear you can spot by examining the outside of the tire casing. Thus, abnormal wear, which indicates certain abnormal conditions in the steering, alignment, and brake system (§ 521), can be easily seen. This abnormal wear is a tip-off that the steering, suspension, or braking system requires service. The effects of overinflation or underinflation on tire treads are also obvious. Less obvious are the internal damages from rim bruises or fabric breaks. Sometimes a tire can be bruised badly enough for fabric to break, and yet there will be little indication of the trouble on the outside of the casing. Thus, the only way to give a tire a thorough inspection is to remove it from the wheel rim so that it can be examined inside and out.

Removing the tire from the wheel rim also permits inspection of the tube (where the tire has a tube). Tubes give little trouble if they are installed correctly. However, careless installation of a tube may give trouble. For example, if the tire rim is rusty or if the tire bead (at the rim) is rough, the tube may chafe through. Rust and roughness should be sanded off. Naturally, if the tube is pinched between the tire and rim or at the valve stem, it will probably wear through at the pinch and fail. Dirt in the tire casing will also cause chafing of the tube. Another condition that may cause trouble is the installation of too large a tube in a tire casing. This could happen if the wrong tube were selected. It could also happen if an old tube were used in a new tire. Sometimes, an old tube has stretched a little. Here is what may happen when you put a tube that is too large in a tire casing: The tube overlaps at some point, and this overlapped area tends to wear both the tire and the tube.

§ **565. Tire removal** The removal and replacement of tires are not difficult on smaller vehicles, but on large, heavy-duty applications special tools are required to remove and handle them. Air must be released from the tube or tire as a first step in

Fig. 34-4. Removing tire from wheel. After the tube is deflated, the bead on the upper side (at A) should be pushed down off the rim flange. The tire bead can then be worked up over the rim as shown at A and B. (*Buick Motor Division of General Motors Corporation*)

Fig. 34–5. Using special tool to remove tire from safety-rim wheel. The jaws of the tool provide sufficient leverage to lift the bead up and over the hump in the rim. (*Plymouth Division of Chrysler Corporation*)

tire removal. The bead on one side of the tire should then be pushed in toward the center of the rim (Fig. 34–4). A tire tool or flat stock can be used to pry one part of the bead up over the rim flange (start near the valve stem). Care must be exercised to avoid damaging the tire bead or inner tube. After the bead is started over the rim flange with the tool, the remainder of the bead can be worked out over the flange with the hands. The other bead of the tire is removed from over the same side of the rim flange in a similar manner.

▶ *CAUTION:* On tubeless tires, do not use tire irons to force the beads away from the rim flanges; this could damage the rim seals on the beads and cause an air leak.

Chrysler-built cars have so-called "safety rims" which have a slight hump over which the tire beads must slide (see Fig. 34–1). This hump is designed to keep the tire on the rim in case of a blowout. The hump makes it harder to remove the tire since the tire bead must be slid up and over it. For this reason, a special tool, such as shown in Fig. 34–5, is desirable.

The tire using a tube requires one mounting procedure, the tubeless tire another, as follows:

1. Tire with tube. Before replacing the tire, inflate the tube until it is

barely rounded, and put it into the casing. The inside and outside of the tire bead may be coated with a vegetable-oil soft soap to facilitate installation of the tire. Never use grease or oil, for these will damage the rubber. In replacing the tire on the rim, install one bead first, following with the second. Pressing down on the side wall of the tire will facilitate slipping the second bead over the rim flange. After the tire is in place, make sure the beads are up on the bead seats in the rim and that they are uniformly seated all around the rim. Inflate the tube, making sure that it is properly centered in the tire and that the valve stem is square in the rim-valve-stem hole. Deflate and then reinflate the tube. This last operation assures good alignment of tire, tube and rim.

▶*CAUTION:* If a tire has been deflated, never inflate it while the car weight is on the tire. Always jack up the car before inflating the tire so that the tube can distribute itself around the tire evenly. If this is not done, some parts of the tube will be stretched more than other parts and this puts a strain on the tube that might cause it to blow out.

2. Tubeless tire. Examine the wheel rim carefully for dents and for roughness or rusting of the rim flanges (where tire beads fit). Straighten out any dents with a hammer. Use steel wool to clean off rim flanges. Use a file to remove roughness of the butt weld (where rim flange attaches to rim). All these areas must be smooth so that the tire bead will seal tightly against the rim and not allow air leakage.

Make sure that the valve is sealed tightly in the rim. Most rims have round holes (and require round washers), but some have oval holes (and require oval washers). Rubber valves do not use washers but are snapped into the hole in the rim (vegetable-oil soap makes this job easier).

To replace the tire, install the two beads over the rim, as noted above (for tire with tube). Coating the beads and rim flanges with a vegetable-oil soft soap makes the mounting procedure easier (never use grease or oil since they will damage the rubber). After the tire is mounted on the rim, apply a blast of air to the valve. The valve core should be removed since this will permit the air to enter more freely. The blast of air should force the tire beads outward and into contact with the bead seats on the rim. If it does not and air escapes so that the tire will not inflate, then the beads must be spread by constricting the tread center line. This can be done with a commercial tire-mounting band or with a simple rope tourniquet (Fig. 34–6). As soon as the beads seat, the tire will inflate normally. Remove the band or tourniquet, replace the valve core, and inflate to recommended pressure.

§ **566. Rotating tires** The amount of wear that a tire receives varies according to its location on the vehicle. The right rear tire, for example, wears more than twice as fast as the left front tire. Of the four tires, the right rear tire wears most rapidly, the left rear tire is next, the right front tire is third, and the left front tire wears least

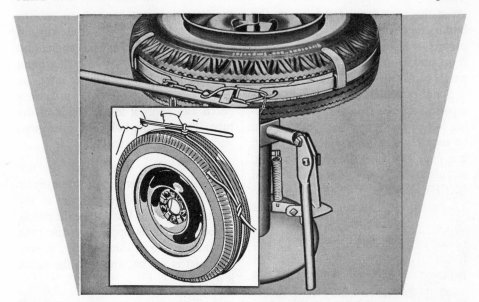

Fig. 34-6. Using a commercial tire-mounting band or a rope tourniquet to spread beads during mounting of tubeless tire.

rapidly of all. To equalize tire wear, it is recommended that tires be rotated every 5,000 miles of operation. The diagram (Fig. 34–7) illustrates one tire-rotation plan. The left rear tire is moved to the right front, the right front tire becomes the spare, the spare is installed on the right rear, the right rear tire is moved to the left front, and the left front tire is placed on the left rear. This not only interchanges front and rear tires but also changes the direction of tire rotation.

§ 567. Tube and tire repair   A number of repairs can be made on tires and tubes, ranging from the patching of nail holes, punctures, or cuts to vulcanizing new tread material to the tire casing. This latter operation is known as recapping, since a new cap, or tread, is placed on the tire. Repair procedures vary according to whether

the tire is or is not of the tubeless type.

1. Tube repair. Leaks in tubes may be located by inflating the tube (after it is out of the tire) and then submerging the tube in water. Bubbles will leak from punctures or holes. Small punctures can be repaired by use of a vulcanizing kit; this is a patch with a metal back containing fuel. You simply

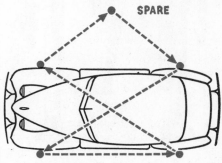

Fig. 34–7. Procedure of rotating tires to equalize wear. (Cadillac Motor Car Division of General Motors Corporation)

clean the tube around the injury (by buffing and with solvent), remove the protective cover from the patch, clamp it on, and light the fuel. Then when the patch cools, the tube is ready for use.

Small punctures or cuts can also be repaired with a regular tube-vulcanizing hot plate. Larger tube injuries can be repaired only with a hot plate. The hot plate provides the proper curing, or vulcanizing, temperature (of around 300°F). To repair a larger injury to a tube, trim injured edges away so that

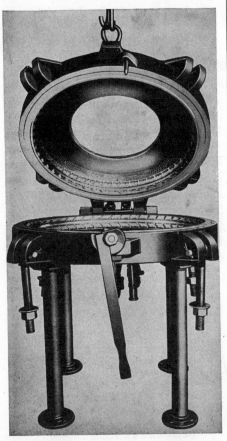

Fig. 34–8. One type of recapping machine. (*Akron Equipment Company*)

the hole does not have sharp cuts or jagged edges. Then buff the edge of the opening to a 45-degree angle, and roughen the area about an inch around the opening. If the injury must be backed (on inside of tube), prepare a patch and apply it to the inside of the tube. Then fill the hole with tube gum, and vulcanize it on the hot plate.

NOTE: The cold patch is not generally recommended for tube repair since it is not as safe a repair as the vulcanized patch. With the cold patch, rubber cement is applied to the tube and allowed to dry until tacky. A second coat is put on, and then the patch is applied.

2. *Tire repair — type using tube.* If a tire has a cut or tear but is otherwise in good condition, it may be repaired by cutting out the material around the injury and buffing the edge (inside and out) to a 45-degree angle. Cement is then applied inside and out, the opening filled with tread gum, a reinforcing fabric applied on the inside, and the repair vulcanized.

If the tread is worn down but the casing is otherwise in good condition, that is, without separated plies or broken or damaged fabric, then a new tread can be vulcanized on the casing. This is called a recapping process since a cap of new material is vulcanized on the old casing. This is done on a special recapping machine, such as shown in Fig. 34–8. As a first step, the tire is cleaned, and the old tread is roughened by rasping or buffing it. Then a strip of new rubber tread, called *camel back,* is placed around the tread. The casing is put into the

recapping machine, the machine is clamped shut, and heat applied for the specified period of time. This vulcanizes the new material into place.

3. Tubeless tire repair. First examine the tire carefully for puncturing objects. This type of tire may carry nails or other puncturing objects for considerable mileage without leaking. Puncturing objects should be removed. Leaks may be located by inflating the tire and submerging the tire and rim assembly in water. Air bubbles will leak from punctures or holes.

NOTE: If air leaks around the spoke welds of the rim, the leaks can be repaired by applying two coatings of cold-patching cement and allowing the cement to dry between coats. Then a strip of rubber is cemented over the welds.

a. Pressure-gun repair. If the puncture is less than 3/32 inch in size, it can be repaired with a pressure gun. If the tire is still on the car, jack up the car so that all the weight is taken off the tire. Clean out the hole in the tire with a rasp (after removing the puncturing object if it is still in place). Reduce the tire pressure to about 10 pounds. Remove the plug from the gun nozzle, and turn the handle until the sealing dough appears. Wipe off the nozzle to make sure only fresh dough will be used. Center the nozzle over the puncture, and press it firmly against the tire. Turn the screw handle two full turns (or follow the recommendations of the supplier) to fill the hole. Allow the tire to stand 20 minutes before reinflating it.

b. Rubber-plug repair. The rubber-plug method of tire repair can be used for injuries up to about 1/4 inch in size. First, remove the puncturing object. Then, use a rasp to clean out the hole. Apply rubber cement to the inside of the hole by coating the needle used to insert the plug with cement. Work the needle around inside the puncture. Repeat until the inside of the hole is well coated. Then select a plug of a size suitable for the hole (it must be at least twice the diameter of the hole). Roll the small end of the plug into the eye of the needle. The end of a 1/4-inch plug should be pulled through the eye of the needle about 3/8 inch. The small end of larger plugs should be pulled through almost to the shoulder of the plug. Dip the plug and the needle into rubber cement, and insert them into the hole. Push the needle in until the short end of the plug snaps through the tire (Fig. 34–9). Remove the needle by

Fig. 34–9. Tire cut away to show use of needle inserting rubber plug in hole in tire.

719

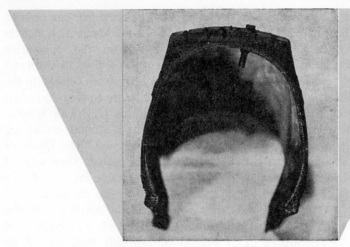

Fig. 34–10. Tire cut away to show repair plug in place.

pulling it straight out. Trim the plug 1/8 inch above tread surface (Fig. 34–10). Check for leakage. If no leakage occurs, the tire is ready for service after it is inflated.

c. Hot-patch repair. This procedure is for larger holes and requires removal of the tire from the rim. The patch must be applied on the inside of the tire. With the tire off, clean out the injury with a rasp. Fill the injury from outside with sealing dough from the pressure gun (as explained in *a, Pressure-gun repair,* above). Clean the inside of the tire around the injury with gasoline, and allow it to dry. Roughen the area with a hand buffer or wire brush. Center the hot patch

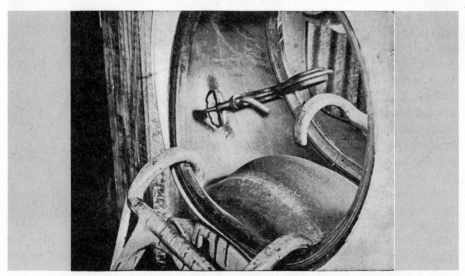

Fig. 34–11. Repairing a tubeless tire by the hot-patch method.

over the injury and hold it in place, using a special hot-patch clamp (Fig. 34–11). Heat the patch with a match or electrically (according to the equipment being used). Follow the instructions of the patch supplier. After the patch is cured, remount and inflate the tire. Check it for leakage. If no leakage occurs, the tire is ready for service.

d. Cold-patch repair. This method should not be used on self-sealing tires (which have an inner coating of puncture-sealing material). It can be used, however, on other tubeless tires.

e. Recapping. The tubeless tire is recapped in the same manner as the tire using a tube (see 2, Tire repair, above).

REVIEW QUESTIONS

1. What two functions do tires perform?
2. How are tire sizes designated? For instance, what does 8.00 × 15 mean?
3. Describe the special features of a tubeless tire. Of a puncture-sealing tire.
4. Describe the procedure of properly inflating a tire.

5. Discuss the procedure of inspecting a tire.
6. Explain how to remove and replace a tire which has a tube.
7. Explain how to remove and replace a tubeless tire.
8. What is meant by rotating tires? Give an example.
9. Explain how to repair a tube that has been punctured.
10. Explain how to repair a tire that uses a tube.
11. Explain how to repair a tubeless tire that has a small puncture.
12. Explain how to repair a tubeless tire that has a fairly large hole in it.

STUDY QUESTIONS

1. Make a sketch of a tire casing, and explain how it is constructed.
2. Write an essay describing various types of tires.
3. Write an essay explaining what could happen to a tire that does not have enough air in it.
4. Write an essay explaining how to remove, repair, and replace a tire that uses a tube. A tubeless tire.

THIS CHAPTER DISCUSSES THE construction and operation of the air-conditioning equipment used in automobiles. For specific servicing instructions on this equipment, refer to the manufacturer's shop manual.

§ **568. Air conditioning.** An air conditioner does two things when it "conditions" or treats the air. First, it takes heat from the air (by refrigeration), thus lowering the temperature of the air. Secondly, it takes moisture from the air, thus drying the air. The air conditioner cools and dries the air.

Air conditioners have been used for many years in public buildings, theaters, restaurants, and homes. A few installations of air-conditioning equipment were made on passenger cars a number of years ago. But it has been only recently that the major car companies have made air conditioning generally available, as accessory equipment, on their cars.

§ **569. Automobile air conditioner** Figure 35–1 is a schematic view of an air-conditioner installation on a car. The three essentials of the system are the compressor, condenser, and evaporator. Let's see how these units operate.

NOTE: The air-conditioning system shown in Fig. 35–1 and discussed in this chapter is only one of several being used in automobiles. It is, however, typical and will serve to describe how these systems function.

§ **570. Compressor** The compressor is mounted on the side of the engine

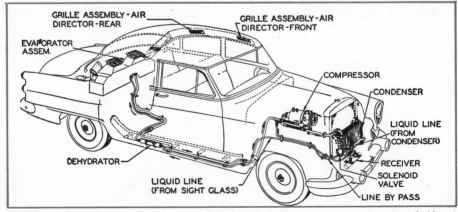

Fig. 35–1. Installation of an air-conditioning system in passenger car. (*Buick Motor Division of General Motors Corporation*)

and is driven by two V belts from a special pulley on the engine crankshaft. The compressor is driven all the time that the engine is operating in the system shown. In other systems, the compressor drive pulley contains a clutch (electrically operated) which declutches the compressor from the pulley when cooling is not wanted.

The function of the compressor is to compress the vaporized refrigerant after it leaves the evaporator. The compressed vapor is then delivered to the condenser.

§ 571. Condenser

The condenser and receiver are mounted at the front of the car (Fig. 35–2). The condenser consists essentially of a series of tubes on which fins have been mounted. The compressed vapor passes through the tubes. Air passes around the fins and between the tubes. In this way, heat is removed from the compressed vapor. As the vapor is cooled, it begins to condense, or return to liquid form. The liquid then runs into the receiver.

§ 572. Solenoid bypass valve

The solenoid bypass valve is the controlling valve in the refrigerating system. When it is closed (or energized), refrigeration takes place; refrigerant circulates as shown in Fig. 35–3. It passes, under high pressure, to the condenser (where it is cooled and condensed). Then, it moves into the receiver. Refrigerant, in liquid form, passes from the receiver through the sight glass and dehydrator filter (which removes dirt and mois-

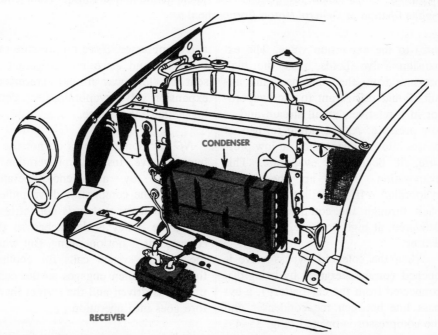

Fig. 35–2. The condenser and receiver are mounted at the front of the car. The condenser is in front of the engine radiator. (*Oldsmobile Division of General Motors Corporation*)

723

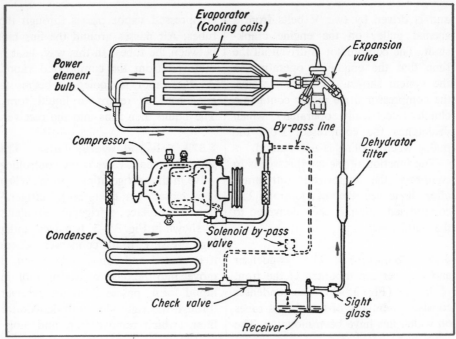

Fig. 35–3. Circulation of refrigerant in the system during normal refrigeration. (Oldsmobile Division of General Motors Corporation)

ture) to the expansion valve. The expansion valve holds back the high pressure from the condenser and admits liquid refrigerant to the evaporator in a relatively small stream and at low pressure. As the liquid refrigerant passes into the evaporator, at low pressure, it begins to evaporate. This evaporation "soaks up" heat. The evaporated refrigerant is then pumped back through the compressor and is delivered, at high pressure, to the condenser.

When the solenoid bypass valve is opened (or de-energized by being disconnected from the car battery), a bypass line between the condenser and the compressor is opened (Fig. 35–4). This means that the pressure in the system is relieved. Refrigerant can circulate freely between the condenser and compressor. Since no pressure can build up and since no refrigerant is sent the "long way around" (receiver–expansion valve–evaporator), no cooling action takes place.

NOTE: Some systems do not use a bypass valve. Instead, refrigeration is controlled by a solenoid-operated clutch in the compressor drive pulley. Thus, when the system is not refrigerating, the pulley is declutched so the compressor is not operating. But when the control system calls for cooling, the pulley clutch engages so the compressor is driven and the system therefore goes into operation.

§ 573. Evaporator In the system under discussion, the evaporator is located at the back of the car, just

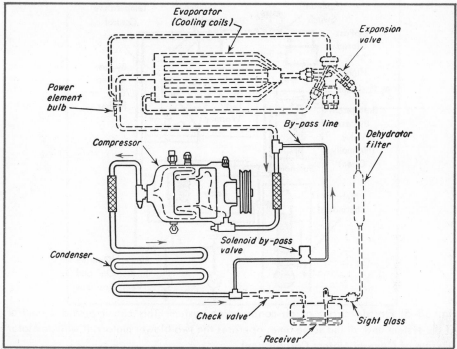

Fig. 35–4. When the solenoid bypass valve opens, refrigerant can circulate through the bypass (from condenser back to compressor) and no refrigerating action takes place. (Oldsmobile Division of General Motors Corporation)

behind the rear seat (Fig. 35–1). In some other systems, the evaporator is located at the front of the car. The evaporator consists of tubing and radiating fins. There is a pair of intake air grills on the deck back of the rear seat and, beneath these, a pair of blowers. The blowers take air in through the air grills, pass this air through the evaporator, and then discharge the cooled air through a pair of outlet ducts in the car.

§ 574. Electric control circuit Figure 35–5 shows the electric circuit used with the car air conditioner. This circuit contains the controls for the solenoid bypass valve (§ 572)—both manual and thermostatic. It also contains the controls for the blowers.

When the switch is turned to "On," the blowers operate, and at the same time the refrigerating system comes into operation. The amount of cooling that will result depends upon the position of the temperature control lever. The temperature control lever operates a variable resistance which puts more or less resistance into a circuit to a heater coil on the thermostat. The thermostat consists of a tube of mercury in which contacts are set. When the control lever is turned to the right (Cooler), full line voltage is imposed on the heater coil. Heat from the heater coil, plus the warmth of the car, heats the mercury so it expands and rises (just as increasing temperature sends the mercury in a thermometer up in the thermometer tube). When

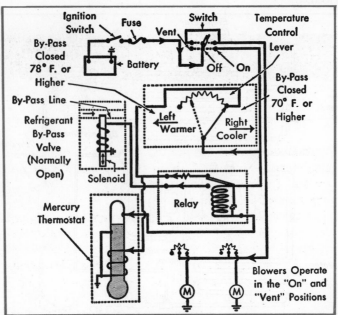

Fig. 35–5. Electric circuit of air-conditioning system. This circuit provides control of the system and, at the same time, operates the two blower motors. (*Cadillac Motor Division of General Motors Corporation*)

the mercury reaches the upper contact, the relay winding is grounded through the mercury. This completes the relay-winding circuit. The relay closes its lower points. Now, the solenoid bypass valve is energized and the refrigerant bypass line is closed. This means that refrigeration takes place (Fig. 35–3). If the temperature control lever is placed at any other position (toward Warmer), there will be less voltage on the thermostat heater coil. This means that the car temperature must be somewhat higher to make the thermostat complete the relay-winding circuit. Thus, the operating temperature will be higher. The circuit shown in Fig. 35–5 is only one of several used to control air conditioners in different cars.

REVIEW QUESTIONS

1. Explain the purpose of the condenser.
2. Explain the purpose of the compressor.
3. Describe the operation of the solenoid bypass valve.
4. Explain the purpose of the evaporator.
5. Describe the manner in which the control circuit shown in this chapter functions.

STUDY QUESTIONS

1. Write a step-by-step story on the servicing procedures required on the different components of a car air-conditioning system.
2. Explain how the car air-conditioning system functions.

THIS CHAPTER DISCUSSES THE late-model cars generally referred to by the term "compact." Compact cars are smaller than the standard models manufactured by the same car companies. For example, the four-door-sedan model of the compact car produced by the Chevrolet Motor Division, the Corvair, has a bumper-to-bumper length of 180 inches compared with a bumper-to-bumper length of 211 inches in the standard model.

This does not mean that the compact cars are cut-down versions of the standard cars. On the contrary, they represent new engineering ideas in new "packages" designed to provide the full comfort and convenience the American public has come to expect from the automotive industry. This chapter describes some of the engineering in-novations of the new compact cars and provides design and servicing information on them.

§ 575. Exterior appearance The compact cars have generally clean, simple lines, with passenger compartments of a size comparable to those of the standard cars. Figure 36–1 compares the Valiant with the outline of a standard model. Note that the passenger compartment has been reduced only slightly, with ample room being provided for six passengers.

§ 576. Engines Interesting innovations in engines used in the new compact cars include the rear-mounted horizontal-opposed air-cooled six-cylinder engine in the Corvair (Fig. 36–2), and the six-cylinder in-line en-

Fig. 36–1. The Valiant. Note the white outline, which compares the size of the Valiant with a standard car. Although the front and rear ends are much reduced in size, the passenger compartment remains adequately large for six passengers. (*Plymouth–De Soto–Valiant Division of Chrysler Corporation*)

Fig. 36–2. Partial cutaway view, from top, of the Corvair horizontal-opposed air-cooled six-cylinder engine. (*Chevrolet Motor Division of General Motors Corporation*)

gines in the Valiant and Dart (Figs. 36–4 and 36–5) which are inclined 30 degrees off vertical. Another new six-cylinder engine has appeared on the scene also, a V-6 introduced by GMC Truck and Coach Division (Figs. 36–6 and 36–7).

1. Corvair engine. The Corvair horizontal-opposed air-cooled six-cylinder engine (Fig. 36–2) has an aluminum 'crankcase, six individual cast-iron cylinders, and two cast-aluminum cylinder heads. Both the cylinder heads and cylinders have cooling fins. The two cylinder heads are identical and contain integral intake manifolds, combustion chambers, and valves for each cylinder.

The valves are operated by push rods and rocker arms in a manner similar to the valve train used in the standard Chevrolet V-8 engine. The camshaft is located in the lower part of the crankcase (Fig. 36–3). The push rods are housed in steel tubes extending between the cylinder heads and crankcase. The tubes not only protect the push rods, but also drain oil from the heads back into the crankcase oil pan.

The crankcase is split into halves and houses, in addition to the camshaft, the crankshaft. The crankshaft is held in position by four bearings which are supported, in turn, entirely by the crankcase halves. This arrangement requires no separate main-bearing caps.

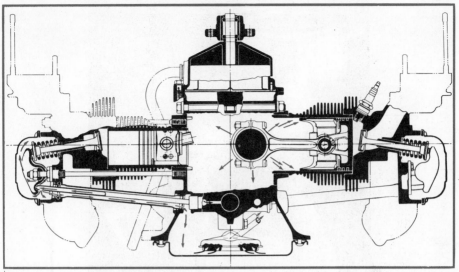

Fig. 36–3. Lubrication system of the Corvair engine. Arrows show direction of oil flow to engine components. (*Chevrolet Motor Division of General Motors Corporation*)

The rear housing of the engine is of cast aluminum and contains the oil pump and crankshaft seal. Since the engine is rear-mounted, it drives through its front end. With the standard transmission, a clutch housing and clutch are mounted on the front end of the engine. With the automatic transmission, the torque converter is mounted on the front of the engine. With either transmission, the differential and rear axle separate the transmission from the clutch or converter. See § 581 for further details.

2. *Valiant engine.* The Valiant engine (Fig. 36–4) is inclined 30 degrees from the vertical to permit improved manifolding along with a lower hood line. The carburetor and air cleaner mount to one side of the engine with this arrangement and take up little additional headroom. This engine has overhead valves operated by push rods and rocker arms in an arrangement

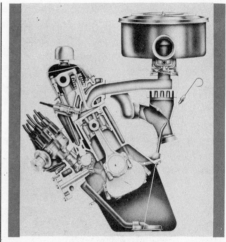

Fig. 36–4. Cutaway view of the Valiant engine, an overhead-valve, six-cylinder unit with the cylinders inclined 30 degrees from vertical. Note how this arrangement permits manifolding, carburetor, and air cleaner to be carried to the side of the engine without increasing engine height. (*Plymouth–De Soto–Valiant Division of Chrysler Corporation*)

729

Fig. 36–5. Cutaway view of the Dodge Dart "slant" engine. This engine is similar to that shown in Fig. 36–4. The view here is from the opposite end of the engine. (*Dodge Division of Chrysler Corporation*)

Fig. 36–6. The GMC V-6 engine. (*GMC Truck and Coach Division of General Motors Corporation*)

similar to that used in other Chrysler Corporation engines.

3. *Dodge Dart engine.* The Dart engine (Fig. 36–5) is similar to the Valiant engine. The view shown in Fig. 36–5 is taken from the opposite end as compared to the Valiant engine shown in Fig. 36–4.

4. *GMC Truck and Coach Division engine.* This engine has two banks of three cylinders each set at an angle of 60 degrees. The valves are in-head and the design is "oversquare." This means that the bore (4.25 inches on the model 305 engine) is greater than the stroke (3.58 inches on all models). Figure 36–6 is an external view of the engine showing accessories mounted in place. Figure 36–7 shows the engine block and the four bearing caps. This

engine is so designed that two of them can be mounted end to end to provide, on one vehicle, a V-12 engine.

§ **577. Fuel systems** Fuel systems for the compact cars are of the standard arrangements seen in the standard cars with the exception of that on the Corvair. The Corvair, being a horizontal-opposed six-cylinder engine, has two carburetors, one for each bank of three cylinders. It uses two identical single-barrel carburetors but only one air cleaner and one automatic choke. Figure 36–8 shows the carburetor system minus the air cleaner and the two air tubes that feed filtered air to the carburetors. One of the tubes can be seen in partial phantom view in the engine shown in Fig. 36–2. The air cleaner

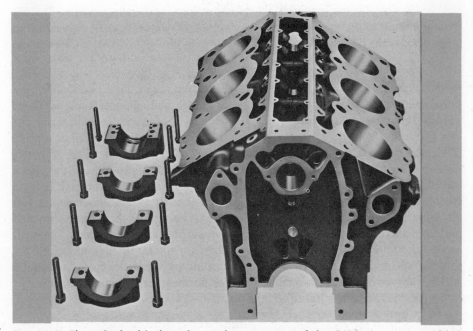

Fig. 36–7. The cylinder block and main-bearing caps of the GMC V-6 engine. (GMC *Truck and Coach Division of General Motors Corporation*)

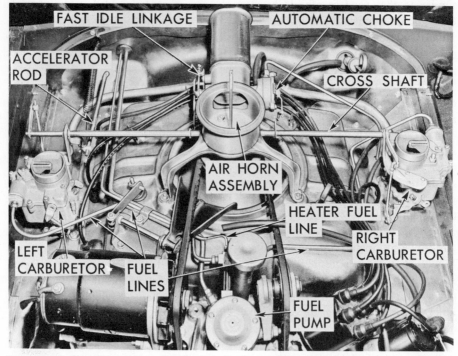

Fig. 36–8. The Corvair opposed six-cylinder-engine carburetion system. The air cleaner and air tubes from the air horn to the two carburetors have been removed so other details may be seen. (*Chevrolet Motor Division of General Motors Corporation*)

mounts on the centrally located air horn, and filtered air from the air horn passes through the two tubes to the two carburetors. The automatic choke is located in the air passage from the outside to the air horn as shown. When the choke valve closes, as during cold-engine starting, passage of air into the air horn is restricted. This creates a partial vacuum in the two carburetors so that the mixture is enriched, just as in other carburetors.

The carburetor valves are controlled by a cross shaft which is linked to both valves as well as to the accelerator rod from the pedal in the driver's compartment. When the accelerator pedal is depressed, both carburetor valves are opened a like amount. There is also a linkage to the cross shaft from the choke for fast idle. That is, during warm-up, when the choke is partly closed, the fast-idle cam on the choke causes the carburetor valves to be held open enough to run the engine at fast idle. After the engine warms up and the automatic choke opens, the fast-idle cam rotates enough to permit the carburetor valves to close sufficiently for normal warm-engine slow idle.

§ 578. Engine lubricating systems Full-pressure lubricating systems are used on the compact car engines. The

Corvair engine lubricating system is of special interest (Fig. 36–3). The main and connecting-rod bearings are pressure-lubricated, with the cylinder bores and pistons being lubricated by overspray from the rod bearings. The valve push rods are hollow and feed oil under pressure to the valve mechanisms in the cylinder heads. Oil drains from the cylinder heads to the oil pan through the steel tubes that house the push rods. The lubricating system has an oil cooler.

§ 579. Cooling systems

The cooling systems of the compact cars all use liquid with the exception of the Corvair engine, which is air-cooled. The operating and servicing information presented in Chaps. 11 and 18 will be found to apply, in general, to all the engines except the Corvair. The Corvair engine has cooling fins on the cylinders and cylinder heads as shown in Fig. 36–2. Sheet-metal forms entirely shroud the engine so that cooling air can be directed past these fins. A centrifugal blower, or fan, mounted on top of the engine delivers cooling air downward over the cylinders and cylinder heads. This air exhausts from an opening at the rear of the engine. The rate of engine cooling is controlled by a bellows-type thermostat which operates a cooling air valve that opens or closes the blower air intake. When the engine is cold, the valve is closed to prevent the flow of cooling air. This permits the engine to reach efficient operating temperature quickly. Then the valve opens to permit cooling air to flow. The blower is rotated by a belt from a pulley at the rear of the engine crankshaft.

§ 580. Electric systems

The compact cars use 12-volt electric systems. Generally speaking, operation and servicing information found in Chaps. 7 and 15 of this book will be found to cover this equipment.

The Valiant uses an alternator (alternating-current generator) instead of a direct-current generator as has been standard on cars for many years. The alternator supplies alternating current which must be rectified or changed to direct current. Alternators have been supplied as special equipment only until now.

§ 581. Power train

All the compact cars except the Corvair use a conventional power train including clutch (with standard transmissions), standard or automatic transmission, drive shaft, differential, and rear axles and wheels. The Corvair is also available with either a standard or an automatic transmission. However, since it has a rear-mounted engine, a somewhat different drive arrangement is required. Figure 36–9 shows the power train us-

Fig. 36–9. Schematic view of the Corvair power train showing locations of the engine, clutch, and transmission. (*Chevrolet Motor Division of General Motors Corporation*)

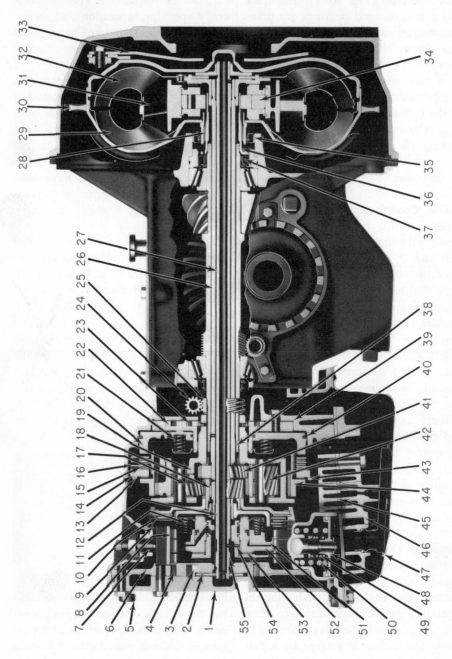

Fig. 36-10.

Fig. 36–10. Cross-sectional view of the Corvair Powerglide automatic transmission. (Chevrolet Motor Division of General Motors Corporation)

1. Front-pump cover
2. Front-pump shaft-drive hub
3. Front-pump drive gear
4. Front-pump driven gear
5. Transmission vent
6. Front-pump body
7. Low-band adjusting screw and lock nut
8. Low band
9. Clutch-drum faced plate (3 used)
10. Clutch-drum faced plate (2 used)
11. Clutch-piston return spring (15 used)
12. Turbine-shaft front bushing
13. Reverse-clutch retaining-ring clip
14. Reverse-clutch front reaction plate (thick)
15. Reverse-clutch faced plate (3 used)
16. Reverse-clutch reaction plate (3 used)
17. Short pinion
18. Low sun-gear bushing
19. Planet-carrier hub (transmission output)
20. Reverse piston
21. Reverse-piston return spring (17 used)
22. Rear-pump driven gear
23. Rear-pump drive gear
24. Governor driven gear
25. Governor drive gear
26. Turbine shaft
27. Front-pump shaft
28. Converter hub bushing
29. Converter pump
30. Starter gear
31. Stator
32. Turbine
33. Engine flex plate
34. Stator cam race
35. Converter hub seal
36. Stator shaft
37. Pinion-shaft rear oil seal
38. Pinion-shaft bushing
39. Rear-pump wear plate
40. Reverse-piston outer seal
41. Planet-carrier input sun gear
42. Long pinion gear
43. Reverse-clutch-plate retaining ring
44. Ring gear
45. Valve-body ditch plate
46. Valve body
47. Oil pickup pipe
48. Low servo piston
49. Low-servo-piston cushion spring
50. Low-servo-piston return spring
51. Clutch-drum piston
52. Clutch-drum hub
53. Clutch-drum selective thrust washer
54. Clutch-drum bushing
55. Front-pump body bushing

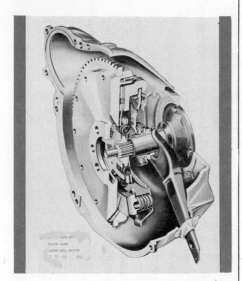

Fig. 36–11. Partial cutaway view of the Falcon flywheel and clutch. (*Ford Division of Ford Motor Company*)

ing a clutch and standard transmission. The engine and clutch (on standard transmission) are to the rear of the axles while the transmission is to the front of the axles. On cars equipped with an automatic transmission, the torque converter is to the rear, and the transmission itself to the front, of the rear axles. The rear axles are driven from the differential through universal joints so that only the wheels and axles are sprung weight (see Fig. 36–12). The engine, transmission, and differential are solidly attached to the car body. Figure 36–10 is a sectional view of the torque converter, differential, and automatic transmission.

§ **582. Automatic transmissions** The Corvair automatic transmission, shown in Fig. 36–10, has a three-member torque converter and a single plane-

tary-gear system with long and short pinions. The arrangement provides automatic shifting between low and direct drive when the selector lever is in D (drive). The selector lever also has L (low), R (reverse), and N (neutral) positions. In low, the transmission is held in low gear at all speeds below about 45 mph (miles per hour).

§ **583. Standard transmissions** The manually shifted standard transmissions are similar in construction and operation to other transmissions of this type used on standard models. The Corvair has a special arrangement because of its rear-mounted engine. Figure 36–9 illustrates this arrangement. Note that the transmission is mounted ahead of the rear axles, with the engine and clutch being mounted behind the axles.

§ **584. Clutches** The general construction and operation of the clutches used on the compact cars are similar to those of the clutches used on the standard models. Figure 36–11 is a partial cutaway view of the flywheel and clutch used on the Falcon.

§ **585. Differentials** The differentials used on the compact cars are similar to those used on the standard models. The Corvair arrangement is different, as already noted. A transaxle connects the differential to the transmission and at the same time connects the transmission to the clutch (standard) or torque converter (automatic).

With the standard transmission, the transaxle consists of two shafts. One is an inner shaft, the clutch shaft, which connects the clutch to the transmission.

Fig. 36–12. Cutaway view of the Corvair differential used with the manually shifted transmission and clutch. (*Chevrolet Motor Division of General Motors Corporation*)

1. Clutch shaft (transmission input)
2. Washer
3. Clutch-release-bearing-shaft inner seal
4. Clutch-release-bearing shaft
5. Clutch-release-bearing-shaft outer seal
6. Differential carrier
7. Pinion rear bearing and race
8. Pinion gear
9. Differential-side-bearing adjusting sleeve
10. Axle shaft
11. Universal joint
12. Pinion shaft
13. Speedometer driven-gear assembly
14. Speedometer drive gear (integral with pinion shaft)
15. Pinion front bearing and race
16. Pinion-bearing adjusting sleeve
17. Pinion-adjusting-sleeve seal ring
18. Transmission output shaft
19. Differential-pinion-gear shaft
20. Differential-pinion gear
21. Differential side bearing and race
22. Differential side gear (short)
23. Differential-side-bearing adjusting-sleeve seal
24. Differential cover
25. Ring gear

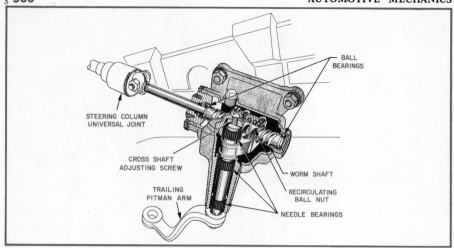

Fig. 36–13. Manual steering gear used on the Valiant. (*Plymouth–De Soto–Valiant Division of Chrysler Corporation*)

The outer shaft, the pinion shaft, is hollow and carries the differential pinion gear. This pinion gear is meshed with and drives the ring gear. The pinion shaft is driven by splines on a stub transmission output shaft which enters the end of the pinion shaft. Figure 36–12 shows this arrangement and also the differential.

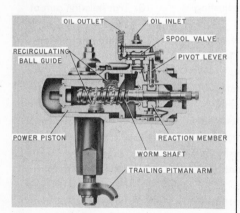

Fig. 36–14. Power steering gear used on the Valiant. (*Plymouth–De Soto–Valiant Division of Chrysler Corporation*)

The arrangement on the Corvair with automatic transmission is shown in Fig. 36–10. The transaxle on this model has three concentric hollow shafts. As with the standard transmission, the outer shaft carries the differential pinion gear which drives the differential ring gear.

§ 586. Steering Figure 36–13 is a cutaway view of the manual steering gear used on the Valiant. It is similar in construction and operation to other ball-nut steering gears used on other cars and described in detail earlier in the book. Figure 36–14 illustrates the power-steering unit used on the Valiant. This unit is much like those used on other late-model Chrysler Corporation cars.

§ 587. Unitized construction There is no separate frame, as such, on the compact cars. Instead, the frame and body are assembled as a unit by the welding of the separate components

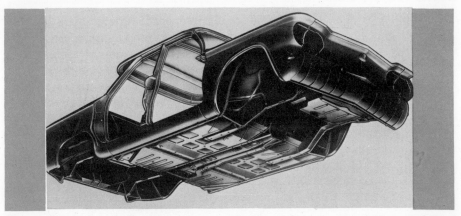

Fig. 36–15. Corvair body viewed from underneath. (*Chevrolet Motor Division of General Motors Corporation*)

into a single assembly. This is called unitized construction. Figure 36–15 shows the body shell construction of the Corvair as viewed from underneath. Note that the framework on which the engine and wheel supports mount are part of the assembly. Figure 36–16 is a partial cutaway view of the body structure of the Falcon. Here also the frame members are permanent parts of the body structure.

§ **588. Suspension** In general, the suspension systems are much like those

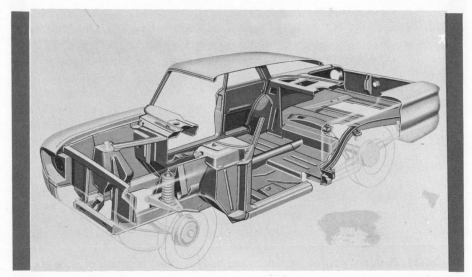

Fig. 36–16. Falcon body structure partly cut away so framing can be seen. Wheels and supports are also shown in phantom view. (*Ford Division of Ford Motor Company*)

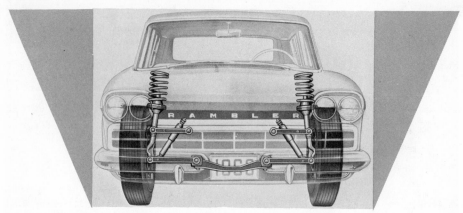

Fig. 36–17. Front phantom view of the Rambler showing front-suspension system. *(American Motors Corporation)*

used on the standard cars. Figures 36–17 and 36–18 show suspension systems on two models. Note that in both models the front springs are located above the upper arms, between the upper arms and towers in the sheet-metal body. The Corvair uses a front suspension similar to that on the stand-

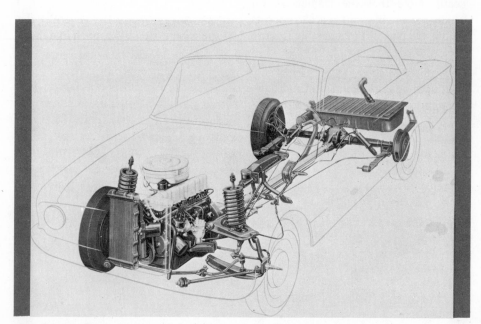

Fig. 36–18. Phantom view of the Falcon car body showing locations of various components, the suspension systems on front and rear, and so on. *(Ford Division of Ford Motor Company)*

Fig. 36–19. Corvair engine sheet-metal components. (*Chevrolet Motor Division of General Motors Corporation*)

A. Cooling air throttle valve
B. Thermostat rod
C. Thermostat and stop
D. Engine upper shroud
E. Air-cleaner air-horn support
F. Oil-cooler access-hole cover
G. Front-shroud assembly—RH
H. Engine-cyclinder air baffle—RH
I. Engine lower shroud —RH
J. Engine rear shroud— RH

K. Engine front shield
L. Engine side-shield assembly—RH
M. Engine side-shield assembly—LH
N. Oil cooler
O. Engine air-exhaust duct—LH
P. Engine air-exhaust duct—RH
Q. Engine rear-center shield
R. Engine skid-plate assembly
S. Rear-mount bolt
T. Rear-mount upper retainer

U. Sleeve
V. Mounting
W. Lower retainer
X. Rebound pad
Y. Rear lower mounting (rebound retainer)
Z. Engine rear-mounting bracket
AA. Engine front shroud— LH
BB. Engine-cylinder air baffle—LH
CC. Engine rear shroud— LH
DD. Engine lower shroud —LH

ard Chevrolet cars, with spherical or ball joints. The Valiant uses ball joints and torsion bars, as in other Chrysler Corporation cars.

§ 589. **Service** The servicing information on the compact-car components described in this chapter is similar to that given in earlier pages in the book. There is one exception, the Corvair engine, and this is discussed in some detail in a following section. However, for other engines, suspension and steering systems, and so on, the servicing information already supplied in the book applies.

§ 590. **Corvair engine service** The complete servicing procedures on the Corvair engine are found in the Corvair Shop Manual. Some of the highlights will be mentioned here.

The engine is shrouded with sheet metal to direct the flow of cooling air past the finned cylinders and cylinder heads. Thus, this sheet metal must be removed to get to certain parts of the engine for servicing. Figure 36–19 illustrates these engine sheet-metal components.

For most servicing operations requiring entrance into the engine, for example, when removing cylinder heads, the crankcase must be drained.

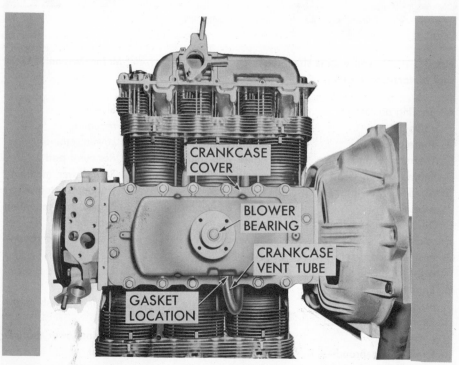

Fig. 36–20. Appearance of the engine off the vehicle with sheet-metal components removed. (*Chevrolet Motor Division of General Motors Corporation*)

Fig. 36–21. Removing a cylinder, piston, and rod assembly from the crankcase. (Chevrolet Motor Division of General Motors Corporation)

Special precautions must be used when handling the aluminum parts of the engine. For instance, gasket surfaces must not be cleaned by scraping. Instead, cleaning fluid should be used to wash the surfaces clean.

As with other engines, many servicing operations can be performed on the car. Others require removal of the engine. The items in red in the chart on pages 744 and 745 are those that require removal of the engine for servicing. The key at the bottom of the chart explains how to use it. Figure 36–20 shows the engine off the vehicle, with sheet-metal components removed. Figure 36–21 shows the removal of a cylinder with piston and rod. Such an operation requires substantial disassembly of the engine. Figure 36–22 illustrates the appearance of the crank-

Fig. 36–22. Crankcase after cylinder heads, cylinders, and other parts have been removed from it. The long studs are for attachment of the cylinders and heads. (Chevrolet Motor Division of General Motors Corporation)

743

ENGINE SERVICE REFERENCE GUIDE

(Chevrolet Motor Division of General Motors Corporation)

Some service operations can be done either in or out of the vehicle. Items in the left column printed in boldface letters, indicate service operations that require removal of the power train from vehicle. The most practical method should be followed, depending on the conditions involved.

REMOVE THESE PARTS FOR EASY ACCESS WHEN SERVICING THESE PARTS

Item to be Replaced or Serviced	Drain Crankcase	Rear Grille	Rear Center Shield	Rear Mount	Remove Engine	See Engine Disassembly	Air Cleaner	Accelerator Linkage	Air Horn Support	Carburetor Cross Shaft	Wire Harness	Fuel Lines	Carburetor	Vacuum Balance Tube	Blower Belt	Thermostat	Upper Shroud	Spark Plugs	Blower and Pulley	Crankcase Cover	Coil (Right Bank Only)	Side Shield Left	Side Shield Right	Lower Shroud Left	Lower Shroud Right	Valve Cover	Rocker Arms	Rocker Studs	Push Rods	Push Rod Guides	Push Rod Tubes	Exhaust Manifold	Cylinder Head	Cylinder	Fuel Pump	Generator	Oil Filter	Oil Filter & Gen. Adptr.	Crankshaft Pulley	Skid Plate	Oil Pan	Oil Cooler	Exhaust Duct Left	Exhaust Duct Right	Rear Shroud Left	Rear Shroud Right	Front Shroud Left	Front Shroud Right	Front Shield	Oil Cooler Adapter	See Comment Procedure
Bearings																																																			
Crankshaft	•	•	•	•	•	•																																													
Connecting Rod	•	•	•	•	•	•																																													
Blower Bearing		•	•		•	•	•								•		•	•	•																																
Camshaft	•	•	•	•	•	•																																													
Carburetor							•	•	•				•																																						
Connecting Rod	•	•	•	•	•	•					•																																								
Crankshaft	•	•	•	•	•	•																																													
Crankshaft Pulley		•	•	•																																			•												
Crankcase Cover & Vent																				•																															
Cylinder (Right Bank)	•	•	•				•	•	•	•	•	•	•	•		•	•	•			•		•		•	•	•	•	•	•	•	•	•	•																•	•
Cylinder (Left Bank)	•	•	•				•	•	•	•	•	•	•	•		•	•	•				•		•		•	•	•	•	•	•	•	•	•																•	•
Cylinder Head (Left Bank)	•	•	•				•	•	•	•	•	•	•	•		•						•		•		•	•	•	•	•	•	•	•																	•	•
Cylinder Head (Right Bank)	•	•	•				•	•	•	•	•	•	•	•		•					•		•		•	•	•	•	•	•	•	•	•																	•	•
Exhaust Manifold	•	•	•				•	•	•	•	•	•	•	•		•							•		•							•																		•	•
Flywheel Housing					•	•																													•																
Front Mounts	•	•	•	•	•																																														
Fuel Pump Eccentric	•	•	•		•	•						•	•	•																					•																
Fuel Pump Push Rod	•	•										•																							•																
Gaskets																																																		•	
Cylinder Head (Left)	•	•											•	•								•		•		•	•	•	•	•	•	•	•																	•	•
Cylinder Head (Right)	•	•											•	•									•		•	•	•	•	•	•	•	•	•																	•	•

Disassembly Sequence Chart (column on left = item to be serviced; column on top = item to be removed in sequence)

Left-column items (item to be serviced):

- Crankcase Cover & Vent.
- Exhaust Manifold
- Flywheel Housing
- Rear Housing
- Oil Filter & Gen. Adapter
- Oil Cooler Adapter
- Oil Pump Cover
- Oil Pan
- Valve Rocker Cover
- Gears
- Camshaft Drive
- Crankshaft
- Distributor Drive
- Oil Cooler
- Piston
- Piston Rings
- Push Rods
- Rear Housing
- Seals
- Flywheel Housing
- Rear Housing
- Push Rod Drain Tube
- Rocker Arm Ball Stud
- Spark Plugs
- Sending Unit
- Oil Pressure
- Oil Temperature
- Suction Screen and Tube
- Thermostat and Cooling Air Valve
- Valve Rocker Arms
- Valve Rocker Studs
- Valve Lifter

CHART KEY: Column on left indicates item to be serviced.
Column on the top indicates item to be removed in sequence to perform service operation listed in the left column.

EXAMPLE: To Service Exhaust Manifold.
● Remove Lower Shroud ● Remove Exhaust Manifold

745

Fig. 36–23. Using special tool to remove valve from cylinder head. (*Chevrolet Motor Division of General Motors Corporation*)

case after the cylinders, pistons, and rods have been removed and the two crankcase sections are separated. Figure 36–23 shows the use of a special tool to remove valves from the cylinder head. Valves, valve-seat inserts, and valve-guide bores are serviced in the usual manner. If valve inserts or valve guides are beyond repair, replacement of the cylinder head is required. Refer to the chart on pages 744 and 745 for information on parts that should be removed before other parts can be serviced.

There is a good future in the automotive business for anyone who studies hard and applies himself. One out of every seven workers in the United States owes his job to the automotive industry. So there are plenty of good jobs for those who merit them.

INDEX

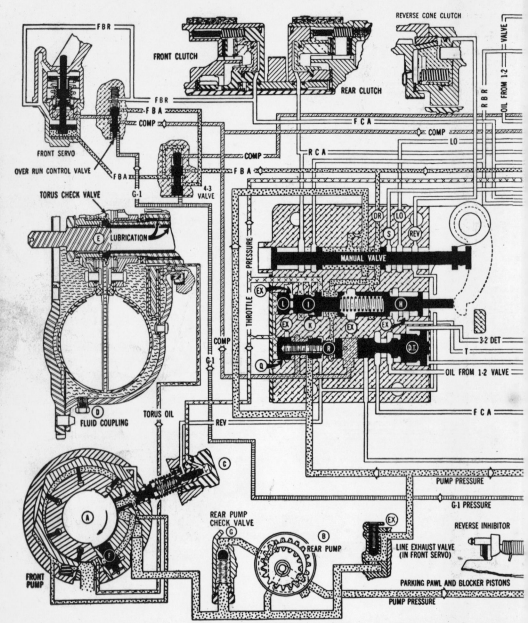

Fig. 24–49. Hydraulic control circuits in the Hydra-Matic.

See text page 524.